ELECTRIC MACHINERY

McGraw-Hill Electrical and Electronic Engineering Series

Frederick Emmons Terman, Consulting Editor
W. W. Harman and J. G. Truxal, Associate Consulting Editors

Ahrendt and Savant · Servomechanism Practice
Angelo · Electronic Circuits
Aseltine · Transform Method in Linear System Analysis
Atwater · Introduction to Microwave Theory
Bailey and Gault · Alternating-current Machinery
Beranek · Acoustics
Brenner and Javid · Analysis of Electric Circuits
Bruns and Saunders · Analysis of Feedback Control Systems
Cage · Theory and Application of Industrial Electronics
Cauer · Synthesis of Linear Communication Networks
Chirlian and Zemanian · Electronics
Clement and Johnson · Electrical Engineering Science
Cote and Oakes · Linear Vacuum-tube and Transistor Circuits
Cuccia · Harmonics, Sidebands, and Transients in Communication Engineering
Cunningham · Introduction to Nonlinear Analysis
Eastman · Fundamentals of Vacuum Tubes
Evans · Control-system Dynamics
Feinstein · Foundations of Information Theory
Fitzgerald and Higginbotham · Basic Electrical Engineering
Fitzgerald and Kingsley · Electric Machinery
Frank · Electrical Measurement Analysis
Friedland, Wing, and Ash · Principles of Linear Networks
Geppert · Basic Electron Tubes
Ghose · Microwave Circuit Theory and Analysis
Greiner · Semiconductor Devices and Applications
Hammond · Electrical Engineering
Hancock · An Introduction to the Principles of Communication Theory
Happell and Hesselberth · Engineering Electronics
Harman · Fundamentals of Electronic Motion
Harman · Principles of the Statistical Theory of Communication
Harman and Lytle · Electrical and Mechanical Networks
Harrington · Introduction to Electromagnetic Engineering
Harrington · Time-harmonic Electromagnetic Fields
Hayt · Engineering Electromagnetics
Hill · Electronics in Engineering
Javid and Brown · Field Analysis and Electromagnetics
Johnson · Transmission Lines and Networks
Koenig and Blackwell · Electromechanical System Theory
Kraus · Antennas
Kraus · Electromagnetics
Kuh and Pederson · Principles of Circuit Synthesis
Ledley · Digital Computer and Control Engineering
LePage · Analysis of Alternating-current Circuits
LePage and Seely · General Network Analysis
Ley, Lutz, and Rehberg · Linear Circuit Analysis

ELECTRIC MACHINERY

*The Dynamics and Statics of
Electromechanical Energy Conversion*

A. E. FITZGERALD

*Jackson & Moreland, Inc., Engineers
Formerly Professor of Electrical Engineering
Massachusetts Institute of Technology*

CHARLES KINGSLEY, JR.

*Associate Professor of Electrical Engineering
Massachusetts Institute of Technology*

SECOND EDITION   1961

NEW YORK   TORONTO   LONDON

McGRAW-HILL BOOK COMPANY, INC.

ELECTRIC MACHINERY

III

21139   THE MAPLE PRESS COMPANY, YORK, PA.

Preface

In common with the rapidly shifting pattern of all engineering education, the requirements to be met in teaching energy-conversion processes have changed significantly. Emphasis must be placed on the dynamics of energy-conversion devices and systems. The theory must be developed from simple beginnings in such a manner that it can readily be applied to new and complex situations. Physical concepts must be highlighted and not subordinated to mathematical techniques, for these concepts, rather than routine analysis, usually underlie creative engineering and become the most valuable and permanent part of a student's background. Attention must be given to the art of reducing a practical situation to a mathematical model. Opportunity must be presented in text, examples, and problems for applying, illustrating, and developing modern engineering and analytical techniques. And all this must usually be accomplished in a shorter time than formerly available.

Our revision attempts to meet these requirements. To do so, the book has been reorganized and, to a large extent, rewritten. Electromechanical energy conversion is still the theme, with increased emphasis given to dynamic systems. We have continued to aim at the typical undergraduate course of one or two semesters' duration (or of one semester followed by an optional extension in a second semester).

To provide the greatest flexibility in meeting different circumstances and desires, the book is now divided into three parts. As a glance at the Contents will show, the first part is devoted to the principles underlying energy storage in magnetic and electrostatic fields, linear magnetically coupled systems (including an introduction to transformers), electromechanical transducers, and rotating machines. This subject matter is considered to be basic to any course, however short or long. The second and third parts present complementary treatments of rotating machinery. The second part, based on dynamic coupled-circuit theory and dq variables, leads quickly to the dynamic equations for machine performance. The third part is more concerned with the machine as a physical entity composed of iron, copper, and insulation and intended for a variety of engineering applications. Even when no parts of it are assigned, the presence of the third part will indicate that there is more to a knowledge of energy conversion than purely analytical detail.

An effective single-semester course can be composed of the majority of Part I and selected portions of Part II or III. In a two-term program, most or all of the book can be taken up. The chapters in Parts II and III may be taken in any order (except that Chapter 11 is more meaningful after a background in 3-phase induction machines is acquired). Many of the later articles in these chapters may be skipped without affecting continuity. Various articles throughout the book are subdivided, either to indicate the attainment of a specific part of the objective or to permit omission of a portion.

In dealing with the many problems associated with energy-conversion processes, an experienced engineer naturally uses any of a wide variety of analytical techniques to expedite the mathematical routine. Among these techniques are block diagrams or signal-flow charts, transfer functions, frequency-response techniques, the Laplace transform, matrix or tensor methods, and analog and digital computers. To assume a working knowledge of all these techniques would, in many cases, not be justified; to treat one or two exclusively and in depth would unduly restrict the book and risk serious loss of emphasis on the machines themselves. On the other hand, to ignore these techniques entirely would present a false impression of the field. Our general procedure has been to assume a reasonable knowledge of the theory of linear systems (such as presented in a course in modern circuit theory) and to use simple classical methods with, however, occasional consideration of alternative approaches, such as by transform or matrix methods. Similarly, block-diagram, computer, and frequency-response methods have been introduced in Chapter 2 and brought in from time to time, especially in the treatment of feedback systems in Chapter 4. We hope thereby to achieve an additional degree of flexibility whereby individual instructors may supply such emphasis on alternative analytical methods as they may consider appropriate.

We are indeed grateful to the many persons who have helped us in one way or another during the writing of the book. We especially wish to acknowledge the valuable advice and suggestions of many instructors who used the first edition.

A. E. Fitzgerald
Charles Kingsley, Jr.

Contents

PART II. THE IDEALIZED MACHINE

PART III. THE REALISTIC MACHINE

PART I

Electromechanical Energy Conversion

CHAPTER 1

Basic Principles

The role of electricity in modern technology is that of an extremely versatile intermediary. Although energy is seldom directly available in electrical form and ultimately it is seldom wanted in electrical form, yet we often convert it to that form. In the electrical form energy can be transmitted and controlled with relative simplicity, reliability, and efficiency. The electrical components then are part of a system receiving input energy in nonelectrical form and ultimately delivering a nonelectrical output. Thus energy-conversion devices are required at both ends of the electrical system. Often their dynamic behavior has a predominant effect on the performance of the system as a whole.

Among the most important of these energy-conversion devices are those for the conversion of energy from mechanical to electrical or from electrical to mechanical form. They include electric generators and motors. The telephone receiver is another example. Electrical techniques are also widely used in the measurement and control of nonelectrical quantities—for example, the measurement of pressure and the control of a valve to regulate the pressure. Many other examples could be cited. While energy is in the electrical form, a feeble source can be made to control a much larger source. Devices for translating a mechanical input to electrical form, or the reverse, are called electromechanical *transducers*.

The object of this book is to present a basic theory of electromechanical energy conversion. The final objective is not only to provide familiarity with existing devices but also wherever possible to establish criteria by which proposed innovations may be judged. Although other forms of energy can be converted directly to and from electrical energy (for example, heat to electricity), their treatment is outside the scope of this book. The treatment of electromechanical energy conversion is divided into three parts.

Part I develops a basic theory applicable to most electromechanical transducers and lays the groundwork for the rest of the book. Attention is also given to the transformer because it is an important auxiliary in energy-conversion systems. Moreover, in many respects its theory is closely related to that of electromechanical energy conversion. The third chapter of Part I introduces the concepts which are applied in Parts II and III to rotating machines.

Part II treats machines on a somewhat idealized and mathematical basis. The treatment here is from the dynamic-circuit viewpoint, i.e., circuits in motion. This viewpoint is well suited to the treatment of problems involving the dynamic behavior of machines as system components.

Part III discusses some of the matters which were left out of consideration in Part II and which often have important influence on machine applications. The treatment in Part III is less mathematical than that in Part II and emphasizes physical concepts. Parts II and III are essentially independent. They may be studied separately or in either sequence.

1-1. Survey of Physical Phenomena. An electromechanical transducer is a link between an electrical and a mechanical system. The coupling between the two systems is through the medium of the fields of electric charges. Both electric and magnetic fields are in general present, and energy storage in these fields is inevitably associated with energy conversion. The energy in the coupling field of the device may change or tend to change during the energy-conversion process. In fact it may be said that the tendency for the energy in the coupling field to release itself and do work is the reason for the existence of coupling between the electrical and mechanical systems.

Electromechanical energy conversion accordingly depends on the existence in nature of phenomena interrelating magnetic and electric fields on the one hand and mechanical force and motion on the other. The principal phenomena utilized practically are the following:

1. A mechanical force is exerted on a current-carrying conductor in a magnetic field, and between current-carrying circuits by means of their magnetic fields. The energy-conversion process is reversible because a voltage is induced in a circuit undergoing motion in a magnetic field.

2. A mechanical force is exerted on ferromagnetic material tending to align it with or bring it into the position of the densest part of the magnetic field. When the magnetic field is created by a current-carrying coil, the energy-conversion process is reversible because motion of the material will cause a change in the flux linking the coil and the change of flux linkages will induce a voltage in the coil.

3. A mechanical force is exerted on the plates of a charged capacitor and on dielectric material in an electric field; conversely, relative motion of the plates and the dielectric results in a change of either the charge or the voltage between the plates or both.

4. Certain crystals are slightly deformed when voltage gradients are applied in particular directions, and, conversely, when they are deformed, an electric charge appears. This phenomenon is known as the *piezoelectric effect*. Although the deformation of the crystal when voltage is applied is small, the associated mechanical force may be very large.

5. Most ferromagnetic materials show a very small deformation under the influence of a magnetic field, and, conversely, the magnetic properties are affected when the materials are strained mechanically. This phenomenon is called *magnetostriction*. As in the piezoelectric effect, the full elastic force of the material is available even though the changes in dimensions are small.

In their engineering applications, the foregoing five energy-conversion processes are supplementary rather than competitive. The most important from the point of view of the magnitude of energy involved is the rotating machine, utilizing the first and second phenomena. Electric motors range in size from midgets having a fraction of a watt output and used in instrument-type control mechanisms, up to giants of 65,000 hp used in pumping plants and steel mills. Electric generators with ratings of hundreds of megawatts are not at all unusual. By way of contrast, devices based on piezoelectric or magnetostrictive effects are limited to power levels below a few watts.

Other important electromechanical transducers are those producing translatory and vibratory motions. Translational devices in general may be based on application of any of the foregoing five phenomena. Among those using the first two phenomena are electromagnets, relays, and telephone receivers. It is in the field of translational and vibrational devices that the last three phenomena find their principal application, especially in devices for producing or detecting mechanical or acoustical vibration; examples are microphones, phonograph pickups, and driving systems for setting up supersonic vibrations. Operation of these devices at relatively low power levels is not a disadvantage, and considerations of dynamics, with emphasis on maximum power transfer and frequency-response characteristics, are highly favorable to them.

In this text we shall be concerned with devices utilizing the first three phenomena, with emphasis on electromagnetic rotating machines, both the steady-state theory of the machines themselves and the dynamical theory of systems containing them. The machine is the best specific vehicle for illustrating the solution of energy-conversion problems. The size and cost elements alone in many motors and generators necessitate the most careful and thoroughgoing analysis. The luxury of true-to-life performance tests on the equivalent of breadboard setups can rarely be afforded—the engineer must be right the first time. Thus no fruitful analytic avenue of approach can be overlooked. At the same time, we shall want to bear in mind that fuller perspective and deeper insight are gained by considering electromechanical energy conversion in a fairly broad sense, recognizing that all such devices have certain basic features in common.

1-2. Analytical Basis. A general principle applicable to all physical systems in which mass is neither created nor destroyed is the *principle of conservation of energy*, which states that energy then is neither created nor destroyed; it is merely changed in form. This principle, together with the laws of electric and magnetic fields, electric circuits, and Newtonian mechanics, is a convenient means for finding the characteristic relationships of electromechanical coupling. Because the frequencies and velocities involved are relatively low, quasi-static field conditions prevail and electromagnetic radiation is entirely negligible. Electromechanical energy conversion then involves energy in four forms, and conservation of energy leads to the following relation among these forms:

$$
\begin{pmatrix} \text{Energy input} \\ \text{from electrical} \\ \text{source} \end{pmatrix} = \begin{pmatrix} \text{mechanical} \\ \text{energy} \\ \text{output} \end{pmatrix}
$$

$$
+ \begin{pmatrix} \text{increase in} \\ \text{energy stored} \\ \text{in coupling} \\ \text{field} \end{pmatrix} + \begin{pmatrix} \text{energy} \\ \text{converted} \\ \text{to heat} \end{pmatrix} \quad (1\text{-}1)
$$

Equation 1-1 is applicable to all conversion devices; it is written so that the electrical and mechanical energy terms have positive values for motor action. The equation applies equally well to generator action: the electrical and mechanical energy terms then have negative values.

Irreversible conversion of energy to heat arises from three causes: part of the electrical energy is converted directly to heat in the resistances of the current paths, part of the mechanical energy developed within the device is absorbed in friction and windage and converted to heat, and part of the energy absorbed by the coupling field is converted to heat in magnetic core loss (for magnetic coupling) or dielectric loss (for electric coupling). If the energy losses in the electrical system, the mechanical system, and the coupling field are grouped with the corresponding terms in Eq. 1-1, the energy balance may be written in the following form:

$$
\begin{pmatrix} \text{Electrical} \\ \text{energy input} \\ \text{minus resist-} \\ \text{ance losses} \end{pmatrix} = \begin{pmatrix} \text{mechanical} \\ \text{energy out-} \\ \text{put plus fric-} \\ \text{tion and wind-} \\ \text{age losses} \end{pmatrix} + \begin{pmatrix} \text{increase in} \\ \text{energy stored} \\ \text{in coupling} \\ \text{field plus as-} \\ \text{sociated losses} \end{pmatrix} \quad (1\text{-}2)
$$

The left-hand side of Eq. 1-2 can be expressed in terms of the currents and voltages in the electric circuits of the coupling device. Consider, for example, the energy-conversion device shown schematically in Fig. 1-1. The differential energy input from the electrical source in time dt is $v_t i\, dt$, where v_t is the instantaneous terminal voltage and i is the instantaneous current. The energy loss in the resistance of the device is $i^2 r\, dt$, where r is the resistance. Hence the left-hand side of Eq. 1-2 is

$$dW_{\text{elec}} = v_t i\, dt - i^2 r\, dt \tag{1-3}$$

$$dW_{\text{elec}} = (v_t - ir)i\, dt \tag{1-4}$$

where dW_{elec} is the net electrical energy input to the coupling device after resistance losses have been taken into account. For the coupling

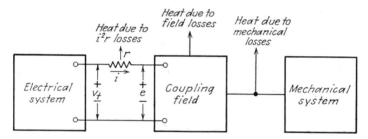

FIG. 1-1. General representation of electromechanical energy conversion.

device to absorb energy from the electric circuit, the coupling field must produce a reaction in the circuit. This reaction is the emf indicated by the voltage e in Fig. 1-1. In electromagnetic devices, for example, it is a voltage induced by the magnetic field. Reaction on the input is an essential part of the process of interconversion of energy between an electric circuit and any other medium. The coupling field may be likened to a reservoir of energy, releasing energy to the output system and being replenished through the reaction of the field on the input system. For the voltages to balance properly, the emf e must be

$$e = v_t - ir \tag{1-5}$$

Substitution of Eq. 1-5 in 1-4 gives

$$dW_{\text{elec}} = ei\, dt \tag{1-6}$$

If electrical energy is supplied to the coupling field from more than one circuit, the total electrical energy input is the sum of terms of the form of Eq. 1-6.

The first term on the right-hand side of Eq. 1-2 is the total energy converted to mechanical form. It differs from the useful mechanical energy by the mechanical friction and windage losses caused by the motion of the mechanical parts of the energy-conversion device. The second term on the right-hand side of Eq. 1-2 is the total energy absorbed by the coupling field, including both stored energy and losses.

From the foregoing discussion, it should be evident that the resistances of the electric circuits and the friction and windage of the mechanical system, though always present, play no basic parts in the energy-conversion process. They can be accounted for as losses in the electrical and mechanical systems on the two sides of the coupling element, as indicated in block-diagram form in Fig. 1-1. The basic energy-conversion process is one involving the coupling field and its action and reaction on the electrical and mechanical systems. For motor action, the sum of the energy absorbed by the coupling field and the internal energy converted to mechanical form can always be equated to the internal electrical energy associated with the flow of electricity against the emf e caused by the coupling field. In differential form, Eq. 1-2 may be written

$$dW_{\text{elec}} = ei\,dt = dW_{\text{fld}} + dW_{\text{mech}} \qquad (1\text{-}7)$$

where dW_{mech} is the differential energy converted to mechanical form and dW_{fld} is the differential energy absorbed by the coupling field.

Equation 1-7, together with Faraday's law for induced voltage, is the fundamental basis for analysis of energy-conversion devices. It is applied to a variety of such devices in Chap. 2. The procedure involves two steps: (1) Obtain an expression for the energy stored in the coupling field in terms of the electrical variables and the configuration of the mechanical parts. (2) Then investigate how the electrical and field energy terms are affected by changes in the configuration of the mechanical parts. The mechanical energy is then obtainable from Eq. 1-7. In this chapter we shall be concerned primarily with step 1 and related aspects. Both magnetic and electric fields will be considered and compared, with emphasis on the former because of its predominant importance.

1-3. Energy in Singly Excited Magnetic Systems. According to Maxwell's field equations, an electric field is induced by a time-varying magnetic field. Faraday's law of electromagnetic induction, which historically preceded Maxwell's generalization, is the equivalent statement applied to circuits. Faraday's law, based on experimental evidence, states that an emf is induced in an electric circuit whenever the magnetic flux linking the circuit changes. The emf is proportional to the time rate of change of the flux linkage, and, according to Lenz's law, its direction is such as to tend to induce a current which would prevent the flux from changing.

a. Induced Voltage and Electric Input. Consider first a magnetic system comprising a single exciting coil and its associated magnetic field, as indicated schematically in Fig. 1-2. If the flux is increasing, the emf induced in the coil is in a direction to oppose the current, as shown by the $+$ and $-$ signs associated with the emf e in Fig. 1-2. When the flux is increasing, its time derivative is positive and hence the instantaneous value of the counter emf e is given by

$$e = +\frac{d\lambda}{dt} \qquad (1\text{-}8)$$

where λ is the instantaneous value of the flux linkage with the circuit and t is time.

Equation 1-8 is correct in any consistent system of units. In this text the rationalized mks system will be used in all theoretical derivations. In general, when no units are given after a symbol or equation, mks units are to be understood; at times specific units are indicated either for emphasis or because the mks system is being departed from, as in expressing the output of a motor in horsepower.

For a winding in which all the flux φ links all N turns of the winding the flux linkage λ is $N\varphi$, and Eq. 1-8 may be written

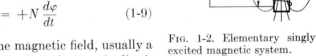

$$e = +N\frac{d\varphi}{dt} \qquad (1\text{-}9)$$

FIG. 1-2. Elementary singly excited magnetic system.

Actually part of the magnetic field, usually a small portion in practical devices, is distributed throughout the space occupied by the turns of the winding and therefore links only a fraction of the turns. In computing the total linkage, proper account must be taken of the actual flux linking each turn. The effect of the partial linkages can be taken into account in Eq. 1-9 by defining the flux as

$$\varphi \equiv \frac{\lambda}{N} \qquad (1\text{-}10)$$

where φ is an equivalent flux linking all N turns. In most practical devices having ferromagnetic cores the effect of the partial linkages is relatively slight, because most of the flux is confined to the core and therefore links all the turns.

As shown in Eq. 1-6, the differential energy dW_{elec} supplied by the electrical source in time dt (after heat loss $i^2 r\, dt$ in the coil has been accounted for) is

$$dW_{elec} = ei\, dt \qquad (1\text{-}11)$$

From Eqs. 1-8 and 1-9,

$$dW_{elec} = i\, d\lambda = Ni\, d\varphi = \mathfrak{F}\, d\varphi \qquad (1\text{-}12)$$

where $\mathfrak{F} \equiv Ni$ is defined as the *magnetomotive force*, or *mmf*, of the coil.

Equation 1-12 shows that a change in flux linking a circuit is associated with flow of energy in the circuit. The change in flux may be caused by a change in excitation, or by mechanical motion, or by both. For example, in the relay shown in Fig. 1-3 mechanical forces are created by the magnetic field tending to shorten the air gap, and if the armature is allowed to move, the flux will change. The electrical energy input is always given by Eq. 1-12 when all factors causing the change in flux are taken into account. In Chap. 2 we shall consider what happens when mechanical motion takes place in an energy-conversion device. Our first problem, however, is to study the energy in the magnetic field.

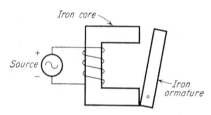

Fig. 1-3. Magnetic relay.

b. *Energy in the Magnetic Field.* In the energy-balance equation 1-7, the energy associated with the magnetic field is determined by the mmf of the coil and the configuration of the magnetic material and coil. Mechanical forces are created by the field, but if there is no mechanical motion, no mechanical work will be done. For example, if the armature of the relay of Fig. 1-3 is held in a fixed position, Eq. 1-7 reduces to the special case

$$dW_{elec} = dW_{fld} + 0 \qquad (1\text{-}13)$$

The field energy for a specified configuration can then be found from the energy supplied by the source in establishing the field *with the configuration considered to be fixed.* Substitution of Eq. 1-12 in Eq. 1-13 then gives

$$dW_{fld} = i \, d\lambda = \mathfrak{F} \, d\varphi \qquad (1\text{-}14)$$

That is, for a fixed configuration, the electrical energy input $i \, d\lambda$ associated with a change in flux is absorbed by the field.

The energy absorbed by the field in changing the flux linkage from λ_1 to λ_2, or the flux from φ_1 to φ_2, is

$$\Delta W_{fld} = \int_{\lambda_1}^{\lambda_2} i(\lambda) \, d\lambda = \int_{\varphi_1}^{\varphi_2} \mathfrak{F}(\varphi) \, d\varphi \qquad (1\text{-}15)$$

where the functional notation $i(\lambda)$ and $\mathfrak{F}(\varphi)$ is used to emphasize the fact that λ and φ are the variables of integration. If the initial flux is zero, the energy absorbed by the field when flux linkage λ, or flux φ, is established is

$$W_{fld} = \int_0^{\lambda} i(\lambda) \, d\lambda = \int_0^{\varphi} \mathfrak{F}(\varphi) \, d\varphi \qquad (1\text{-}16)$$

In these equations, the mmf is a function of the flux, the relation between them depending on the geometry of the coil and magnetic circuit and on the magnetic properties of the core material. For example, the mmf-flux characteristic of the relay of Fig. 1-3 with the armature held stationary depends on the position of the armature. If the magnetic circuit contains ferromagnetic material, the relation will be more or less nonlinear, as in the rising curve Oa of Fig. 1-4, and the integrations in Eqs. 1-15 and 1-16 must then be performed graphically. Because of hysteresis and eddy currents, the relation between flux and mmf is not single-valued.

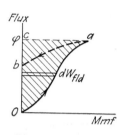

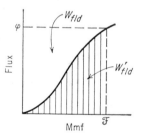

FIG. 1-4. Flux-mmf characteristic and magnetic field energy.

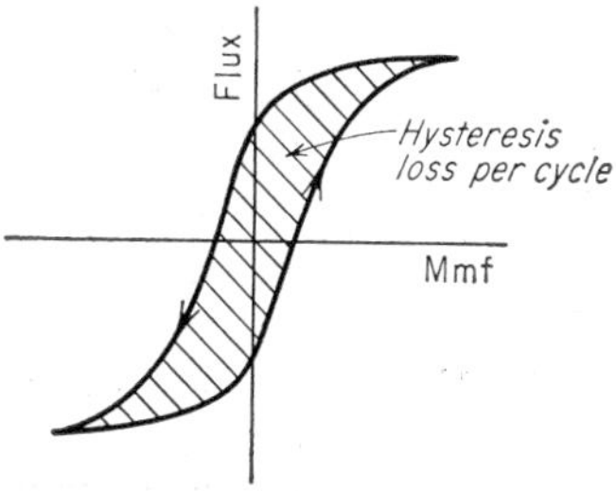

FIG. 1-5. Symmetrical hysteresis loop.

The falling curve is indicated by the broken line ab in Fig. 1-4. When the mmf is reduced to zero, only a part of the energy that was absorbed by the field during the build-up process is returned to the circuit, the energy returned being given by area abc. Some energy remains stored in the kinetic energy associated with the spinning electrons producing the residual flux, and some has been dissipated in the core losses caused by hysteresis and eddy currents. The net energy absorbed during the build-up and build-down process Oab is the area $OabO$ in Fig. 1-4. If the time rate of change is sufficiently slow so that the effects of eddy currents can be neglected, the flux-mmf characteristics Oa and ab become the rising and falling magnetization curves. Under cyclic conditions, the hysteresis loss can be found from the area of a closed hysteresis loop, as shown in Fig. 1-5.

In Eq. 1-16 the field energy is explicitly expressed in terms of flux linkage or flux as the variable of integration; i.e., it is the area

FIG. 1-6. Flux-mmf characteristic and magnetic co-energy.

between the magnetization curve and the λ or φ axis in Fig. 1-4. The quantity

$$W'_{\text{fld}} = \int_0^i \lambda(i) \, di = \int_0^{\mathcal{F}} \varphi(\mathcal{F}) \, d\mathcal{F} \qquad (1\text{-}17)$$

is called the *coenergy* and is explicitly expressed in terms of the current or mmf as the integration variable. The coenergy is shown by the vertically shaded area below the magnetization curve in Fig. 1-6, which also shows that

$$W_{\text{fld}} + W'_{\text{fld}} = i\lambda = \mathcal{F}\varphi \qquad (1\text{-}18)$$

Although coenergy does not have the clear-cut physical significance that energy has, it will be found to be a useful quantity in the computation of electromechanical forces.

Most electromagnetic-energy-conversion devices contain air gaps in series with the magnetic circuit, and usually most of the mmf is required to overcome the air-gap reluctance. Most of the energy is then stored in the air gap and is returned to the circuit when the field is reduced. Because of the simplicity of the resulting relations, magnetic nonlinearity and core losses are often neglected in the analysis of practical devices. The final results of such approximate analyses can, if necessary, be corrected for the effects of these neglected factors by semiempirical methods.

When the flux and mmf are directly proportional, as in air, the stored energy and coenergy are equal, and from Eqs. 1-16 and 1-17

$$W_{\text{fld}} = W'_{\text{fld}} = \tfrac{1}{2}i\lambda = \tfrac{1}{2}\mathcal{F}\varphi \qquad (1\text{-}19)$$

The stored energy can also be expressed in terms of the *reluctance*, defined as

$$\mathcal{R} \equiv \frac{\mathcal{F}}{\varphi} \qquad (1\text{-}20)$$

or the *permeance*, defined as

$$\mathcal{P} \equiv \frac{\varphi}{\mathcal{F}} = \frac{1}{\mathcal{R}} \qquad (1\text{-}21)$$

With nonlinearity and hysteresis neglected, the reluctance and permeance are constant, and

$$W_{\text{fld}} = W'_{\text{fld}} = \tfrac{1}{2}\mathcal{R}\varphi^2 = \tfrac{1}{2}\mathcal{P}\mathcal{F}^2 \qquad (1\text{-}22)$$

The *self-inductance* L of the coil in henrys is defined as the flux linkage in weber-turns per ampere, or

$$L \equiv \frac{\lambda}{i} = \frac{N\varphi}{i} = N^2\mathcal{P} \qquad (1\text{-}23)$$

and is constant if the permeance is constant. Substitution of this relation in Eq. 1-19 gives the familiar expression for energy stored in the field of a constant inductance; thus

$$W_{\text{fld}} = W'_{\text{fld}} = \tfrac{1}{2}Li^2 \qquad (1\text{-}24)$$

The energy associated with the field is distributed throughout the space occupied by the field. For a magnetic medium with constant permeability and no losses, the energy density is assumed to be

$$w_{\text{fld}} = w'_{\text{fld}} = \tfrac{1}{2}\mathcal{H}\mathcal{B} = \tfrac{1}{2}\mu\mathcal{H}^2 = \frac{1}{2}\frac{\mathcal{B}^2}{\mu} \qquad (1\text{-}25)$$

where w_{fld} is the magnetic stored energy density in joules per cubic meter and w'_{fld} is the coenergy density at a point where the magnetic field intensity is $\mathcal{H}$ amp-turns/m, the flux density is $\mathcal{B}$ webers/m², and the permeability is μ in rationalized mks units. Equation 1-25 follows from Eq. 1-19, because $\mathcal{H}$ is the mmf per unit length and $\mathcal{B}$ is the flux per unit area.

In the foregoing discussion the field energy relations have been expressed in three ways, and it is appropriate to comment briefly on the three viewpoints. In Eq. 1-25 the magnetic stored energy is expressed in terms of the specific or per-unit-volume properties of the magnetic field. This viewpoint is that of the designer. He thinks in terms of properties of materials and field intensities, stress intensities, flow densities, and like concepts. He then builds up the geometrical form and arrangement of any specific device from a knowledge of what he can do with unit volume of the available materials. In Eq. 1-24, the field energy is expressed in terms of current and inductance, familiar and useful concepts, particularly when nonlinearity is unimportant. The viewpoint here is that of the circuit analyst. Except for difficulties in taking into account nonlinearity, the theory of the operating characteristics of most electromagnetic-energy-conversion devices can be developed on the basis of assuming the device to be a circuit element with time-varying inductance parameters. This viewpoint, however, gives very little insight into the internal phenomena and gives no conception of physical size. In Eqs. 1-14 to 1-22, the field energy is expressed in terms of the whole field. The viewpoint here is somewhere between the other two. The expressions readily can be translated into the language of either the designer or the circuit analyst. In this text all three viewpoints will be taken at various times.

1-4. Magnetically Coupled Circuits—Introduction to Transformers.
Before proceeding with a study of energy conversion, it is desirable to discuss certain aspects of the theory of magnetically coupled circuits, with emphasis on transformer action. Although the static transformer is not an energy-conversion device, it is an indispensable component in many energy-conversion systems. It is one of the principal reasons for the widespread use of a-c power systems, for it makes possible electric generation at the most economical generator voltage, power transfer at the most economical transmission voltage, and power utilization at the most suitable voltage for the particular utilization device. The transformer is also widely used in low-power low-current electronic and control circuits for performing such functions as matching the impedances of a source and its load for maximum power transfer, insulating one circuit from another, or isolating direct current while maintaining a-c continuity between two circuits.

Moreover, the transformer is one of the simpler devices comprising two or more electric circuits coupled by a common magnetic circuit, and its analysis involves many of the principles essential to the study of energy conversion.

Essentially, a transformer consists of 2 or more windings interlinked by a mutual magnetic field. If one of these windings, the *primary*, is connected to an alternating-voltage source, an alternating flux will be produced whose amplitude will depend on the primary voltage and number of turns. The mutual flux will link the other winding, the *secondary*, and will induce a voltage in it whose value will depend on the number of secondary turns. By properly proportioning the numbers of primary

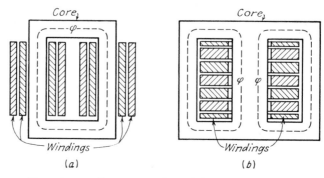

FIG. 1-7. (a) Core-type and (b) shell-type transformer.

and secondary turns, almost any desired voltage ratio, or *ratio of transformation*, can be obtained.

Transformer action evidently demands only the existence of alternating mutual flux linking the 2 windings and is simply utilization of the mutual-inductance concept. Such action will be obtained if an air core is used, but it will be obtained much more effectively with a core of iron or other ferromagnetic material, because most of the flux is then confined to a definite path linking both windings and having a much higher permeability than that of air. Such a transformer is commonly called an *iron-core transformer*. The majority of transformers are of this type. The following discussion will be concerned almost wholly with iron-core transformers.

In order to reduce the losses caused by eddy currents in the core, the magnetic circuit usually consists of a stack of thin laminations, two common types of construction being shown in Fig. 1-7. In the *core type* (Fig. 1-7a) the windings are wound around two legs of a rectangular magnetic core, while in the *shell type* (Fig. 1-7b) the windings are wound around the center leg of a three-legged core. Silicon-steel laminations 0.014 in. thick are generally used for transformers operating at frequencies below a few hundred cycles per second. Silicon steel has the desirable properties of low cost, low core loss, and high permeability at high flux densities (65 to 90 kilolines/in.^{2}). The cores of small transformers used in communication circuits at high frequencies and low energy levels are sometimes made of compressed powdered ferromagnetic alloys such as permalloy.

Most of the flux is confined to the core and therefore links both windings. Although leakage flux which links one winding without linking the other is a small fraction of the total flux, it has an important effect on the behavior of the transformer. Leakage is reduced by subdividing the windings into sections placed as close together as possible. In the core-type construction, each winding consists of two sections, one section on each of the two legs of the core, the primary and secondary windings being concentric coils. In the shell-type construction, variations of the concentric-winding arrangement may be used, or the windings may consist of a number of thin "pancake" coils assembled in a stack with primary and secondary coils interleaved.

Figure 1-8 illustrates the internal construction of a *distribution transformer* such as is used in public-utility systems to provide the appropriate voltage at the consumer's premises. A large power transformer is shown in Fig. 1-9.

Figure 1-10 shows schematically a transformer having two windings on a common magnetic circuit. The windings have resistances r_1 and r_2 and winding turns N_1 and N_2, respectively. The winding currents are i_1 and i_2. The magnetic field is determined by the currents in both windings. According to Faraday's law the induced voltages e_1 and e_2 are

$$e_1 = \frac{d\lambda_1}{dt} \quad \text{and} \quad e_2 = \frac{d\lambda_2}{dt} \tag{1-26}$$

where λ_1 and λ_2 are the flux linkages with the respective windings produced by the total effect of both currents. The terminal voltages v_1 and v_2 are

$$v_1 = r_1 i_1 + e_1 = r_1 i_1 + \frac{d\lambda_1}{dt} \tag{1-27}$$

$$v_2 = r_2 i_2 + e_2 = r_2 i_2 + \frac{d\lambda_2}{dt} \tag{1-28}$$

a. *Ideal Transformer.* In order to obtain a physical concept and a first approximation to a theory of transformers, assume that (1) all the flux is confined to the core and links both windings, (2) winding resistances are negligible, (3) core losses are negligible, and (4) the permeability of the core is so high that only a negligible mmf is required to establish the flux.   These properties are closely approached but never actually attained in real transformers.   A hypothetical transformer having these properties is often called an *ideal transformer*.

FIG. 1-8. Cutaway view of self-protected transformer typical of sizes 2 through 25 kva, 7,200:240/120 volts.   Only one high-voltage insulator and lightning arrester is needed, because one side of the 7,200-volt line and one side of the primary are grounded. (*Courtesy of General Electric Company.*)

According to the first two assumptions, Eqs. 1-27 and 1-28 reduce to

$$v_1 = e_1 = N_1 \frac{d\varphi}{dt} \tag{1-29}$$

$$v_2 = e_2 = N_2 \frac{d\varphi}{dt} \tag{1-30}$$

FIG. 1-9. This 50,000-kva 3-phase power transformer is used to step up 115,000 volts to 460,000 volts in an experimental transmission line in south-central Pennsylvania. (*Courtesy of General Electric Company.*)

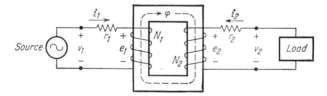

FIG. 1-10. Transformer and load.

where φ is the resultant core flux. From Eqs. 1-29 and 1-30

$$\frac{v_1}{v_2} = \frac{e_1}{e_2} = \frac{N_1}{N_2} \quad \text{or} \quad v_1 = \frac{N_1}{N_2} v_2 \tag{1-31}$$

For the reference directions shown in Fig. 1-10 the net mmf acting on the core is $N_1 i_1 + N_2 i_2$. But according to assumption 4, the net mmf required to produce the core flux is negligibly small; thus

$$N_1 i_1 + N_2 i_2 = 0 \quad \text{or} \quad N_1 i_1 = -N_2 i_2 \tag{1-32}$$

Hence
$$-\frac{i_1}{i_2} = \frac{N_2}{N_1} \quad \text{or} \quad i_1 = -\frac{N_2}{N_1} i_2 \tag{1-33}$$

Thus current in the secondary calls for a compensating current in the primary.

Moreover it can be seen from Eqs. 1-31 and 1-33 that

$$v_1 i_1 = -v_2 i_2 \tag{1-34}$$

That is, in an ideal transformer, instantaneous power input equals instantaneous power output.

When the applied voltage v_1 is a sinusoid, the corresponding steady-state phasor relations become

$$V_1 = \frac{N_1}{N_2} V_2 \quad \text{or} \quad V_2 = \frac{N_2}{N_1} V_1 \tag{1-35}$$

$$I_1 = -\frac{N_2}{N_1} I_2 \quad \text{or} \quad -I_2 = \frac{N_1}{N_2} I_1 \tag{1-36}$$

From Eqs. 1-35 and 1-36

$$\frac{V_1}{I_1} = \left(\frac{N_1}{N_2}\right)^2 \frac{V_2}{-I_2} = \left(\frac{N_1}{N_2}\right)^2 Z_2 \tag{1-37}$$

where Z_2 is the complex impedance of the load.

The ideal transformer is thus seen to transform voltages in the direct ratio of turns, currents in the inverse ratio, and impedances in the direct ratio squared. As a result of the impedance transformation, for example, all three circuits of Fig. 1-11 are indistinguishable as far as their performance viewed from terminals ab is concerned. The values of the secondary voltage, current, and impedance as viewed from the primary are called the values *referred to the primary.*

To adapt this simple model to a realistic transformer, the effects of departures from the idealizing assumptions must be examined. A more complete theory must include the effects of winding resistances, magnetic leakage, and the magnetic characteristics of the core. We shall examine these effects in a preliminary way in the rest of this article and in more detail in Art. 7-7. The effects of winding capacitances, sometimes important in problems involving high frequencies or rapidly changing transients, will be neglected.

b. Component Magnetic Fields. Figure 1-12a shows in somewhat simplified form the magnetic field produced in a transformer by the current in winding 1 acting alone. It consists of a *leakage flux* φ_{l1} linking

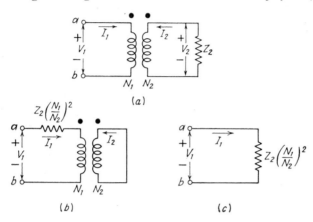

FIG. 1-11. Three circuits which are identical at terminals *ab* when the transformers are ideal.

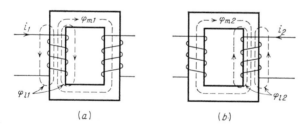

FIG. 1-12. Component leakage and mutual fluxes.

only its own turns and a *mutual flux* φ_{m1} linking both windings. In a transformer with interleaved windings the details of the flux map are more complicated, but the essential features remain the same. Similarly, Fig. 1-12b shows the field produced by the current in winding 2 acting alone. It also consists of a *leakage flux* φ_{l2} linking only its own turns and a *mutual flux* φ_{m2} linking both windings. The mutual fluxes are assumed to be confined to the core and therefore link all the turns of both windings. On the assumption that the core has constant permeability and negligible core losses, the component mutual fluxes are proportional to the mmfs producing them, the constant of proportionality being called the *permeance* $\mathcal{P}_m$. Thus

$$\varphi_{m1} = \mathcal{P}_m N_1 i_1 \quad \text{and} \quad \varphi_{m2} = \mathcal{P}_m N_2 i_2 \tag{1-38}$$

On the assumption of constant permeability, with currents in both windings, the resultant fluxes φ_1 and φ_2 linking windings 1 and 2 can be found by superposition; thus for the reference directions chosen in Fig. 1-12

$$\varphi_1 = \varphi_{l1} + \varphi_{m1} + \varphi_{m2} \tag{1-39}$$
$$\varphi_2 = \varphi_{l2} + \varphi_{m2} + \varphi_{m1} \tag{1-40}$$

The component fluxes now can be combined in either of two ways as shown below in parts c and d of this article. The first way leads to a simple equivalent-circuit model with a physical interpretation in terms of the resultant magnetic field. The treatment of rotating machines in Part III and a more complete treatment of transformers in Art. 7-7 follow this line of reasoning. The second way leads to the classical theory of magnetically coupled circuits. This theory is the basis for the treatment of electromechanical transducers in Chap. 2 and of rotating machines in Part II.

The purposes of the remainder of this article are to correlate these two theories and to lay the foundations for the subsequent treatments of energy conversion.

c. *Leakage Inductances and an Equivalent Circuit.* In Eqs. 1-39 and 1-40, the resultant mutual flux produced by the combined action of both currents is the sum of the component mutual fluxes produced by each current. Thus the *resultant* mutual flux φ is

$$\varphi = \varphi_{m1} + \varphi_{m2} \tag{1-41}$$

From Eqs. 1-38

$$\varphi = \mathcal{P}_m(N_1 i_1 + N_2 i_2) \tag{1-42}$$

The total flux linkages λ_1 and λ_2 in Eqs. 1-27 and 1-28 can then be expressed as

$$\lambda_1 = N_1 \varphi_{l1} + N_1 \varphi \tag{1-43}$$
$$\lambda_2 = N_2 \varphi_{l2} + N_2 \varphi \tag{1-44}$$

The leakage fluxes φ_{l1} and φ_{l2} are proportional to the currents in their respective windings. The constants of proportionality relating the leakage-flux linkages to the currents are defined as the *leakage inductances.* Thus, by definition, the leakage inductances of the windings are, respectively,

$$L_{l1} \equiv \frac{N_1 \varphi_{l1}}{i_1} \quad \text{and} \quad L_{l2} \equiv \frac{N_2 \varphi_{l2}}{i_2} \tag{1-45}$$

On the assumption of constant permeability the component mutual fluxes are also proportional to the currents producing them. The constant of proportionality relating the flux linkage per ampere with a winding due to the component mutual flux produced by its own current is defined as the *magnetizing inductance.* Thus the magnetizing inductances of the primary and secondary are, respectively,

$$L_{m1} \equiv \frac{N_1 \varphi_{m1}}{i_1} \quad \text{and} \quad L_{m2} \equiv \frac{N_2 \varphi_{m2}}{i_2} \tag{1-46}$$

$$L_{m1} = N_1^2 \mathcal{P}_m \quad \text{and} \quad L_{m2} = N_2^2 \mathcal{P}_m \tag{1-47}$$

The total primary and secondary flux linkages can now be expressed as

$$\lambda_1 = L_{l1} i_1 + N_1 \varphi \tag{1-48}$$
$$\lambda_2 = L_{l2} i_2 + N_2 \varphi \tag{1-49}$$

The voltage equations 1-27 and 1-28 then are

$$v_1 = r_1 i_1 + L_{l1} \frac{di_1}{dt} + e_1 \tag{1-50}$$

$$v_2 = r_2 i_2 + L_{l2} \frac{di_2}{dt} + e_2 \tag{1-51}$$

where e_1 and e_2 are the voltages induced by the resultant mutual flux; thus

$$e_1 = N_1 \frac{d\varphi}{dt} \quad \text{and} \quad e_2 = N_2 \frac{d\varphi}{dt} \tag{1-52}$$

These induced voltages are in the same ratio as the voltages of an ideal transformer whose turns ratio is N_1/N_2. The current ratio for this ideal transformer is N_2/N_1; that is, its primary current is $(N_2/N_1)i_2$.

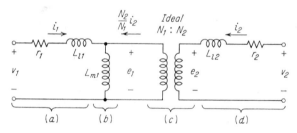

FIG. 1-13. Transformer equivalent circuit.

The voltage equations 1-50 and 1-51 and the voltage and current transformations are represented by the series impedances and the ideal transformer in parts *a*, *c*, and *d* of the circuit of Fig. 1-13. To complete the circuit representation of the transformer, the effect of the core must be taken into account by means of a circuit element. To find this circuit element, the resultant mutual flux φ can be expressed in terms of the currents and either of the magnetizing inductances. From Eqs. 1-42 and 1-47

$$\varphi = \frac{L_{m1}}{N_1^2}(N_1 i_1 + N_2 i_2) = \frac{L_{m1}}{N_1}\left(i_1 + \frac{N_2}{N_1} i_2\right) \tag{1-53}$$

The primary flux linkage is $N_1\varphi$, and the induced voltage is

$$e_1 = N_1 \frac{d\varphi}{dt} = L_{m1} \frac{d}{dt}\left(i_1 + \frac{N_2}{N_1} i_2\right) \tag{1-54}$$

From a circuit point of view the effect of the core is equivalent to an inductance L_{m1} connected across the voltage e_1 and with current $i_1 + (N_2/N_1)i_2$ in it. But $(N_2/N_1)i_2$ is the secondary current referred to the primary and is the current on the primary side of the ideal transformer in Fig. 1-13c. Thus the effect of the core is taken into account by the shunt inductance L_{m1} in the circuit of Fig. 1-13.

The actual transformer therefore is equivalent to an ideal transformer plus external impedances. This equivalent circuit is reexamined in

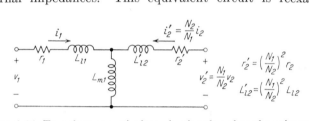

FIG. 1-14. Transformer equivalent circuit referred to the primary.

Art. 7-7, where it is shown that the effects of magnetic saturation and core losses may be included. By referring all quantities to the primary or secondary, the ideal transformer of Fig. 1-13c may be moved out to the right or left, respectively, of the equivalent circuit. For example, Fig. 1-14 shows the equivalent circuit referred to the primary. The referred values of the secondary quantities are indicated by prime superscripts. As explained in Appendix A, the parameters and variables in power-system studies often are expressed in per-unit form rather than in volts, amperes, ohms, etc. When the per-unit system is used, all quantities are scaled in accordance with a set of reference or base values chosen so that the referring factors arising from transformer turns ratios are taken into account in the scaling. (See Appendix A for details.)

The elements in the equivalent circuit have clearly defined physical significance. The effects of magnetic leakage are explicitly shown as leakage inductances, the effects of the core are shown by means of the magnetizing inductance, and the transformation ratio by means of the ideal transformer. The equivalent-circuit model shows, probably more clearly than do the equations, the influence of these factors. It also points the way to simplifying approximations which can often be made. These approximations are discussed in Example 1-1.

Example 1-1. Figure 1-15a shows a transformer connected between a voltage source and a load for the purpose of matching the source and load impedances to provide maximum power to the load over a range of frequencies. The source and load impedances are

$$r_s = 1{,}600 \text{ ohms} \qquad r_L = 16 \text{ ohms}$$

The transformer data are

$$r_1 = 200 \text{ ohms} \qquad r_2 = 2 \text{ ohms}$$
$$L_{m1} = 4.95 \text{ henrys}$$
$$L_{l1} = 50 \text{ mh} \qquad L_{l2} = 0.5 \text{ mh}$$
$$\text{Turns ratio } \frac{N_1}{N_2} = 10$$

a. Find the power delivered to the load by a sinusoidal voltage source of 100 volts rms value at a frequency of 5,000 cps.

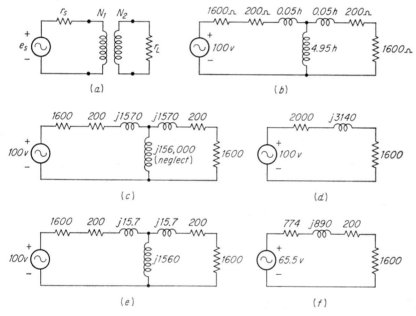

FIG. 1-15. Circuits for Example 1-1. (*a*) Circuit diagram. (*b*) Equivalent circuit referred to the primary. (*c* and *d*) Equivalent circuits at 5,000 cps. (*e* and *f*) Equivalent circuits at 50 cps.

b. Find the power delivered to the load for the same voltage but at a frequency of 50 cps.

Solution. The equivalent-circuit technique will be found very helpful because it points the way to simplifying approximations which will shorten the numerical work. The equivalent circuit with all resistances and inductances referred to the primary is shown in Fig. 1-15*b*. Thus r_2, L_{l2}, and r_L are referred to the primary by multiplying their actual values by $(N_1/N_2)^2 = 100$.

a. At a frequency $f = 5{,}000$ cps, $\omega = 2\pi f = 31{,}400$. Figure 1-15*c* shows the corresponding equivalent circuit with the values of the inductive reactances ωL shown in ohms. From this equivalent circuit it can be seen that the value of the impedance of the shunt magnetizing reactance is so high that it can be neglected. The circuit then reduces to that shown in Fig. 1-15d. The total impedance referred to the primary is

$$\sqrt{(3{,}600)^2 + (3{,}140)^2} = 4{,}780 \text{ ohms}$$

The load current referred to the primary is

$$\frac{100}{4{,}780} = 0.0209 \text{ amp rms}$$

The actual load current is 0.209 amp. The load power $I^2 r_L = (0.209)^2(16) = 0.70$ watt.

b. At $f = 50$ cps, $\omega = 314$. Figure 1-15e shows the corresponding equivalent circuit. Here the shunt magnetizing reactance is small enough to be important, but the series leakage reactances are negligible. The circuit can then be reduced by Thévenin's theorem to that shown in Fig. 1-15f. The total impedance is

$$\sqrt{(2{,}574)^2 + (890)^2} = 2{,}720 \text{ ohms}$$

The load current referred to the primary is

$$\frac{65.5}{2{,}720} = 0.024 \text{ amp}$$

or the actual load current is 0.24 amp. The load power $I^2 r_L = (0.24)^2(16) = 0.92$ watt.

For further discussion of the effects of variable frequency on impedance-matching transformers, see Art. 7-8b.

d. *Self- and Mutual Inductances.* In Eq. 1-39, $\varphi_{l1} + \varphi_{m1}$ is the total flux linking winding 1 owing to its own current acting alone. Similarly, in Eq. 1-40, $\varphi_{l2} + \varphi_{m2}$ is the total flux linking winding 2 owing to its own current acting alone. With currents in both windings the total flux linkages λ_1 and λ_2 can then be expressed as

$$\lambda_1 = N_1(\varphi_{l1} + \varphi_{m1}) + N_1\varphi_{m2} \qquad (1\text{-}55)$$
$$\lambda_2 = N_2(\varphi_{l2} + \varphi_{m2}) + N_2\varphi_{m1} \qquad (1\text{-}56)$$

For a linear system, self-inductance is defined as the flux linkage with a winding per ampere in the same winding. Accordingly the self-inductances of the 2 windings are, respectively,

$$L_{11} \equiv \frac{N_1(\varphi_{l1} + \varphi_{m1})}{i_1} \quad \text{and} \quad L_{22} \equiv \frac{N_2(\varphi_{l2} + \varphi_{m2})}{i_2} \qquad (1\text{-}57)$$

or in terms of the leakage and magnetizing inductances (Eqs. 1-45 and 1-46),

$$L_{11} = L_{l1} + L_{m1} \quad \text{and} \quad L_{22} = L_{l2} + L_{m2} \qquad (1\text{-}58)$$

Similarly, mutual inductance is defined as the flux linkage with a winding per ampere in another winding, or

$$L_{12} \equiv \frac{N_1\varphi_{m2}}{i_2} \quad \text{and} \quad L_{21} \equiv \frac{N_2\varphi_{m1}}{i_1} \tag{1-59}$$

Substitution of Eqs. 1-38 in Eqs. 1-59 shows that

$$L_{12} = L_{21} = N_1N_2\mathcal{P}_m \tag{1-60}$$

From Eqs. 1-47 and 1-60

$$\frac{N_1}{N_2}L_{12} = L_{m1} \quad \text{and} \quad \frac{N_2}{N_1}L_{12} = L_{m2} \tag{1-61}$$

Substitution of Eqs. 1-58 and 1-59 in Eqs. 1-55 and 1-56 then gives

$$\lambda_1 = L_{11}i_1 + L_{12}i_2 \tag{1-62}$$
$$\lambda_2 = L_{12}i_1 + L_{22}i_2 \tag{1-63}$$

In matrix notation

$$\begin{bmatrix} \lambda_1 \\ \lambda_2 \end{bmatrix} = \begin{bmatrix} L_{11} & L_{12} \\ L_{12} & L_{22} \end{bmatrix} \times \begin{bmatrix} i_1 \\ i_2 \end{bmatrix} \quad \text{or} \quad [\lambda] = [L] \times [i] \tag{1-63a}$$

In these equations the relative directions of the self- and mutual-flux linkages are accounted for by the algebraic sign of the mutual inductance. The mutual inductance is a positive quantity if positive currents in the two windings produce self- and mutual fluxes in the same direction as in Fig. 1-12; otherwise it is a negative quantity.

This method of treating the flux linkages is based on the principle of superposition and specifically assumes linear flux-mmf characteristics. It is the basis for the theory of linear coupled circuits and of electromechanical energy conversion in Chap. 2 and Part II.

The induced voltages (Eqs. 1-26) now can be expressed conveniently in terms of the currents and inductances; thus

$$e_1 = \frac{d\lambda_1}{dt} = \frac{d}{dt}(L_{11}i_1 + L_{12}i_2) \tag{1-64}$$

$$e_2 = \frac{d\lambda_2}{dt} = \frac{d}{dt}(L_{12}i_1 + L_{22}i_2) \tag{1-65}$$

In matrix notation

$$[e] = \frac{d}{dt}[L] \times [i] \tag{1-65a}$$

For static coupled circuits the inductances are constant. Equations 1-64 and 1-65 then reduce to the familiar voltage equations of stationary linear coupled circuits,

$$e_1 = L_{11}\frac{di_1}{dt} + L_{12}\frac{di_2}{dt} \tag{1-66}$$

$$e_2 = L_{12}\frac{di_1}{dt} + L_{22}\frac{di_2}{dt} \tag{1-67}$$

The terminal voltages v_1 and v_2 then are

$$v_1 = r_1i_1 + L_{11}\frac{di_1}{dt} + L_{12}\frac{di_2}{dt} \tag{1-68}$$

$$v_2 = r_2i_2 + L_{22}\frac{di_2}{dt} + L_{12}\frac{di_1}{dt} \tag{1-69}$$

These equations together with the constraints imposed by the networks connected to their terminals determine the behavior of the coupled circuits. Similar equations can be written for three or more magnetically coupled circuits.

In the theory of linear coupled circuits it is convenient to introduce two new factors, the *coefficient of coupling* k and the *leakage coefficient* σ. These are defined as

$$k \equiv \frac{L_{12}}{\sqrt{L_{11}L_{22}}} \tag{1-70}$$

$$\sigma \equiv 1 - k^2 = 1 - \frac{L_{12}^2}{L_{11}L_{22}} \tag{1-71}$$

Their significance in terms of the self- and mutual fluxes can be appreciated by finding the ratio L_{m1}/L_{11}. This ratio is a coupling factor k_1 expressing the effectiveness of winding 1 in producing mutual flux. From Eqs. 1-61

$$k_1 \equiv \frac{L_{m1}}{L_{11}} = \frac{N_1}{N_2}\frac{L_{12}}{L_{11}} \tag{1-72}$$

Similarly the coupling factor k_2 for winding 2 is

$$k_2 \equiv \frac{L_{m2}}{L_{22}} = \frac{N_2}{N_1}\frac{L_{12}}{L_{22}} \tag{1-73}$$

From Eqs. 1-70, 1-72, and 1-73

$$k = \sqrt{k_1k_2} \tag{1-74}$$

The coefficient of coupling k is the geometric mean of the coupling factors k_1 and k_2. It is a two-way measure of the mutual reactions of 2 windings on each other. If there were no magnetic leakage, $k = 1$, its greatest possible value, and $\sigma = 0$. For closely coupled circuits, the following relations are very nearly correct:

$$\frac{N_1}{N_2} \approx \frac{L_{11}}{L_{12}} \approx \frac{L_{12}}{L_{22}} \approx \sqrt{\frac{L_{11}}{L_{22}}} \tag{1-75}$$

Example 1-2. Figure 1-16a shows 2 windings on a common magnetic circuit. This sort of arrangement occurs often in electromechanical-energy-conversion devices when it is desired to control the flux by means of the effect of several windings. For example, the windings in Fig. 1-16a might represent two control-field windings of a d-c machine. The transient response of circuits of this sort is often important.

The windings of Fig. 1-16a have the following constants:

$$L_{11} = 100 \text{ henrys} \qquad L_{22} = 25 \text{ henrys} \qquad L_{12} = 47.5 \text{ henrys}$$
$$r_1 = 25 \text{ ohms} \qquad r_2 = 25 \text{ ohms}$$
$$N_1 = 1{,}000 \text{ turns} \qquad N_2 = 500 \text{ turns}$$

Winding 2 is short-circuited, and a d-c voltage source of 25 volts is suddenly applied to winding 1. Find the currents $i_1(t)$ and $i_2(t)$ and the resultant core flux $\varphi(t)$ as functions of time t.

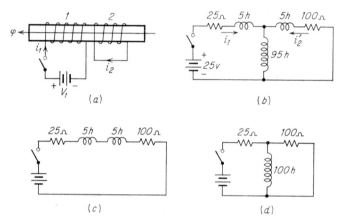

Fig. 1-16. Circuits for Example 1-2. (a) Circuit diagram. (b) Equivalent circuit. (c) Approximate equivalent circuit for rapidly decaying component. (d) Approximate equivalent circuit for slowly decaying component.

Solution. The solution will be in terms of the coupled-circuit equations 1-68 and 1-69 and the results correlated with the equivalent circuit. For the reference directions of Fig. 1-16a the differential equations are

$$v_1(t) = (r_1 + L_{11}p)i_1(t) + L_{12}pi_2(t)$$
$$0 = L_{12}pi_1(t) + (r_2 + L_{22}p)i_2(t)$$

where p is the derivative operator d/dt. From Eqs. 1-53 and 1-61

$$\varphi(t) = \frac{L_{m1}}{N_1}\left(i_1 + \frac{N_2}{N_1}i_2\right) = \frac{L_{12}}{N_2}\left(i_1 + \frac{N_2}{N_1}i_2\right)$$

The equations can be solved either by the classical method or by Laplace transforms. We shall use the classical method and indicate the procedure to be followed by the Laplace-transform method.

The final steady-state solutions are

$$I_1(\infty) = 1.0 \text{ amp} \qquad I_2(\infty) = 0$$
$$\varphi(\infty) = \frac{L_{12}}{N_2}I_1(\infty) = 0.095 \text{ weber}$$

The transient terms are exponential currents of the form $I_1\epsilon^{st}$ and $I_2\epsilon^{st}$. The exponents s are found from the solution of

$$0 = (r_1 + L_{11}s)I_1 + L_{12}sI_2$$
$$0 = L_{12}sI_1 + (r_2 + L_{22}s)I_2$$

Elimination of the currents gives

$$0 = (r_1 + L_{11}s)(r_2 + L_{22}s) - L_{12}^2s^2$$
or
$$0 = (L_{11}L_{22} - L_{12}^2)s^2 + (r_1L_{22} + r_2L_{11})s + r_1r_2$$

From the definition of the leakage coefficient σ (Eq. 1-71),

$$0 = \sigma L_{11}L_{22}s^2 + (r_1L_{22} + r_2L_{11})s + r_1r_2$$

Division by r_1r_2 gives

$$0 = \sigma\tau_1\tau_2s^2 + (\tau_1 + \tau_2)s + 1$$

where the time constants of the 2 windings are

$$\tau_1 = \frac{L_{11}}{r_1} \quad \text{and} \quad \tau_2 = \frac{L_{22}}{r_2}$$

Solving for s gives

$$s_1,\, s_2 = \frac{-(\tau_1 + \tau_2) \pm \sqrt{(\tau_1 + \tau_2)^2 - 4\sigma\tau_1\tau_2}}{2\sigma\tau_1\tau_2}$$

For small values of σ, the values of s_1 and s_2 are very nearly

$$s_1 = -\frac{1}{\tau_1 + \tau_2}$$

$$s_2 = -\frac{1}{\sigma}\left(\frac{1}{\tau_1} + \frac{1}{\tau_2}\right)$$

Substitution of numerical values gives

$$\sigma = 1 - \frac{L_{12}^2}{L_{11}L_{22}} = 0.1$$

$$\tau_1 = 4 \text{ sec} \qquad \tau_2 = 1 \text{ sec}$$
$$s_1 = -0.2 \qquad s_2 = -12.5$$

The solution for $i_1(t)$ is of the form

$$i_1(t) = 1 + A\epsilon^{-0.2t} + B\epsilon^{-12.5t}$$

Its derivative is

$$pi_1(t) = -0.2A\epsilon^{-0.2t} - 12.5B\epsilon^{-12.5t}$$

The initial conditions are

$$i_1(0) = 0 \qquad i_2(0) = 0$$

From the differential equation for winding 2 at $t = 0+$,

$$pi_2(0) = -\frac{L_{12}}{L_{22}}\, pi_1(0)$$

Substitution in the differential equation for winding 1 at $t = 0+$ gives

$$V_1 = \left(L_{11} - \frac{L_{12}^2}{L_{22}}\right)pi_1(0) = \sigma L_{11}pi_1(0)$$

or

$$pi_1(0) = \frac{V_1}{\sigma L_{11}} = 2.5 \quad \text{and} \quad pi_2(0) = -4.75$$

The constants A and B can now be found from the initial conditions. The results are

Similarly

$$i_1(t) = 1 - 0.813\epsilon^{-0.2t} - 0.187\epsilon^{-12.5t}$$
$$i_2(t) = -0.386\epsilon^{-0.2t} + 0.386\epsilon^{-12.5t}$$

$$\varphi(t) = \frac{L_{12}}{N_2}\left(i_1 + \frac{N_2}{N_1}i_2\right)$$

$$= 0.095 - 0.0956\epsilon^{-0.2t} + 0.0006\epsilon^{-12.5t}$$

If the solution had been carried out by Laplace transforms, the equations to be solved would have been

$$\frac{V_1}{s} = (r_1 + L_{11}s)I_1(s) + L_{12}sI_2(s)$$

$$0 = L_{12}sI_1(s) + (r_2 + L_{22}s)I_2(s)$$

yielding

$$I_1(s) = \frac{V_1}{s}\frac{L_{22}s + r_2}{\sigma L_{11}L_{22}s^2 + (r_1L_{22} + r_2L_{11})s + r_1r_2}$$

Simplification, substitution of numerical values, and finding the inverse transform would have given the same result for $i_1(t)$.

Examination of these results and of the equivalent circuit, Fig. 1-16b, shows several interesting things. In this circuit everything is referred to the primary; thus

$$L_{m1} = \frac{N_1}{N_2}L_{12} = 95 \qquad L_{l1} = L_{11} - L_{m1} = 5$$

$$L_{22}' = \left(\frac{N_1}{N_2}\right)^2 L_{22} = 100 \qquad L_{l2}' = L_{22}' - L_{m1} = 5$$

$$r_2' = \left(\frac{N_1}{N_2}\right)^2 r_2 = 100 \qquad i_2' = \frac{N_2}{N_1}i_2 = 0.5i_2$$

For the rapidly decaying components of the currents of frequency s_2 the impedance $L_{m1}s_2$ of the magnetizing branch is much larger (in absolute value) than the secondary leakage impedance $L_{l2}s_2 + r_2'$, a fact which can readily be checked through substitution of numerical values. Thus

$$L_{m1}s_2 = -1,190 \quad \text{and} \quad L_{l2}'s_2 + r_2' = +37.5$$

Nearly all the rapidly decaying current goes through the secondary branch and very little through the magnetizing branch L_{m1}. But the current through L_{m1} is proportional to the net mmf producing the resultant mutual flux. The amplitude of the s_2 term in the expression for $\varphi(t)$ therefore is small, and furthermore it disappears rapidly. If this term is neglected, the expression for the flux becomes simply that of a single-time-constant exponential rise toward its final steady-state value; thus

$$\varphi(t) = 0.095(1 - \epsilon^{-0.2t}), \text{ very nearly}$$

The frequencies s_1 and s_2 can also be found from the equivalent circuit. Because nearly all the rapidly decaying component of current goes through the secondary branch, its frequency s_2 is determined almost wholly by the simple rL circuit comprising the resistances and leakage inductances in series, as in Fig. 1-16c. Therefore

$$s_2 \approx -\frac{r_1 + r_2'}{L_{l1} + L_{l2}'} = -\frac{25 + 100}{5 + 5} = -12.5$$

which agrees with the previous value. For the slowly decaying component of frequency s_1, however, the impedances $L_{l1}s_1$ and $L_{l2}'s_1$ are small compared with the resistances r_1 and r_2'. Consequently the leakage inductances may be neglected and the equivalent circuit reduced to that of Fig. 1-16d. Neglecting leakage is equivalent

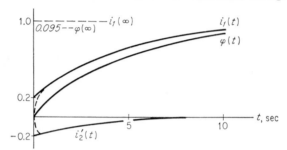

FIG. 1-17. Results of Example 1-2.

to assuming perfect magnetic coupling, or $L_{m1} = L_{11} = L_{22}'$. From this circuit, the natural frequency with the voltage source short-circuited is

$$s_1 = -\frac{r_{\text{par}}}{L_{11}} = -\frac{r_1 r_2'}{(r_1 + r_2')L_{11}} = -\frac{1}{L_{11}/r_1 + L_{11}/r_2'}$$

where r_{par} is the parallel combination of r_1 and r_2'. From Eq. 1-75

$$r_2' = \left(\frac{N_1}{N_2}\right)^2 r_2 = \frac{L_{11}}{L_{22}} r_2$$

whence

$$s_1 = -\frac{1}{L_{11}/r_1 + L_{22}/r_2} = -\frac{1}{\tau_1 + \tau_2}$$

which also agrees with the result found previously.

Furthermore the amplitudes of the transient currents can be found with satisfactory accuracy by neglecting magnetic leakage. From Fig. 1-16d the initial currents are

$$i_1(0+) = -i_2'(0+) = \frac{V_1}{r_1 + r_2'} = \frac{25}{125} = 0.20$$

These initial currents are followed by exponentials whose time constant is $\tau = \tau_1 + \tau_2$. The current $i_1(t)$ rises to its steady-state value $V_1/r_1 = 1.00$, and the induced current $i_2(t)$ dies out. Thus

$$i_1(t) = 1.00 - 0.80\epsilon^{-0.2t}$$
$$i_2'(t) = -0.20\epsilon^{-0.2t} \quad \text{or} \quad i_2(t) = -0.40\epsilon^{0.2t}$$
$$\varphi(t) = 0.095(1 - \epsilon^{-0.2t})$$

These results are shown graphically in Fig. 1-17. Of course the currents cannot actually rise abruptly, because of the leakage inductances. The effect of the leakage inductances is shown by the dotted curves in Fig. 1-17. Except during the short initial period, however, the approximate solutions are very nearly correct.

We therefore come to the following important conclusion: Except for the initial period, the transients in closely coupled circuits can be treated as if they were exponentials having only one time constant τ equal to _start the sum of the time constants of all of the windings.

1-5. Energy in Multiply Excited Magnetic Systems. Most electro-mechanical-energy-conversion devices of the magnetic type consist of several windings arranged in two groups. One group is mounted on a stationary member and the other on a movable member. The various types differ only as to the number of windings, their physical arrangement, and the manner of connecting the windings to the external circuits. The simplest type of such a device, analysis of which will serve to demonstrate the basic principles underlying the action of all of them, consists of 2 magnetically coupled windings connected to two separate electrical sources as shown in Fig. 1-18. Winding 1 is mounted on a rotor which can rotate with respect to the stator on which winding 2 is mounted.

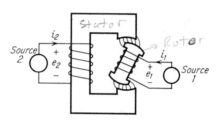

FIG. 1-18. Elementary multiply excited magnetic system.

Both stator and rotor cores are made of magnetic material. The energy in the magnetic field is influenced by the relative positions of the stator and rotor, and equal and opposite mechanical torques act on the two members in much the same manner as two permanent magnets react on each other. The component magnetic fields of stator and rotor tend to align themselves.

a. Induced Voltages and Electric Input. In Fig. 1-18, the magnetic field is determined by the angular position θ of the rotor and the winding currents i_1 and i_2. According to Faraday's law, voltages are induced in the windings whenever the flux linkages are changing, as in Eqs. 1-26. If magnetic saturation is neglected, the induced voltages can be expressed conveniently in terms of the self- and mutual inductances, as in Eqs. 1-64 and 1-65. In Fig. 1-18 the inductances are functions of the angular position θ of the rotor, and if the rotor is turning, they must be treated as variables. Equations 1-64 and 1-65 then become

$$e_1 = \frac{d}{dt}\left[L_{11}(\theta) \cdot i_1 + L_{12}(\theta) \cdot i_2\right]$$

$$= L_{11}(\theta)\frac{di_1}{dt} + L_{12}(\theta)\frac{di_2}{dt} + \left[i_1\frac{dL_{11}(\theta)}{d\theta} + i_2\frac{dL_{12}(\theta)}{d\theta}\right]\frac{d\theta}{dt} \quad (1\text{-}76)$$

where the functional notation $L(\theta)$ is used to emphasize the fact that the inductances are functions of θ. Similarly

$$e_2 = L_{12}(\theta)\frac{di_1}{dt} + L_{22}(\theta)\frac{di_2}{dt} + \left[i_1\frac{dL_{12}(\theta)}{d\theta} + i_2\frac{dL_{22}(\theta)}{d\theta} \right]\frac{d\theta}{dt} \qquad (1\text{-}77)$$

Compare with Eqs. 1-66 and 1-67. Like Eqs. 1-66 and 1-67, the first two terms on the right-hand sides of Eqs. 1-76 and 1-77 are *transformer voltages* due to the time rate of change of the currents. The last terms in Eqs. 1-76 and 1-77 are *speed voltages* proportional to the angular speed $d\theta/dt$. They are present whenever mechanical motion takes place.

When the flux linkages are changing, the differential electrical energy dW_{elec} supplied to the magnetic field by the two sources in time dt is

$$dW_{elec} = e_1 i_1\, dt + e_2 i_2\, dt = i_1\, d\lambda_1 + i_2\, d\lambda_2 \qquad (1\text{-}78)$$
$$dW_{elec} = i_1 d[L_{11}(\theta) \cdot i_1 + L_{12}(\theta) \cdot i_2] + i_2 d[L_{12}(\theta) \cdot i_1 + L_{22}(\theta) \cdot i_2] \qquad (1\text{-}79)$$

where $d\lambda_1$ and $d\lambda_2$ are the total differentials of λ_1 and λ_2, including both changes in the currents and change in angle, as in Eqs. 1-76 and 1-77. Compare with Eqs. 1-11 and 1-12. As in the singly excited system, Art. 1-3, Eq. 1-78 shows that a change in flux linking a circuit causes flow of electrical energy in the circuit. The change in flux may be caused by changes in excitation, or by mechanical motion, or by both. If mechanical motion is involved, mechanical work will be done by the forces created by the magnetic field. Part of the electrical energy input then will be converted to mechanical work. But if no mechanical motion is allowed to take place, all the electrical energy input is absorbed by the magnetic field. In this article we shall be concerned with stationary circuits and the evaluation of the magnetic field energy. Then in Chap. 2 we shall consider the effects of mechanical motion on the electromechanical-energy-conversion process. Equations 1-76, 1-77, and 1-79 are the basis for the treatment of transducers in Chap. 2 and of rotating machines in Part II.

b. Energy in the Magnetic Field. An expression for the energy stored in the magnetic field can be obtained by considering the energy supplied by the sources in establishing the currents i_1 and i_2. If no motion takes place during the process, no mechanical work is done and all the energy supplied by the sources goes into storage in the field. Under these conditions

$$dW_{fld} = dW_{elec} = i_1\, d\lambda_1 + i_2\, d\lambda_2 \qquad (1\text{-}80)$$

For fixed configuration the inductances are constant. Differentiation of Eq. 1-79 and substitution of the results in Eq. 1-80 then gives

$$dW_{fld} = i_1 L_{11}\, di_1 + i_2 L_{22}\, di_2 + L_{12}(i_1\, di_2 + i_2\, di_1) \qquad (1\text{-}81)$$

But $i_1 \, di_2 + i_2 \, di_1$ is the differential $d(i_1 i_2)$ of the product of the currents. Consequently

$$dW_{\text{fld}} = L_{11} i_1 \, di_1 + L_{22} i_2 \, di_2 + L_{12} \, d(i_1 i_2) \qquad (1\text{-}82)$$

and the field energy corresponding to currents i_1 and i_2 is

$$W_{\text{fld}} = L_{11} \int_0^{i_1} i_1 \, di_1 + L_{22} \int_0^{i_2} i_2 \, di_2 + L_{12} \int_0^{i_1 i_2} d(i_1 i_2) \qquad (1\text{-}83)$$

$$W_{\text{fld}} = \tfrac{1}{2} L_{11} i_1^2 + \tfrac{1}{2} L_{22} i_2^2 + L_{12} i_1 i_2 \qquad (1\text{-}84)$$

If the field is produced by currents in more than two circuits, the equation for the field energy in terms of the self- and mutual inductances can be obtained by an identical reasoning process. With three circuits, for example, the result is

$$W_{\text{fld}} = \tfrac{1}{2} L_{11} i_1^2 + \tfrac{1}{2} L_{22} i_2^2 + \tfrac{1}{2} L_{33} i_3^2 + L_{12} i_1 i_2 + L_{23} i_2 i_3 + L_{31} i_3 i_1 \qquad (1\text{-}85)$$

For a magnetically linear system the stored energy W_{fld} equals the coenergy W'_{fld}. We shall need these expressions for the energy and coenergy in the analysis of energy-conversion processes in Chap. 2.

1-6. Energy in the Electrostatic Field. The electric field under quasi-static conditions can be treated in a manner paralleling the foregoing discussion of the magnetic field, and similar energy relations will be obtained. In this article we shall obtain expressions for the energy stored in the field; then in Chap. 2 we shall see what happens to the energy balance when the charged bodies are allowed to move under the influence of the mechanical forces created by the field.

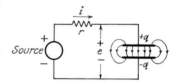

FIG. 1-19. Charged capacitor.

For these purposes consider the electric field of the simple capacitor shown in Fig. 1-19. If the current is i, the differential electrical energy supplied to the capacitor in time dt is

$$dW_{\text{elec}} = ei \, dt = e \, dq \qquad (1\text{-}86)$$

where e is the voltage due to the charge q on the capacitor and $i \, dt = dq$ is the differential charge added to the capacitor. If no mechanical motion takes place, no mechanical work will be done and the energy supplied by the source will be absorbed by the field. For a fixed configuration, the differential energy input to the field then is

$$dW_{\text{fld}} = dW_{\text{elec}} = e \, dq \qquad (1\text{-}87)$$

According to Gauss' theorem, the total electric field flux crossing a closed surface is proportional to the charge enclosed, and in rationalized mks units the constant of proportionality is unity. The total electric flux ψ passing through a closed surface surrounding the positively charged capacitor plate equals the charge $+q$. This flux leaves the surface of the positively charged plate and terminates on the negative charge $-q$ on the surface of the negatively charged plate. For differential changes

$$dW_{\text{fld}} = e\,dq = e\,d\psi \tag{1-88}$$

Note the similarity between Eqs. 1-88 and 1-14. In the electric field, voltage or emf is analogous to current or mmf in the magnetic field. Similarly, charge or electric flux in the electric field is analogous to flux linkage or magnetic flux in the magnetic field. These corresponding quantities are said to be *duals*. The concepts of duality can be extended much further and are often found useful in circuit theory.

The energy absorbed in establishing from zero a charge q or an electric flux ψ with the configuration fixed is

$$W_{\text{fld}} = \int_0^q e(q)\,dq = \int_0^\psi e(\psi)\,d\psi \tag{1-89}$$

where the functional notation $e(q)$ and $e(\psi)$ is used to emphasize the fact that q and ψ are the variables of integration. The field energy equals the

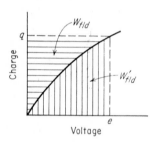

FIG. 1-20. Energy and co-energy in a capacitor.

horizontally shaded area in Fig. 1-20. Compare with Eq. 1-16 and Fig. 1-4. The coenergy W'_{fld} is

$$W'_{\text{fld}} = \int_0^e q(e)\,de = \int_0^e \psi(e)\,de \tag{1-90}$$

wherein q and ψ are explicitly expressed in terms of the voltage e. The coenergy equals the vertically shaded area in Fig. 1-20, which also shows that

$$W_{\text{fld}} + W'_{\text{fld}} = eq = e\psi \tag{1-91}$$

Compare Eqs. 1-90 and 1-91 with Eqs. 1-17 and 1-18 and Fig. 1-20 with Fig. 1-6.

If the permittivity (capacitivity) of the dielectric material in the space occupied by the field is constant and dielectric losses are zero, the charge and flux are proportional to the voltage e and

$$W_{\text{fld}} = W'_{\text{fld}} = \tfrac{1}{2}eq = \tfrac{1}{2}e\psi \tag{1-92}$$

Compare with Eq. 1-19. The capacitance C of the capacitor in farads is defined as

$$C = \frac{q}{e} \tag{1-93}$$

and is constant if the permittivity is constant. Substitution of Eq. 1-93 in Eq. 1-92 gives the familiar expression for the energy stored in a capacitance; thus

$$W_{\text{fld}} = W'_{\text{fld}} = \tfrac{1}{2}Ce^2 \qquad (1\text{-}94)$$

Compare with Eq. 1-24. Capacitance is the dual of inductance.
The energy density w_{fld} and coenergy density w'_{fld} in an electrostatic field in a linear lossless dielectric can be expressed as

$$w_{\text{fld}} = w'_{\text{fld}} = \tfrac{1}{2}\mathcal{E}\mathfrak{D} = \tfrac{1}{2}\epsilon\mathcal{E}^2 = \frac{1}{2}\frac{\mathfrak{D}^2}{\epsilon} \qquad (1\text{-}95)$$

in joules per cubic meter at a point where the electric field intensity is $\mathcal{E}$ volts/m, the electrostatic flux density or displacement is $\mathfrak{D}$ coulombs/m², and the permittivity is ϵ. Compare with Eq. 1-25. The electric field quantities $\mathcal{E}$, $\mathfrak{D}$, and ϵ are duals of the magnetic field quantities $\mathfrak{IC}$, $\mathfrak{B}$, and μ, respectively.

1-7. Résumé. The principle of conservation of energy is applicable to all energy-conversion processes in which matter is neither created nor destroyed. This principle is the basis for the treatment of electromechanical energy conversion in this book.

In electrical form, energy is associated with the electromagnetic field of electric charges, as described by Maxwell's field equations. The frequencies and velocities involved in the processes discussed in this book are sufficiently low so that quasi-static field conditions prevail. The electrical energy relations then can be described in terms of lumped-parameter electric circuits and the mechanical energy relations in terms of Newton's laws. The coupling between the electrical and mechanical systems is through the medium of energy storage in the electromagnetic field, as discussed in Art. 1-2 and expressed in Eqs. 1-2 and 1-7.

In this chapter we have been primarily concerned with energy storage, a necessary preliminary to the study of energy conversion in Chap. 2. The field energy is determined by the currents or charges and the configuration of the material bodies constituting the boundaries of the field. The field energy can be found by considering the electrical energy input in establishing the field with fixed configuration of the boundaries as in Eqs. 1-14, 1-80, and 1-87. With ferromagnetic material the mmf-flux characteristic is more or less nonlinear as shown in Figs. 1-4 and 1-6. In these figures the horizontally shaded area is the energy W_{fld}; the vertically shaded area is called the coenergy W'_{fld}. Similar areas are shown in Fig. 1-20 for the quasi-static electric field.

For linear materials the magnetic field energy can be conveniently expressed in terms of the field variables and parameters, as in Eq. 1-22, or in terms of the current variables and inductance parameters, as in Eqs. 1-24 and 1-84. The corresponding expression for the electrostatic field is Eq. 1-94 in terms of voltage and capacitance.

Most electromechanical-energy-conversion devices of the magnetic type consist of several windings on a common magnetic circuit, and a study of stationary coupled circuits is a necessary prelude to the study of energy conversion in these devices. The introductory treatment of transformers in Art. 1-4 serves this broader purpose. In Art. 1-4 it has been shown that there are two ways in which the theory of closely coupled magnetic systems can be treated.

The first way, discussed in Art. 1-4c, is a magnetic-circuit treatment. It considers that the principal magnetic field is a resultant mutual flux produced by the combined mmf of all the windings, as in Eq. 1-41. Superposed on the principal field are leakage fluxes linking the individual windings. Their effects are accounted for by means of leakage inductances defined in Eq. 1-45. This method of analysis leads to a simple equivalent circuit in which the component elements have clearly defined physical meaning. Often this equivalent circuit suggests simplifying approximations. By this method the nonlinear effects of the magnetic core can be taken into account, as will be shown in Art. 7-7. This method is the basis for the treatment of rotating machines in Part III.

The second way, discussed in Art. 1-4d, is based on superposition and consequently neglects the effects of magnetic nonlinearity. It considers that the magnetic field is the sum of the component fields produced by the separate effects of each winding acting alone. This method of analysis leads to the classical theory of linear coupled circuits as expressed in Eqs. 1-64 through 1-69. These equations can be manipulated mathematically to obtain the solution for the system behavior when sufficient terminal conditions are specified. This method of analysis is the basis for the dynamic-circuit theory of transducers in Chap. 2 and of rotating machines in Part II. The two methods of analysis are supplementary, and it is advantageous to be able to shift from one to the other.

PROBLEMS

1-1. The cylindrical iron-clad solenoid magnet shown in Fig. 1-21 is used for tripping circuit breakers, for operating valves, and in other applications in which a relatively large force is applied to a member which moves a relatively short distance. When the coil current is zero, the plunger drops against a stop such that the gap g is 0.50 in. When the coil is energized by a direct current of sufficient magnitude, the plunger is raised until it hits another stop set so that g is 0.10 in. The plunger is supported so that it can move freely in the vertical direction. The air gap between the shell and the plunger can be assumed to be uniform and 0.01 in. long. For the purposes of this problem neglect magnetic leakage and fringing in the air gaps. The exciting coil has 1,000 turns and carries a constant current of 3.0 amp.

If the mmf in the iron is neglected:

a. Compute the flux densities, in webers per square meter, between the working faces of the center core and plunger for gaps g of 0.10, 0.20, and 0.50 in.

b. Compute the corresponding values of the energy stored in the magnetic field, in watt-seconds.

c. Compute the corresponding values of the coil inductance, in henrys.

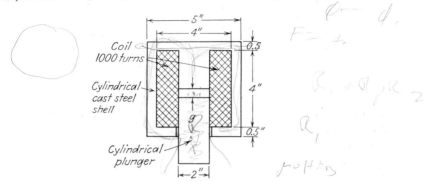

Fig. 1-21. Plunger magnet for Probs. 1-1, 1-2, 2-2, 2-3, and 2-4.

1-2. Data for the magnetization curve of the iron portion of the magnetic circuit of the plunger magnet of Problem 1-1 are given below:

Flux, kilolines...........	100	150	200	240	250	260	270	275
Mmf, amp-turns..........	60	95	150	250	305	425	600	725

Plot magnetization curves for the complete magnetic circuit (flux in webers vs. total mmf in ampere-turns) for the following conditions:

a. Gap $g = 0.50$ in.

b. Gap $g = 0.10$ in.

c. From these curves find graphically the magnetic field energy and coenergy for each of the gaps in (*a*) and (*b*) with 3.0 amp coil current.

1-3. A square voltage wave having a fundamental frequency of 60 cps and equal positive and negative half cycles of amplitude E volts is impressed on a resistanceless winding of 1,000 turns surrounding a closed iron core of 10^{-3} m^2 cross section.

a. Sketch curves of voltage and flux as functions of time.

b. Find the maximum permissible value of E if the maximum flux density is not to exceed 1.00 weber/m^2.

1-4. Data for the top half of a symmetrical hysteresis loop for the core of Prob. 1-3 are given below:

B, webers/m^2...	0	0.2	0.4	0.6	0.7	0.8	0.9	1.0	0.95	0.9	0.8	0.7	0.6	0.4	0.2	0
H, amp-turns/m	48	52	58	73	85	103	135	193	80	42	2	−18	−29	−40	−45	−48

The mean length of the flux paths in the core is 0.30 m.

Find graphically the hysteresis loss in watts for a maximum flux density of 1.00 weber/m^2 at a frequency of 60 cps.

1-5. The time constant L/r of the field winding of a 10-kw 1,150-rpm d-c shunt generator is 0.15 sec. At normal operating conditions, the i^2r loss in its field winding is 350 watts. Compute the energy stored in its magnetic field, in watt-seconds, at normal operating conditions.

1-6. Figure 1-22 shows an inductor wound on a high-permeability laminated iron core of rectangular cross section. Assume that the permeability of the iron is infinite. Neglect magnetic leakage and fringing in the air gap g. The winding is insulated copper wire whose resistivity is ρ ohm-m. Assume that the fraction k_w of the winding space is available for copper, the rest of the space being used for insulation.

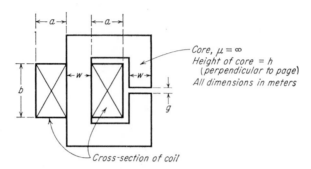

FIG. 1-22. Iron-core inductor for Probs. 1-6 and 1-7.

a. Estimate the mean length l of a turn of the winding.

b. Derive an expression for the electric power input to the coil for a specified steady flux density B. This expression should be in terms of B, ρ, μ_0, l, k_w, and the given dimensions. Note that the expression is independent of the number of turns if the winding factor k_w is assumed to be independent of the turns.

c. Derive an expression for the magnetic stored energy in terms of B and the given dimensions.

d. From (*b*) and (*c*) derive an expression for the time constant L/r of the coil.

1-7. The inductor of Fig. 1-22 has the following dimensions:

$$a = h = w = 1 \text{ cm}$$
$$b = 2 \text{ cm} \qquad g = 0.2 \text{ cm}$$

The winding space factor $k_w = 0.7$. The resistivity of copper = 1.73 microhm-cm.

The coil is to be operated with a constant applied voltage of 50 volts, and the air-gap flux density is to be 1.0 weber/m².

Find the power input to the coil, the coil current, the number of turns, the coil resistance, the inductance, the time constant, and the wire size to the nearest standard size.

1-8. A 5-kva 2,400:240-volt transformer has the following parameters:

Turns ratio $N_1/N_2 = 10:1$
Resistances $r_1 = 10$ ohms, $r_2 = 0.10$ ohm
Leakage inductances $L_{l1} = 0.0266$ henry, $L_{l2} = 0.000266$ henry
Mutual inductance $L_{12} = 15.9$ henrys

a. Find the primary self-inductance and the secondary self-inductance.

b. Draw equivalent circuits showing numerical values of all parameters referred to' (1) the primary, (2) the secondary.

1-9. The primary of the transformer of Prob. 1-8 is connected to a sinusoidal voltage source of 2,400 volts rms and 60 cps frequency. Its secondary is connected to a load whose impedance at 60 cps is 8.0 + j8.0 ohms.

a. Find the Thévenin equivalent circuit as viewed from the secondary terminals. Show that the effect of the magnetizing inductance is negligible.

b. Find the secondary terminal voltage.

1-10. An audio-frequency transformer has primary and secondary resistances of 200 ohms each, primary and secondary leakage inductances of 5 mh each, and a magnetizing inductance of 0.632 henry, all referred to the primary. These values may be considered to be independent of frequency. The primary-to-secondary turns ratio is $\sqrt{40}$. Iron losses are to be neglected.

The transformer is used to couple a 50-ohm resistive load to a source which may be represented by a constant voltage of 5 volts in series with an internal resistance of 2,000 ohms. Determine the ratio of primary-to-secondary terminal voltage under the following conditions:

a. At 100 cps, neglecting leakage reactance.

b. At 15,000 cps, omitting the magnetizing reactance.

c. At 5,000 cps, omitting the magnetizing reactance and neglecting the leakage reactance.

d. For the numerical orders of magnitude involved, justify the simplifying approximations of (*a*), (*b*), and (*c*).

1-11. A copper tube 1 m long, 1 mm thick, and 5 cm external diameter is completely covered with a winding of 1,150 turns of No. 20 enameled copper wire. The resistivity of the copper tubing is 1.73 microhm-cm, and the resistance of the winding is 6.15 ohms. Assume that exactly the same flux links both winding and tube and that the reluctance of the flux paths is that of the column of air enclosed by the copper tube.

Treat the winding and tube as a short-circuited transformer with the winding as the primary and the tube as the short-circuited secondary. Draw an equivalent circuit with all parameters referred to the primary winding. Label the equivalent circuit with numerical values of all resistance and inductance parameters.

1-12. A d-c voltage source of 10 volts is suddenly applied to the winding of Prob. 1-11. Find the equations for (*a*) the winding current $i(t)$ and (*b*) the winding flux linkage $\lambda(t)$ as functions of time. Sketch curves of $i(t)$ and $\lambda(t)$ showing initial values at $t = 0+$, final values, and the time constant.

1-13. Draw an equivalent circuit representing Eqs. 1-68 and 1-69 with v_1 and i_1 as inputs at terminal pair 1, v_2 and i_2 as inputs at terminal pair 2, and L_{12} as the coupling parameter. Find numerical values of the parameters of this equivalent circuit for the transformer of Prob. 1-8.

1-14. In Eqs. 1-68 and 1-69 make the following changes in the variables and parameters:

Multiply v_2 by any real number a.

Divide i_2 by a.

Multiply L_{12} by a.

Multiply r_2 and L_{22} by a^2.

Show that the coupled-circuit equations are still valid. Draw an equivalent circuit representing the modified coupled-circuit equations with v_1 and i_1 as inputs at terminal pair 1 and av_2 and i_2/a as inputs at terminal pair 2. Show that if a is the turns ratio N_1/N_2 the result is identical to the equivalent circuit of Fig. 1-14.

1-15. Three coils are wound close together on a common magnetic circuit. Assume that the permeability is constant. Write the voltage equations for the three circuits in terms of the input currents, the resistance and inductance parameters, and the derivative operator $p = d/dt$. Matrix notation is suggested.

1-16. For the 3 windings of Prob. 1-15, assume that the magnetic circuit has high and constant permeability, that the resultant core flux links all the turns of all windings, and that magnetic leakage between windings is negligible.

The winding turns are

$$N_1 = 1,000 \qquad N_2 = 500 \qquad N_3 = 100$$

The winding resistances, in ohms, are

$$r_1 = 1,000 \qquad r_2 = 150 \qquad r_3 = 4$$

The self-inductance of winding 1 is

$$L_{11} = 200 \text{ henrys}$$

Find an equivalent circuit with the voltages, currents, and parameters of windings 2 and 3 referred to winding 1. Give numerical values of the parameters.

Also, find the actual values of the self-inductances of windings 2 and 3.

1-17. At $t = 0$, a constant voltage of 124 volts is suddenly applied to the terminals of winding 1, Prob. 1-16, with the terminals of windings 2 and 3 short-circuited. Find the equations for the core flux and the currents in windings 1, 2, and 3 as functions of time. Sketch the corresponding curves.

CHAPTER 2

Electromechanical-energy-conversion Principles

All electromechanical-energy-conversion devices have certain basic features in common. The moving-coil telephone receiver, for example, behaves according to the same basic physical laws which govern the behavior of a 100,000-kw electric generator. The purpose of this chapter is to describe the physical principles of electromechanical energy conversion in general terms, to develop a basic theory from which the mechanical forces produced by magnetic and electrostatic fields can be determined, and to compare the potentialities of magnetic and electrostatic fields as force-producing media.

The method of attack has already been discussed in Art. 1-1. As shown in Eq. 1-7, application of the principle of conservation of energy to the electromechanical-energy-conversion process leads to the basic differential equation

$$dW_{elec} = dW_{fld} + dW_{mech} \qquad (2-1)$$

where dW_{elec} is the net electrical energy input after copper losses have been accounted for, dW_{fld} is the differential energy absorbed by the coupling field, and dW_{mech} is the net internal energy converted to mechanical form including mechanical losses. This equation is written so that the electrical and mechanical energy terms have positive values for motor action. It applies equally well to generator action: the electrical and mechanical energy terms then have negative values. This equation, together with Faraday's law for induced voltage, is the foundation on which the whole structure of this chapter is laid.

2-1. Singly Excited Magnetic Systems. In Chap. 1 we have considered the energy interchanges between the electric circuit and the magnetic field for a fixed configuration of the mechanical parts. The interchange of energy between an electrical system and a mechanical system is possible when the energy in the coupling field is influenced by the configuration of the mechanical elements.

41

a. Mechanical Work. As a simple example, consider the relay attracting the iron armature in Fig. 2-1a. The magnetization curves of the magnetic circuit for the open and closed positions of the armature are shown in Fig. 2-1b. Suppose the switch S is closed and the armature is held forcibly in the open position until the current in the coil has settled down to its final d-c steady-state value E_s/r. The corresponding operating point for the magnetic circuit is the point a (Fig. 2-1b). Now let the armature be released. It will move under the influence of the magnetic force of attraction and eventually will stop in the closed position. After the transients have disappeared, the final operating point is at b in Fig. 2-1b.

During the transient period while the armature is moving, the flux is increasing, and a counter emf is induced in the coil. This emf depends on

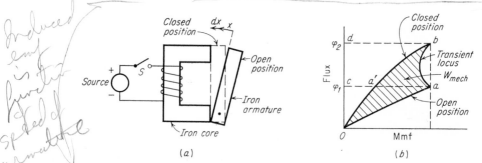

FIG. 2-1. (a) Relay and (b) corresponding flux-mmf characteristics.

how fast the armature moves. If it moves very slowly, the induced emf is negligible; the current then stays substantially constant, and the flux-mmf locus during the transient period approaches the vertical dotted line ab in Fig. 2-1b. On the other hand, if the motion is very fast, it will have taken place before the flux has changed appreciably; the flux-mmf locus while the armature is moving then approaches the horizontal dotted line aa', and after the motion is all over the flux and mmf rise along the magnetization curve $a'b$. The complete solution for the transient condition is complicated and involves the inertia and frictional forces of the mechanical system as well as the transient behavior of the electrical system. We shall not go any further into these details at present. Rather, we shall assume that the flux-mmf locus during the transient period is known and lies somewhere between the two limits described above, as shown by the curve ab in Fig. 2-1b.

Consider the significance of the various areas in Fig. 2-1b. Area $OacO$ to the left of the original magnetization curve represents the energy abstracted from the electrical source and absorbed by the magnetic field during the initial excitation of the coil while the armature is in the open position. For simplicity, neglect hysteresis and eddy currents. This energy then is stored in the magnetic field. After the armature has moved into the closed position, the energy stored in the field is represented by the area $ObdO$ to the left of the final magnetization curve. Consequently the increase in energy stored in the field is

$$\Delta W_{\text{fld}} = ObdO - OacO \qquad (2\text{-}2)$$

While the armature is moving, the flux is increasing from φ_1 to φ_2 and an emf is induced in the coil. The corresponding energy abstracted from the source during this time is, from Eq. 1-12,

$$W_{\text{elec}} = \int_{\varphi_1}^{\varphi_2} \mathfrak{F}\, d\varphi = \text{area } cabdc \qquad (2\text{-}3)$$

Substitution of Eqs. 2-2 and 2-3 in the energy-balance equation 2-1 gives

$$W_{\text{elec}} = \Delta W_{\text{fld}} + W_{\text{mech}} \qquad (2\text{-}4)$$
$$\text{Area } cabdc = ObdO - OacO + W_{\text{mech}} \qquad (2\text{-}5)$$
whence $\qquad W_{\text{mech}} = OacO + cabdc - ObdO = OabdO - ObdO \qquad (2\text{-}6)$
$$= OabO \qquad (2\text{-}7)$$

This important relation shows that the energy converted to mechanical form equals the area included by the original and final magnetization curves and the flux-mmf locus during motion, as shown by the cross-hatched area in Fig. 2-1b. Any singly excited magnetic system whose magnetization curve is affected by the relative position of its parts is a potential electromechanical-energy-conversion device.

b. Mechanical Forces—Virtual Work. The magnitude and direction of the mechanical forces on any part of a magnetic system can be determined by considering what would happen to the energy balance if the part in question were allowed to move an infinitesimal distance dx in the direction of the magnetic force f acting upon it. This method of determining forces by means of the effect on the energy balance of an imaginary or virtual displacement is commonly used in the analysis of physical systems to which conservation of energy applies. It is called the principle of *virtual work.*

Although the relations which will be derived below have a very broad significance, it may be helpful initially to consider a simple specific case such as the relay of Fig. 2-1a. The magnetic force of attraction on the armature can be determined by considering the effect on the energy balance if the air gap were shortened a differential amount dx. Mechanical work $f\, dx$ would then be done by the magnetic force of attraction f. At the same time the reluctance of the magnetic circuit would change. The current and flux also may change because of the induced transients described in Art. 2-1a.

Figure 2-2 shows the effect of the differential displacement dx on the magnetization curve. The curve for air gap x is the one so marked; the curve for the shortened gap is marked $x + dx$. The operating point at x is point a; at $x + dx$ it is point b. The mmf and flux at the operating point a are F and ϕ, respectively. This figure is similar to Fig. 2-1b, except that the difference between the curves Oa and Ob is the infinitesimal amount resulting from the differential virtual displacement dx.

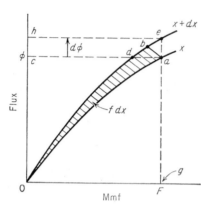

FIG. 2-2. Illustrating virtual work.

Just as in Art. 2-1a, the mechanical work done by the magnetic force is area $OabO$, whence

$$f\,dx = OabO \qquad (2\text{-}8)$$

But area $OabO$ differs from area $OadO$ by the area of triangle abd, whose altitude and base are both infinitesimals. In the limit as dx approaches zero, $OabO = OadO$ and

$$f\,dx = OadO = OacO - OdcO \qquad (2\text{-}9)$$

Areas $OacO$ and $OdcO$ represent the energies stored in the magnetic field respectively before and after the virtual displacement dx with flux ϕ constant. Their difference is the decrease in stored energy at constant flux; thus

$$f\,dx = -dW_{\text{fld}}(\phi,x) \qquad \text{with } \phi \text{ constant} \qquad (2\text{-}10)$$

$$f\,dx = -\frac{\partial W_{\text{fld}}}{\partial x}(\phi,x)\,dx \qquad (2\text{-}11)$$

The functional notation $W_{\text{fld}}(\phi,x)$ is used here to emphasize the fact that the field energy must be expressed explicitly in terms of flux ϕ (or flux linkage λ) and x. From Eq. 2-11

$$f = -\frac{\partial W_{\text{fld}}}{\partial x}(\phi,x) \qquad (2\text{-}12)$$

By similar reasoning, area $OabO$ differs from area $OaeO$ by the second-order infinitesimal area of triangle abe. Therefore in the limit as dx approaches zero

$$f\,dx = OaeO = OgeO - OgaO \qquad (2\text{-}13)$$

Areas $OgeO$ and $OgaO$ represent the coenergies, respectively, after and before the virtual displacement dx with mmf F constant. Their difference is the increase in coenergy at constant mmf; thus

$$f\,dx = +dW'_{\text{fld}}(F,x) \qquad \text{with } F \text{ constant} \qquad (2\text{-}14)$$

where $W'_{fld}(F,x)$ is the *coenergy* and the functional notation is used to emphasize the fact that the coenergy must be explicitly expressed in terms of mmf F (or current i) and x. From Eq. 2-14

$$f = + \frac{\partial W'_{fld}}{\partial x}(F,x) \tag{2-15}$$

Equations 2-12 and 2-15 are fundamental relations of electromechanical coupling. Although the simple relay of Fig. 2-1a has been used as a concrete example, it should be clearly understood that these equations have very broad significance. Consider any magnetic system, one part of which is movable as a rigid body with respect to the other parts. In general, the movable part will be acted upon by magnetic translational forces and rotational torques. The value of the component magnetic force acting in any direction on any part can be determined by imagining the part in question to be given a virtual displacement, say, dx, and evaluating the corresponding partial derivative in Eq. 2-12 or 2-15. Torque can be determined by giving the part a virtual angular displacement $d\theta$ and finding the corresponding derivatives with respect to θ.

Equations 2-12 and 2-15 express the mechanical force of electrical origin in terms of partial derivatives of the energy and coenergy functions $W_{fld}(\phi,x)$ and $W'_{fld}(F,x)$. It is important to note two things about them, (1) the variables in terms of which they must be expressed and (2) their algebraic signs. Mathematically, the derivations have shown that it makes no difference how the flux and mmf are assumed to change with virtual displacement because, in the limit process of shrinking the displacement dx to an infinitesimal, the effects of flux and mmf changes become second-order effects. Physically, of course, the force depends on the dimension x and the magnetic field and is independent of the way in which the field may change, a statement which agrees with the mathematics. The field can be specified in terms of flux ϕ, or mmf F, or related variables. Mathematically, however, it makes a great deal of difference as to which energy function is used and the variables in terms of which it is expressed. Thus in Eq. 2-12 the stored energy $W_{fld}(\phi,x)$ must be explicitly expressed in terms of flux ϕ or the related field variable, flux linkage λ, as in Eq. 1-16. The partial derivative in Eq. 2-12 is then taken with the field variables treated as constants. In Eq. 2-15 the coenergy $W'_{fld}(F,x)$ must be explicitly expressed in terms of mmf F or the related field variable, current i, as in Eqs. 1-17. The partial derivative in Eq. 2-15 is then taken with these field variables treated as constants.

Although the restrictions in Eqs. 2-12 and 2-15 are mathematical constraints resulting from the choice of variables, they can also be given a simple physical interpretation which will explain the algebraic signs.

For differential displacement dx the energy balance (Eq. 2-1) becomes

$$F \, d\phi = dW_{\text{fld}} + f \, dx \tag{2-16}$$

wherein the electrical energy input is $F \, d\phi$, as in Eq. 1-12, with F and ϕ the values of $\mathcal{F}$ and φ at the operating point. But since we have shown that the force f is independent of $d\phi$, an expression for the force can be found by considering what would happen if the flux were constant, or $F \, d\phi = 0$. Equation 2-16 then reduces to Eq. 2-10. This equation simply states that if the virtual displacement dx were to take place at constant flux the electrical energy input $F \, d\phi$ would be zero and the mechanical work done $f \, dx$ would be at the expense of the energy stored in the magnetic field. The force therefore equals the rate, with respect to motion, at which energy can be abstracted from the magnetic field at constant flux, as shown by the minus sign in Eq. 2-12.

On the other hand, if the mmf were considered constant, the flux would increase and the operating point would move vertically from a to e (Fig. 2-2). The electrical input $F \, d\phi$ would then be the area of the rectangle $aehc$ (Fig. 2-2). But the sum of the energy plus the coenergy (Eq. 1-18) increases from rectangle $Ogac$ to rectangle $Ogeh$, whence

$$dW_{\text{fld}} + dW'_{\text{fld}} = aehc = F \, d\phi \tag{2-17}$$

or
$$dW_{\text{fld}} = F \, d\phi - dW'_{\text{fld}} \tag{2-18}$$

Substitution of Eq. 2-18 in Eq. 2-16 gives, for constant mmf F,

$$F \, d\phi = F \, d\phi - dW'_{\text{fld}} + f \, dx \tag{2-19}$$

which reduces to Eq. 2-14. Thus the force f is equal to the rate of increase of coenergy at constant mmf, as shown by the plus sign in Eq. 2-15.

A word of caution: Although the force is independent of differential changes in flux and mmf resulting from differential motion dx, it is evident from Fig. 2-1b that the mechanical work done with finite motion does depend on the flux-mmf locus.

Example 2-1. A simple, purely hypothetical example will illustrate the mathematical processes involved in Eqs. 2-12 and 2-15.

Assume that the functional relationship of mmf $\mathcal{F}$, flux φ, and the position coordinate x is given by

$$\mathcal{F} = \varphi^2 x^2$$

From Eqs. 2-12 and 2-15, find the mechanical force f acting in the x direction, and show that the results are identical.

Solution. From Eq. 1-16, the stored energy is

$$W_{\text{fld}}(\phi,x) = \int_0^\phi \mathcal{F}(\varphi,x) \, d\varphi = \int_0^\phi \varphi^2 x^2 \, d\varphi = \tfrac{1}{3}\phi^3 x^2$$

where ϕ is the flux at the operating point.   From Eq. 2-12

$$f = -\frac{\partial W_{\text{fld}}}{\partial x}(\phi,x) = -\tfrac{2}{3}\phi^3 x$$

Alternatively, from Eq. 1-17 the coenergy is

$$W'_{\text{fld}}(F,x) = \int_0^F \varphi(\mathfrak{F},x)\, d\mathfrak{F}$$

From the flux-mmf expression

$$\varphi = \frac{\mathfrak{F}^{1/2}}{x}$$

Thus

$$W'_{\text{fld}}(F,x) = \int_0^F \frac{\mathfrak{F}^{1/2}}{x}\, d\mathfrak{F} = \frac{2}{3}\frac{F^{3/2}}{x}$$

From Eq. 2-15

$$f = +\frac{\partial W'_{\text{fld}}}{\partial x}(F,x) = -\frac{2}{3}\frac{F^{3/2}}{x^2}$$

From the flux-mmf expression

$$F^{3/2} = \phi^3 x^3$$

and substitution in the expression for f found from Eq. 2-15 gives

$$f = -\tfrac{2}{3}\phi^3 x$$

which is the same result as was found from Eq. 2-12.   In these results, the minus signs show that the force due to the field tends to decrease the coordinate x.

In dealing with magnetic devices the flux-mmf characteristics usually are given in graphical form, rather than as analytic expressions.   The force can then be found by graphical methods based on Eq. 2-12 or 2-15 if a family of flux-mmf characteristics for various constant values of the coordinate x are available.   For example, the coenergy can be found at constant mmf F and various values of the coordinate x, by measuring the area under the flux-mmf curves for each value of x.   The force f corresponding to mmf F and any desired value of x, say, x_1, can then be found by measuring the slope of the coenergy curve $W'_{\text{fld}}(F,x)$ at $x = x_1$ in accordance with Eq. 2-15.   An alternative graphical solution can be made based on the stored energy $W_{\text{fld}}(\phi,x)$ in accordance with Eq. 2-12. The procedure is fairly long and laborious.   Fortunately, however, the much simpler relations derived below on the basis of magnetic linearity usually give satisfactory results when properly applied, even though the magnetic circuit may be saturated.

c. *Mechanical Forces, Linear Analysis.*   When the flux and mmf are linearly proportional, as in air, the energy and coenergy are equal, as in Eqs. 1-22 and 1-24.   The only difference between energy and coenergy then is the variables in terms of which they are expressed.   Nevertheless, care must be taken to use the proper variables in finding the force from Eqs. 2-12 and 2-15; otherwise the algebraic signs will be incorrect.

If the energy is explicitly expressed in terms of flux or flux linkage then the force is given by Eq. 2-12 with the negative sign; thus

$$f = -\frac{\partial W_{\text{fld}}}{\partial x}(\phi,x) = -\frac{\partial W_{\text{fld}}}{\partial x}(\lambda,x) \tag{2-20}$$

with ϕ or λ constant in the differentiation. This equation is *always* true. When flux and mmf are linearly proportional, Eq. 2-15 can be written interchangeably in terms of stored energy or coenergy so long as the proper variables are used; thus

$$f = +\frac{\partial W'_{\text{fld}}}{\partial x}(F,x) = +\frac{\partial W'_{\text{fld}}}{\partial x}(i,x) \tag{2-21}$$

$$f = +\frac{\partial W_{\text{fld}}}{\partial x}(F,x) = +\frac{\partial W_{\text{fld}}}{\partial x}(i,x) \tag{2-22}$$

with F or i constant in the differentiation. Equation 2-21 in terms of coenergy is *always* true, but Eq. 2-22 in terms of stored energy is true *only* when flux and mmf are linearly proportional.

Other useful forms can be derived from Eqs. 2-20 and 2-22. Differentiation of Eq. 1-22 in terms of flux ϕ and reluctance $\mathcal{R}$ in accordance with Eq. 2-20 gives

$$f = -\tfrac{1}{2}\phi^2 \frac{d\mathcal{R}}{dx} \tag{2-23}$$

in which the reluctance is a function of x. For example, in the simple relay of Fig. 2-1a the reluctance is a function of the position of the armature. In terms of mmf F and permeance $\mathcal{P}$, from Eqs. 1-22 and 2-22

$$f = +\tfrac{1}{2}F^2 \frac{d\mathcal{P}}{dx} \tag{2-24}$$

In terms of current i and inductance L, from Eqs. 1-24 and 2-22

$$f = +\tfrac{1}{2}i^2 \frac{dL}{dx} \tag{2-25}$$

The force is thus seen to act in a direction to tend to decrease the stored energy at constant flux, to increase the stored energy and coenergy at constant mmf, to decrease the reluctance, and to increase the permeance and inductance.

In a singly excited magnetic system containing iron elements, it is the configuration of the iron elements which principally affects the reluctance. Most of the force then acts directly on these iron elements. In the normal type of energy-conversion device, most of the force which is available to do useful work acts on iron bodies mounted to allow the desired type of motion. In such a device, there is normally a single force or torque which is involved in the desired energy conversion. There are also forces acting to produce stresses within the iron members. These stresses cause strains which modify the shape of the members in a manner

to reduce the reluctance.   This phenomenon is known as *magnetostriction*.
The result of the internal stresses in an alternating field is vibration,
which is usually undesirable since it causes noise.

There are also forces acting directly on the exciting coil.   In accordance
with the general principle, these forces tend to move the coil as a rigid
body into the position on the magnetic circuit where the reluctance is a
minimum and also tend to deform it by compressing it axially and expand-
ing it in cross-sectional area of flux path.   A coil wound on a rectangular
form, for example, tends to deform into a circle.   The shape and position
of the exciting coil on an iron magnetic circuit usually have relatively
little effect on the reluctance.   Consequently, under normal conditions
the forces acting directly on the exciting coil are much smaller than those
acting on the iron members.   Under abnormal conditions, however, such
as short circuits on large power apparatus, the forces on the coil may be
extremely large.

Equations 2-20 through 2-24 are often used to compute the forces on
moving-iron devices with air gaps even when the magnetic circuit is
nonlinear.   To justify their use in this manner, assume that the distribution of flux throughout the magnetic material and in the leakage field is
unchanged when the movable part is given a displacement dx and the
flux is held constant.   This condition usually is approximately met in
singly excited systems, except when the saturation or the magnetic
leakage is abnormally high.   Also assume that the volume of magnetic
material in the field is constant.   Then the only changes in magnetic
conditions caused by the displacement dx occur in the immediate vicinity
of the variable air gap, whose reluctance is independent of the flux.   The
problem then reduces to one involving changes in only the linear portion
of the field.   All the force relations which have been derived in this
article for the linear case therefore apply within the limitations of the
assumptions.   Thus Eqs. 2-20, 2-22, 2-23, and 2-24 may be written in
terms of the air-gap flux, the magnetic potential difference between the
faces of the air gap, the air-gap reluctance, the air-gap permeance, and
the magnetic energy stored in the air gap.   The problem then reduces to
the calculation of conditions in the air gap, which in turn can be computed from dimensions.[1]

Although nonlinearity does not enter directly into these approximate
force equations, it should not be forgotten that saturation often may have
an important indirect effect on the force produced by a specified coil current, since the air-gap flux and mmf will be determined by the magnetic
characteristics of the entire magnetic circuit.

Although the discussion of this article is based on the magnetic field

---

[1] For an extensive treatment of a wide variety of moving iron devices see H. C.
Roters, "Electromagnetic Devices," John Wiley & Sons, Inc., New York, 1941.

produced by a current-carrying coil, the final results show that the force depends primarily on energy changes at the variable air gap and is independent of the source of the field. Force equations in terms of conditions at the air gap therefore apply equally well when the field is produced by permanent magnets.

Example 2-2. Derive expressions for the force of attraction between two parallel plane faces of high-permeability ferromagnetic material with flux passing normally between them, as shown in Fig. 2-3. Neglect fringing.

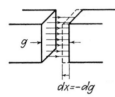

Solution. The force relations readily can be derived in terms of the air-gap reluctance, the air-gap permeance, or the air-gap field energy. The first approach will be chosen here.

The reluctance $\mathfrak{R}_{ag}$ of the air gap is

$dx=-dg$

FIG. 2-3. Air gap with parallel faces.

$$\mathfrak{R}_{ag} = \frac{g}{\mu_0 A} \qquad (2\text{-}26)$$

where g is the air-gap length, A is the area of each surface, and μ_0 is the permeability of air. Differentiation with respect to x (Fig. 2-3) gives

$$\frac{d\mathfrak{R}_{ag}}{dx} = \frac{1}{\mu_0 A}\frac{dg}{dx} = -\frac{1}{\mu_0 A} \qquad (2\text{-}27)$$

since dx is a negative increment in gap length. Substitution of Eq. 2-27 in Eq. 2-23 gives

$$f = +\frac{\phi_{ag}^2}{2\mu_0 A} \qquad (2\text{-}28)$$

where ϕ_{ag} is the air-gap flux. In rationalized mks units the force is in newtons. An alternative form is

$$f = +\frac{B_{ag}^2 A}{2\mu_0} \qquad (2\text{-}29)$$

where B_{ag} is the air-gap flux density and equals ϕ_{ag}/A.

Example 2-3. The magnetic circuit shown in Fig. 2-4 is made of cast steel. The rotor is free to turn about a vertical axis. The dimensions are shown in the figure.

a. Derive an expression in mks rationalized units for the torque acting on the rotor in terms of the dimensions and the magnetic field in the two air gaps. Neglect the effects of fringing.

b. The maximum flux density in the overlapping portions of the air gaps is limited to approximately 130 kilolines/in.[2], because of saturation in the steel. Compute the maximum torque in inch-pounds for the following dimensions: $r_1 = 1.00$ in.; $h = 1.00$ in.; $g = 0.10$ in.

Solution. In a manner paralleling Example 2-2, the torque can be derived from the

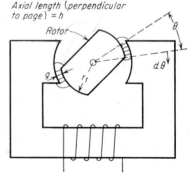

FIG. 2-4. Magnetic system, Example 2-3.

derivative of air-gap reluctance, of air-gap permeance, or of field energy. This time the last approach will be used.

a. The field energy density is $\mu_0 H_{ag}^2/2$ (Eq. 1-25), and the volume of the two overlapping air gaps is $2gh(r_1 + 0.5g)\theta$. Consequently the field energy is

$$W_{ag} = \mu_0 H_{ag}^2 gh(r_1 + 0.5g)\theta \qquad (2\text{-}30)$$

At constant mmf H_{ag} is constant, and therefore differentiation of Eq. 2-30 with respect to θ at constant mmf in accordance with Eq. 2-22 gives for the torque

$$T = \mu_0 H_{ag}^2 gh(r_1 + 0.5g) = \frac{B_{ag}^2 gh(r_1 + 0.5g)}{\mu_0} \qquad (2\text{-}31)$$

The torque acts in a direction to align the rotor with the stator pole faces.

b. Convert the flux density and dimensions to mks units.

$$B_{ag} = \frac{130{,}000}{6.45} \times 10^4 \times 10^{-8} = 2.02 \text{ webers/m}^2$$

$$g = 0.1 \times 2.54 \times 10^{-2} = 0.00254 \text{ m}$$
$$h = r_1 = 1.00 \times 2.54 \times 10^{-2} = 0.0254 \text{ m}$$
$$\mu_0 = 4\pi \times 10^{-7}$$

Substitution of these numerical values in Eq. 2-31 gives

$$T = 5.56 \text{ newton-m}$$
$$= 5.56 \times 0.738 \times 12 = 49.3 \text{ in.-lb}$$

Moving-iron devices are used in a wide variety of applications for producing mechanical force or torque. Some of them, such as lifting magnets and magnetic chucks, are required merely to hold a piece of ferromagnetic material; others, such as iron-core solenoids, relays, and contactors, are required to exert a force through a specified distance; still others, such as iron-vane instruments, are required to produce a rotational torque against a restraining spring so that the deflection of a pointer is indicative of the steady-state value of the current or voltage of the circuit to which they are connected; with others, such as moving-iron telephone receivers and the electromagnets used for controlling the operation of hydraulic motors in servomechanisms, the force or torque should be very nearly proportional to an electrical signal, and the dynamic response should be as rapid as possible. The dynamics of electromagnetically coupled systems are discussed in Art. 2-4.

2-2. Reluctance Torque in Rotating Machines. The variable-reluctance principle can be applied for producing continuous rotation of a shaft, and the result, the *single-phase a-c reluctance motor*, is one of the simplest forms of electric motor. This motor is of the *synchronous* type; i.e., it operates at a speed proportional to the frequency of the applied voltage. The commonest application of such motors is in driving electric clocks and other timing devices since their speed is constant when they are operated from a source whose frequency is constant. The theory of the electromagnetic type of reluctance motor is developed in this article, and an analogous type of electrostatic single-phase synchronous motor is described in Art. 2-7.

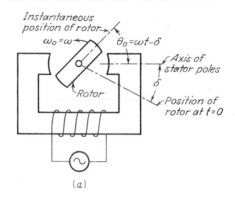

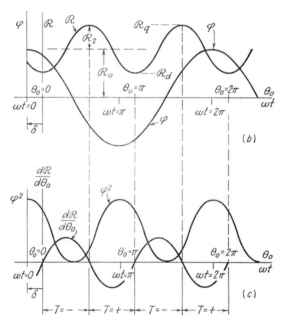

Fig. 2-5. (a) Elementary reluctance motor.   (b and c) Flux and reluctance variations.

Although the analysis is devoted specifically to the simple single-phase motor, its broad significance should be borne in mind.   Thus similar phenomena may be present in any rotating machine whose magnetic circuit is of such a form that its reluctance depends on the relative angular position of its stationary and moving parts.   For example, reluctance torque is a significant component of the torque produced by any salient-pole synchronous machine.

The principal constructional features of one form of single-phase reluctance motor are shown in Fig. 2-5a.   The essential feature is that the

rotor be shaped so that the reluctance of the magnetic circuit depends
on the angular position of the rotor. Thus in Fig. 2-5a, the reluctance
$\Re$ is a periodic function of the angle θ_o between the long axis of the rotor
and the axis of the stator poles, as indicated in Fig. 2-5b. The reluctance
has a minimum value $\Re_d$, called the *direct-axis reluctance*, when the axis of
the rotor is directly in line with the axis of the stator poles ($\theta_o = 0, \pi,$
$2\pi, \ldots$), and a maximum value $\Re_q$, called the *quadrature-axis reluctance*,
when the axis of the rotor is at right angles to the axis of the stator poles
($\theta_o = \pi/2, 3\pi/2, \ldots$). The exciting winding is connected to a source of
single-phase alternating voltage. The flux therefore is also alternating,
as shown by the curve φ in Fig. 2-5b. In accordance with the rotational
equivalent of Eq. 2-23

$$T = -\tfrac{1}{2}\varphi^2 \frac{d\Re}{d\theta_o} \qquad (2\text{-}32)$$

where T is the instantaneous torque acting in the direction to increase the
angle θ_o. The corresponding curves of φ^2 and $d\Re/d\theta_o$ are shown in Fig.
2-5c. From Eq. 2-32, the direction of the torque is determined by the
sign of $d\Re/d\theta_o$. It is positive while the reluctance is decreasing.

Examination of Eq. 2-32 and Fig. 2-5c shows that, if the speed of the
rotor and the phase relation between the reluctance variation and the flux
wave are such that the average square of the flux is greater while the reluctance is decreasing than it is while the reluctance is increasing, the average
torque acts in the direction to increase θ_o and thereby to keep the rotor
revolving. To meet these requirements, the rotor speed must be such
that the reluctance goes through one cycle of its variation in each half
cycle of the flux wave; that is, the rotor must revolve one-half a revolution
in one-half a cycle of the flux wave. Its average angular velocity in
radians per second therefore must equal the time angular velocity ω of
the flux wave, whence the rotor must make one revolution for each cycle
of the applied voltage. The rotor speed which satisfies these requirements is known as *synchronous speed*. For the simple reluctance motor
of Fig 2-5a,

$$\text{Synchronous speed in rev/sec} = f \qquad (2\text{-}33)$$

where f is the frequency of the applied voltage in cycles per second.
Except for the usually negligible effect of harmonics, no average torque is
produced at any other speed. The motor therefore is not self-starting, a
limitation characteristic of all types of synchronous motors. It must be
started by auxiliary means. In the simplest types of clock motors, the
motor is started manually by spinning the rotor at or above synchronous
speed; as the rotor coasts through synchronous speed, it "pulls into step"
and continues to run at this speed. Large synchronous motors and self-

starting clock motors are started electrically by means of auxiliary windings which produce induction-motor action.

The basic theory of the single-phase reluctance motor can be developed on the assumption of sinusoidal variations of the flux and reluctance. Actually, of course, the reluctance variation depends on the geometry of the magnetic circuit, and the waveform of the flux depends on the waveform of the applied voltage. The assumption of sinusoidal waveforms is made primarily because of its convenience; it is usually also a fairly realistic assumption. If the waveforms depart substantially from sine waves, the flux and reluctance variations can be expressed in terms of Fourier series but this refinement seldom is necessary. Let the instantaneous value φ of the flux be

$$\varphi = \phi_{\max} \cos \omega t \tag{2-34}$$

where $\phi_{\max}$ is its maximum value. From Eq. 2-34

$$\varphi^2 = \phi_{\max}^2 \cos^2 \omega t = \tfrac{1}{2}\phi_{\max}^2 (1 + \cos 2\omega t) \tag{2-35}$$

Most electromechanical-energy-conversion devices are designed so that the resistances of the windings are as small as possible. If the voltage drop due to the winding resistance is negligible, the flux must vary in such a manner as to induce a counter emf e equal to the voltage v_t applied to the winding. For sinusoidal variations, substitution of Eq. 2-34 in Faraday's law gives

$$e = N \frac{d\varphi}{dt} = -N\omega\phi_{\max} \sin \omega t \tag{2-36}$$

whence the relation between the rms value of the counter emf in volts and the maximum value of the flux in webers is

$$E_{\mathrm{rms}} = \frac{2\pi}{\sqrt{2}} f N \phi_{\max} = 4.44 f N \phi_{\max} \tag{2-37}$$

Thus, when a sinusoidally varying voltage is impressed on a winding whose resistance is negligible, a sinusoidally varying flux must be established whose maximum value $\phi_{\max}$ satisfies Eq. 2-37. The applied voltage and the induced counter emf are then equal, and Kirchhoff's law is satisfied.

The instantaneous value $\mathfrak{R}$ of the reluctance is a function of the instantaneous angle θ_o. Inspection of the reluctance curve in Fig. 2-5b shows that, if a sinusoidal variation is assumed, the reluctance can be expressed as

$$\mathfrak{R} = \tfrac{1}{2}(\mathfrak{R}_q + \mathfrak{R}_d) - \tfrac{1}{2}(\mathfrak{R}_q - \mathfrak{R}_d) \cos 2\theta_o \tag{2-38}$$

from curve

Differentiation of Eq. 2-38 gives

$$\frac{d\Re}{d\theta_o} = (\Re_q - \Re_d) \sin 2\theta_o \qquad (2\text{-}39)$$

Assume that the rotor has been started by some auxiliary means and is running at a constant angular velocity of ω_o rad/sec. Actually, the instantaneous torque pulsates, and therefore the instantaneous speed is not absolutely constant. The inertias of the rotor and its mechanical load, however, maintain substantially constant speed. If the effects of the torque pulsations are neglected, the instantaneous position of the rotor is

$$\theta_o = \omega_o t - \delta \qquad (2\text{-}40)$$

where δ is its instantaneous position at zero time when the flux is passing through its maximum value. For convenience, δ is taken as a *lag* angle, as indicated in Fig. 2-5a.

Substitution of Eq. 2-40 in Eq. 2-39 gives

$$\frac{d\Re}{d\theta_o} = (\Re_q - \Re_d) \sin (2\omega_o t - 2\delta) \qquad (2\text{-}41)$$

and substitution of Eqs. 2-35 and 2-41 in the basic torque relation (Eq. 2-32) then gives

$$T = -\tfrac{1}{4}\phi_{max}^2(\Re_q - \Re_d)[\sin (2\omega_o t - 2\delta) + \sin (2\omega_o t - 2\delta)\cos 2\omega t] \qquad (2\text{-}42)$$

By use of the trigonometric identity

$$\sin \alpha \cos \beta = \tfrac{1}{2}\sin (\alpha + \beta) + \tfrac{1}{2}\sin (\alpha - \beta) \qquad (2\text{-}43)$$

the torque expression becomes

$$T = -\tfrac{1}{4}\phi_{max}^2(\Re_q - \Re_d) \{\sin (2\omega_o t - 2\delta) + \tfrac{1}{2}\sin [2(\omega_o + \omega)t - 2\delta] + \tfrac{1}{2}\sin [2(\omega_o - \omega)t - 2\delta]\} \qquad (2\text{-}44)$$

When the shaft angular velocity ω_o is not equal to the time angular velocity ω of the flux wave, the three sine terms in Eq. 2-44 are functions of time and the average value of each of them over a complete cycle is zero. Therefore no average torque is developed. However, if ω_o equals ω, the torque becomes

$$T = -\tfrac{1}{4}\phi_{max}^2(\Re_q - \Re_d)[\sin (2\omega t - 2\delta) + \tfrac{1}{2}\sin (4\omega t - 2\delta) + \tfrac{1}{2}\sin (-2\delta)] \qquad (2\text{-}45)$$

The first two sine terms are functions of time, and therefore their average values are zero. They represent pulsating components of the torque of twice and four times line frequency. The last sine term is independent of time.   The average value T_{av} of the torque therefore is

$$T_{av} = +\tfrac{1}{8}\phi^2_{max}(\mathfrak{R}_q - \mathfrak{R}_d)\sin 2\delta \qquad (2\text{-}46)$$

Equation 2-46 is characteristic of the reluctance torque in all synchronous motors, whether they be of the simple single-phase type described here or of the more complicated form met in large polyphase salient-pole synchronous machines described in Chaps. 5 and 9.   If the applied voltage and frequency are constant and the resistance drop is negligible, ϕ_{max} must be constant, as given by Eq. 2-37.   The reluctances $\mathfrak{R}_q$ and $\mathfrak{R}_d$ depend primarily on the configuration of the magnetic circuit.   Thus

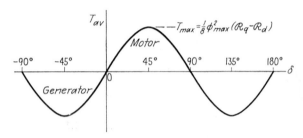

FIG. 2-6. Torque-angle characteristic of a reluctance motor.

the rotor phase angle δ is the only variable on the right-hand side of Eq. 2-46.   The relation between the average torque developed by the motor and the angle δ is shown in Fig. 2-6.   The phase angle δ adjusts itself so that the electromagnetic torque T_{av} developed by the motor equals the torque required to drive the mechanical load connected to its shaft plus the torque required to overcome rotational losses in the motor. For this reason the rotor angle δ is often called the *torque angle*.   If the load torque increases, the motor momentarily slows down, thereby increasing the lag angle δ until sufficient electromagnetic torque is developed to carry the increased load.   After the brief transient required for adjustment of the torque angle δ, operation is resumed at synchronous speed.   Note that the maximum value of the average electromagnetic torque the motor can develop occurs when δ equals 45° and is

$$T_{max} = \tfrac{1}{8}\phi^2_{max}(\mathfrak{R}_q - \mathfrak{R}_d) \qquad (2\text{-}47)$$

The motor stalls if a mechanical load is applied that requires a torque exceeding this value.

As with any electromechanical-energy-conversion device, the process is essentially reversible.   If mechanical power is supplied to the shaft, the rotor advances in phase; i.e., the angle δ becomes negative.   The average electromagnetic torque changes sign and therefore represents mechanical power absorbed and converted into electrical power, as shown by the portion of the torque-angle characteristic to the left of the origin in Fig. 2-6. As with motor action, there is a definite limit to the mechanical power that can be absorbed, occurring when $\delta = -45°$. Any further increase in driving torque causes overspeeding and loss of synchronism.

Example 2-4. When the rotor of a reluctance motor like that shown in Fig. 2-5a is in the direct-axis position, the inductance of its exciting winding is $L_d = 1.00$ henry. When the rotor is in the quadrature-axis position, the inductance is $L_q = 0.50$ henry. The exciting winding has $N = 1,000$ turns. Determine approximately the maximum torque that the motor can develop with 115 volts at 60 cps applied to its exciting winding.

Solution. According to Eq. 2-37,

$$\phi_{max} = \frac{115}{(4.44)(1,000)(60)} = 4.32 \times 10^{-4} \text{ weber}$$

From the definition of inductance

$$L = \frac{N\phi}{I} = \frac{N^2\phi}{NI} = \frac{N^2}{\mathfrak{R}} \tag{2-48}$$

or

$$\mathfrak{R} = \frac{N^2}{L} \tag{2-49}$$

whence

$$\mathfrak{R}_q = \frac{10^6}{0.50} = 2.00 \times 10^6 \text{ mks units}$$

$$\mathfrak{R}_d = \frac{10^6}{1.00} = 1.00 \times 10^6 \text{ mks units}$$

Substitution of numerical values in Eq. 2-47 then gives

$$T_{max} = \tfrac{1}{8}(4.32)^2(10^{-8})(2.00 - 1.00)(10^6) = 2.34 \times 10^{-2} \text{ newton-m}$$

In English units of a convenient size (inch-ounces),

$$T_{max} = (2.34)(10^{-2})(0.738)(16)(12) = 3.31 \text{ in.-oz}$$

2-3. Multiply Excited Magnetic Systems. Except for the simple moving-iron mechanisms discussed in Arts. 2-1 and 2-2, most electromagnetic-energy-conversion devices have several windings. One group of windings is mounted on a stationary member and the other group on a movable member. The tendency for the magnetic field energy to change when one group of windings moves with respect to the other gives rise to mechanical forces. The theory of numerous types of energy-conversion devices, including most rotating machines, is based on this general principle.

Consider the simple device shown in Fig. 2-7, which has previously been used in Art. 1-5 as an illustration of multiply excited magnetic systems. The torque can be found by a line of reasoning identical to that used in the analysis of singly excited systems in Art. 2-1. Imagine the rotor to be allowed to move through a differential angular displacement $d\theta_o$ in the direction of the magnetic torque T acting upon it. Mechanical work $T\,d\theta_o$ will be done by the magnetic field. In general, the flux linkages with the windings may change, and counter emfs e_1 and e_2 will be induced in them. Energy will be abstracted from the two electrical sources. The field energy also may change. As in Eq. 2-1, the energy balance is

$$dW_{\text{elec}} = T\,d\theta_o + dW_{\text{fld}} \tag{2-50}$$

In order to continue the analysis, the field energy must be related to the energy abstracted from the electrical sources. Since most of the field energy is stored in the air gaps, satisfactory results usually can be obtained by use of linear approximations. The energy relations then can be expressed conveniently in terms of the currents i_1 and i_2 and the self- and

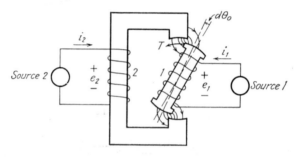

FIG. 2-7. Elementary multiply excited magnetic system.

mutual inductances $L_{11}(\theta_o)$, $L_{22}(\theta_o)$, and $L_{12}(\theta_o)$ of the windings. The inductances are independent of the currents but are functions of the angular position θ_o of the rotor.

The differential changes in the electrical and field energy resulting from a virtual displacement $d\theta_o$ can now be expressed in terms of the inductances and currents, and the magnetic torque T can then be found from Eq. 2-50. From Eqs. 1-78 and 1-79, the electrical energy input is

$$dW_{\text{elec}} = i_1\,d\lambda_1 + i_2\,d\lambda_2 \tag{2-51}$$

$$dW_{\text{elec}} = i_1 d(L_{11}i_1 + L_{12}i_2) + i_2 d(L_{12}i_1 + L_{22}i_2) \tag{2-52}$$

where $d\lambda_1$ and $d\lambda_2$ are the total differentials of the flux linkages λ_1 and λ_2, including both changes in the currents and changes in angle. For simplicity the functional notation has been dropped. From Eq. 1-84, the field energy is

$$W_{\text{fld}} = \tfrac{1}{2}L_{11}i_1^2 + \tfrac{1}{2}L_{22}i_2^2 + L_{12}i_1i_2 \tag{2-53}$$

For a magnetically linear system the stored energy and coenergy are equal. In Eqs. 2-52 and 2-53 the inductances must be considered as variables, because they are functions of the angle θ_o. In fact, it is these changes of inductance with angle which account for the mechanical energy output. The currents also may change because of the induced electrical transients. Differential changes in the currents, however, have no effect on the mechanical forces, since the forces depend solely on the values of the currents and the geometrical configuration. For the sake of completeness, however, the effects of differential changes in the currents are included in the following analysis.

Differentiation of Eq. 2-52 with respect to the inductances and currents gives for the electrical energy input

$$dW_{elec} = L_{11}i_1\, di_1 + L_{12}i_1\, di_2 + i_1^2\, dL_{11} + i_1 i_2\, dL_{12}$$
$$+ L_{22}i_2\, di_2 + L_{12}i_2\, di_1 + i_2^2\, dL_{22} + i_1 i_2\, dL_{12} \quad (2\text{-}54)$$

Similarly from Eq. 2-53 the increment in field energy is

$$dW_{fld} = L_{11}i_1\, di_1 + \tfrac{1}{2}i_1^2\, dL_{11} + L_{22}i_2\, di_2 + \tfrac{1}{2}i_2^2\, dL_{22}$$
$$+ L_{12}i_1\, di_2 + L_{12}i_2\, di_1 + i_1 i_2\, dL_{12} \quad (2\text{-}55)$$

When Eqs. 2-54 and 2-55 are substituted in Eq. 2-50, the four terms $L_{11}i_1\, di_1 + L_{22}i_2\, di_2 + L_{12}i_1\, di_2 + L_{12}i_2\, di_1$ expressing the electrical energy input caused by the current increments di_1 and di_2 are balanced by identical terms expressing the corresponding increments in field energy. These terms therefore cancel. In other words, differential changes in the currents have no effect on the mechanical forces. Substitution of the remaining terms in Eq. 2-50 gives

$$i_1^2\, dL_{11} + i_2^2\, dL_{22} + 2i_1 i_2\, dL_{12} = \tfrac{1}{2}i_1^2\, dL_{11} + \tfrac{1}{2}i_2^2\, dL_{22}$$
$$+ i_1 i_2\, dL_{12} + T\, d\theta_o \quad (2\text{-}56)$$

whence
$$T = \tfrac{1}{2}i_1^2 \frac{dL_{11}}{d\theta_o} + \tfrac{1}{2}i_2^2 \frac{dL_{22}}{d\theta_o} + i_1 i_2 \frac{dL_{12}}{d\theta_o} \quad (2\text{-}57)$$

The translational equivalent of Eq. 2-57 is obtained if torque T is replaced by translational force f and angular displacement $d\theta_o$ by linear displacement dx in the direction of the force. The extension of Eq. 2-57 to a situation involving several circuits whose self- and mutual inductances depend upon the angular position of some member should be obvious from consideration of the line of reasoning followed in the derivation of Eq. 2-57. For example, with three circuits,

$$T = \tfrac{1}{2}i_1^2 \frac{dL_{11}}{d\theta_o} + \tfrac{1}{2}i_2^2 \frac{dL_{22}}{d\theta_o} + \tfrac{1}{2}i_3^2 \frac{dL_{33}}{d\theta_o}$$
$$+ i_1 i_2 \frac{dL_{12}}{d\theta_o} + i_2 i_3 \frac{dL_{23}}{d\theta_o} + i_3 i_1 \frac{dL_{31}}{d\theta_o} \quad (2\text{-}58)$$

Examination of Eq. 2-56 shows that the sum of the three terms on the right-hand side expressing the increment in field energy at constant currents is half of the left-hand side expressing the electrical energy input at constant currents. The other half of the electrical energy input at constant currents therefore is delivered as mechanical energy. The increment in field energy at constant currents therefore equals the mechanical energy delivered; hence the torque or force equals the rate of increase of field energy with respect to motion at constant current. Thus differentiation of Eq. 2-53 gives

$$T = + \frac{\partial W_{\mathrm{fld}}}{\partial \theta_o} (i_1, i_2, \theta_o)$$ (2-59)

in which the field energy must be explicitly expressed in terms of the currents and angle θ_o and the partial derivative must be taken with the currents treated as constants. The translational equivalent of Eq. 2-59 is

$$f = \frac{\partial W_{\mathrm{fld}}}{\partial x} (i_1, i_2, x)$$ (2-60)

where f is the magnetic force acting in the positive direction of x. In Art. 2-1c this equation has been found to apply to linear singly excited systems (see Eq. 2-22). For a linear system, Eqs. 2-59 and 2-60 simply say that magnetic torques and forces act on the magnetic material and conductors in such a direction as to tend to increase the field energy at constant currents.

It can be shown[1] that torque or force in a nonlinear multiply excited system can be expressed in terms of the coenergy W'_{fld}. For a rotational system

$$T = + \frac{\partial W'_{\mathrm{fld}}}{\partial \theta_o} (i_1, i_2, \theta_o)$$ (2-61)

Compare with Eqs. 2-15 and 2-21 for the singly excited system. For a magnetically linear system Eqs. 2-59 and 2-61 are identical. When the magnetic circuit contains iron, the terms involving the angular rates of change of the self-inductances in Eq. 2-57 are the reluctance torques that have previously been discussed in Arts. 2-1 and 2-2 in connection with singly excited systems. They express the fact that the field due to one current acting alone produces forces on magnetic material tending to move it so as to reduce the reluctance of the magnetic circuit. Thus, if both stator and rotor cores in Fig. 2-7 are made of magnetic material, the field due to either current acting alone tends to move the rotor into a vertical position.

The terms involving the angular rates of change of the mutual inductances express the torques due to the interaction of the magnetic field of

[1] See D. C. White and H. H. Woodson, "Electromechanical Energy Conversion," pp. 12–24, John Wiley & Sons, Inc., New York, 1959.

one current with that of another. These terms merely say that the magnetic fields of stator and rotor tend to line up. These are the principal torques in a large class of rotating machines.

2-4. Dynamic Equations of Magnetic Systems. Up to this point we have been concerned primarily with the mechanical force or torque produced electrically. A necessary counterpart to the study of force or torque is a study of the reactions of the energy-conversion process on the electrical system. The dynamic behavior of a system containing energy-conversion components can then be determined by the characteristics of the electrical and mechanical systems connected to its input and output

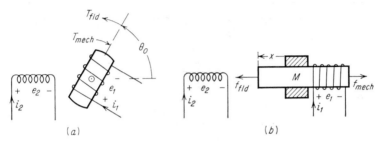

FIG. 2-8. (a) Rotational and (b) translational electromechanical transducers.

terminals. This article is concerned with magnetic field coupling. The subject will be introduced in fairly general terms and illustrated by specific examples. A discussion of the quasi-static electric field as a coupling medium is given in Art. 2-6.

Consider the electromechanical systems shown schematically in Fig. 2-8. In Fig. 2-8a the rotor turns under the influence of the torques acting upon it. The translational equivalent is shown in Fig. 2-8b, in which the mass M is constrained by guides to move in the x direction. Everything which will be said below concerning the rotational system also applies to the translational system if torque T is replaced by force f, angular displacement θ_o by linear displacement x, and moment of inertia J by mass M.

In Fig. 2-8a the torques are (1) the magnetic torque T_{fld} acting in the positive direction of θ_o, (2) the mechanical torque T_{mech} opposing rotation, and (3) the inertial torque $J \, d^2\theta_o/dt^2$, where J is the moment of inertia of the rotor. The torque balance equation is

$$T_{\text{fld}} = J \frac{d^2\theta_o}{dt^2} + T_{\text{mech}} \qquad (2\text{-}62)$$

The reference directions are shown in Fig. 2-8a. Positive values correspond to an accelerating motor, but of course the equation applies to any operating condition when the algebraic signs are interpreted properly.

In this equation the opposing mechanical torque T_{mech} includes mechanical friction and windage, mechanical loads, restraining springs, and applied mechanical torques. In general, these torques are functions of the angle θ_o and its time derivative, the angular speed $\omega_o = d\theta_o/dt$. The right-hand side of the differential equation 2-62 then depends on the constraints imposed by the specific mechanical system under consideration. Thus Eq. 2-62 is a differential equation in terms of the dependent variable θ_o, expressing the motion of a mechanical system under the influence of the torque T_{fld} developed by the magnetic field.

The magnetic torque T_{fld} can be expressed explicitly in terms of either the flux linkages or the currents and the angle θ_o. Usually magnetic saturation effects are neglected. The magnetic torque is then given by the rotational equivalent of Eqs. 2-20 through 2-25 for a singly excited system or Eq. 2-57 (or its equivalent, Eq. 2-58) for a multiply excited system. For example, for the 2-winding system shown in Fig. 2-8a, substitution of Eq. 2-57 in Eq. 2-62 gives

$$\frac{1}{2}i_1^2 \frac{dL_{11}}{d\theta_o} + \frac{1}{2}i_2^2 \frac{dL_{22}}{d\theta_o} + i_1 i_2 \frac{dL_{12}}{d\theta_o} = J \frac{d^2\theta_o}{dt^2} + T_{mech} \qquad (2\text{-}63)$$

in which the inductances are functions of θ_o. The currents depend on the electrical networks connected to the windings and also on the counter emfs generated in them. These emfs can be expressed in terms of the inductances and currents. From Eqs. 1-76 and 1-77,

$$e_1 = \overbrace{L_{11}\frac{di_1}{dt} + L_{12}\frac{di_2}{dt}}^{\text{transformer voltages}} + \overbrace{\left(i_1 \frac{dL_{11}}{d\theta_o} + i_2 \frac{dL_{12}}{d\theta_o}\right)\frac{d\theta_o}{dt}}^{\text{speed voltages}} \qquad (2\text{-}64)$$

$$e_2 = L_{12}\frac{di_1}{dt} + L_{22}\frac{di_2}{dt} + \left(i_1 \frac{dL_{12}}{d\theta_o} + i_2 \frac{dL_{22}}{d\theta_o}\right)\frac{d\theta_o}{dt} \qquad (2\text{-}65)$$

The first two terms on the right-hand sides are due to the time rate of change of the currents. They are like the voltages induced in transformers and are called *transformer voltages*. Unlike the static transformer, however, the inductances are not constant; some or all of them are functions of the dependent variable θ_o. The last terms are proportional to the angular speed $d\theta_o/dt$ and are called *speed voltages*. They are the coupling terms relating the flow of energy between the mechanical and electrical systems. These terms are not easy to deal with mathematically, however, because they are functions of the dependent current variables as well as θ_o.

When Eqs. 2-64 and 2-65 are introduced into the Kirchhoff-law equations for the networks connected to windings 1 and 2, two differential equations will result relating the dependent variables i_1, i_2, and θ_o to the applied electrical sources. These equations together with Eq. 2-63 (with the mechanical variables expressed in terms of θ_o) are a set of three differential equations describing the dynamic behavior of the system in terms of the applied electrical and mechanical sources and loads. The extension of these thought processes to a more complicated system follows the same general procedure. The application to specific cases is illustrated in the following examples.

Example 2-5. Figure 2-9 shows in cross section a cylindrical solenoid magnet in which the cylindrical plunger of mass M kg moves vertically in brass guide rings of thickness t and mean diameter d. The permeability of brass is the same as that of free space and is $\mu_0 = 4\pi \times 10^{-7}$ rationalized mks units. The plunger is supported by a spring whose elastance is k_s newtons/m. Its unstretched length is l_0. A mechanical load force f_t is applied to the plunger from the mechanical system connected to it, as shown in Fig. 2-9. Assume that frictional force is linearly proportional to velocity and that the coefficient of friction is b newton-sec/m. The coil has N turns and resistance r ohms. Its terminal voltage is v_t, and its current is i. The effects of magnetic leakage and reluctance of the steel are negligible.

Derive the dynamic equations of motion of the electromechanical system, i.e., the differential equations expressing the dependent variables i and x in terms of v_t, f_t, and the given constants and dimensions.

Solution. Express the inductance as a function of x. The coupling terms, i.e., magnetic force f_{fld} and induced emf e, can then be expressed in terms of x and i and these relations substituted in the equations for the mechanical and electrical systems.

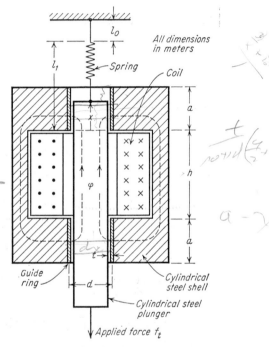

Fig. 2-9. Solenoid magnet, Example 2-5.

The reluctance of the magnetic circuit is that of the two guide rings in series, with the flux directed radially through them, as shown by the dotted flux lines φ in Fig. 2-9. Because $t \ll d$, the flux density in the guide rings is very nearly constant with respect to radial distance. In a region where the flux density is constant the reluctance is

$$\frac{\text{Length of flux path in direction of field}}{\mu(\text{area perpendicular to field})}$$

The reluctance of the upper gap is

$$\mathcal{R}_1 = \frac{t}{\mu_0 \pi d x}$$

in which it is assumed that the field is concentrated in the area between the upper end of the plunger and the lower end of the upper guide ring. Similarly the reluctance of the lower gap is

$$\Re_2 = \frac{t}{\mu_0 \pi d a}$$

The total reluctance is

$$\Re = \Re_1 + \Re_2 = \frac{t}{\mu_0 \pi d}\left(\frac{1}{a} + \frac{1}{x}\right) = \frac{t}{\mu_0 \pi d a}\frac{a+x}{x}$$

The permeance is

$$\Phi = \frac{1}{\Re} = \frac{\mu_0 \pi d a}{t}\frac{x}{a+x}$$

From Eq. 1-23, the inductance is

$$L = N^2 \Phi = \frac{\mu_0 \pi d a N^2}{t}\frac{x}{a+x} = L'\frac{x}{a+x} \tag{2-66}$$

where

$$L' = \frac{\mu_0 \pi d a N^2}{t} \tag{2-67}$$

From Eq. 2-25 the magnetic force acting upward on the plunger in the positive direction of x is

$$f_{\text{fld}} = +\tfrac{1}{2}i^2 \frac{dL}{dx} = +\tfrac{1}{2}L'\frac{ai^2}{(a+x)^2} \tag{2-68}$$

The counter emf induced in the coil is

$$e = \frac{d}{dt}(Li) = L\frac{di}{dt} + i\frac{dL}{dx}\frac{dx}{dt} \tag{2-69}$$

$$e = L'\frac{x}{a+x}\frac{di}{dt} + L'\frac{ai}{(a+x)^2}\frac{dx}{dt} \tag{2-70}$$

Substitution of the magnetic force in the differential equation of motion of the mechanical system gives

$$-f_t + \tfrac{1}{2}L'\frac{ai^2}{(a+x)^2} = M\frac{d^2x}{dt^2} + b\frac{dx}{dt} - k_s(l_1 - x) + Mg \tag{2-71}$$

The voltage equation for the electrical system is

$$v_t = ri + e = ri + L'\frac{x}{a+x}\frac{di}{dt} + L'\frac{ai}{(a+x)^2}\frac{dx}{dt} \tag{2-72}$$

Equations 2-71 and 2-72 are the desired results. They are valid only so long as the upper end of the plunger is well within the upper guide ring, say, between the limits $0.1a < x < 0.9a$. This is the normal working range of the solenoid.

Example 2-6. The cross section of a cylindrical solenoid used to control the valve mechanism of a hydraulic servo system is shown in Fig. 2-10. When the currents in the 2 identical coils 1 and 2 are equal, the plunger is centered horizontally as shown in the figure. When the coil currents are unbalanced, the plunger moves horizontally a distance x. The brass sleeves keep the plunger centered radially. Their thickness is t, and their mean diameter is d. The coefficient of friction is b, and friction is assumed to be proportional to velocity. The mass of the plunger is M. The spring

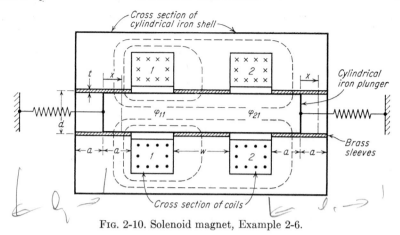

FIG. 2-10. Solenoid magnet, Example 2-6.

constant of each spring is k_s. All constants and dimensions are in mks units. The reluctances of all magnetic paths except the brass sleeves are negligible, and leakage and fringing may be neglected. The resistance of each coil is r, and the number of turns is N. The currents in coils 1 and 2 are i_1 and i_2, respectively, and are time-varying.

Derive the three differential equations of motion of the system, i.e., the equations for the voltages at the terminals of the 2 coils and for the mechanical motion of the plunger as functions of time. Express the results in terms of the given constants and dimensions and the variables i_1, i_2, and x.

Solution. Express the self- and mutual inductances as functions of x. The coupling terms can then be expressed as functions of i_1, i_2, and x.

To find the inductances, consider the magnetic field due to i_1 acting alone. The flux paths are shown dotted in Fig. 2-10. An analogous electrical circuit is shown in Fig. 2-11, in which $\mathcal{R}_1$, $\mathcal{R}_2$, and $\mathcal{R}_3$ are the reluctances of the left-hand, right-hand, and center sleeves, respectively. From the dimensions

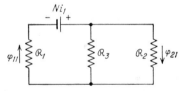

FIG. 2-11. Electrical equivalent of the magnetic circuit, Example 2-6.

$$\mathcal{R}_1 = \frac{t}{\mu_0 \pi d(a - x)} \qquad \mathcal{R}_2 = \frac{t}{\mu_0 \pi d(a + x)}$$

$$\mathcal{R}_3 = \frac{t}{\mu_0 \pi d w}$$

From the analogous electric circuit of Fig. 2-11

$$\varphi_{11} = \frac{N i_1}{\mathcal{R}_1 + \mathcal{R}_2 \mathcal{R}_3/(\mathcal{R}_2 + \mathcal{R}_3)} \qquad \varphi_{21} = \frac{\mathcal{R}_3}{\mathcal{R}_2 + \mathcal{R}_3} \varphi_{11}$$

and from the definitions of inductance

$$L_{11} = \frac{N \varphi_{11}}{i_1} \qquad L_{12} = \frac{N \varphi_{21}}{i_1} = \frac{\mathcal{R}_3}{\mathcal{R}_2 + \mathcal{R}_3} L_{11}$$

Substitution of the expressions for the reluctances in the expressions for the inductances gives, after algebraic simplification,

$$L_{11}(x) = L_0\left(1 - \frac{x}{a}\right)\left(1 + \frac{w}{a} + \frac{x}{a}\right) \tag{2-73}$$

$$L_{12}(x) = L_0\left(1 - \frac{x^2}{a^2}\right) \tag{2-74}$$

where $$L_0 = \frac{\mu_0\pi da^2N^2}{t(2a + w)} = \text{mutual inductance when } x \text{ is } 0 \tag{2-75}$$

By symmetry the self-inductance of coil 2 is obtained by changing the sign of x; thus

$$L_{22}(x) = L_0\left(1 + \frac{x}{a}\right)\left(1 + \frac{w}{a} - \frac{x}{a}\right) \tag{2-76}$$

The derivatives of the inductances with respect to x are

$$\frac{dL_{11}(x)}{dx} = -L_0\frac{2x + w}{a^2} \tag{2-77}$$

$$\frac{dL_{22}(x)}{dx} = -L_0\frac{2x - w}{a^2} \tag{2-78}$$

$$\frac{dL_{12}(x)}{dx} = -L_0\frac{2x}{a^2} \tag{2-79}$$

From the translational equivalent of Eq. 2-57

$$f_{11d} = -\frac{L_0}{a^2}\left(\frac{2x + w}{2}i_1^2 + \frac{2x - w}{2}i_2^2 + 2xi_1i_2\right)$$

$$= +\frac{L_0}{a^2}\left[\frac{w}{2}(i_2^2 - i_1^2) - x(i_2 + i_1)^2\right] \tag{2-80}$$

The equation of motion of the mechanical system then is

$$\frac{L_0}{a^2}\left[\frac{w}{2}(i_2^2 - i_1^2) - x(i_2 + i_1)^2\right] = M\frac{d^2x}{dt^2} + b\frac{dx}{dt} + 2k_sx \tag{2-81}$$

The terminal voltages of the coils are

$$v_{t1} = ri_1 + L_{11}(x)\frac{di_1}{dt} + L_{12}(x)\frac{di_2}{dt} + \left[i_1\frac{dL_{11}(x)}{dx} + i_2\frac{dL_{12}(x)}{dx}\right]\frac{dx}{dt} \tag{2-82}$$

$$v_{t2} = ri_2 + L_{22}(x)\frac{di_2}{dt} + L_{12}(x)\frac{di_1}{dt} + \left[i_2\frac{dL_{22}(x)}{dx} + i_1\frac{dL_{12}(x)}{dx}\right]\frac{dx}{dt} \tag{2-83}$$

in which the inductances and their derivatives are given in terms of the dimensions and x in Eqs. 2-73 through 2-79. Equations 2-81, 2-82, and 2-83 are the desired results. They are valid only so long as the ends of the plunger remain well within the two sleeves at the ends of the solenoid, between the limits $-0.9a < x < +0.9a$ approximately. This is the normal working range.

2-5. Analytical Techniques. The results of Examples 2-5 and 2-6 show that the equations of motion of an electromechanical system are rather complicated. They are nonlinear differential equations; i.e., they involve products of the variables and their derivatives. There are no general analytical techniques for solving such equations, although a numerical solution can always be found for specific numerical values. To make such numerical solutions usually is time-consuming and expensive and often involves recourse to machine computation. Only under special circumstances can a general analytical solution be found. Nevertheless much useful information can often be obtained by the use of judiciously chosen simplifying approximations. One of these approximate methods is linearization of the equations.

a. Linearization Techniques. Useful information often can be obtained by assuming that the range of the variables is small, i.e., that the system is operating around a quiescent point with only incremental changes in the variables. The reader is probably already familiar with this technique as applied in other fields. The incremental differential equations can then be reduced to linear differential equations with constant coefficients. All the well-known and highly developed analytical techniques for solving this type of equation can then be used. The linearization technique as applied to a singly excited transducer is discussed below.

In a singly excited transducer the coupling terms expressing the mutual interactions of the electrical and mechanical systems are the induced voltage e and the magnetic force f_{fld}, where

$$e = \frac{d\lambda}{dt} = L(x)\frac{di}{dt} + i\frac{dL(x)}{dx}\frac{dx}{dt} \tag{2-84}$$

$$f_{\text{fld}} = +\tfrac{1}{2}i^2\frac{dL(x)}{dx} \tag{2-85}$$

These are the troublesome terms, because they are products of the variables i and x and their derivatives. Now assume incremental operation around a quiescent point. Let capital letters with subscript 0 be the quiescent values of current and displacement and lower-case letters with subscript 1 be the time-varying incremental values. Then

$$i = I_0 + i_1 \qquad x = X_0 + x_1 \tag{2-86}$$

Whether a stable quiescent point actually exists depends on the specific details of the transducer and its connected electrical and mechanical systems. For example, a family of magnetic-force–distance curves for the solenoid of Fig. 2-12a is shown in Fig. 2-12b with I_0 as the parameter. The restraining force of the spring is also shown by the straight line. A quiescent point exists at the intersections, where the magnetic attraction is balanced by the spring. There is no quiescent point for $I_0 = 2$. There are two intersections, a and b, for $I_0 = 1$. Point a is stable, but point b is not. Thus a positive displacement dx of the plunger from point a results in a larger increase in restoring force from the spring than in the corresponding magnetic attractive force, and therefore the plunger is returned to its original operating point a at X_0. Point b, however, is unstable. The quiescent point must, of course, lie within the operating range.

To continue, assume that a meaningful quiescent point exists. The inductance and its derivative in Eqs. 2-84 and 2-85 can be expressed as a

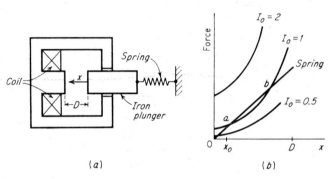

(a)   (b)

FIG. 2-12. (a) Solenoid magnet and (b) force-distance curves. The rest position of the plunger is D when the coil current is zero.

Taylor's series about the quiescent point X_0, and for small incremental values x_1 all but the first two terms can be neglected; thus

$$L(x) \approx L(X_0) + \frac{dL}{dx}(X_0)x_1 \tag{2-87}$$

$$\frac{dL(x)}{dx} \approx \frac{dL}{dx}(X_0) + \frac{d^2L}{dx^2}(X_0)x_1 \tag{2-88}$$

where $L(X_0)$, $\frac{dL}{dx}(X_0)$, and $\frac{d^2L}{dx^2}(X_0)$ are the values of the inductance and its derivatives at $x = X_0$. Also in Eq. 2-85, for small increments

$$i^2 \approx I_0^2 + 2I_0i_1 \tag{2-89}$$

When Eqs. 2-86 through 2-89 are substituted in Eqs. 2-84 and 2-85, the products of the small incremental terms such as x_1i_1, $x_1\,di_1/dt$, etc., can be neglected with very little error. The results are

$$e = L(X_0)\frac{di_1}{dt} + I_0\frac{dL}{dx}(X_0)\frac{dx_1}{dt} \tag{2-90}$$

$$f_{\text{fld}} = \tfrac{1}{2}I_0^2\frac{dL}{dx}(X_0) + I_0\frac{dL}{dx}(X_0)i_1 + \tfrac{1}{2}I_0^2\frac{d^2L}{dx^2}(X_0)x_1 \tag{2-91}$$

In Eq. 2-91

$$\tfrac{1}{2}I_0^2\frac{dL}{dx}(X_0) = F_0 \tag{2-92}$$

is the value of the static magnetic force F_0 required to balance the mechanical system at the quiescent point, and

$$\tfrac{1}{2} I_0^2 \frac{d^2 L}{dx^2} (X_0) = S_0 \qquad (2\text{-}93)$$

is the slope of the magnetic-force–distance curve at the operating point. The symbol S_0 is introduced here to simplify the notation. Also to simplify the notation let

$$L(X_0) = L_0 = \text{inductance at quiescent point} \qquad (2\text{-}94)$$

Substitution of Eqs. 2-92, 2-93, and 2-94 in Eqs. 2-90 and 2-91 gives

$$e = L_0 \frac{di_1}{dt} + \frac{2F_0}{I_0} \frac{dx_1}{dt} \qquad (2\text{-}95)$$

$$f_{\text{fld}} = F_0 + \frac{2F_0}{I_0} i_1 + S_0 x_1 \qquad (2\text{-}96)$$

The coefficient of the velocity dx_1/dt in Eq. 2-95 is the same as the coefficient of incremental current i_1 in Eq. 2-96. The third term on the right-hand side of Eq. 2-96 is like an incremental spring force. For positive values of S_0 this force is like a spring acting in the same direction as the static magnetic force F_0. Positive values of S_0 may lead to instability.

Equations 2-95 and 2-96 are linear differential equations with constant coefficients. The incremental performance of a complete electromechanical system, such as relative stability and frequency response, can be found by combining these equations with the linear differential equations of the electrical and mechanical systems connected to the transducer. Their application to a particular transducer is illustrated in Example 2-7.

Example 2-7. Consider the electromechanical system of Example 2-5, Fig. 2-9. Can the system be adjusted to have a stable quiescent point? If so, find the relations among the quiescent values of the terminal voltage, current, applied mechanical force, and displacement in terms of the spring constant k_s, the dimensions of the spring and magnet, and the weight of the plunger. Then linearize the differential equations for incremental operation around the quiescent point.

Solution. Let the variables be expressed as the sum of quiescent and incremental values.

$$v_t = V_{t0} + v_{t1} \qquad i = I_0 + i_1$$
$$f_t = F_{t0} + f_{t1} \qquad x = X_0 + x_1$$

where v_t = terminal voltage
  i = coil current
  f_t = downward mechanical force exerted on plunger (Fig. 2-9)
  x = upward displacement (Fig. 2-9)

The upward magnetic force f_{fld} is given by Eq. 2-68. Figure 2-13 shows the shape of the curve of f_{fld} as a function of x for constant current I_0. For static conditions the net downward mechanical force as a function of x is

$$\text{Static } f_{\text{mech}} = -k_s(l_1 - x) + Mg + F_{t0}$$

as shown by the straight line in Fig. 2-13. It is drawn intersecting the x axis at a small positive value so as to prevent the plunger from falling out of the upper guide ring when the current is turned off. The intersection of the two curves is the quiescent point, where the quiescent upward magnetic force F_0 balances the net downward mechanical force. Obviously it is possible to adjust the quiescent current I_0, the length l_1, and the spring stiffness k_s so as to obtain a quiescent point at X_0 within the working range of the plunger. This quiescent point is stable, because a change in x away from X_0 results in a net restoring force. At the quiescent point, from Eq. 2-68,

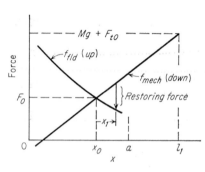

$$F_0 = \frac{1}{2} \frac{L'aI_0^2}{(a + X_0)^2}$$

$$= -k_s(l_1 - X_0) + Mg + F_{t0} \quad (2\text{-}97)$$

in which, from Eq. 2-67,

$$L' = \frac{\mu_0 \pi d a N^2}{t} \quad (2\text{-}98)$$

FIG. 2-13. Static force-distance curves, Example 2-7.

The quiescent point for the electrical system is obviously

$$V_{t0} = rI_0 \quad (2\text{-}99)$$

Equations 2-97 and 2-99 are the desired expressions for the quiescent values. Graphical solutions like Fig. 2-13 based on a family of curves will show the effects of varying the design of the system. This graphical process is analogous to the process of locating a load line on the output characteristics of an amplifier.

The slope of the magnetic-force–displacement curve at the quiescent point is

$$S_0 = \frac{\partial f_{\text{fld}}}{\partial x} (i,x) \quad (2\text{-}100)$$

evaluated at I_0, X_0. From Eq. 2-68

$$S_0 = -\frac{L'aI_0^2}{(a + X_0)^3} = -\frac{2F_0}{a + X_0} \quad (2\text{-}101)$$

When Eqs. 2-95 and 2-96 are substituted in Eqs. 2-71 and 2-72, the quiescent values on each side of the equations balance each other. The remaining terms give the incremental equations. After rearrangement and further simplification of the notation the results are

$$K_0 i_1 - f_{t1} = M \frac{d^2 x_1}{dt^2} + b \frac{dx_1}{dt} + k'_s x_1 \quad (2\text{-}102)$$

$$v_{t1} = r i_1 + L_0 \frac{di_1}{dt} + K_0 \frac{dx_1}{dt} \quad (2\text{-}103)$$

where

$$K_0 = \frac{2F_0}{I_0} \quad (2\text{-}104)$$

$$k'_s = k_s - S_0 \quad (2\text{-}105)$$

The constant K_0 is twice the magnetic force per ampere at the quiescent point. The constant k'_s is an effective spring constant including the effect of the slope S_0 of the magnetic-force–displacement curve at the quiescent point. Because S_0 is a negative quantity in this transducer, its effect is equivalent to a stiffening of the spring, as can be seen in Fig. 2-13. Equations 2-102 and 2-103 are the desired incremental equations.

b. Equivalent Circuits. It is often helpful to represent electromechanical systems by equivalent electric circuits in which the transducers and their connected mechanical systems are represented by electric-circuit elements and sources.[1] The complete system including both electrical and mechanical components then reduces to an electric network. The electromechanical equivalence is based on term-by-term identity of the differential equations of the system and of the equivalent circuit.

Consider the linearized incremental equations of a spring-loaded transducer such as that of Fig. 2-9. Assume that frictional force is proportional to velocity. The incremental equations of motion are then given by Eqs. 2-102 and 2-103. The last term on the right-hand side of Eq. 2-103 is the voltage induced in the electric circuit by incremental motion of the plunger. Let this voltage be designated by e_{m1}; thus

$$e_{m1} = K_0 \frac{dx_1}{dt} \qquad (2\text{-}106)$$

The voltage equation 2-103 can then be expressed as

$$v_{t1} = ri_1 + L_0 \frac{di_1}{dt} + e_{m1} \qquad (2\text{-}107)$$

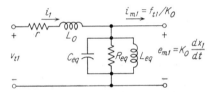

FIG. 2-14. Equivalent circuit for incremental motion, Example 2-7.

This equation is identical to that of the series rL_0 combination in the circuit of Fig. 2-14.

From Eq. 2-106, the incremental mechanical displacement, velocity, and acceleration in Eq. 2-102 can be expressed in terms of the motional voltage as follows:

$$x_1 = \frac{1}{K_0} \int e_{m1}\, dt \qquad (2\text{-}108)$$

$$\frac{dx_1}{dt} = \frac{1}{K_0} e_{m1} \qquad (2\text{-}109)$$

$$\frac{d^2x_1}{dt^2} = \frac{1}{K_0} \frac{de_{m1}}{dt} \qquad (2\text{-}110)$$

[1] Further general considerations of electromechanical equivalence may be found in F. A. Firestone, The Mobility Method of Computing the Vibration of Linear Mechanical and Electrical Systems, *J. Appl. Phys.*, vol. 9, pp. 373–387, 1938; M. F. Gardner and J. L. Barnes, "Transients in Linear Systems," pp. 50–85, John Wiley & Sons, Inc., New York, 1942.

Division of Eq. 2-102 by K_0 and substitution of Eqs. 2-108, 2-109, and 2-110 in the result gives

$$i_1 - \frac{f_{t1}}{K_0} = \frac{M}{K_0^2}\frac{de_{m1}}{dt} + \frac{b}{K_0^2}e_{m1} + \frac{k_s'}{K_0^2}\int e_{m1}\,dt \qquad (2\text{-}111)$$

Now compare Eq. 2-111 with the node equation for the parallel CRL combination in Fig. 2-14,

$$i_1 - i_{m1} = C_{eq}\frac{de_{m1}}{dt} + \frac{1}{R_{eq}}e_{m1} + \frac{1}{L_{eq}}\int e_{m1}\,dt \qquad (2\text{-}112)$$

The equations are identical if

$$i_{m1} = \frac{f_{t1}}{K_0} \qquad \text{or} \qquad f_{t1} = K_0 i_{m1} \qquad (2\text{-}113)$$

$$C_{eq} = \frac{M}{K_0^2} \qquad (2\text{-}114)$$

$$R_{eq} = \frac{K_0^2}{b} \qquad \text{or} \qquad \frac{1}{R_{eq}} = \frac{b}{K_0^2} \qquad (2\text{-}115)$$

$$L_{eq} = \frac{K_0^2}{k_s'} \qquad \text{or} \qquad \frac{1}{L_{eq}} = \frac{k_s'}{K_0^2} \qquad (2\text{-}116)$$

In the equivalent circuit the mechanical variables and parameters are replaced by electrical variables and parameters—mechanical forces by currents, velocities by voltages, masses by capacitances, spring constants by reciprocal inductances, and friction coefficients by conductances, as in Eqs. 2-108 through 2-116. The complete electromechanical system can then be transformed into an equivalent all-electrical system, and the system performance can be computed by electric-circuit techniques or by setting up a model in the laboratory.

Example 2-8. The transducer of Fig. 2-9 supports a mass M_L through a spring whose stiffness constant is k_2, as shown in Fig. 2-15a. A voltage source e_s is applied to the coil, and a mechanical-force source f_s is applied to M_L. Find an all-electrical equivalent circuit for the system for incremental changes in e_s and f_s.

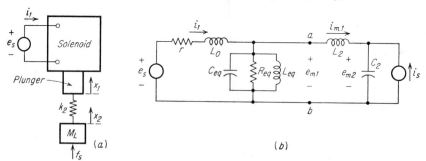

FIG. 2-15. (a) Loaded solenoid and (b) its equivalent circuit for incremental motion, Example 2-8.

Solution.   The equivalent circuit for the mechanical system can be found from its differential equations.   The incremental load on the plunger is

$$f_{t1} = k_2(x_1 - x_2) \tag{2-117}$$

where x_1 and x_2 are incremental displacements.   For the mass M_L

$$M_L \frac{d^2x_2}{dt^2} = f_s + k_2(x_1 - x_2) = f_s + f_{t1} \tag{2-118}$$

Change mechanical variables to equivalent electrical variables in accordance with Eqs. 2-108, 2-110, 2-113, and divide by K_0.   From Eq. 2-117

$$i_{m1} = \frac{k_2}{K_0^2} \int (e_{m1} - e_{m2}) \, dt = \frac{1}{L_2} \int (e_{m1} - e_{m2}) \, dt \tag{2-119}$$

where

$$e_{m2} = K_0 \frac{dx_2}{dt} \tag{2-120}$$

$$L_2 = \frac{K_0^2}{k_2} \tag{2-121}$$

From Eq. 2-118, with mechanical variables x_2, f_s, and f_{t1} changed to equivalent electrical variables,

$$\frac{M_L}{K_0^2} \frac{de_{m2}}{dt} = i_s + i_{m1} = C_2 \frac{de_{m2}}{dt} \tag{2-122}$$

where

$$i_s = \frac{f_s}{K_0} \tag{2-123}$$

is the current-source equivalent of the incremental applied-force source f_s and

$$C_2 = \frac{M_L}{K_0^2} \tag{2-124}$$

Inspection shows that Eqs. 2-119 through 2-124 apply to the circuit to the right of terminals ab in Fig. 2-15b.   The circuits to the left of ab represent the transducer and voltage source, as in Fig. 2-14.

c. Transfer Functions and Block Diagrams.   In the study of systems involving more than a few relatively simple equations an analytical attack by means of the equations themselves becomes cumbersome and confusing.   It is then helpful to represent the system by means of either a block diagram or a signal-flow chart.   This technique is useful in analytical studies of system characteristics such as stability, accuracy, and frequency response.   The technique has been highly developed in connection with studies of feedback control systems.   Closely related to the analytical technique based on block diagrams is the technique of programming a problem for solution on a computing machine.

The *block diagram* is a pictorial representation of the equations of the system.   Each block represents a mathematical operation.   The blocks are then interconnected in accordance with the dictates of the system.

There is no need to solve simultaneous equations in setting up the block diagram. The block diagram itself is a chart of the procedure to be followed in combining the simultaneous equations. Often useful information can be obtained from the block diagram without making a complete analytical solution.

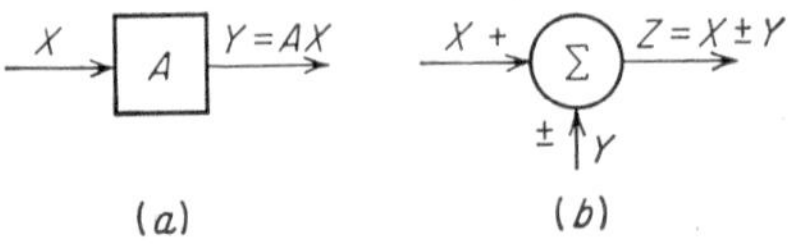

The symbols needed in block diagrams of linear systems are shown in Fig. 2-16. In Fig. 2-16a, X is an *input* variable, and Y is an *output* variable. They may be functions of time or complex-amplitude functions of frequency. The operator A is the *transfer function* representing the mathematical operation performed on X to obtain Y. If X and Y are time functions, A is a differential operator $A(p)$, where p is the derivative operator d/dt. If X and Y are complex amplitudes, A is a complex operator $A(s)$, where s is complex frequency. For steady-state sinusoidal variables, X and Y are phasors and $s = j\omega$. The symbol in Fig. 2-16b represents addition or subtraction.

Fig. 2-16. Block-diagram symbols.

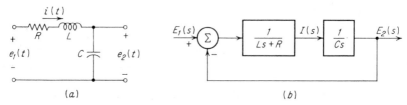

(a)

(b)

Fig. 2-17. (a) Circuit diagram and (b) complex-frequency block diagram of its transfer function, Example 2-9.

Example 2-9. Draw a block diagram in the complex-frequency domain for the circuit of Fig. 2-17a with input $e_1(t)$ and output $e_2(t)$.

Solution. The differential equations can be written in the form

$$e_1(t) - e_2(t) = Lpi + Ri \qquad e_2(t) = \frac{1}{Cp} i$$

When transformed to complex quantities and rearranged, the equations become

$$\frac{E_1(s) - E_2(s)}{Ls + R} = I(s) \qquad E_2(s) = \frac{1}{Cs} I(s)$$

The block diagram is shown in Fig. 2-17b.

Example 2-10. Draw a block diagram in the complex-frequency domain for incremental operation of the transducer of Example 2-7, Fig. 2-9, with terminal voltage v_{t1} and load force f_{l1} as inputs.

Solution. Rearrangement of Eq. 2-103 and transformation to complex quantities gives

$$I_1(s) = \frac{V_{t1}(s) - K_{0s}X_1(s)}{L_{0s} + r}$$

where the capital letters with subscript 1 are the complex amplitudes of the incremental variables. The block diagram for this equation is shown in the left-hand part of Fig. 2-18. Rearrangement of Eq. 2-102 and transformation to complex quantities gives

$$X_1(s) = \frac{K_0 I_1(s) - F_{t1}(s)}{Ms^2 + bs + k_s' s}$$

The corresponding block diagram is shown in the part of Fig. 2-18 to the right of $I_1(s)$. The diagram is completed by feeding back $K_0 s X_1$ into the left-hand summation.

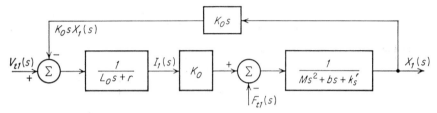

Fig. 2-18. Block diagram, Example 2-10.

With a little practice it becomes very easy to draw block diagrams with scarcely any preliminary algebra. One simply starts in somewhere with faith that everything is going to come out right in the end. Eventually all loops should close, leaving only the driving functions as inputs. These driving functions may come from other parts of a complex system. The block diagrams of the other components can then be drawn and their outputs fed in. Thus the block diagrams of complicated systems can be built up with attention focused on each element one at a time.

In a linear system the response of an output variable to any one input can be found by considering all other inputs to be zero. The over-all

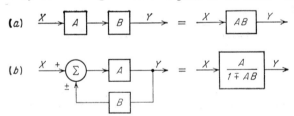

Fig. 2-19. Basic operations of block-diagram algebra.

response to several inputs can be found by superposition. The blocks can be combined by means of a few simple rules. Two basic ones are shown in Fig. 2-19. For example, in Fig. 2-19b,

$$Y = A(X \pm BY) \quad \text{or} \quad Y = \frac{A}{1 \mp AB} X \qquad (2\text{-}125)$$

Example 2-11. Find the transfer function $X_1(s)/V_{t1}(s)$ for the system of Fig. 2-18 with $F_{t1} = 0$. Then find an expression for the response to a small sinusoidal variation of v_{t1}.

Solution. With $F_{t1} = 0$ the system immediately reduces to Fig. 2-20a, which is of the same form as Fig. 2-19b with

$$A = \frac{K_0}{(L_0 s + r)(M s^2 + b s + k_s')}$$

and $$B = K_0 s$$

and negative feedback. Substitution in Eq. 2-125 with the positive sign and simplification of the result gives the transfer function shown in Fig. 2-20b. It is of the form

$$\frac{X_1(s)}{V_{t1}(s)} = \frac{K_0}{K_1 s^3 + K_2 s^2 + K_3 s + K_4}$$

where the K's are constants.

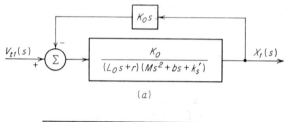

(a)

(b)

FIG. 2-20. Block diagrams, Example 2-11.

For a sinusoidal input, $s = j\omega$. The transfer function then becomes

$$\frac{X_1(j\omega)}{V_{t1}(j\omega)} = \frac{K_0}{-j\omega^3 K_1 - \omega^2 K_2 + j\omega K_3 + K_4}$$

$$= \frac{K_0}{K_4 - K_2\omega^2 + j\omega(K_3 - K_1\omega^2)}$$

When a system becomes too complicated for an analytical attack, computing machines can be used. Computers of the digital or analog type can quickly solve complex problems. Not only analysis of a specific system but also synthesis of the system and its components for optimum performance can be studied.[1] Because analog computers are frequently

---

[1] A number of books on computers are available. See, for example, W. J. Karplus and W. W. Soroka, "Analog Methods," 2d ed., McGraw-Hill Book Company, Inc., New York, 1959; N. R. Scott, "Analog and Digital Computer Technology," McGraw-Hill Book Company, Inc., New York, 1960. Analysis and synthesis of systems and components by use of computers is discussed in a large number of papers in technical publications such as *Trans. AIEE, Proc. IRE,* and proceedings of several computer conferences.

used in studies of electromechanical systems, it is appropriate to include here a brief discussion of block diagrams for analog computers.

The basic components of an analog computer perform the following operations: integration, addition, and multiplication by a constant. There may also be components for multiplication of two variables and for generation of a function of one or more variables. Differentiation is avoided. It is difficult to build an accurate analog differentiator, because differentiation exaggerates the effects of stray noise. The symbols used for computer block diagrams in this book are shown in Fig. 2-21, where

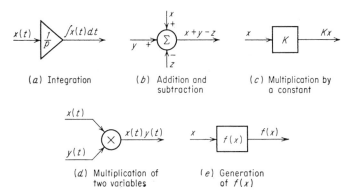

(a) Integration   (b) Addition and subtraction   (c) Multiplication by a constant

(d) Multiplication of two variables   (e) Generation of $f(x)$

FIG. 2-21. Block-diagram symbols.

$1/p$ indicates the operation of integration. The method of setting up a block diagram is illustrated in Example 2-12.

Example 2-12. Draw a block diagram for the transducer of Example 2-7, Fig. 2-9, for incremental motion, with the incremental terminal voltage v_{t1} and the incremental applied force f_{t1} as the inputs.

Solution. In general, the procedure is as follows: Express the highest derivatives of the variables in terms of their lower derivatives, the other variables, and the inputs. Thus Eqs. 2-102 and 2-103 become

$$pi_1 = \frac{1}{L_0}(v_{t1} - K_0 px_1 - ri_1) \tag{2-126}$$

$$p^2 x_1 = \frac{1}{M}(K_0 i_1 - f_{t1} - bpx_1 - k_s' x_1) \tag{2-127}$$

where p is the derivative operator d/dt. The equations can now be dealt with one at a time with no further algebra.

In Eq. 2-126, if pi_1 is integrated, i_1 can be generated, as shown by the integrator in Fig. 2-22a. The terms in parentheses on the right-hand side of Eq. 2-126 are shown by the summer with input v_{t1}, feedback ri_1 from the output i_1, and $K_0 px_1$ obtained from the block diagram of Eq. 2-127 as shown by the connection from Fig. 2-22b. Multiplication by $1/L_0$ then gives pi_1 as in Eq. 2-126 and in Fig. 2-22a.

In Eq. 2-127, if $p^2 x_1$ is integrated twice, px_1 and x_1 can be generated as shown by the two cascaded integrators in Fig. 2-22b. The terms in parentheses on the right-hand side of Eq. 2-127 are shown by the summer with input f_{t1}, bpx_1, and $k'_s x_1$ fed back from the outputs of the integrators, and $K_0 i_1$ obtained from Fig. 2-22a. The interconnections of px_1 and i_1 between the two parts of the block diagram are the coupling terms between the electrical and mechanical systems. The input $K_0 i_1$ is the magnetic force acting on the mechanical system, and the feedback $K_0 px_1$ is the motional counter emf generated in the electrical system.

The block diagram of Fig. 2-22 is typical of many magnetic field transducers. Except for the feedback k'_s, the block diagram of a d-c motor with constant field current is identical to Fig. 2-22.

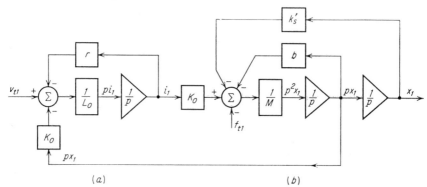

(a) (b)

STOP

FIG. 2-22. Block diagram, Example 2-12.

2-6. The Quasi-static Electric Field as a Coupling Medium.

The electric field as a coupling medium can be treated in a manner paralleling the foregoing treatment of the magnetic field, and similar coupling terms will be obtained. The mechanical forces due to the field can be found from the principles of virtual work and conservation of energy (Eq. 2-1). For example, suppose the plates of the capacitor in Fig. 2-23 are allowed to move closer together a differential distance dx under the influence of the force of attraction between the oppositely charged plates. Mechanical work $f\,dx$ will then be done by the field. The force depends only on the strength of the field and is independent of the way in which the field variables may change.

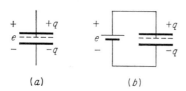

(a) (b)

FIG. 2-23. Charged capacitor. (a) At constant charge. (b) At constant voltage.

First assume that the capacitor has been charged and the source disconnected, as in Fig. 2-23a. Then assume the virtual displacement dx. The charge is constant, and the electrical energy input is zero. With rearrangement, Eq. 2-1 then reduces to

$$f\,dx = -dW_{\text{fld}}(q,x) \qquad \text{with } q \text{ const} \qquad (2\text{-}128)$$

or

$$f = -\frac{\partial W_{\text{fld}}}{\partial x}(q,x) \qquad (2\text{-}129)$$

where the field energy must be explicitly expressed in terms of q and x (compare with Eqs. 2-10 and 2-12).

Now assume the voltage to be constant, as in Fig. 2-23b. The charge will then increase, and electrical energy $e\, dq$ will be supplied by the source. Just as in the discussion of the magnetic field (Eq. 2-18), the increase in energy stored in the field at constant voltage is

$$dW_{\text{fld}} = e\, dq - dW'_{\text{fld}} \tag{2-130}$$

where dW'_{fld} is the increase in coenergy. Substitution in Eq. 2-1 then gives

$$e\, dq = e\, dq - dW'_{\text{fld}} + f\, dx \tag{2-131}$$

or

$$f = +\frac{\partial W'_{\text{fld}}}{\partial x}\,(e,x) \tag{2-132}$$

where the coenergy must be explicitly expressed in terms of e and x. Equations 2-129 and 2-132 are general expressions which apply to non-linear as well as linear dielectrics, and they give the same result. The only difference is the variables in terms of which they are expressed. For linear dielectrics $W_{\text{fld}} = W'_{\text{fld}}$, but it is still essential to use the proper field variables, q or e, in Eqs. 2-129 and 2-132; otherwise the algebraic signs will be wrong.

For linear dielectrics, the energy and coenergy can be expressed conveniently in terms of voltage e and capacitance C. As in Eq. 1-94,

$$W_{\text{fld}} = W'_{\text{fld}} = \tfrac{1}{2}Ce^2 \tag{2-133}$$

From Eq. 2-132

$$f = +\tfrac{1}{2}e^2\frac{dC}{dx} \tag{2-134}$$

Compare with the dual expression (Eq. 2-25) for the singly excited magnetic field. The force acts in a direction to increase the capacitance. The electrical behavior of the capacitor is

$$i = \frac{d}{dt}\,(Ce) = C\frac{de}{dt} + e\frac{dC}{dx}\frac{dx}{dt} \tag{2-135}$$

Compare with the dual expression (Eq. 2-69) for the magnetic system.

Equations 2-134 and 2-135 are the electromechanical coupling terms. The equations of motion of an electromechanical system with electric field coupling can be found by combining these equations with the equations for the electrical and mechanical systems connected to the coupling device. All the analytical techniques discussed in connection with magnetic field coupling will be found to apply in dual form.

2-7. Single-phase Electrostatic Synchronous Machine. An electrostatic synchronous machine of the variable-capacitance type[1] analogous to the magnetic variable-reluctance synchronous machine of Art. 2-2 is shown in Fig. 2-24. It is essentially a variable capacitance of the parallel-plate interleaving type whose rotor is free to rotate continuously. A high-voltage single-phase a-c source is connected across the stator and rotor. The rotor preferably should be grounded. As shown subsequently, high potential gradients are necessary in electrostatic devices to obtain mechanical forces of the same order of magnitude as those which can be obtained in magnetic devices of comparable size. Air at atmospheric pressure will not withstand such potential gradients, but high vacuum is a much superior insulating medium.

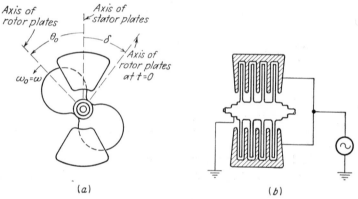

(a)   (b)

FIG. 2-24. (a) End view and (b) cross section of an electrostatic synchronous machine.

By analogy with Eq. 2-133, the instantaneous electrostatic torque T acting on a system whose capacitance C depends on the angular position θ of its parts is

$$T = +\tfrac{1}{2}e^2 \frac{dC}{d\theta} \qquad (2\text{-}136)$$

where e is the instantaneous voltage. In Fig. 2-24, the capacitance C is a periodic function of the angle θ_o. If the plates are shaped so that the capacitance varies sinusoidally between maximum and minimum values $C_{\max}$ and $C_{\min}$,

$$C = \tfrac{1}{2}(C_{\max} + C_{\min}) + \tfrac{1}{2}(C_{\max} - C_{\min}) \cos 2\theta_o \qquad (2\text{-}137)$$

[1] An analysis of this and a number of other types of electrostatic variable-capacitance rotating machines is the subject of the doctorate thesis by J. G. Trump, "Vacuum Electrostatic Engineering," Massachusetts Institute of Technology, Cambridge, Mass., 1933. For a brief survey of the potentialities of electrostatic machinery, see J. G. Trump, Electrostatic Sources of Electric Power, *Elec. Eng.*, vol. 66, no. 6, pp. 525–534, June, 1947.

If the applied voltage is sinusoidal,

$$e = E_{max} \cos \omega t$$

where E_{max} is its maximum value and zero time is chosen at the peak of the voltage wave. If the speed of the rotor is ω_o rad/sec and its instantaneous angular position at zero time is δ rad behind the position of maximum capacitance,

$$\theta_o = \omega_o t - \delta$$

If ω_o and δ are such that in each half cycle of the voltage wave the average square of the voltage is greater while the capacitance is increasing than it is while the capacitance is decreasing, average torque is developed in the direction to increase θ_o and thereby to keep the rotor revolving.

The analysis parallels that of the magnetic-reluctance motor. The synchronous speed ω_o equals the time angular velocity ω of the voltage wave. The average torque is

$$T_{av} = \tfrac{1}{8} E_{max}^2 (C_{max} - C_{min}) \sin 2\delta \qquad (2\text{-}138)$$

Compare with Eq. 2-46. The machine has all the operating characteristics of the magnetic type of reluctance motor.

In spite of the simplicity of electrostatic phenomena, the practical applications of electrostatic machines to date have been only as low-power high-voltage generators of the belt type, producing high constant potentials for X rays and nuclear research. No practical applications of the variable-capacitance type of machine have been made up to the present, although an experimental model has been built and tested. Some of the reasons for the preponderance of electromagnetic machinery are discussed in the following article.

2-8. Comparison of Electromagnetic and Electrostatic Machinery. In order to produce electrically a mechanical force between two rigid bodies, a concentration of energy must exist in the region between them. The energy storage can be in either a magnetic or an electrostatic field. Comparatively speaking, electromagnetic machines are high-current devices, while electrostatic machines are high-voltage devices. The availability of inexpensive materials with satisfactory magnetic, electrical, and mechanical properties, such as silicon-steel core materials and copper conductors, has made possible the enormous development of electromagnetic devices. On the other hand, no satisfactory means are available for insulating the potential gradients necessary to store energy electrostatically with densities equal to those that can be concentrated in the magnetic field in an air gap between two iron surfaces.

For purposes of obtaining a numerical comparison, consider the essentially uniform fields produced in the two simple cases shown in Fig. 2-25.

As in Eq. 2-29, the expression for the magnetic force of attraction between the two parallel plane faces of ferromagnetic material shown in Fig. 2-25a is

$$f_{\text{mag}} = \frac{1}{2} \frac{\mathcal{B}^2 A}{\mu_g} \tag{2-139}$$

where $\mathcal{B}$ is the flux density in the air gap, A is the area of each face, and μ_g is the permeability of the medium in the gap in rationalized units.

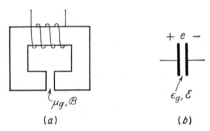

(a)   (b)

FIG. 2-25. Elementary magnetic and electrostatic systems for comparison of energy relations.

The permeability of the ferromagnetic material is assumed to be high compared with μ_g. The force per unit area of gap faces is

$$\frac{f_{\text{mag}}}{A} = \frac{1}{2} \frac{\mathcal{B}^2}{\mu_g} \tag{2-140}$$

The corresponding expression for the electrostatic force of attraction per unit area acting on each of the two parallel charged plates (Fig. 2-25b) is

$$\frac{f_{\text{elec}}}{A} = \frac{1}{2} \frac{\mathcal{D}^2}{\epsilon_g} = \frac{1}{2} \epsilon_g \mathcal{E}^2 \tag{2-141}$$

In Eq. 2-141, $\mathcal{D}$ is the electrostatic flux density in the gap and equals the charge density on the plates, $\mathcal{E}$ is the corresponding electric field intensity, and ϵ_g is the permittivity of the medium in the gap in rationalized units.

With magnetically operated devices the flux density that can be produced in an air gap depends primarily on the characteristics of the ferromagnetic material in the other parts of the magnetic circuit. For example, the commercially available grades of silicon steel used in the cores of rotating machines have their maximum permeabilities at flux densities of about 0.6 weber/m² (about 40 kilolines/in.²), and the "knee" of the magnetization curve—i.e., the region where the permeability decreases rapidly with increasing magnetizing force—is in the range from about 1.1 to 1.4 webers/m² (about 70 to 90 kilolines/in.²). Although it is theoretically possible to raise the flux density indefinitely by increasing the mmf of the exciting winding, it becomes uneconomical to do so, since for flux densities in the iron portion of the magnetic circuit much above the knee of the magnetization curve the power required by the exciting winding increases much more rapidly than the flux density in the gap.

It is a simple matter to produce flux densities in an air gap of the order of 1 weber/m^2 (64.5 kilolines/in.^{2}). At this flux density,

$$\frac{f_{\text{mag}}}{A} = \frac{1}{2} \times \frac{1^2}{4\pi \times 10^{-7}} = 3.98 \times 10^5 \text{ newtons/m}^2 \qquad (2\text{-}142)$$

or the magnetic stored energy density equals 3.98 × 10^5 watt-sec/m^3. In English units, this force intensity is 57.7 psi. This force is the order of magnitude of the intensity of radial magnetic force between the iron stator and rotor surfaces in rotating machines.

The charge concentration needed to produce electrostatically force intensities comparable with those which can be produced magnetically results in potential gradients which are extremely difficult to insulate. For example, air at atmospheric pressure will withstand a maximum potential gradient of approximately 30,000 volts/cm, or 3 × 10^6 volts/m. Its permittivity in rationalized mks units is 8.85 × 10^{-12}. From Eq. 2-141, the maximum force intensity that can be obtained between the plates in Fig. 2-25b with air as the insulating medium is

$$\frac{f_{\text{elec}}}{A} = \frac{1}{2} \times 8.85 \times 10^{-12} \times 9 \times 10^{12} = 39.8 \text{ newtons/m}^2 \qquad (2\text{-}143)$$

or the maximum density at which energy can be stored electrostatically in air at atmospheric pressure is about 40 watt-sec/m^3. In English units, this force intensity is 0.00577 psi.

Considerably higher potential gradients can be insulated if high vacuum or certain gases under pressures of several atmospheres are used as the insulating medium. High vacuum is preferable for rotating machinery, since windage loss then is negligible. Breakdown in vacuum is not solely dependent on potential gradient but is also a function of the total voltage between electrodes. It appears possible that cathode gradients of several million volts per centimeter may be insulated, even at the intermediate and high voltages that would be required in power machinery. If the gradient could be raised to 3 × 10^8 volts/m, the electrostatic force intensity would be 57.7 psi, the same as the magnetic force intensity at a magnetic flux density of 1 weber/m^2. Such potential gradients would be necessary for development of electrostatic rotating machines of compactness comparable with electromagnetic machines. If such vacuum-insulated machines could be built, they would have the advantages over electromagnetic machines of no windage loss, no magnetic core loss, very little dielectric loss, and very small I^2R loss. Their efficiencies therefore would be very high. They would probably be confined to high-voltage high-power applications.

2-9. Résumé. Magnetic and electrostatic fields are seats of energy storage. Whenever the energy in the field is influenced by the configuration of the mechanical parts constituting the boundaries of the field, mechanical forces are created which tend to move the mechanical elements so that energy is transmitted from the field to the mechanical system.

The force relations can readily be formulated from the conservation-of-energy principle and virtual work. The singly excited magnetic system is considered first in Art. 2-1. The results are the two basic relations 2-12 and 2-15, which express the magnetic forces in terms of the spatial partial derivatives of field energy or coenergy. They show that mechanical forces act on current-carrying conductors and ferromagnetic material, tending to move them so as to decrease the field energy at constant flux or to increase the coenergy at constant current. Later in the chapter these basic relations are shown to apply also to multiply excited magnetic systems and to quasi-static electric fields. In using these equations care must be taken to express the energy and coenergy in terms of the appropriate variables.

If magnetic nonlinearity is neglected, the force or torque acting on any part of a singly excited magnetic system readily can be expressed in terms of the space rate of change of reluctance, permeance, or inductance, as in Eqs. 2-23, 2-24, and 2-25. The force or torque acts in a direction to decrease the reluctance, to increase the permeance, and to increase the self-inductance. A dual expression for the electrostatic field is given in Eq. 2-134, which shows that the force acts in a direction to increase the capacitance.

The magnetic forces which tend to move rigid bodies into the positions of minimum reluctance are used to advantage in a wide variety of moving-iron devices consisting of an exciting coil wound on a magnetic circuit, part of which is movable. Most of the force acts between the fixed and movable iron members, since the reluctance of such a magnetic circuit is determined primarily by the air gap between these members. Forces also act directly on the exciting coil which tend to move it into the position of minimum reluctance and to deform it into the shape for minimum reluctance; i.e., the deforming forces tend to compress the coil axially, to deform it into a circle, and to expand it radially. Under normal conditions, however, the forces acting directly on the exciting coil are small. These forces may nevertheless become exceedingly important under abnormal conditions such as short circuits on large power apparatus.

In rotating machines, the variable-reluctance effect is a potential producer of torque whenever the configuration of the magnetic circuit is such that the reluctance depends on the angular position of the rotor. The basic relation is Eq. 2-32, in which the instantaneous torque is proportional to the square of the flux and the angular rate of decrease of reluctance. If the flux is a periodic function of time, as when alternating voltage is impressed on the exciting winding, and if the rotor is revolving so that the average square of the flux is greater while the reluctance is decreasing than it is while the reluctance is increasing, average torque will be produced in a direction to sustain rotation, as shown in Art. 2-2. Since the square of the flux goes through a cycle of its variation in a half cycle of the flux wave, the speed of the rotor must be such that the reluctance variation goes through a cycle of its variation in a half cycle of the flux wave. This is the only speed at which average torque is produced and is known as synchronous speed. The machine is a synchronous machine of the reluctance type. It accommodates itself to changes in shaft torque by adjusting the phase relation between the flux-squared wave and the reluctance variation, as shown in Eq. 2-46. For this reason the phase angle δ in Eq. 2-46 is known as the torque angle. For motor action, the reluctance variation lags behind the flux-squared wave; for generator action, it leads. The average torque is proportional to sin 2δ, as in Eq. 2-46. Its maximum value occurs when δ equals 45° and is given by Eq. 2-47.

An analogous type of synchronous machine using the electrostatic field as the energy-conversion medium is described in Art. 2-7, and the potentialities of magnetic and electrostatic fields for electromechanical coupling are compared in Art. 2-8. A comparison of the two types of devices can be made by comparing the density with which energy can be stored in the coupling fields. It is shown that potential gradients of about 3 million volts per centimeter are required to store energy in an electrostatic field at a density comparable with that which can easily be attained in a magnetic field. Electrostatic machines will be unable to compete with magnetic machines unless the problem of insulating such potential gradients can be solved satisfactorily.

Most electromechanical-energy-conversion devices, including nearly all rotating machines, are provided with several windings, and the useful torque or force is produced by the interaction of the magnetic fields of the two groups. Investigation of the basic theory of these multiply excited magnetic systems is the subject of Art. 2-3. We have seen that the effects of nonlinearity usually are of secondary importance when air gaps are present, and therefore multiply excited systems usually can be treated on a linear basis. The torque acting on the simple device of Fig. 2-7 can then readily be expressed in terms of the angular rates of change of the self- and mutual inductances, as in Eqs. 2-57 and 2-58, or in terms of the angular rate of increase of field energy at constant currents, as in Eq. 2-59. In Eqs. 2-57 and 2-58, the terms involving the angular derivatives of the self-inductances are recognized as the reluctance torques of Art. 2-1c.

They merely say that the field due to one current acting alone produces forces on magnetic material tending to move it so as to reduce the reluctance of the magnetic circuit. The terms involving the angular derivatives of the mutual inductances express the torques produced by the interaction of the magnetic field of one current with that of another. These terms merely say that the magnetic fields of stator and rotor tend to line up in the same direction. These are the principal torques in most rotating machines and in many other devices.

Through Art. 2-3 the discussion has been almost wholly concerned with the production of *mechanical* force in magnetic systems; the counterpart of this problem is the production of *electromotive* force. Mechanical force or torque is a *space* rate of change of flux linkages; electromotive force is the total *time* rate of change. The total time derivative of flux linkages is the sum of two groups of terms, one caused by variation in the amplitude of the field and the other caused by motion, as in Eqs. 2-64 and 2-65. The former are the transformer voltages, the latter the speed voltages. The speed voltage and the torque or force taken together are the electromechanical coupling terms constituting the action-reaction mechanism by which the coupling field calls for input to supply output. The differential equations of motion of an electromechanical system can then be written by introducing the torque or force produced by the coupling field into the differential equations for the mechanical system (as in Eqs. 2-62 and 2-63) and the induced voltage into the Kirchhoff-law equations for the electrical system (as in Eqs. 2-64 and 2-65). The process is described in Art. 2-4 and illustrated in Examples 2-5 and 2-6.

The equations of electromechanical coupling are difficult to solve analytically, because they are nonlinear differential equations containing terms which are the products of the variables and their derivatives. Approximate methods of treating these equations for small incremental changes away from a quiescent point are discussed in Art. 2-5a and illustrated in Example 2-7. The incremental equations then become linear differential equations with constant coefficients. The highly developed techniques of linear-system theory can then be applied. Some of these techniques, such as equivalent circuits, block diagrams, and transfer functions, are discussed in Art. 2-5b and c and illustrated by Examples 2-8 through 2-11. An introduction to block diagrams for analog computers is given in Art. 2-5c and Example 2-12.

This chapter has been concerned with basic principles applying broadly to the electromechanical-energy-conversion process, with emphasis on magnetic field coupling. Basically rotating machines and linear-motion transducers, for example, work in the same way. The remainder of this text is devoted almost entirely to the rotating-machine aspects of electromechanical energy conversion, both the dynamic characteristics of the machines as system components and their behavior under steady-state conditions. The rotating machine is a fairly complicated assembly of electric and magnetic circuits with a number of variations in machine types. For all of them the electromechanical coupling terms—torque and induced voltage—can be found by the principles developed in this chapter. The purpose of Chap. 3 is to provide this continuity of treatment and to lay the foundations for the specific treatments of the common machine types in Parts II and III.

PROBLEMS

2-1. An iron-clad plunger magnet is shown in Fig. 2-26. For the purposes of this problem, neglect fringing and leakage fluxes, and assume that all the reluctance of the magnetic circuit is in the working gap g between the movable plunger and the center core. The coil has an inductance of 1.00 henry when $g = 1.00$ cm.

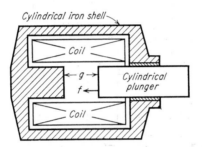

FIG. 2-26. Cylindrical plunger magnet, Prob. 2-1.

If the coil is excited from a constant-current source of 1.00 amp, compute:
 a. The energy stored in the magnetic field, in watt-seconds, when $g = 1.00$ cm
 b. The magnetic force f on the plunger, in newtons, when $g = 1.00$ cm
 c. The force f when $g = 0.50$ cm
 d. The mechanical work done by the force f, in watt-seconds, when the plunger is allowed to move slowly from $g = 1.00$ cm to $g = 0.50$ cm

2-2. An iron-clad plunger magnet is shown in Fig. 1-21 and described in Prob. 1-1. The air gap between the shell and the plunger can be assumed to be uniform and 0.01 in. long. Magnetic leakage and fringing may be neglected. The coil has 1,000 turns and carries a constant current of 3.0 amp.
 a. If the plunger is allowed to move slowly so as to reduce the gap g from 0.50 to 0.10 in., how much mechanical work will be done by the plunger, in watt-seconds?
 b. For the conditions of (a), how much energy will be supplied by the electrical source (in excess of heat loss in the coil)?

2-3. For the plunger magnet of Prob. 2-2 (Fig. 1-21), find a numerical expression for the magnetic force f acting on the plunger, in newtons, as a function of the gap g in meters with a constant coil current of 3.0 amp. Plot a curve of f as a function of g. From the area under this force-displacement curve, compute the mechanical work done by the plunger when it moves slowly so as to reduce the gap g from 0.50 to 0.10 in. Compare with the result of Prob. 2-2a.

2-4. Data for the magnetization curve of the iron portion of the magnetic circuit of the plunger magnet of Prob. 2-2 (Fig. 1-21) are given in Prob. 1-2. Plot magnetization curves for the complete magnetic circuit (flux in webers vs. total mmf in ampere-turns) for the following conditions:

a. Gap $g = 0.50$ in.

b. Gap $g = 0.10$ in.

c. From these curves find graphically the work done by the plunger if it is allowed to move slowly from $g = 0.50$ in. to $g = 0.10$ in. while the coil carries a constant current of 3.0 amp. Compare with the result of Prob. 2-2a.

d. Also find the energy supplied by the electrical source (in excess of heat loss in the coil). Compare with the result of Prob. 2-2b.

2-5. Consider the iron-cored solenoid shown in Fig. 2-27. The iron plunger of mass M is supported by a spring and guided vertically by nonmagnetic spacers of

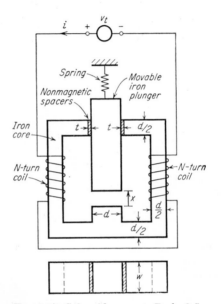

FIG. 2-27. Solenoid magnet, Prob. 2-5.

thickness t and permeability μ_0. Assume the iron to be infinitely permeable, and neglect magnetic fringing and leakage fields. All quantities are in rationalized mks units.

a. Find the inductance of the coil as a function of the plunger position x. Under what conditions is your expression fairly accurate?

b. Find an expression for the magnetic force acting on the plunger in terms of the coil current i.

c. Suppose the dimensions are

$$w = 5 \text{ cm} \qquad d = 4 \text{ cm} \qquad t = 0.1 \text{ cm}$$

Approximately what maximum force would you expect to get on the plunger without saturating the iron?

2-6. The armature and field structures of a simplified 2-pole d-c machine are shown in the end view (a) and cross section (b) in Fig. 2-28. Because of an error in assembly, the armature core is displaced 0.5 in. in an axial direction from its correct position. Other numerical data are as follows:

Length of each air gap = 0.10 in.
Diameter of armature = 10.0 in.
Air-gap flux density = 50 kilolines/in.²
Angle subtended by each pole shoe = 100°

The air-gap length can be considered constant under the pole shoes, and the armature can be considered as a smooth cylinder.

Find the axial force in pounds tending to center the armature.

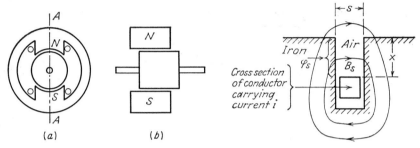

Fɪɢ. 2-28. Simplified d-c machine, Prob. 2-6. 　　Fɪɢ. 2-29. Conductor in a slot, Prob. 2-7.

2-7. Figure 2-29 shows the general nature of the slot-leakage flux produced by current i in a rectangular conductor embedded in a rectangular slot in iron. Assume that the slot-leakage flux φ_s goes straight across the slot in the region between the top of the conductor and the top of the slot.

a. Derive an expression for the flux density B_s in the region between the top of the conductor and the top of the slot.

b. Derive an expression for the slot-leakage flux φ_s crossing the slot above the conductor, in terms of the height x of the slot above the conductor, the slot width s, and the embedded length l perpendicular to the paper.

c. Derive an expression for the force f created by this magnetic field on a conductor of length l. Use rationalized mks units. In what direction does this force act on the conductor?

d. Compute the force in pounds on a conductor 1.0 ft long in a slot 1.0 in. wide when the current in the conductor is 1,000 amp.

2-8. Derive an expression for the instantaneous current taken by a single-phase reluctance motor in terms of ϕ_{max}, $\mathfrak{R}_q$, $\mathfrak{R}_d$, and δ. Assume that the flux and reluctance variations are sinusoidal, as in Fig. 2-5b, and that the effects of core loss and magnetic nonlinearity are negligible. Using this expression for the current, derive an expression for the average power input, neglecting the effects of winding resistance. Show that the result is consistent with the torque relations derived in the text.

2-9. Express the torque developed by a single-phase reluctance motor in terms of the impressed voltage V_t, the direct- and quadrature-axis reactances X_d and X_q, the torque angle δ, and the angular velocity ω_o. Assume that the winding resistance is negligible and that the flux and reluctance variations are sinusoidal. The direct- and quadrature-axis reactances are, respectively, the reactances of the winding when the rotor axis is in line with, and when it is in quadrature with, the axis of the stator poles.

2-10. Two coils have self- and mutual inductances in henrys as functions of a displacement x in meters as follows:

$$L_{11} = 1 + x$$
$$L_{22} = 2(1 + x)$$
$$L_{12} = 1 - x$$

The resistances are negligible.

a. For constant currents $I_1 = +10.0$ amp and $I_2 = -5.0$ amp, compute the mechanical work done in increasing x from 0 to $+1.0$ m.

b. Does the force developed in part a tend to increase or decrease x?

c. During the motion of part a, how much energy is supplied by source 1? By source 2?

d. Compute the average value of the force developed for $x = 0.50$ m when coil 2 is short-circuited and a sinusoidal voltage of 377 volts rms at 60 cps is applied to coil 1.

2-11. The self-inductances L_{11} and L_{22} and the absolute value of the mutual inductance L_{12} of the device shown in Fig. 2-7 are given in the table below for two angular positions θ_o of the rotor, where θ_o is measured from a horizontal reference axis to the axis of the rotor:

θ_o	L_{11}	L_{22}	L_{12}
45°	0.60	1.10	0.30
75°	1.00	2.00	1.00

The inductances are given in henrys and may be assumed to vary linearly with θ_o over the range $45° < \theta_o < 75°$.

For each of the following cases, compute the electromagnetic torque in newton-meters when the rotor is stationary at an angular position $\theta_o = 60°$ (approximately the position shown in Fig. 2-7), and state whether this torque tends to turn the rotor in a clockwise or counterclockwise direction.

a. $i_1 = 10.0$ amp, $i_2 = 0$.

b. $i_1 = 0$, $i_2 = 10.0$ amp.

c. $i_1 = 10.0$ amp, and $i_2 = 10.0$ amp in arrow directions (Fig. 2-7).

d. $i_1 = 10.0$ amp in arrow direction, and $i_2 = 10.0$ amp in reverse direction.

e. $I_1 = 10.0$ amp rms value of sinusoidal alternating current, with coil 2 short-circuited. In this case the resistance of coil 2 may be neglected, and it is the time average of the torque which is wanted.

2-12. Two coils, one mounted on a stator and the other on a rotor, have self- and mutual inductances of

$$L_{11} = 0.20 \text{ mh}$$
$$L_{22} = 0.10 \text{ mh}$$
$$L_{12} = 0.05 \cos \theta \text{ mh}$$

where θ is the angle between the axes of the coils. The coils are connected in series and carry a current

$$i = \sqrt{2}\, I \sin \omega t$$

a. Derive an expression for the instantaneous torque T on the rotor as a function of the angular position θ.

b. Give an expression for the time-average torque T_{av} as a function of θ.

c. Compute the numerical value of T_{av} for $I = 10$ amp and $\theta = 90°$.

d. Sketch three curves of T_{av} versus θ for currents $I = 5, 7.07$, and 10 amp, respectively.

e. A helical restraining spring which tends to hold the rotor at $\theta = 90°$ is now attached to the rotor. The restraining torque of the spring is proportional to the angular deflection from $\theta = 90°$ and is 0.004 newton-meter when the rotor is turned to $\theta = 0$. Show on the curves of part *d* how you could find the angular position of the rotor-plus-spring combination for coil currents $I = 5, 7.07$, and 10 amp, respectively. Sketch a curve showing θ versus I. A reasonable-looking sketch with estimated numerical values is all that is required.

NOTE: This problem illustrates the principles of the dynamometer-type a-c ammeter.

2-13. Figure 2-30 shows in cross section a cylindrical-plunger magnet. The plunger is constrained to move in the x direction and is restrained by a spring whose spring

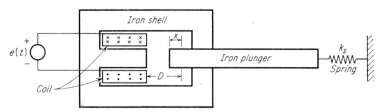

FIG. 2-30. Solenoid magnet, Prob. 2-13.

constant is k_s. The position of the plunger when the coil is unexcited is D. The mass of the plunger is M. Friction is negligible. The cross-sectional area of the working air gap is A. Neglect magnetic leakage and fringing. Also neglect the reluctance of the iron. The coil has N turns and negligible resistance.

The plunger is operating under steady-state sinusoidal conditions. The flux density in the air gap is

$$B(t) = B_m \sin \omega t$$

a. Find an expression for the magnetic force acting on the plunger in terms of B_m, ω, and t.

b. Write the equation for the coil voltage $e(t)$ in terms of B_m, ω, and t.

c. Write the differential equation of motion of the plunger in terms of B_m, ω, t, and x.

d. Assume that the system is in the steady state. Solve for the position of the plunger $x(t)$. Note that the solution must contain a constant part X_0 and a time-varying part $x_1(t)$.

2-14. Consider a solenoid magnet similar to that shown in Fig. 2-9, except that the length of the cylindrical steel plunger is $a + h$.

Derive the dynamic equations of motion of the system.

2-15. The following dimensions and data apply to the solenoid magnet of Prob. 2-14:

$$a = 2 \text{ cm} \qquad h = 6 \text{ cm} \qquad d = 2 \text{ cm} \qquad t = 0.05 \text{ cm}$$

Turns $N = 1,000$
Coil resistance $r = 100$ ohms
Mass of plunger $M = 0.2$ kg
Spring constant $k_s = 6.25$ newtons/cm
With $i = 0$, plunger is at rest at $x = 0.25$ cm
External applied force $= 0$
Friction negligible

The voltage applied to the coil has a quiescent value of 10 volts.

a. Find the quiescent operating point. Is it stable?

b. Linearize the dynamic equations of motion for small incremental changes in the applied voltage. Give numerical values of the parameters in mks units.

c. Find an equivalent electric circuit, with numerical values.

2-16. The solenoid magnet of Example 2-6, Fig. 2-10, is driven by a push-pull amplifier as shown in Fig. 2-31. The tubes are identical and have the amplification factor μ and plate resistance r_p. The quiescent current is I_{b0}.

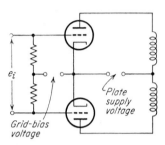

FIG. 2-31. Push-pull amplifier circuit, Prob. 2-16.

a. From the results of Example 2-6, derive the equations of motion for small input signals e_i.

b. Linearize the equations.

c. Draw an equivalent electric circuit. Express the values of the mechanical parameters and variables in terms of equivalent electrical quantities.

d. Draw a block diagram of the system with e_i as the input and mechanical displacement x as the output.

2-17. Two windings, one mounted on a stator and the other on a rotor, have self- and mutual inductances as given below:

$$L_{11} = 2.20 \text{ henrys} \qquad L_{22} = 1.00 \text{ henry}$$
$$L_{12} = 1.414 \cos \theta_o \text{ henrys}$$

where θ_o is the angle between the axes of the windings. The resistances of the windings may be neglected.

Winding 2 is short-circuited, and the current in winding 1 as a function of time is $i_1 = 14.14 \sin \omega t$.

a. If the rotor is stationary, derive an expression for the numerical value, in newton-meters, of the instantaneous torque on the rotor in terms of the angle θ_o.

b. Compute the average torque in newton-meters when $\theta_o = 45°$.

c. If the rotor is allowed to move, will it rotate continuously or will it tend to come to rest? If the latter, at what value of θ_o?

2-18. Figure 2-32 shows a capacitor with one fixed and one movable plate constrained to move in the x direction. Its capacitance is given by

$$C = \frac{1}{x} \quad \mu\text{f}$$

with x in meters. There are no electrical or mechanical losses. Initially $E = 200$ volts and $x = 0.01$ m.

The capacitor is then put through the following cycle:

a. With $E = 200$ volts, x is increased to 0.02 m.

b. With $x = 0.02$ m, E is decreased to 100 volts.

c. With $E = 100$ volts, x is decreased to 0.01 m.

d. With $x = 0.01$, E is increased to 200 volts, thereby closing the cycle.

For this closed cycle, find the mechanical work done. Is the net energy flow into or out of the battery?

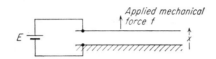

FIG. 2-32. Movable-plate capacitor, Prob. 2-18.

2-19. Consider a single-phase electrostatic synchronous machine of the type shown in Fig. 2-24. The purpose of this problem is to investigate some of the physical proportions of such a machine designed to develop 1 hp at 3,600 rpm with 60-cps applied voltages. Several operating voltages will be considered, and both air and vacuum insulation will be investigated. The following assumptions can be made:

1. The applied voltages vary sinusoidally.

2. The plates are shaped so that the capacitance varies sinusoidally with rotor angle, the minimum capacitance being negligibly small.

3. For mechanical reasons, the minimum permissible clearance between stator and rotor plates will be taken (more or less arbitrarily) as 0.1 cm.

4. Edge effects will be neglected, and the potential gradients between stator and rotor plates will be considered to be uniform. The maximum permissible potential gradients will be taken as 10 kv/cm in air and 1,000 kv/cm in vacuum. These values allow a factor of safety of about 3 for edge effects.

The following results are to be computed:

a. Determine the maximum value of the capacitance for operation at an rms voltage of 115 volts.

b. Determine the corresponding total rotor surface area.

c. If one face of each of the approximately circular surfaces constituting half of each rotor plate in Fig. 2-24 has a surface area of 200 cm², how many rotor plates will be required?

d. Roughly what would be the diameter of the rotor?

e. If each stator and rotor plate had a thickness of 0.1 cm (determined by mechanical considerations), how long would the motor be? (Do not be surprised if you arrive at a monstrosity!)

f. Determine the minimum rms voltage which would take full advantage of the maximum permissible potential gradient in air. For this operating voltage, repeat the calculations called for in (a) to (e).

g. Determine the minimum rms voltage which would take full advantage of the maximum permissible potential gradient in vacuum. For this operating voltage, repeat the calculations called for in (a) to (e).

CHAPTER 3

Basic Rotating Machines

The object of this chapter is to discuss the approximations involved in reducing a physical machine to a simple mathematical model, to apply the basic principles of Chap. 2 to the analysis of this model, and to give some simple concepts relating to the basic machine types.

3-1. Elementary Concepts. Faraday's law, $e = d\lambda/dt$, describes quantitatively the induction of voltages by a time-varying magnetic field. Electromechanical energy conversion takes place when the change in

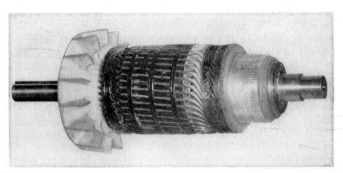

FIG. 3-1. Armature of a d-c motor. (*Courtesy of General Electric Company.*)

flux is associated with mechanical motion. In rotating machines voltages are generated in windings or groups of coils by rotating these windings mechanically through a magnetic field, by mechanically rotating a magnetic field past the winding, or by designing the magnetic circuit so that the reluctance varies with rotation of the rotor. By any of these methods the flux linking a specific coil is changed cyclically, and a voltage is generated. A group of such coils interconnected so that their generated voltages all make a positive contribution to the desired result is called an *armature winding*. The armature winding of a d-c machine is shown in Fig. 3-1; the armature is the rotating member, or *rotor*. Figure 3-2 shows the armature winding of an a-c generator, *alternator*, or *synchronous generator*. Here the armature is the stationary member, or *stator*.

94

These coils are wound on iron cores in order that the flux path through them may be as effective as possible. Because the armature iron is subjected to a varying magnetic flux, eddy currents will be induced in it; to minimize the eddy-current loss, the armature iron is built up of thin laminations as illustrated in Fig. 3-3 for the armature of an a-c machine. The magnetic circuit is completed through the iron of the other machine member, and exciting coils, or *field windings*, are placed on that member to act as the primary sources of flux. Permanent magnets may be used in small machines.

Fig. 3-2. Stator with armature winding for a 27,500-kva 3-phase 11,000-volt 187.5-rpm hydroelectric generator. (*Courtesy of ASEA Electric Inc.*)

a. Elementary Synchronous Machines. Preliminary ideas of generator action can be gained by discussing the armature induced voltage in the very much simplified a-c synchronous generator shown in Fig. 3-4. With rare exceptions, the armature winding of a synchronous machine is on the stator, and the field winding is on the rotor, as in Fig. 3-4. The field winding is excited by direct current conducted to it by means of carbon *brushes* bearing on *slip rings* or *collector rings*. Constructional factors usually dictate this orientation of the 2 windings: the field current is usually much smaller than the armature current, and it is advantageous to have the low-power winding on the rotor. The armature winding, consisting of a single coil of N turns, is indicated in cross section by the

Fig. 3-3. Partially completed stator core for an a-c motor. (*Courtesy of Westinghouse Electric Corporation.*)

two coil sides a and $-a$ placed in diametrically opposite narrow slots on the stator of Fig. 3-4. The conductors forming these coil sides are parallel to the shaft of the machine and are connected in series by end connections which are not shown in the figure. The rotor is turned at a constant speed by a source of mechanical power connected to its shaft. Flux paths are shown by dotted lines in Fig. 3-4.

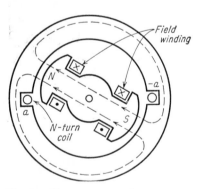

Fig. 3-4. Elementary synchronous generator.

The radial distribution of the air-gap flux density $\mathfrak{B}$ is shown in Fig. 3-5a as a function of the space angle θ around the air-gap periphery. The flux-density wave of practical machines can be made to approximate a sinusoidal distribution by properly shaping the pole face. As the rotor revolves, the flux waveform sweeps by the coil sides a and $-a$. The resulting coil voltage (Fig. 3-5b) is a time function having the same waveform as the spatial distribution $\mathfrak{B}$. The coil voltage passes through a complete cycle of values for each revolution of the 2-pole machine of Fig. 3-4. Its frequency in cycles per second is the same as the speed of

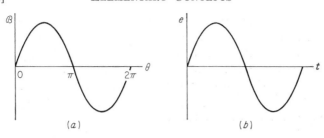

Fig. 3-5. (a) Space distribution of flux density and (b) corresponding waveform of the generated voltage.

the rotor in revolutions per second; i.e., the electrical frequency is synchronized with the mechanical speed, and this is the reason for the designation *synchronous* machine. Thus a 2-pole synchronous machine must revolve at 3,600 rpm to produce a 60-cps voltage.

A great many synchronous machines have more than 2 poles. As a specific example, Fig. 3-6 shows the most elementary 4-pole single-phase alternator. The field coils are connected so that the poles are of alternate north and south polarity. There are two complete wavelengths or cycles in the flux distribution around the periphery, as shown in Fig. 3-7. The armature winding now consists of 2 coils a_1, $-a_1$ and a_2, $-a_2$ connected in series by their end connections. The span of each coil is one-half wavelength of flux. The generated voltage now goes through two complete cycles

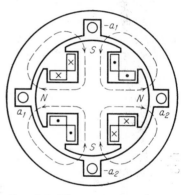

Fig. 3-6. Elementary 4-pole synchronous generator.

per revolution of the rotor. The frequency f in cycles per second then is twice the speed in revolutions per second.

When a machine has more than 2 poles, it is convenient to concentrate on a single pair of poles and to recognize that the electric, magnetic, and

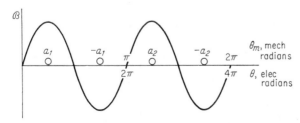

Fig. 3-7. Space distribution of flux density in a 4-pole synchronous generator.

mechanical conditions associated with every other pole pair are repetitions of those for the pair under consideration. For this reason it is convenient to express angles in *electrical degrees* or *electrical radians* rather than in mechanical units. One pair of poles in a P-pole machine or one cycle of flux distribution equals 360 electrical degrees or 2π electrical radians. Since there are $P/2$ complete wavelengths or cycles in one complete revolution, it follows that

$$\theta = \frac{P}{2}\,\theta_m \qquad (3\text{-}1)$$

where θ is the angle in electrical units and θ_m is the mechanical angle. The coil voltage of a P-pole machine passes through a complete cycle every time a pair of poles sweeps by, or $P/2$ times each revolution. The frequency of the voltage wave is therefore

$$f = \frac{P}{2}\frac{n}{60} \qquad \text{cps} \qquad (3\text{-}2)$$

where n is the mechanical speed in rpm and $n/60$ is the speed in revolutions per second. The radian frequency ω of the voltage wave is

$$\omega = \frac{P}{2}\,\omega_m \qquad (3\text{-}3)$$

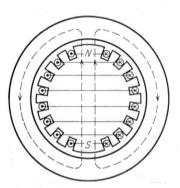

FIG. 3-8. Elementary 2-pole cylindrical-rotor field winding.

where ω_m is the mechanical speed in radians per second.

The rotors shown in Figs. 3-4 and 3-6 have *salient*, or projecting, poles with *concentrated* windings. Figure 3-8 shows diagrammatically a *nonsalient-pole*, or *cylindrical*, rotor. The field winding is a *distributed* winding placed in slots and arranged so as to produce an approximately sinusoidal 2-pole field. The constructional reasons for some synchronous generators having salient-pole rotor structures and others having cylindrical rotors can be appreciated with the aid of Eq. 3-2. Most power systems in the United States operate at a frequency of 60 cps. A salient-pole construction is characteristic of hydroelectric generators because hydraulic turbines operate at relatively low speeds and a relatively large number of poles are required to produce the desired frequency; the salient-pole construction is better adapted mechanically to this situation. A large hydroelectric generator is shown in Fig. 3-9 during assembly. One section of its stator laminations is shown in Fig. 3-10. Steam turbines and gas turbines, on the other hand, operate best at relatively high speeds, and turbine-driven alternators are commonly

2- or 4-pole cylindrical-rotor machines.   The rotor of such a *turbine-generator* is shown in Fig. 3-11.

With very few exceptions, synchronous generators are 3-phase machines, because of the advantages of 3-phase systems for generation, transmission, and heavy-power utilization.   For the production of a set

FIG. 3-9. The 445-metric-ton rotor for one of the three 150,000-kva 125-rpm generators at the Stornorrfors hydroelectric power station in the north of Sweden being lowered into the stator.   The rotor has a diameter of 32 ft.   (*Courtesy of ASEA Electric Inc.*)

of three voltages phase-displaced by 120 electrical degrees in time, it follows that a minimum of 3 coils phase-displaced 120 electrical degrees in space must be used.   An elementary 3-phase 2-pole machine with 1 coil per phase is shown in Fig. 3-12a.   The 3 phases are designated by the letters a, b, and c.   In an elementary 4-pole machine, two such sets of coils must be used, as illustrated in Fig. 3-12b; in an elementary P-pole machine, $P/2$ such sets must be used.   The 2 coils in each phase of Fig.

FIG. 3-10. One section of the stator core for the Stornorrfors generator of Fig. 3-9. (*Courtesy of ASEA Electric Inc.*)

FIG. 3-11. Rotor of a 2-pole 3,600-rpm turbine-generator. (*Courtesy of Westinghouse Electric Corporation.*)

3-12*b* are connected in series so that their voltages aid, and the 3 phases may then be either Y- or Δ-connected. Figure 3-12*c* shows how the coils are interconnected to form a Y connection.

When a synchronous generator supplies electrical power to a load, the armature current creates a component flux wave in the air gap which rotates at synchronous speed, as will be shown in Art. 3-4. This flux reacts with the flux created by the field current, and electromagnetic torque results from the tendency of the two magnetic fields to align themselves. In a generator this torque opposes rotation, and mechanical torque must be applied from the prime mover in order to sustain rotation. The electromagnetic torque is the mechanism through which greater electrical power output calls for greater mechanical power input.

The counterpart of the synchronous generator is the *synchronous motor*. A cutaway view of a 3-phase 60-cps synchronous motor is shown

(*a*)   (*b*)   (*c*)

Fig. 3-12. Elementary 3-phase generators. (*a*) 2-pole. (*b*) 4-pole. (*c*) Y connection of the windings.

in Fig. 3-13. Alternating current is supplied to the armature winding (usually the stator), and d-c excitation is supplied to the field winding (usually the rotor). The magnetic field of the armature currents rotates at synchronous speed. In order to produce a steady electromagnetic torque, the magnetic fields of stator and rotor must be constant in amplitude and stationary with respect to each other. In a synchronous motor the steady-state speed is determined by the number of poles and the frequency of the armature current exactly as in Eq. 3-2 or 3-3 for a synchronous generator. Thus a synchronous motor operated from a constant-frequency a-c source must run at a constant steady-state speed.

In a motor the electromagnetic torque is in the direction of rotation and balances the opposing torque required to drive the mechanical load. The rotational or speed voltage then acts in opposition to the applied voltage and current. In both generators and motors an electromagnetic torque and a rotational voltage are produced. These are the essential phenomena for electromechanical energy conversion. Quantitative analysis of these phenomena will be discussed in a preliminary way later in this chapter and in more detail in Chaps. 5 and 9.

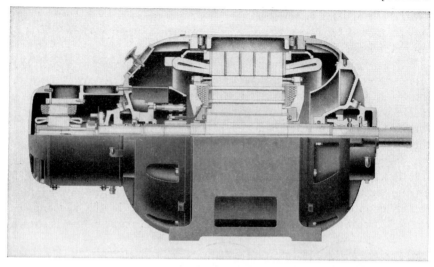

Fig. 3-13. Cutaway view of a high-speed synchronous motor with overhung exciter. (*Courtesy of General Electric Company.*)

Fig. 3-14. A large d-c motor showing brush rigging and commutator. (*Courtesy of Westinghouse Electric Corporation.*)

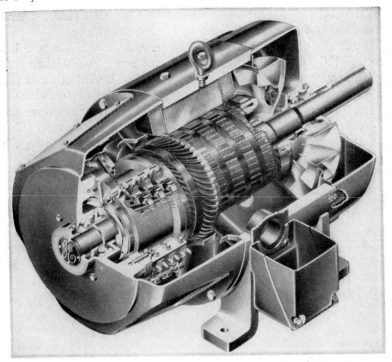

FIG. 3-15. Cutaway view of a typical d-c motor. (*Courtesy of General Electric Company.*)

b. Elementary D-C Machines. The armature winding of a d-c generator is on the rotor with current conducted from it by means of carbon brushes. The field winding is on the stator and is excited by direct current. A photograph of a large d-c machine is shown in Fig. 3-14 and a cutaway view of a d-c motor in Fig. 3-15.

A very elementary 2-pole d-c generator is shown in Fig. 3-16. The armature winding, consisting of a single coil of N turns, is indicated by the two coil sides a and $-a$ placed at diametrically opposite points on the rotor with the conductors parallel to the shaft. The rotor is normally turned at a constant speed by a source of mechanical power connected to the shaft. The air-gap flux distribution usually approximates a flat-topped wave rather than the sine wave found in a-c machines and is shown in Fig. 3-17a. Rota-

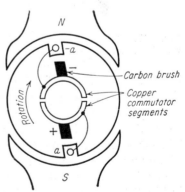

FIG. 3-16. Elementary d-c machine with commutator.

tion of the coil generates a coil voltage which is a time function having the same waveform as the spatial flux-density distribution.

Although the ultimate purpose is the generation of a direct voltage, the voltage induced in an individual armature coil is an alternating voltage. This voltage must therefore be rectified. Rectification is sometimes provided externally, for example, by means of semiconductor rectifiers. The machine then is an a-c generator plus external rectifiers. In the conventional d-c machine rectification is provided mechanically by means of a *commutator*, which is a cylinder formed of copper segments

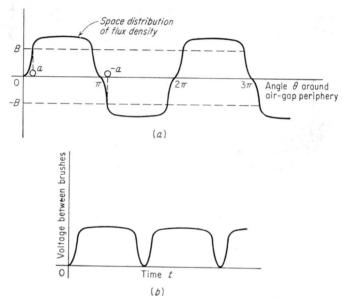

(a)

(b)

Fig. 3-17. (a) Space distribution of flux density in an elementary d-c machine and (b) waveform of voltage between brushes.

insulated from each other by mica and mounted on, but insulated from, the rotor shaft. Stationary carbon brushes held against the commutator surface connect the winding to the external armature terminals. The commutator and brushes may readily be seen in Figs. 3-14 and 3-15. The necessity for commutation is the reason why the armature windings of d-c machines are placed on the rotor.

For the elementary d-c generator the commutator takes the form shown in Fig. 3-16. For the direction of rotation shown, the commutator at all times connects the coil side which is under the south pole to the positive brush and that under the north pole to the negative brush. The commutator provides full-wave rectification, transforming the voltage waveform between brushes to that of Fig. 3-17b and making available a unidirectional voltage to the external circuit.   The d-c machine of Fig. 3-16 is, of course, simplified to the point of being unrealistic in the practical sense, and it will be essential later to examine the action of more realistic commutators.

If direct current flows in the external circuit connected to the brushes, torque is created by the interaction of the magnetic fields of stator and rotor.   If the machine is acting as a generator, this torque opposes rotation.   If it is acting as a motor, the electromagnetic torque acts in the direction of rotation.   Remarks similar to those already made concerning the roles played by the generated voltage and electromagnetic torque in the energy-conversion process in synchronous machines apply equally well to d-c machines.   A wide variety of operating characteristics can be obtained, as will be shown in a preliminary way later in this chapter and in more detail in Chaps. 4 and 8.

c. *Elementary Induction Machines.*   A third variation on exciting stator and rotor windings is the *induction machine,* in which there are alternating currents in both stator and rotor windings.   The most common example is the induction motor in which alternating current is supplied directly to the stator and by induction (i.e., transformer action) to the rotor.   The induction machine may be regarded as a generalized transformer in which electric power is transformed between stator and rotor together with a change of frequency and a flow of mechanical power. Although the induction motor is the most common of all motors, the induction machine is seldom used as a generator; its performance characteristics as a generator are unsatisfactory for most applications.   The induction machine may also be used as a frequency changer.

In the induction motor, the stator winding is essentially the same as that of a synchronous motor.   On the rotor, the winding is electrically closed on itself and very often has no external terminals; currents are induced in it by transformer action from the stator winding.   A cutaway view of an induction motor is shown in Fig. 3-18.   The usual induction-motor speed-torque characteristic is that the speed drops off slightly as load is added to its shaft.   These characteristics will be discussed in a preliminary way later in this chapter and in more detail in Chaps. 6 and 10.

Thus a variety of basic machine types is available, all operating on the same basic principles and each having its own special characteristics and uses.   Obviously further study of the interacting magnetic fields is needed for an understanding of the basic theory.   Since the geometry of rotating machines is far too complicated to permit a direct solution by means of field theory, it will be necessary to develop a simplified mathematical model through making reasonable simplifying approximations, as discussed in the next article.

3-2. MMF of Distributed Windings. Most armatures have distributed windings—i.e., windings which are spread over a number of slots around the periphery of the machine as in the photographs of Figs. 3-1, 3-2, and 3-9. The individual coils are interconnected so that the result is belts of conductors in the slots carrying oppositely directed currents parallel to the shaft and arranged to produce the same number of poles as the field winding.

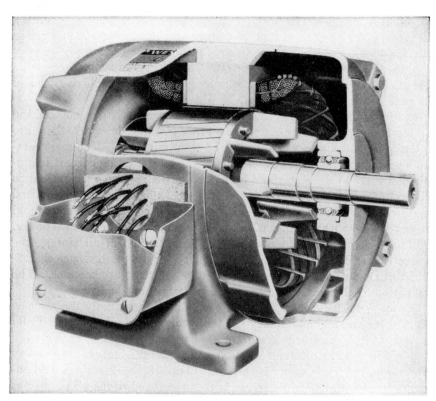

Fig. 3-18. Cutaway view of an induction motor with squirrel-cage rotor. (*Courtesy of Westinghouse Electric Corporation.*)

For example, Fig. 3-19 shows diagrammatically in cross section the armature (rotor) of a 2-pole d-c machine. (In practice a larger number of slots would probably be used.) The current directions are shown by dots and crosses indicating current toward and away from the reader, respectively. The armature winding is equivalent to a coil wrapped around the armature and producing a magnetic field whose axis is vertical, and a clockwise electromagnetic torque acts on the armature, tending to align its magnetic field with that of the field winding. As the armature rotates, the coil connections to the external circuit are changed through commutator action so that the magnetic field of the armature is always perpendicular to that of the field winding and a continuous unidirectional torque results.   Commutator action is described in Art. 3-7.

This armature winding is arranged in two layers, each coil having one side in the top of a slot and the other coil side in the bottom of another slot a half wavelength of flux away, as indicated by the two representative coil sides a_1, $-a_1$ in Fig. 3-19.   The two-layer arrangement simplifies the geometrical problem of getting the end turns of the individual coils past

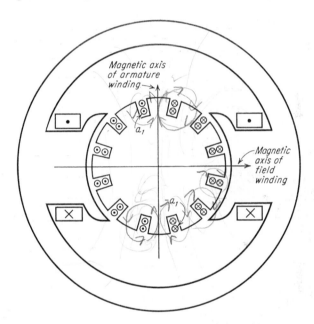

Fig. 3-19. Cross section of a 2-pole d-c machine.

each other.   These end turns and the interconnections among the individual coils and to the commutator need not concern us at present.   For our purposes it is sufficient to know that the current distribution in the slots is as shown in Fig. 3-19.

Figure 3-20a shows this winding in developed form—i.e., laid out flat. From the symmetry of the structure it is evident that the magnetic field intensity $\mathcal{3C}$ in the air gap at angle θ is the same in magnitude as that at $\theta + \pi$, but the fields are in the opposite direction.   This assumes that the air gap at θ is the same as at $\theta + \pi$.   Since the permeability of the armature and field iron is much greater than that of air, it is sufficiently accurate for our present purposes to assume that all the reluctance of the magnetic circuit is in the air gaps and that the resultant magnetic field can be found by superposition of the fields due to the armature and field windings acting separately. With the armature alone excited the field iron then is a boundary of zero magnetic potential.

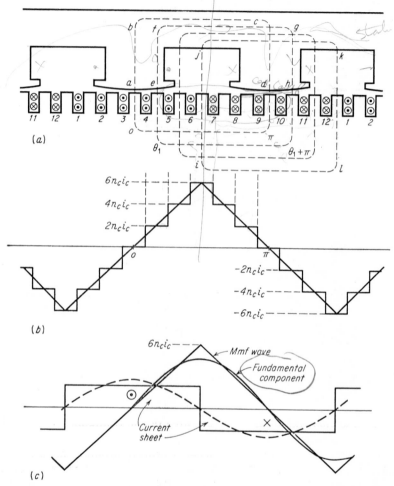

Fig. 3-20. (a) Developed sketch of the d-c machine of Fig. 3-19. (b) Magnetomotive-force wave. (c) Equivalent triangular mmf wave, its fundamental component, and equivalent rectangular current sheet.

Now recall that in rationalized mks units the mmf acting on any closed path equals the total current enclosed by the path. First consider specifically the path abcd crossing the air gap at the centers of the field poles at angles 0 and π (Fig. 3-20a). The net current enclosed is zero, and the magnitude of the magnetic potential difference across the gap at these points is zero. Next consider the path efgh crossing the gap at

θ_1 and $\theta_1 + \pi$. The net current enclosed is $4n_ci_c$, where n_c is the number of turns in each coil and i_c is the coil current. The net current is away from the reader, and the total mmf $4n_ci_c$ around the path is in the clockwise direction. On the assumption of symmetry at angles θ and $\theta + \pi$, the magnetic potential difference across *each* gap is $2n_ci_c$, and the $\mathcal{3C}$ field is upward under the left-hand pole and downward under the right-hand pole. On the assumption that the slot openings are very narrow the mmf jumps abruptly when the path of integration is moved across a slot. Now move the path of integration so that it crosses the gap between slots 5 and 6 and closes between slots 11 and 12. The net current enclosed then is $8n_ci_c$, and the mmf at *each* gap is $4n_ci_c$—upward between slots 5 and 6, and downward between slots 11 and 12. Finally consider the path *ijkl* enclosing the belt of current directed away from the reader. Here the current enclosed reaches its peak value of $12n_ci_c$, and the mmf at *each* gap is $6n_ci_c$.

Figure 3-20b shows a plot of the mmf wave produced by the armature. It consists of a series of steps. This mmf wave can be represented approximately by the triangular wave drawn in Fig. 3-20b and repeated in Fig. 3-20c. For a more realistic winding with a larger number of armature slots per pole the triangular distribution becomes a close approximation. It is the exact equivalent of the mmf wave of a uniformly distributed current sheet wrapped around the armature and carrying current in the dot and cross directions, as shown by the rectangular space distribution of current density in Fig. 3-20c.

Because of the ease with which sinusoids can be manipulated analytically, it is often convenient to resolve the mmf waves of distributed windings into a Fourier series. The fundamental component of the triangular mmf wave of Fig. 3-20c is shown by the sine wave. Its peak value is $8/\pi^2 = 0.81$ times the height of the triangular wave, and its half-wave area is 1.03 times the half-wave area of the triangular wave. The fundamental mmf wave is the exact equivalent of the mmf wave of a sinusoidally distributed current sheet wrapped around the armature whose peak value equals the fundamental component of the rectangular current sheet of Fig. 3-20c. This sinusoidally distributed current sheet is shown dotted in Fig. 3-20c.

It should be noted that the mmf wave depends only on the winding arrangement and symmetry of the magnetic structure at angles θ and $\theta + \pi$. The flux-density wave, however, depends not only on the mmf but also on the magnetic boundary conditions, primarily the length of the air gap, the effect of the slot openings, and the shape of the pole face. The designer takes these effects into account by means of flux maps, but these details need not concern us here.

Machines often have a magnetic structure with more than 2 poles.

For example, Fig. 3-21a shows schematically a 4-pole d-c machine. The field winding produces alternate north-south-north-south polarity, and the armature conductors are distributed in four belts of slots carrying currents alternately toward and away from the reader, as symbolized by the crosshatched areas. This machine is shown in laid-out form in Fig. 3-21b. The corresponding triangular armature-mmf wave is also shown. On the assumption of symmetry of the winding and field poles each successive pair of poles is like every other pair of poles. Magnetic conditions in the air gap can then be determined by examining any pair of adjacent poles—i.e., 360 electrical degrees.

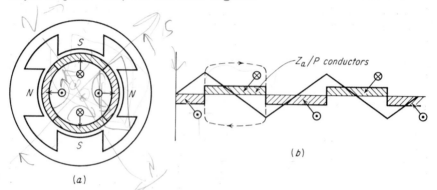

FIG. 3-21. (a) Cross section of 4-pole d-c machine and (b) development of current heet and mmf wave.

The peak value of the triangular armature-mmf wave is

$$F_a = \frac{1}{2} \frac{Z_a}{P} \frac{i_a}{a} \qquad \text{amp-turns per pole} \qquad (3\text{-}4)$$

where Z_a is the total number of conductors in the armature winding, P is the number of poles, i_a is the armature current, and a is the number of parallel paths through the armature winding. Thus i_a/a is the current in each conductor. This equation comes directly from the line integral around the dotted closed path in Fig. 3-21b which crosses the air gap twice and encloses Z_a/P conductors each carrying current i_a/a in the same direction. In more compact form

$$F_a = \frac{N_a}{P} i_a \qquad (3\text{-}5)$$

where $N_a = Z_a/2a$ is the number of series armature turns. For the triangular mmf wave of Fig. 3-21b the peak value of the space fundamental is $\dfrac{8}{\pi^2} \dfrac{N_a}{P} i_a$.

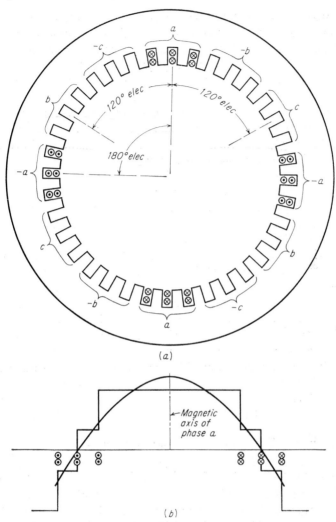

(a)

(b)

Fig. 3-22. (a) Cross section of stator of a 4-pole 3-phase machine showing coil sides of phase a and (b) mmf waveform and its space-fundamental component.

Figure 3-22a shows in cross section phase a of the armature winding (stator) of a somewhat simplified 3-phase 4-pole a-c machine. Phases b and c occupy the empty slots. The windings of the 3 phases are identical and are located with their magnetic axes 120 electrical degrees apart. One pole of this winding is shown in laid-out form in Fig. 3-22b. The mmf wave is shown by the flat-topped step wave. Its peak value determined from the dotted closed path surrounding a phase belt is given by Eqs. 3-4 and 3-5 with Z_a now equal to the total number of conductors per phase and N_a equal to the number of series turns in each phase. The space-fundamental component is shown by the sine wave. Its peak value can be expressed as

$$F_{a1} = \frac{4}{\pi} k_w \frac{N_a}{P} i_a \qquad (3\text{-}6)$$

in which the factor $4/\pi$ arises from the Fourier-series analysis of the rectangular mmf wave of a concentrated full-pitch coil and the winding factor k_w takes into account the distribution of the winding. (See Art. C-2 for details. For most 3-phase windings k_w is about 0.8 to 0.9.) Through the use of fractional-pitch windings and other artifices the effects of the space harmonics in a-c machines can be made small.

We shall base our preliminary investigations of both a-c and d-c machines on the assumption of sinusoidal space distributions of mmf. This model will be found to give very satisfactory results for most problems involving a-c machines, because their windings can be distributed so as to minimize the effects of harmonics. Because of the restrictions placed on the winding arrangement by the commutator, the mmf waves of d-c machines inherently approach more nearly a triangular waveform. Nevertheless the theory based on a sinusoidal model brings out the essential features of d-c machine theory. The results can readily be modified whenever necessary to account for any significant discrepancies.

We shall also use a 2-pole machine as our mathematical model. The results can immediately be extrapolated to a P-pole machine when it is recalled that electrical angles θ and electrical angular velocities ω are related to mechanical angles θ_m and mechanical angular velocities ω_m through Eqs. 3-1 and 3-3.

For a preliminary study we shall further simplify our model by assuming that the stator and rotor air-gap surfaces are smooth, concentric cylinders, as in the following article.

3-3. Torque and Voltage in Nonsalient-pole Machines. The behavior of any electromagnetic device as a component in an electromechanical system can be described in terms of its Kirchhoff-law voltage equations and its electromagnetic torque. The purpose of this article is to derive the voltage and torque equations for an idealized elementary machine—results which can readily be extended later to more complex machines. We shall derive these equations from two viewpoints and show that basically they stem from the same ideas.

The first viewpoint is essentially the same as that of Art. 2-3. The machine will be regarded as a circuit element whose inductances depend on the angular position of the rotor. The flux linkages λ and magnetic field energy will be expressed in terms of the currents and inductances. The torque can then be found from the partial derivative of the magnetic field energy or coenergy with respect to angle and the terminal voltages from the sum of the resistance drops ri and the Faraday-law voltages $d\lambda/dt$. The result will be a set of nonlinear differential equations describing the dynamic performance of the machine. These equations are the basis for most of the analysis of idealized machines in Part II.

The second viewpoint regards the machine as two groups of windings producing magnetic fields in the air gap, one group on the stator and the other on the rotor. By making suitable assumptions regarding these fields simple expressions can be derived for the flux linkages and magnetic field energy stored in the air gap in terms of the field quantities. The torque and generated voltage can then be found in terms of these quantities. Thus torque is expressed explicitly as the tendency for two magnetic fields to line up in the same way as permanent magnets tend to align

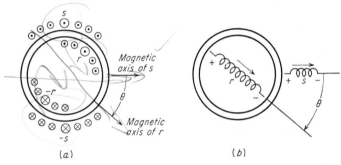

(a)　　　　　　　　　　　　　　　(b)

FIG. 3-23. Elementary 2-pole machine. (a) Winding distribution. (b) Schematic representation.

themselves, and generated voltage is expressed as the result of relative motion between a field and a winding. These expressions lead to a simple physical picture of the normal steady-state behavior of rotating machines. They are also the basis for much of the treatment of rotating machines in Part III.

As a by-product resulting from the parallel development of these two viewpoints, approximate expressions will be obtained for the inductance parameters. The purpose here is not to derive accurate design formulas but rather to give some feeling for how the inductances are affected by physical dimensions.

a. The Coupled-circuit Viewpoint. Consider the elementary machine of Fig. 3-23 with 1 winding on the stator and 1 on the rotor. These windings are distributed over a number of slots so that their mmf waves can be approximated by space sinusoids. In Fig. 3-23a the coil sides s, $-s$ and r, $-r$ mark the positions of the centers of the belts of conductors comprising the distributed windings. An alternative way of drawing these windings is shown in Fig. 3-23b, which also shows reference directions for voltages and currents. Here it is assumed that current in the arrow direction produces a magnetic field in the air gap in the arrow direction so that a single arrow defines reference directions for both current and flux. The stator and rotor are concentric cylinders, and slot openings are neglected. Consequently our elementary model does not include the effects of salient poles—effects which will be investigated in later chapters. We shall also assume that the reluctances of the stator and rotor iron are negligible.

On these assumptions the stator and rotor self-inductances L_{ss} and L_{rr} are constant, but the stator-rotor mutual inductance depends on the angle θ between the magnetic axes of the stator and rotor windings. The mutual inductance is a positive maximum when $\theta = 0$ or 2π, is zero when $\theta = \pm\pi/2$, and is a negative maximum when $\theta = \pm\pi$. On the assumption of sinusoidal mmf waves and a uniform air gap the space distribution of the air-gap flux wave is sinusoidal, and the mutual inductance is

$$\mathcal{L}_{sr}(\theta) = L_{sr}\cos\theta \tag{3-7}$$

where the script letter $\mathcal{L}$ is used to denote an inductance which is a function of the electrical angle θ. The italic capital letter L denotes a constant value. Thus L_{sr} is the value of the mutual inductance when the magnetic axes of stator and rotor are in line. In terms of the inductances, the stator and rotor flux linkages λ_s and λ_r are

$$\lambda_s = L_{ss}i_s + \mathcal{L}_{sr}(\theta)\,i_r = L_{ss}i_s + L_{sr}\cos\theta\,i_r \tag{3-8}$$
$$\lambda_r = \mathcal{L}_{sr}(\theta)\,i_s + L_{rr}i_r = L_{sr}\cos\theta\,i_s + L_{rr}i_r \tag{3-9}$$

In matrix notation

$$\begin{bmatrix} \lambda_s \\ \lambda_r \end{bmatrix} = \begin{bmatrix} L_{ss} & \mathcal{L}_{sr}(\theta) \\ \mathcal{L}_{sr}(\theta) & L_{rr} \end{bmatrix} \times \begin{bmatrix} i_s \\ i_r \end{bmatrix}$$

The terminal voltages v_s and v_r are

$$v_s = r_s i_s + p\lambda_s \tag{3-10}$$
$$v_r = r_r i_r + p\lambda_r \tag{3-11}$$

where r_s and r_r are the winding resistances and p is the time-derivative operator d/dt. When the rotor is revolving, θ must be treated as a variable. Differentiation of Eqs. 3-8 and 3-9 and substitution of the results in Eqs. 3-10 and 3-11 then give

$$v_s = r_s i_s + L_{ss}pi_s + L_{sr}\cos\theta\,(pi_r) - L_{sr}i_r\sin\theta\,(p\theta) \tag{3-12}$$
$$v_r = r_r i_r + L_{rr}pi_r + L_{sr}\cos\theta\,(pi_s) - L_{sr}i_s\sin\theta\,(p\theta) \tag{3-13}$$

where $p\theta$ is the instantaneous speed ω in *electrical* radians per second. In a 2-pole machine θ and ω are equal to the instantaneous shaft angle θ_m and speed ω_m, respectively. In a P-pole machine they are related by

Eqs. 3-1 and 3-3.   The second and third terms on the right-hand sides of Eqs. 3-12 and 3-13 are $L\,di/dt$ induced voltages like those induced in stationary coupled circuits such as the windings of transformers.   They are the *transformer voltages* of Art. 2-4.   The fourth terms are caused by mechanical motion and are proportional to the instantaneous speed. They are the *speed voltages* of Art. 2-4 and are the coupling terms relating the interchange of power between the electrical and mechanical systems.

The electromagnetic torque can be found from the energy stored in the magnetic field in the air gap.   From Eq. 2-53

$$W_{\text{fld}} = \tfrac{1}{2}L_{ss}i_s^2 + \tfrac{1}{2}L_{rr}i_r^2 + L_{sr}i_s i_r \cos\theta \qquad (3\text{-}14)$$

and from Eq. 2-59

$$T = +\frac{\partial W_{\text{fld}}}{\partial\theta_m}\,(\theta_m,i_s,i_r) = +\frac{\partial W_{\text{fld}}}{\partial\theta}\,(\theta,i_s,i_r)\,\frac{d\theta}{d\theta_m} \qquad (3\text{-}15)$$

where T is the electromagnetic torque acting in the positive direction of θ_m and the derivative must be taken with respect to actual *mechanical* angle θ_m, because we are dealing here with mechanical variables.   Differentiation of Eqs. 3-14 and 3-1 for a P-pole machine then gives

$$T = -\frac{P}{2}\,L_{sr}i_s i_r \sin\theta = -\frac{P}{2}\,L_{sr}i_s i_r \sin\frac{P}{2}\,\theta_m \qquad (3\text{-}16)$$

with T in newton-meters.   The negative sign in Eq. 3-16 means that the electromagnetic torque acts in the direction to bring the magnetic fields of stator and rotor into alignment.

Equations 3-12, 3-13, and 3-16 are a set of three differential equations relating the electrical variables v_s, i_s, v_r, i_r and the mechanical variables T and θ_m.   These equations, together with the constraints imposed on the electrical variables by the networks connected to its terminals (sources or loads and external impedances) and the constraints imposed on the mechanical variables (applied torques and inertial, frictional, and spring torques), determine the performance of the device as a coupling element. They are nonlinear differential equations and are difficult to solve except under special circumstances.   We are not concerned with their solution here; rather, we are using them merely as steps in the development of the theory of rotating machines.

Now consider a uniform-air-gap machine with several stator and several rotor windings.   The same general principles that apply to the elementary model of Fig. 3-23 also apply to the multiwinding machine. Each winding has its own self-inductance and mutual inductances with other windings.   The self-inductances and mutual inductances between pairs of windings on the same side of the air gap are constant on the assumption of a uniform gap and negligible magnetic saturation.   But the mutual inductances between pairs of stator and rotor windings vary as the cosine of the angle between the magnetic axes of the windings. The torque results from the tendency of the magnetic field of the rotor windings to line up with that of the stator windings. It can be expressed as the sum of terms like Eq. 3-16.

Example 3-1. Consider the elementary rotating machine of Fig. 3-23. Its shaft is coupled to a mechanical device which can be made to absorb or deliver mechanical torque over a wide range of speeds. This machine can be connected and operated in several ways. For example, suppose the rotor winding is excited with direct current I_r and the stator winding is connected to an a-c source which can either absorb or deliver electrical power. Let the stator current be

$$i_s = I_s \cos \omega_s t$$

where $t = 0$ is arbitrarily chosen as the moment when the stator current has its peak value.

a. Derive an expression for the magnetic torque developed by the machine as the speed is varied by control of the mechanical device connected to its shaft.

b. Find the speed at which average torque will be produced if the stator frequency is 60 cps.

c. With the assumed current-source excitations what are the voltages induced in the stator and rotor windings at synchronous speed?

Solution. a. From Eq. 3-16 for a 2-pole machine

$$T = -L_{sr} i_s i_r \sin \theta_m$$

For the conditions of this problem

$$T = -L_{sr} I_s I_r \cos \omega_s t \sin (\omega_m t + \delta)$$

where ω_m is the clockwise angular velocity impressed on the rotor by the mechanical drive and δ is the angular position of the rotor at $t = 0$. From the trigonometric identity

$$\sin A \cos B = \tfrac{1}{2} \sin (A + B) + \tfrac{1}{2} \sin (A - B)$$

$$T = -\tfrac{1}{2} L_{sr} I_s I_r \{\sin [(\omega_m + \omega_s)t + \delta] + \sin [(\omega_m - \omega_s)t + \delta]\}$$

The torque consists of two sinusoidally time-varying terms of frequencies $\omega_m + \omega_s$ and $\omega_m - \omega_s$.

b. Except when $\omega_m = \pm\omega_s$, the torque averaged over a sufficiently long time is zero. But if $\omega_m = +\omega_s$, the torque becomes

$$T = -\tfrac{1}{2} L_{sr} I_s I_r [\sin (2\omega_s t + \delta) + \sin \delta]$$

The first sine term is a double-frequency component whose average value is zero. The second term is the average torque

$$T_{av} = -\tfrac{1}{2} L_{sr} I_s I_r \sin \delta$$

The other possibility is $\omega_m = -\omega_s$, which merely means rotation in the counterclockwise direction. The negative sign in the expression for T_{av} means that the magnetic torque tends to reduce δ. The machine is an idealized single-phase synchronous machine. (With polyphase synchronous machines the direction of rotation is determined by the phase sequence, as shown in Art. 3-4.)

With stator frequency of 60 cps,

$$\omega_m = \omega_s = 2\pi(60) \qquad \text{rad/sec}$$

or 60 rev/sec, or 3,600 rpm.

c. From the second and fourth terms of Eq. 3-12 with $\omega_m = \omega_s$ the voltage induced in the stator is

$$e_s = -\omega_s L_{ss} I_s \sin \omega_s t - \omega_s L_{sr} I_r \sin (\omega_s t + \delta)$$

From the third and fourth terms of Eq. 3-13 the voltage induced in the rotor is

$$e_r = -\omega_s L_{sr} I_s [\sin \omega_s t \cos (\omega_s t + \delta) + \cos \omega_s t \sin (\omega_s t + \delta)]$$
$$= -\omega_s L_{sr} I_s \sin (2\omega_s t + \delta)$$

The stator current induces a double-frequency voltage in the rotor.

b. The Magnetic-field Viewpoint. In the foregoing discussion the characteristics of the device as viewed from its electrical and mechanical terminals have been expressed in terms of its inductances. This viewpoint gives very little insight into the internal phenomena and gives no conception of the effects of physical dimensions. An alternative formulation in terms of the interacting magnetic fields in the air gap should serve to supply some of these missing features.

We shall now assume that the tangential component of the magnetic field in the air gap is negligible compared with the radial component—in other words, the flux goes straight across the gap. We shall also assume that the radial length g of the gap (the clearance between rotor and stator) is small compared with the radius of the rotor or stator. On this assumption there is negligible difference between the flux density at the rotor surface, at the stator surface, or at any intermediate radial distance in the air gap, say, halfway between. The air-gap field then reduces to a radial field $\mathcal{3C}$ or $\mathcal{B}$ whose intensity varies with angle around the periphery. The line integral of $\mathcal{3C}$ across the gap then is simply $\mathcal{3C}g$ and equals the resultant mmf $\mathcal{F}_{sr}$ of the stator and rotor windings; thus

$$\mathcal{3C}g = \mathcal{F}_{sr} \tag{3-17}$$

where the script $\mathcal{F}$ denotes the mmf wave as a function of angle around the periphery.

A developed sketch of the elementary machine of Fig. 3-23 is shown in Fig. 3-24a. The mmf waves of stator and rotor are the sine waves $\mathcal{F}_s$ and $\mathcal{F}_r$ with θ the angle between their magnetic axes. The resultant mmf wave $\mathcal{F}_{sr}$ acting across the air gap is their sum and is also a sine wave. The addition can be carried out conveniently by means of the phasor diagram shown in Fig. 3-24b, where the phasors F_s and F_r represent the peak values of the fundamental components of the stator and rotor spatial mmf waves and the phasor F_{sr} represents the peak value of their resultant. (The sine waves in Fig. 3-24a are space distributions. But

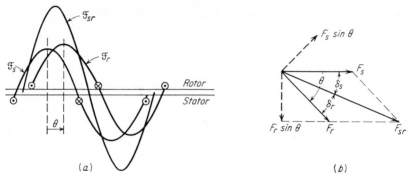

Fig. 3-24. (a) Sinusoidal spatial mmf waves and (b) phasor diagram.

since phasors are simply convenient artifices for adding sine waves, phasor addition is not restricted to sinusoidal currents and voltages and may be used here.) From the trigonometric formula for the diagonal of a parallelogram

$$F_{sr}^2 = F_s^2 + F_r^2 + 2F_sF_r \cos \theta \tag{3-18}$$

in which the F's are the peak values of the phasors. The resultant radial $\mathcal{3C}$ field is a sinusoidal wave whose peak value H_{peak} is, from Eq. 3-17,

$$H_{\text{peak}} = \frac{F_{sr}}{g} \tag{3-19}$$

Now consider the magnetic field energy stored in the air gap. The energy density at a point where the magnetic field intensity is $\mathcal{3C}$ is

$$\frac{\mu_0}{2} \mathcal{3C}^2$$

in rationalized mks units. The average energy density is

$$\frac{\mu_0}{2} \text{ (average value of } \mathcal{3C}^2)$$

The average value of the square of a sine wave is half its peak value. Hence

$$\text{Average energy density} = \frac{\mu_0}{2} \frac{H_{\text{peak}}^2}{2} = \frac{\mu_0}{4} \left(\frac{F_{sr}}{g} \right)^2 \tag{3-20}$$

The total energy is

$$W_{\text{fld}} = \text{(average energy density)(volume of air gap)}$$

$$= \frac{\mu_0}{4} \left(\frac{F_{sr}}{g} \right)^2 \pi dlg = \frac{\mu_0 \pi dl}{4g} F_{sr}^2 \tag{3-21}$$

where d is the average diameter at the air gap, l is the axial length, g is the air-gap clearance, and $\mu_G = 4\pi \times 10^{-7}$. All dimensions are in meters. From Eq. 3-18,

$$W_{\text{fld}} = \frac{\mu_0 \pi dl}{4g}(F_s^2 + F_r^2 + 2F_s F_r \cos \theta) \tag{3-22}$$

The stator and rotor mmfs can be expressed in terms of the stator and rotor currents i_s and i_r, respectively. From Eq. 3-6, with changes in notation,

$$F_s = \frac{4}{\pi} k_s \frac{N_s}{P} i_s \tag{3-23}$$

$$F_r = \frac{4}{\pi} k_r \frac{N_r}{P} i_r \tag{3-24}$$

where N_s, N_r are the number of series turns in the stator and rotor windings, respectively, and k_s, k_r are the winding factors for the space-fundamental components. Substitution of Eqs. 3-23 and 3-24 in Eq. 3-22 then gives

$$W_{\text{fld}} = \frac{\mu_0}{2}\frac{\pi dl}{g}\left[\frac{1}{2}\left(\frac{4}{\pi}k_s\frac{N_s}{P}\right)^2 i_s^2 + \frac{1}{2}\left(\frac{4}{\pi}k_r\frac{N_r}{P}\right)^2 i_r^2 \right.$$
$$\left. + \left(\frac{4}{\pi}k_s\frac{N_s}{P}\right)\left(\frac{4}{\pi}k_r\frac{N_r}{P}\right)i_s i_r \cos \theta\right] \tag{3-25}$$

Comparison of Eq. 3-25 with Eq. 3-14, term by term, gives approximate expressions for the inductances. Thus the self-inductance of the stator due to the radial component of air-gap flux is

$$\frac{\mu_0}{2}\frac{\pi dl}{g}\left(\frac{4}{\pi}k_s\frac{N_s}{P}\right)^2$$

To get the total self-inductance, the leakage inductance L_{sl}, representing flux which does not cross the air gap to the rotor, must be added. That is,

$$L_{ss} = \frac{\mu_0}{2}\frac{\pi dl}{g}\left(\frac{4}{\pi}k_s\frac{N_s}{P}\right)^2 + L_{sl} \tag{3-26}$$

Similarly the self-inductance of the rotor is

$$L_{rr} = \frac{\mu_0}{2}\frac{\pi dl}{g}\left(\frac{4}{\pi}k_r\frac{N_r}{P}\right)^2 + L_{rl} \tag{3-27}$$

where L_{rl} is the leakage inductance of the rotor. The leakage inductances take into account the effects of slot-leakage fluxes, of fluxes linking the coil end connections, and of harmonics in the mmf waves. They usually are about 10 per cent of the total. The mutual-inductance coefficient L_{sr} is

$$L_{sr} = \frac{\mu_0}{2}\frac{\pi dl}{g}\left(\frac{4}{\pi}k_s\frac{N_s}{P}\right)\left(\frac{4}{\pi}k_r\frac{N_r}{P}\right) \tag{3-28}$$

Note that the inductances are proportional to the cylindrical surface area πdl and inversely proportional to the gap length g.

An expression for the electromagnetic torque can now be obtained in terms of the interacting magnetic fields in the air gap. By taking the partial derivative of Eq. 3-22 with respect to mechanical angle θ_m (or by substitution of Eqs. 3-28, 3-23, and 3-24 in Eq. 3-16)

$$T = - \frac{\text{poles}}{2} \frac{\pi}{2} \frac{\mu_0 dl}{g} F_s F_r \sin \theta \qquad (3\text{-}29)$$

where all quantities are in rationalized mks units. The torque is proportional to the peak values of the stator- and rotor-mmf waves F_s and F_r and the sine of the electrical angle θ between them. On referring to Fig. 3-24b it can be seen that $F_r \sin \theta$ is the component of the F_r wave in electrical space quadrature with the F_s wave. Similarly $F_s \sin \theta$ is the component of the F_s wave in quadrature with the F_r wave. Thus the torque is proportional to the product of one magnetic field and the component of the other in quadrature with it, like the cross product of vector analysis. The minus sign means that the fields tend to align themselves. Equal and opposite torques are exerted on stator and rotor. Also note that in Fig. 3-24b

$$F_r \sin \theta = F_{sr} \sin \delta_s \qquad (3\text{-}30)$$

and

$$F_s \sin \theta = F_{sr} \sin \delta_r \qquad (3\text{-}31)$$

The torque can then be expressed in terms of the *resultant* mmf wave F_{sr}; thus

$$T = - \frac{\text{poles}}{2} \frac{\pi}{2} \frac{\mu_0 dl}{g} F_s F_{sr} \sin \delta_s \qquad (3\text{-}32)$$

$$T = - \frac{\text{poles}}{2} \frac{\pi}{2} \frac{\mu_0 dl}{g} F_r F_{sr} \sin \delta_r \qquad (3\text{-}33)$$

Comparison of Eqs. 3-29, 3-32, and 3-33 shows that the torque can be expressed in terms of the component magnetic fields due to each current acting alone as in Eq. 3-29, or in terms of the resultant field and either of the components as in Eqs. 3-32 and 3-33, provided that we use the corresponding angle between the axes of the fields. Ability to reason in any of these terms is a convenience in machine analysis.

In Eqs. 3-29, 3-32, and 3-33 the fields have been expressed in terms of the peak values of their mmf waves. When magnetic saturation is neglected, the fields may, of course, be expressed in terms of their flux-density waves or in terms of total flux per pole. Thus the peak value B of the field due to a sinusoidally distributed mmf wave in a uniform-air-gap machine is $\mu_0 F/g$, where F is the peak value of the mmf wave. For example, the resultant mmf F_{sr} produces a resultant flux-density wave whose peak value is $\mu_0 F_{sr}/g$. Thus

$$T = - \frac{\text{poles}}{2} \frac{\pi d l}{2} B_{sr} F_r \sin \delta_r \qquad (3\text{-}34)$$

One of the inherent limitations in the design of electromagnetic apparatus is the saturation flux density of magnetic materials. Because of saturation in the armature teeth the peak value B_{sr} of the resultant flux-density wave in the air gap is limited to about 1 weber/m² (64.5 kilolines/in.²). The maximum permissible value of the mmf wave is limited by temperature rise of the winding and other design requirements. Because the resultant flux density and mmf appear explicitly in Eq. 3-34, this equation is in a convenient form for design purposes.

Alternative forms arise when it is recognized that the resultant flux per pole is

$$\Phi = (\text{average value of } \mathfrak{B} \text{ over a pole})(\text{pole area}) \qquad (3\text{-}35)$$

and that the average value of a sinusoid over a half wavelength is $2/\pi$ times its peak value. Thus

$$\Phi = \frac{2}{\pi} B \frac{\pi d l}{P} = \frac{2 d l}{P} B \qquad (3\text{-}36)$$

where B is the peak value of the corresponding flux-density wave. For example, substitution of Eq. 3-36 in Eq. 3-34 gives

$$T = - \frac{\pi}{2} \left(\frac{\text{poles}}{2} \right)^2 \Phi_{sr} F_r \sin \delta_r \qquad (3\text{-}37)$$

where Φ_{sr} is the resultant flux produced by the combined effect of the stator and rotor mmfs.

To recapitulate, we now have several forms in which the torque of a uniform-air-gap machine may be expressed in terms of its magnetic fields. All of them are merely statements that the torque is proportional to the interacting fields and the sine of the electrical space angle between their magnetic axes. The negative sign indicates that the electromagnetic torque acts in a direction to decrease the displacement angle between the fields. In a preliminary discussion of machine types and in much of the analysis of Part III, Eq. 3-37 will be the preferred form.

Although our derivation has been based on the elementary model of Fig. 3-23, it should be clear that the results apply equally well to a machine with several windings on the stator and rotor if F_s is the mmf due to all the stator windings, F_r is the mmf due to all the rotor windings, and F_{sr}, B_{sr}, and Φ_{sr} are the resultant mmf, flux density, and flux per pole.

One further remark may be made concerning the torque equations and the thought process leading up to them. There is no restriction that the mmf wave or flux-density wave need remain stationary in space. They may remain stationary, or they may be traveling waves as shown in Art. 3-4. If the magnetic fields of stator and rotor are constant in amplitude and travel around the air gap at the same speed, a steady torque will be produced by the efforts of the stator and rotor fields to align themselves in accordance with the torque equations.

The counterpart of torque in the electromechanical-energy-conversion process is generated voltage. In part a of this article the generated voltage is expressed explicitly in terms of the currents and the instantaneous angle θ of the rotor as the sum of $d(\mathcal{L}i)/dt$ terms. It may also be expressed explicitly in terms of the amplitude of the air-gap flux wave and the relative speed of the flux wave and the winding. This latter viewpoint is especially useful for the conceptual insight it gives into the normal steady-state behavior of a variety of rotating machines; it is also the basis for much of the analytical theory of Part III.

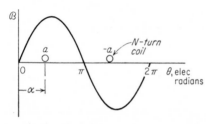

FIG. 3-25. Full-pitch coil and air-gap flux-density wave.

Consider a single coil of N turns as indicated by the coil sides a and $-a$ in Fig. 3-4 for an elementary synchronous machine and in Fig. 3-16 for an elementary d-c machine. In either case voltage is induced by relative motion of the coil and the inducing field. This simple winding is shown developed in Fig. 3-25, and a sinusoidal spatial flux-density wave is shown superimposed. The coil spans a half wavelength of the flux wave and hence is a full-pitch coil. At the instant of time when coil side a is α electrical radians from the zero crossing of the flux-density wave, the total flux linkage with the coil is

$$\lambda = N \frac{dlB}{P} \int_{\alpha}^{\pi+\alpha} \sin \theta \, d\theta \qquad (3\text{-}38)$$

$$\lambda = N \frac{2dlB}{P} \cos \alpha = N\Phi \cos \alpha \qquad (3\text{-}39)$$

where d is the air-gap diameter, l is the axial length, B is the peak value of the flux-density wave, P is the number of poles, and Φ is the total flux per pole of the inducing wave as in Eq. 3-36.

Now if the relative speed of the coil and flux-density wave is ω electrical radians per second, we have $\alpha = \omega t$, where time t is arbitrarily reckoned as zero when the magnetic axis of the coil and the peak of the flux-density wave coincide. Hence

$$\lambda = N\Phi \cos \omega t \qquad (3\text{-}40)$$

and the induced voltage e is

$$e = \frac{d\lambda}{dt} = -\omega N\Phi \sin \omega t + N \frac{d\Phi}{dt} \cos \omega t \qquad (3\text{-}41)$$

The first term on the right-hand side of Eq. 3-41 is a speed voltage due to relative motion of the coil and the field. The second term is a transformer voltage and is present only when the amplitude of the flux-density wave changes with time. These terms are similar to the corresponding terms in Eqs. 3-12 and 3-13; the difference is the variables in terms of which the voltages are expressed.

In the normal steady-state operation of most rotating machines the amplitude of the air-gap flux wave is constant. The transformer voltage in Eq. 3-41 then is zero, and the induced voltage is simply the speed voltage

$$e = -\omega N\Phi \sin \omega t \qquad (3\text{-}42)$$

These equations can be modified to apply to a distributed winding of N series turns by multiplying by the winding distribution factor k_w as shown in Art. C-1. For a distributed winding

$$e = -\omega k_w N\Phi \sin \omega t \qquad (3\text{-}43)$$

Its maximum value is

$$E_m = \omega k_w N\Phi = 2\pi f k_w N\Phi \qquad (3\text{-}44)$$

and its rms value is

$$E_{\text{rms}} = \frac{2\pi}{\sqrt{2}} f k_w N\Phi = 4.44 f k_w N\Phi \qquad (3\text{-}45)$$

where f is the frequency in cycles per second. These equations are identical in form to the corresponding emf equations of a transformer. Relative motion of a coil and a constant-amplitude spatial flux-density wave in a rotating machine produce the same voltage effect as does a time-varying flux in association with stationary coils in a transformer. In rotating machines this voltage is associated with electromechanical energy conversion, whereas in the transformer it is not, because no mechanical motion takes place.

Even if the ultimate purpose is the generation of a direct voltage, as in a d-c machine, it is evident that the speed voltage generated in an armature coil is an alternating voltage. The alternating waveform must therefore be rectified. Mechanical rectification is provided by the commutator, the device already referred to in Art. 3-2 for keeping the field of the rotor stationary in space and described in elementary form in Art. 3-1b. For the single coil of Fig. 3-16, the commutator provides full-wave rectification. With the continued assumption of sinusoidal flux distribution, the voltage waveform between brushes is transformed to that of

Fig. 3-26. The average, or d-c, value of the voltage between brushes is

$$e_a = \frac{1}{\pi} \int_0^\pi \omega N \Phi \sin \omega t \, d(\omega t) = \frac{2}{\pi} \omega N \Phi \tag{3-46}$$

It is usually more convenient in the d-c case to express the voltage e_a in terms of the mechanical speed ω_m rad/sec or n rpm. Substitution of Eq. 3-3 in Eq. 3-46 for a P-pole machine then yields

$$e_a = \frac{PN}{\pi} \Phi \omega_m = 2PN\Phi \frac{n}{60} \tag{3-47}$$

The single-coil d-c winding implied here is, of course, simplified to the point of being unrealistic in the practical sense, and it will be essential later to examine more carefully the action of commutators. Actually, Eq. 3-47 gives correct results for the more practical distributed d-c windings as well, provided that N be taken as the total number of turns in series between armature terminals, as in Eq. 3-5. Thus

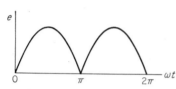

FIG. 3-26. Voltage between brushes in an elementary d-c machine.

$$e_a = \frac{PZ_a}{2\pi a} \Phi \omega_m = \frac{PZ_a}{a} \Phi \frac{n}{60} \tag{3-48}$$

where Z_a is the total number of conductors in the armature winding and a is the number of parallel paths through the winding.

We now have the basic analytical tools for studying rotating machines. These tools are expressions for the induced voltages and for the electromagnetic torque. Taken together, they express the coupling between the electrical and mechanical systems. In this article these expressions have been derived from two viewpoints. The first regards the machine as a group of magnetically coupled circuits; the second regards the machine from the viewpoint of the magnetic fields in the air gap. The two viewpoints are supplementary, and ability to reason in terms of both of them is helpful in reaching an understanding of how machines work.

3-4. Rotating Magnetic Fields. The torque and voltage principles of Art. 3-3b may readily be applied to examination of the operation of machines. Before doing so for a-c machines, however, it is necessary to study the nature of the magnetic field produced by a winding in which the currents are time-varying. In particular, we shall study the mmf patterns of a 3-phase winding such as those found on the stator of 3-phase induction and synchronous machines. Elementary versions of such windings are shown diagrammatically in Figs. 3-12 and 3-22. Once again attention will be focused on a 2-pole machine or on one pair of poles of a P-pole winding.

In a 3-phase machine, the windings of the individual phases are displaced from each other by 120 electrical degrees in space around the air-gap circumference as shown by the coil sides a, $-a$, b, $-b$, and c, $-c$ in the developed winding of Fig. 3-27. The three component sinusoidal mmf waves are accordingly displaced by 120 electrical degrees in *space* from each other also. But each phase is excited by an alternating current which varies in magnitude sinusoidally with *time*. Under balanced 3-phase conditions the instantaneous currents are

$$i_a = I_m \cos \omega t \tag{3-49}$$
$$i_b = I_m \cos (\omega t - 120°) \tag{3-50}$$
$$i_c = I_m \cos (\omega t - 240°) \tag{3-51}$$

where I_m is the maximum value of the current and the time origin is arbitrarily taken as the instant when the phase a current is a positive maximum. The corresponding component mmf waves therefore also vary sinusoidally with time.

To study the resultant field analytically, let the origin for angle θ around the air-gap periphery arbitrarily be placed at the axis of phase a (Fig. 3-27). At any time t, all 3 phases contribute to the air-gap mmf at any point θ. The contribution from phase a is

$$F_{a(\text{peak})} \cos \theta$$

where $F_{a(\text{peak})}$ is the amplitude of the component-mmf wave at time t. Similarly, the contributions from phases b and c are

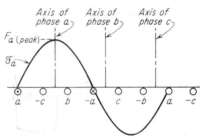

Fig. 3-27. Elementary 3-phase winding and spatial mmf wave of phase a.

$$F_{b(\text{peak})} \cos (\theta - 120°)$$
and
$$F_{c(\text{peak})} \cos (\theta - 240°)$$

respectively. The 120° displacements appear because the machine is so wound that the axes of the three phases are 120 electrical degrees apart in space. The resultant mmf at point θ is then

$$\mathfrak{F}(\theta) = F_{a(\text{peak})} \cos \theta + F_{b(\text{peak})} \cos (\theta - 120°)$$
$$+ F_{c(\text{peak})} \cos (\theta - 240°) \tag{3-52}$$

But the mmf amplitudes vary with time in accordance with the current variations. Thus, with the time origin arbitrarily taken at the instant when the phase a current is a positive maximum,

$$F_{a(\text{peak})} = F_{a(\text{max})} \cos \omega t \tag{3-53}$$
$$F_{b(\text{peak})} = F_{b(\text{max})} \cos (\omega t - 120°) \tag{3-54}$$
and
$$F_{c(\text{peak})} = F_{c(\text{max})} \cos (\omega t - 240°) \tag{3-55}$$

The quantities $F_{a(\max)}$, $F_{b(\max)}$, and $F_{c(\max)}$ are, respectively, the time-maximum values of the amplitudes $F_{a(\text{peak})}$, $F_{b(\text{peak})}$, and $F_{c(\text{peak})}$. The 120° displacements appear here because the three currents are 120° phase-displaced in time. Since the currents in the 3 phases are balanced and therefore of equal amplitude, the three amplitudes $F_{a(\max)}$, $F_{b(\max)}$, and $F_{c(\max)}$ are also equal and the symbol $F_{\max}$ may be used for all three. Equation 3-52 accordingly becomes

$$\mathcal{F}(\theta,t) = F_{\max} \cos \theta \cos \omega t + F_{\max} \cos (\theta - 120°) \cos (\omega t - 120°)$$
$$+ F_{\max} \cos (\theta - 240°) \cos (\omega t - 240°) \quad (3\text{-}56)$$

Each of the three components on the right-hand side of Eq. 3-56 is a pulsating standing wave. In each term the trigonometric function of θ defines the space distribution as a stationary sinusoid, and the trigonometric function of t indicates that the amplitudes pulsate with time. The first of the three terms expresses the phase a component shown in Fig. 3-27; the second and third terms express, respectively, the phase b and c components.

By use of the trigonometric transformation

$$\cos \alpha \cos \beta = \tfrac{1}{2} \cos (\alpha - \beta) + \tfrac{1}{2} \cos (\alpha + \beta) \quad (3\text{-}57)$$

each of the components in Eq. 3-56 can be expressed as cosine functions of sum and difference angles. Thus,

$$\mathcal{F}(\theta,t) = \tfrac{1}{2}F_{\max} \cos (\theta - \omega t) + \tfrac{1}{2}F_{\max} \cos (\theta + \omega t)$$
$$+ \tfrac{1}{2}F_{\max} \cos (\theta - \omega t) + \tfrac{1}{2}F_{\max} \cos (\theta + \omega t - 240°)$$
$$+ \tfrac{1}{2}F_{\max} \cos (\theta - \omega t) + \tfrac{1}{2}F_{\max} \cos (\theta + \omega t - 480°) \quad (3\text{-}58)$$

Now the three cosine terms involving the angles $\theta + \omega t$, $\theta + \omega t - 240°$, and $\theta + \omega t - 480°$ are three equal sinusoids displaced in phase by 120°. (Note that a lag angle of 480° is equivalent to a lag angle of $480° - 360° = 120°$.) Their sum is therefore zero, and Eq. 3-58 reduces to

$$\mathcal{F}(\theta,t) = \tfrac{3}{2}F_{\max} \cos (\theta - \omega t) \quad (3\text{-}59)$$

which is the desired expression for the resultant mmf wave.

The wave described by Eq. 3-59 is a sinusoidal function of the space angle θ. It has a constant amplitude and a space-phase angle ωt which is a linear function of time. The angle ωt provides rotation of the entire wave around the air gap at the constant angular velocity ω. Thus, at a fixed time t_x, the wave is a sinusoid in space with its positive peak displaced ωt_x electrical radians from the fixed point on the winding which is the origin for θ; at a later instant t_y, the positive peak of the same wave is displaced ωt_y from the origin, and the wave has moved $\omega(t_y - t_x)$ around the gap. At $t = 0$, the current in phase a is a maximum, and the positive peak of the resultant mmf wave is located at the axis of phase a; one-third of a cycle later, the current in phase b is a maximum, and the positive peak is located at the axis of phase b; and so on.   The angular velocity of the wave is $\omega = 2\pi f$ electrical radians per second.   For a P-pole machine the rotational speed is

$$\omega_m = \frac{2}{P}\,\omega \quad \text{rad/sec} \tag{3-60}$$

or

$$n = \frac{120f}{P} \quad \text{rpm} \tag{3-61}$$

results which are consistent with Eqs. 3-2 and 3-3.

In general it may be shown that a rotating field of constant amplitude will be produced by a q-phase winding excited by balanced q-phase currents when the respective phases are wound $2\pi/q$ electrical radians apart in space.   The constant amplitude will be $q/2$ times the maximum contribution of any one phase, and the speed will be $\omega = 2\pi f$ electrical radians per second.

A polyphase winding excited by balanced polyphase currents is thus seen to produce the same general effect as spinning a permanent magnet about an axis perpendicular to the magnet or as the rotation of d-c-excited field poles.

3-5. Introduction to Polyphase Synchronous Machines.   In Art. 3-1 we have taken a cursory look at the structural features and mode of operation of the common rotating-machine types.   In the next four articles we shall investigate in an introductory fashion the basic principles underlying rotating-machine theory in the light of the torque and voltage equations of Art. 3-3b and the rotating magnetic fields of Art. 3-4.   At this point the treatment will not be complete or entirely rigorous; some details, which must be clarified later, will be glossed over.   The purpose is primarily to lay a foundation on relatively simple physical reasoning for the more complete analyses which will come later.

As indicated in Art. 3-1a, the synchronous machine is one in which alternating current flows in the armature winding and d-c excitation is supplied to the field winding, usually from a small d-c generator called an *exciter*, which is often mounted on the same shaft as the synchronous machine, as shown in Fig. 3-13.   The armature winding usually is on the stator and is of the type discussed in Art. 3-4.   When carrying balanced polyphase currents, it will produce a component field in the air gap rotating at synchronous speed (Eq. 3-60 or 3-61).   But the field produced by the d-c rotor winding revolves with the rotor.   For the production of a steady unidirectional torque the rotating fields of stator and rotor must be traveling at the same speed, and therefore the rotor must turn at precisely synchronous speed.   A synchronous motor connected to a constant-frequency voltage source therefore operates at a constant steady-state speed regardless of load. A synchronous motor per se has no net starting torque, and means must be provided for bringing it up to synchronous speed by induction-motor action, as described briefly at the end of Art. 3-6.

Behavior of a synchronous motor under running conditions can readily be visualized in terms of the torque equation 3-37; thus

$$T = \frac{\pi}{2} \left(\frac{\text{poles}}{2}\right)^2 \Phi_{sr} F_r \sin \delta_r \qquad (3\text{-}62)$$

in which the minus sign of Eq. 3-37 has been omitted with the understanding that the electromagnetic torque acts in the direction to bring the interacting fields into alignment. Under normal conditions the armature-resistance voltage drop is negligible, and the armature leakage

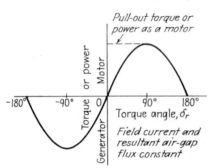

FIG. 3-28. Torque-angle curve of a synchronous machine.

flux is small compared with the resultant air-gap flux Φ_{sr}. Consequently the armature terminal voltage per phase is approximately equal to the emf generated by the rotating air-gap flux wave Φ_{sr}, as in Eq. 3-45. When the armature terminals are connected to a balanced polyphase constant-frequency voltage source, the resultant air-gap flux Φ_{sr} therefore is approximately constant, independent of shaft load. The rotor mmf F_r is determined by the d-c field current and is also constant in normal operation. Variation in the torque requirements of the load must consequently be taken care of entirely by variation of the torque angle δ_r, as shown by the torque-angle curve in Fig. 3-28, in which positive values of T represent motor action and positive values of δ_r represent angles of lag of the rotor-mmf wave with respect to the resultant air-gap flux wave.

With a light shaft load, only a relatively small electromagnetic torque is required, and δ_r is small. When more shaft load is added, the rotor must drop back in space phase with respect to the rotating flux wave just enough so that δ_r assumes the value required to supply the necessary torque. The readjustment process is actually a dynamic one accompanied by a temporary decrease in the instantaneous mechanical speed of the rotor and a damped mechanical oscillation, called *hunting*, of the rotor about its new space-phase position. In a practical machine, some changes in the amplitudes of the resultant flux-density and mmf waves may also occur because of factors (such as saturation and leakage-impedance drop) neglected in the present argument. The adjustment of the rotor to its new phase position following a load change may be observed experimentally in the laboratory by viewing the machine rotor with stroboscopic light having a flashing frequency which causes the rotor to appear stationary when it is turning at its normal synchronous speed.

When δ_r becomes 90°, the maximum possible torque or power, called *pull-out torque* or *pull-out power*, for a fixed terminal voltage and field current is reached. If the load requirements exceed this value, the motor slows down under the influence of the excess shaft torque and synchronous-motor action is lost because rotor and stator fields are no longer stationary with respect to each other. Under these conditions, the motor is usually disconnected from the line by the action of automatic circuit breakers. This phenomenon is known as *pulling out of step* or *losing synchronism*. Pull-out torque limits the short-time overload that may be placed on the motor. Increase of either field current or terminal voltage increases the pull-out torque.

The interrelation of generator and motor action and the associated influence on torque angle are illustrated in Fig. 3-28, where generator action is represented by merely extending the motor curve into the negative region. If the synchronous machine were connected to a constant-voltage constant-frequency a-c system capable of either absorbing or supplying electrical power, it would supply power to that system when its rotor was driven mechanically so that the rotor-mmf wave was pushed ahead of the resultant air-gap flux wave.

3-6. Introduction to Polyphase Induction Machines. As indicated in Art. 3-1c, the induction motor is one in which alternating current is supplied to the stator directly and to the rotor by induction or transformer action from the stator. Like the synchronous machine, the stator winding is of the type discussed in Art. 3-4. When excited from a balanced polyphase source, it will produce a magnetic field in the air gap rotating at synchronous speed as determined by the number of poles and the applied stator frequency f (Eq. 3-61). The rotor may be one of two types. A *wound rotor* carries a polyphase winding similar to and wound for the same number of poles as the stator. The terminals of the rotor winding are connected to insulated slip rings mounted on the shaft. Carbon brushes bearing on these rings make the rotor terminals available external to the motor, as shown in the cutaway view in Fig. 3-29. The motor in Fig. 3-18 has a *squirrel-cage rotor* with a winding consisting of conducting bars embedded in slots in the rotor iron and short-circuited at each end by conducting end rings. The extreme simplicity and ruggedness of the squirrel-cage construction are outstanding advantages of the induction motor.

Now assume that the rotor is turning at the steady speed n rpm in the

FIG. 3-29. Cutaway view of a 3-phase induction motor with a wound rotor and slip rings connected to the 3-phase rotor winding. (*Courtesy of General Electric Company.*)

same direction as the rotating stator field. Let the synchronous speed of the stator field be n_1 rpm as given by Eq. 3-61. The rotor is then traveling at a speed $n_1 - n$ rpm in the backward direction with respect to the stator field, or the *slip* of the rotor is $n_1 - n$ rpm. Slip is more usually expressed as a fraction of synchronous speed; i.e., the per-unit slip s is

$$s = \frac{n_1 - n}{n_1} \qquad (3\text{-}63)$$

or
$$n = n_1(1 - s) \qquad (3\text{-}64)$$

This relative motion of flux and rotor conductors induces voltages of frequency sf, called *slip frequency*, in the rotor. Thus the electrical behavior of an induction machine is similar to that of a transformer, but with the additional feature of frequency transformation. A wound-rotor induction machine can be used as a frequency changer.

When used as an induction motor, the rotor terminals are short-circuited. The rotor currents are then determined by the magnitudes of the induced voltages and the rotor impedance at slip frequency. At starting, the rotor is stationary, the slip $s = 1$, and the rotor frequency equals the stator frequency f. The field produced by the rotor currents therefore revolves at the same speed as the stator field, and a starting torque results, tending to turn the rotor in the direction of rotation of the stator inducing field. If this torque is sufficient to overcome the opposition to rotation created by the shaft load, the motor will come up to its operating speed. The operating speed can never equal the synchronous speed n_1, however, for the rotor conductors would then be stationary with respect to the stator field and no voltage would be induced in them.

With the rotor revolving in the same direction of rotation as the stator field, the frequency of the rotor currents is sf, and the component rotor field set up by them will travel at sn_1 rpm with respect to the rotor in the forward direction. But superimposed on this rotation is the mechanical rotation of the rotor at n rpm. The speed of the rotor field in space is the sum of these two speeds and equals

$$sn_1 + n = sn_1 + n_1(1 - s) = n_1 \quad (3\text{-}65)$$

The stator and rotor fields are therefore stationary with respect to each other, a steady torque is produced, and rotation is maintained. Such a torque which exists at any mechanical speed n other than synchronous speed is called an *asynchronous torque*.

Figure 3-30 shows a typical squirrel-cage induction-motor torque-speed

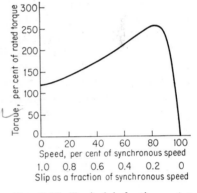

Fig. 3-30. Typical induction-motor torque-speed curve.

characteristic. The factors influencing the shape of this characteristic can be appreciated in terms of the torque equation 3-62. In this equation recognize that the resultant air-gap flux Φ_{sr} is approximately constant when the stator applied voltage and frequency are constant (Eq. 3-45). Also recall that the rotor mmf F_r is proportional to the rotor current I_r. Equation 3-62 then reduces to

$$T = KI_r \sin \delta_r \quad (3\text{-}66)$$

where K is a constant. The rotor current is determined by the voltage induced in the rotor and its leakage impedance, both at slip frequency. The rotor induced voltage is proportional to slip. Under normal running conditions the slip is small—3 to 10 per cent at full load in most squirrel-cage motors. The rotor frequency sf therefore is very low (of the order of 2 to 6 cps in 60-cps motors). Consequently in this range the rotor impedance is largely resistive, and the rotor current is very nearly proportional to and in phase with the rotor voltage and is therefore very nearly proportional to slip. Furthermore the rotor-mmf wave lags approximately 90 electrical degrees behind the resultant flux wave, and therefore $\sin \delta_r \approx 1$. (This point is discussed in Art. 10-1a.) Approximate linearity of torque as a function of slip is therefore to be expected in the range where the slip is small. As slip increases, the rotor impedance increases because of the increasing effect of rotor leakage inductance. Thus the rotor current is less than proportional to slip. Also the rotor current lags further behind the induced voltage, the mmf wave lags further behind the resultant flux wave, and $\sin \delta_r$ decreases. The result is that the torque increases with increasing slip up to a maximum value and then decreases, as shown in Fig. 3-30. The maximum torque, or *breakdown torque*, limits the short-time overload capability of the motor.

The squirrel-cage motor is substantially a constant-speed motor having a few per cent drop in speed from no load to full load. Speed variation may be obtained by using a wound-rotor motor and inserting external resistance in the rotor circuit. In the normal operating range, external resistance simply increases the rotor impedance, necessitating a higher slip for a desired rotor mmf and torque.

In Art. 3-5 it was mentioned that a synchronous motor per se has no starting torque. To make a synchronous motor self-starting, a squirrel-cage winding, called an *amortisseur*, or *damper winding*, is inserted in the rotor pole faces, as shown in Fig. 3-31. The rotor then comes up almost to synchronous speed by induction-motor action with the field winding unexcited. If the load and inertia are not too great, the motor will then pull into synchronism when the field winding is energized from a d-c source.

3-7. Commutator Action. The d-c machine differs in several respects from the ideal model of Art. 3-3. Although the basic concepts of Art. 3-3 are still valid, a reexamination of the assumptions and a modification of the model are desirable. The crux of the matter is the effect of the commutator shown in the photographs of Figs. 3-1, 3-14, and 3-15.

Figure 3-32 shows diagrammatically the armature winding of Fig. 3-19 with the addition of the commutator, brushes, and connections of the coils to the commutator segments. The commutator is represented by the ring of segments in the center of the figure. The segments are insulated from each other and from the shaft. Two stationary brushes are shown by the black rectangles inside the commutator. Actually the brushes usually contact the outer surface, as shown in Figs. 3-14 and 3-15. The coil sides in the slots are shown in cross section by the small circles with dots and crosses in them, indicating currents toward and away from the reader, respectively, as in Fig. 3-19. Only slots 1 and 7 are specifically shown. The connections of the coils to the commutator segments are shown by the circular arcs. The end connections at the back of the armature are shown dotted for the 2 coils in slots 1 and 7, and the connections of these coils to adjacent commutator segments are shown by the heavy arcs. All coils are identical. The back end connections of the other coils have been omitted, to avoid complicating the figure, but they can easily be traced by remembering that each coil has

Fig. 3-31. Rotor of a 6-pole 1,200-rpm synchronous motor showing field coils, pole-face damper winding, and construction. (*Courtesy of General Electric Company.*)

one side in the top of a slot and the other side in the bottom of the diametrically opposite slot.

In Fig. 3-32a the brushes are in contact with commutator segments 1 and 7. Current entering the right-hand brush divides equally between two parallel paths through the winding. The first path leads to the inner coil side in slot 1 and finally ends at the brush on segment 7. The second path leads to the outer coil side in slot 6 and also finally ends at the brush on segment 7. The current directions in Fig. 3-32a can readily

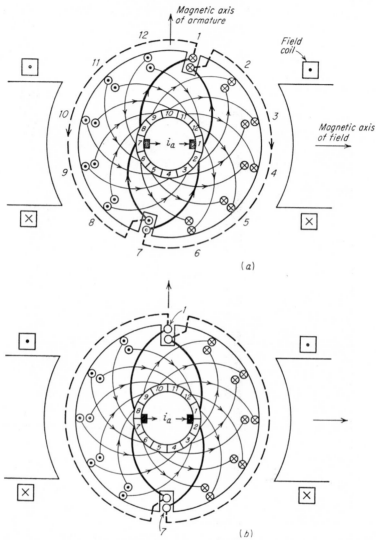

Fig. 3-32. Direct-current-machine armature winding with commutator and brushes. (a) and (b) Current directions for two positions of the armature.

be verified by tracing these two paths. They are the same as in Fig. 3-19. The effect is identical to that of a coil wrapped around the armature with its magnetic axis vertical, and a clockwise magnetic torque is exerted on the armature, tending to align its magnetic field with that of the field winding.

Now suppose the machine is acting as a generator driven in the counter-clockwise direction by an applied mechanical torque. Figure 3-32b shows the situation after the armature has rotated through the angle subtended by half a commutator segment. The right-hand brush is now in contact with both segments 1 and 2, and the left-hand brush is in contact with both segments 7 and 8. The coils in slots 1 and 7 are now short-circuited by the brushes. The currents in the other coils are shown by the dots and crosses, and they produce a magnetic field whose axis again is vertical.

After further rotation the brushes will be in contact with segments 2 and 8, and slots 1 and 7 will have rotated into the positions which were previously occupied by slots 12 and 6 in Fig. 3-32a. The current directions will be similar to those of Fig. 3-32a except that the currents in the coils in slots 1 and 7 will have reversed. The magnetic axis of the armature is still vertical.

During the time when the brushes are simultaneously in contact with two adjacent commutator segments the coils connected to these segments are temporarily removed from the main circuits through the winding, short-circuited by the brushes, and the currents in them are reversed.

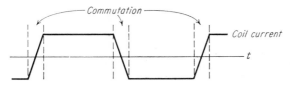

Fig. 3-33. Waveform of current in an armature coil with linear commutation.

Ideally the current in the coils being commutated should reverse linearly with time. Serious departure from linear commutation will result in sparking at the brushes. Means for obtaining sparkless commutation are discussed in Art. 8-1. With linear commutation the waveform of the current in any coil as a function of time is trapezoidal, as shown in Fig. 3-33.

The winding of Fig. 3-32 is simpler than that used in most d-c machines. Ordinarily more slots and commutator segments would be used, and except in small machines more than 2 poles are common. Nevertheless the simple winding of Fig. 3-32 includes the essential features of more complicated windings.

3-8. Introduction to D-C Machines. The essential features of d-c machines are shown schematically in Fig. 3-34. The stator has salient poles excited by 1 or more field coils. The air-gap flux distribution created by the field windings is symmetrical about the center line of the field poles. This axis is called the *field axis*, or *direct axis*. The brushes are located so that commutation occurs when the coil sides are in the neutral zone, midway between the field poles. The axis of the armature-mmf wave then is 90 electrical degrees from the axis of the field poles, i.e., in the *quadrature axis*. In the schematic representation of Fig. 3-34a the brushes are shown in the quadrature axis, because this is the position of the coils to which they are connected. The armature-mmf wave then is along the brush axis, as shown. (The geometrical position of the brushes in an actual machine is approximately 90 electrical degrees from their position in the schematic diagram, because of the shape of the end connections to the commutator. For example, see Fig. 3-32.) For simplicity, the circuit representation usually will be drawn as in Fig. 3-34b.

Although the magnetic torque and the speed voltage appearing at the brushes are independent of the spatial waveform of the flux distribution, for convenience we shall continue to assume a sinusoidal flux-density wave in the air gap. The torque and voltage can then be found from the magnetic-field viewpoint of Art. 3-3b.

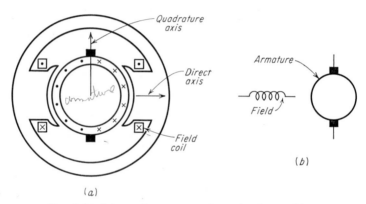

FIG. 3-34. Schematic representations of a d-c machine.

The torque can be expressed in terms of the interaction of the direct-axis air-gap flux per pole Φ_d and the space-fundamental component F_{a1} of the armature-mmf wave, in a form similar to Eq. 3-37. With the brushes in the quadrature axis the angle between these fields is 90 electrical degrees, and its sine equals unity. Substitution in Eq. 3-37 then gives for a P-pole machine

$$T = \frac{\pi}{2}\left(\frac{P}{2}\right)^2 \Phi_d F_{a1} \qquad (3\text{-}67)$$

in which the minus sign has been dropped because the positive direction of the torque can be determined from physical reasoning. The peak value of the triangular armature-mmf wave is given by Eq. 3-4, and its space fundamental F_{a1} is $8/\pi^2$ times its peak. Substitution in Eq. 3-67 then gives

$$T = \frac{PZ_a}{2\pi a}\Phi_d i_a = K_a\Phi_d i_a \qquad \text{newton-m} \qquad (3\text{-}68)$$

where i_a is the current in the external armature circuit, Z_a is the total number of conductors in the armature winding, a is the number of parallel paths through the winding, and

$$K_a = \frac{PZ_a}{2\pi a} \qquad (3\text{-}69)$$

is a constant fixed by the design of the winding.

The rectified voltage generated in the armature has already been found in Art. 3-3b for an elementary single-coil armature, and its waveform is shown in Fig. 3-26. The effect of distributing the winding in several slots is shown in Fig. 3-35, in which each of the rectified sine waves is the voltage generated in one of the coils, with commutation taking place at the moment when the coil sides are in the neutral zone. The generated voltage as observed from the brushes is the sum of the rectified voltages of all the coils in series between brushes and is shown by the rippling line labeled e_a in Fig. 3-35. With a dozen or so commutator segments per

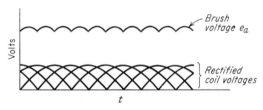

FIG. 3-35. Rectified coil voltages and resultant voltage between brushes in a d-c machine.

pole, the ripple becomes very small, and the average generated voltage observed from the brushes equals the sum of the average values of the rectified coil voltages. From Eq. 3-47 with changes in notation, the average coil voltage is

$$e_{a(\text{coil})} = \frac{PN_c}{\pi} \Phi_d \omega_m \qquad (3\text{-}70)$$

where N_c is the number of turns in one of the coils. For a distributed winding with C coils connected in a parallel paths between brushes, the brush voltage e_a is

$$e_a = \frac{C}{a} e_{a(\text{coil})} = \frac{PN_cC}{\pi a} \Phi_d \omega_m \qquad (3\text{-}71)$$

But $N_cC = Z_a/2$, where Z_a is the total number of active conductors in the winding. Hence

$$e_a = \frac{PZ_a}{2\pi a} \Phi_d \omega_m = K_a \Phi_d \omega_m \qquad (3\text{-}72)$$

where K_a is the design constant defined in Eq. 3-69. Compare with

Eq. 3-48. The rectified voltage of a distributed winding has the same average value as that of a concentrated coil. The difference is that the ripple is greatly reduced.

From Eqs. 3-68 and 3-72, with all variables expressed in mks units,

$$e_a i_a = T\omega_m \tag{3-73}$$

This equation simply says that the instantaneous electrical power associated with the speed voltage equals the instantaneous mechanical power associated with the magnetic torque, the direction of power flow being determined by whether the machine is acting as a motor or generator.

The direct-axis air-gap flux is produced by the combined mmf $\Sigma N_f i_f$ of the field windings, the flux-mmf characteristic being the *magnetization curve* for the particular iron geometry of the machine. A magnetization

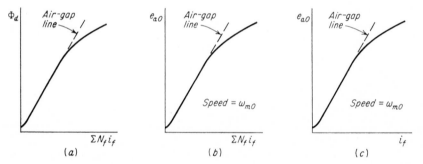

Fig. 3-36. Magnetization curves of a d-c machine.

curve is shown in Fig. 3-36a, in which it is assumed that the armature mmf has no effect on the direct-axis flux, because the axis of the armature-mmf wave is perpendicular to the field axis. It will be necessary to reexamine this assumption later in Chap. 8, where the effects of saturation are investigated more thoroughly. Because the armature emf is proportional to flux times speed, it is usually more convenient to express the magnetization curve in terms of the armature emf e_{a0} at a constant speed ω_{m0} as shown in Fig. 3-36b. The emf e_a for a given flux at any other speed ω_m is proportional to the speed; i.e., from Eq. 3-72

$$\frac{e_a}{\omega_m} = K_a \Phi_d = \frac{e_{a0}}{\omega_{m0}} \tag{3-74}$$

or

$$e_a = \frac{\omega_m}{\omega_{m0}} e_{a0} \tag{3-75}$$

Figure 3-36c shows the magnetization curve with only 1 field winding excited. This curve can easily be obtained by test methods, no knowledge of any design details being required.

Over a fairly wide range of excitation the reluctance of the iron is negligible compared with that of the air gap.   In this region the flux is linearly proportional to the total mmf of the field windings, the constant of proportionality being the *direct-axis air-gap permeance* $\mathscr{P}_d$; thus

$$\Phi_d = \mathscr{P}_d \Sigma N_f i_f \qquad (3\text{-}76)$$

The dotted straight line through the origin coinciding with the straight portion of the magnetization curves in Fig. 3-36 is called the *air-gap line.*

The outstanding advantages of d-c machines arise from the wide variety of operating characteristics which can be obtained by selection of the method of excitation of the field windings.   The field windings may be *separately excited* from an external d-c source; or they may be *self-excited*, i.e., the machine may supply its own excitation.   Connection

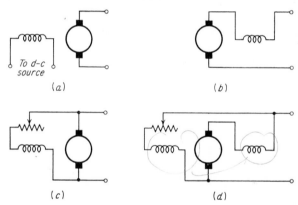

(a)   (b)

(c)   (d)

Fig. 3-37.   Field-circuit connections of d-c machines.   (*a*) Separate excitation.   (*b*) Series.   (*c*) Shunt.   (*d*) Compound.

diagrams are shown in Fig. 3-37.   The method of excitation profoundly influences not only the steady-state characteristics, which we shall describe briefly in this article, but also the dynamic behavior of the machine in control systems, discussed in Chap. 4.

The connection diagram of a separately excited generator is given in Fig. 3-37*a*.   The required field current is a very small fraction of the rated armature current—of the order of 1 to 3 per cent in the average generator.   A small amount of power in the field circuit may control a relatively large amount of power in the armature circuit; i.e., the generator is a power amplifier.   Its field winding is analogous to the grid of a vacuum-tube power amplifier, its armature is analogous to the plate circuit, and the mechanical power input from its mechanical drive is like the plate-circuit power supply.   Separately excited generators are often used in feedback control systems when control of the armature voltage over a wide range is required.

The field windings of self-excited generators may be supplied in three different ways. The field may be connected in series with the armature (Fig. 3-37b), resulting in a *series generator*. The field may be connected in shunt with the armature (Fig. 3-37c), resulting in a *shunt generator*. Or the field may be in two sections (Fig. 3-37d), one of which is connected in series and the other in shunt with the armature, resulting in a *compound generator*. With self-excited generators residual magnetism must be present in the machine iron to get the self-excitation process started.

Typical steady-state volt-ampere characteristics are shown in Fig. 3-38, constant-speed prime movers being assumed. The relation between the steady-state generated emf E_a and the terminal voltage V_t is

$$V_t = E_a - I_a r_a \qquad (3\text{-}77)$$

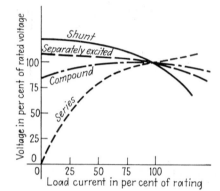

FIG. 3-38. Volt-ampere characteristics of d-c generators.

where I_a is the armature-current output and r_a is the armature-circuit resistance. In a generator, E_a is larger than V_t, and the electromagnetic torque T is a counter torque opposing rotation.

The terminal voltage of a separately excited generator decreases slightly with increase in the load current, principally because of the voltage drop in the armature resistance. The field current of a series generator is the same as the load current, so that the air-gap flux and hence the voltage vary widely with load. As a consequence, series generators are not very often used. The voltage of shunt generators drops off somewhat with load, but not in a manner which is objectionable for many purposes. Compound generators are normally connected so that the mmf of the series winding aids that of the shunt winding. The advantage is that, through the action of the series winding, the flux per pole can increase with load, resulting in a voltage output which is nearly constant or which even rises somewhat as load increases. The shunt winding usually contains many turns of relatively small wire. The series winding, wound on the outside, consists of a few turns of comparatively heavy conductor because it must carry the full armature current of the machine. The voltage of both shunt and compound generators may be controlled over reasonable limits by means of rheostats in the shunt field.

Any of the methods of excitation used for generators may also be used for motors. Typical steady-state speed-torque characteristics are shown in Fig. 3-39, in which it is assumed that the motor terminals are supplied from a constant-voltage source. In a motor the relation between the emf E_a generated in the armature and the terminal voltage V_t is

$$V_t = E_a + I_a r_a \qquad (3\text{-}78)$$

or

$$I_a = \frac{V_t - E_a}{r_a} \qquad (3\text{-}79)$$

where I_a is now the armature-current input. The generated emf E_a is now smaller than the terminal voltage V_t, the armature current is in the opposite direction to that in a generator, and the electromagnetic torque is in the direction to sustain rotation of the armature.

In shunt and separately excited motors the field flux is nearly constant. Consequently increased torque must be accompanied by a very nearly proportional increase in armature current and hence by a small decrease in counter emf to allow this increased current through the small armature resistance. Since counter emf is determined by flux and speed (Eq. 3-72), the speed must drop slightly. Like the squirrel-cage induction motor, the shunt motor is substantially a constant-speed motor having about 5 per cent drop in speed from no load to full load. A typical speed-load characteristic is shown by the solid curve in Fig. 3-39. Starting torque and maximum torque are limited by the armature current that can be commutated successfully.

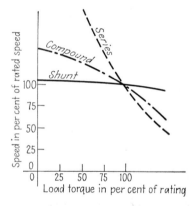

Fig. 3-39. Speed-torque characteristics of d-c motors.

An outstanding advantage of the shunt motor is ease of speed control. With a rheostat in the shunt-field circuit, the field current and flux per pole may be varied at will, and variation of flux causes the inverse variation of speed to maintain counter emf approximately equal to the impressed terminal voltage. A maximum speed range of about 4 or 5 to 1 may be obtained by this method, the limitation again being commutating conditions. By variation of the impressed armature voltage, very wide speed ranges may be obtained.

In the series motor increase in load is accompanied by increases in the armature current and mmf and the stator field flux (provided the iron is not completely saturated). Because flux increases with load, speed must drop in order to maintain the balance between impressed voltage and counter emf; moreover, the increase in armature current caused by increased torque is smaller than in the shunt motor because of the increased flux. The series motor is therefore a varying-speed motor with a markedly drooping speed-load characteristic of the type shown dotted in Fig. 3-39. For applications requiring heavy torque overloads, this characteristic is particularly advantageous because the corresponding power overloads are held to more reasonable values by the associated speed drops. Very favorable starting characteristics also result from the increase in flux with increased armature current.

In the compound motor the series field may be connected either *cumulatively*, so that its mmf adds to that of the shunt field, or *differentially*, so that it opposes. The differential connection is very rarely used. As shown by the dashed curve in Fig. 3-39, a cumulatively compounded motor will have a speed-load characteristic intermediate between those of a shunt and a series motor, the drop of speed with load depending on the relative number of ampere-turns in the shunt and series fields. It does not have the disadvantage of very high light-load speed associated with a series motor, but it retains to a considerable degree the advantages of series excitation.

The applicational advantages of d-c machines lie in the variety of performance characteristics offered by the possibilities of shunt, series, and compound excitation. Some of these characteristics have been touched upon briefly in this article. Still greater possibilities exist if additional sets of brushes are added so that other voltages may be obtained from the commutator. Thus the versatility of d-c machine systems and their adaptability to control, both manual and automatic, are their outstanding features. These characteristics will be discussed in Chaps. 4 and 8 for both steady-state and dynamic operation.

3-9. Résumé. The Nature of Machinery Problems. As we begin to converge on the theory of rotating machines, we need to reflect momentarily on our objectives: what are the machine characteristics that we need to know in reasonably precise, quantitative form? The answer depends on what, specifically, the machines are intended to do for us. The machine is one component in an electromechanical-energy-conversion system, and the machine characteristics often play the predominant part in the behavior of the complete system.

In many applications of electric motors, the motor is supplied with electric power from a constant-voltage source. The motor drives a mechanical load whose torque requirements vary with the speed at which it is driven. The steady-state operating speed is then fixed by the point at which the torque that the motor can furnish electromagnetically is equal to the torque that the load can absorb mechanically. In Fig. 3-40, for instance, the solid curve is the speed-torque characteristic of an induction motor. The dotted curve is a plot of the torque input required by a fan for various operating speeds. When the fan and motor are coupled, the steady-state operating point of the combination is at the intersection of these two curves—where what the motor can give is the same as what the fan can take.

Motor power or torque requirements vary, of course, depending on conditions within the driven equipment. The requirements of some motor loads are satisfied by a speed which remains approximately constant as load varies; an ordinary hydraulic pump is an example. Others, like a phonograph turntable, require absolutely constant speed. Still others require a speed closely coordinated with another speed: the raising of both ends of a vertical-lift bridge, for instance. The automatic direction of guns in accordance with data received from radar signals is a motor application where the instantaneous *position* of the driven equipment must be controlled accurately. Some motor applications, such as cranes and many traction-type drives, inherently demand low speeds and heavy torques at one end of the range and relatively high speeds and light

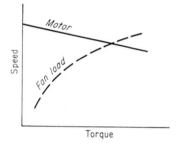

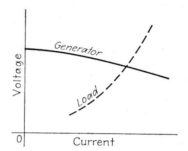

FIG. 3-40. Superposition of motor and load characteristics.

FIG. 3-41. Superposition of generator and load characteristics.

torques at the other—a varying-speed characteristic, in other words. Others may require an adjustable constant speed (e.g., some machine-tool drives in which the speed of operation may require adjustment over a wide range but must always be carefully predetermined) or an adjustable varying speed (a crane is again an example). In almost every application the torque which the motor is capable of supplying while starting, the maximum torque which it can furnish while running, and the current requirements are items of importance.

Many similar remarks can be made for generators. For example, the terminal voltage and power output of a generator are determined by the characteristics of both the generator and its load. Thus, the solid curve of Fig. 3-41 is a plot of the terminal voltage of a d-c shunt generator as a function of its current output. The dotted curve is a plot of the volt-ampere characteristic of a load. When the load is connected to the generator terminals, the operating point of the combination is at the intersection of these two curves—where what the generator can give is the same as what the load can take. Often, as in the usual central station, the requirement is that terminal voltage shall remain substantially constant over a wide load range. Not infrequently, however, a motor is associated with its own individual generator in order to provide greater flexibility and more precise control. Then it may be desired that the terminal voltage vary with load in some particular fashion.

Among the features of outstanding importance, therefore, are the torque-speed characteristics of motors and the voltage-load characteristics of generators, together with knowledge of the limits between which these characteristics can be varied and ideas of how such variations may be obtained. Moreover, pertinent economic features are efficiency, power factor, comparative costs, and the effect of losses on the heating and rating of the machines. One of the objects of our analysis of machinery is accordingly to study and compare these features for the various machine types. Of course there are many important, interesting, and complex engineering problems associated with the design, development, and manufacturing of machines for which these studies are but the introduction; most such problems are beyond the scope of the book.

A knowledge of the steady-state characteristics is insufficient, however, for an understanding of the role played by rotating machines in modern technology. In an increasingly important class of applications in the field of automatic control, the emphasis is rather on the dynamic behavior of the complete electromechanical system of which the machine is one component. For example, it may be desired to control the speed or position of a shaft driving a load in accordance with some specified function of time or of some other variable. A typical industrial application is the accurate control of tension in a process involving the winding of long strips of material, such as paper, on a reel. Dynamic controls of astounding accuracy and rapidity of response have been developed: examples are the tracking of aircraft by radar and the automatic pointing of antiaircraft weapons in accordance with the directions received from the radar signals. In applications of this kind, the electromechanical transient behavior of the system as a whole is a major consideration; the system should respond accurately and rapidly to the control function, and oscillations should die out quickly. Not only the electrical characteristics but also the mechanical properties of the system, such as stiffness, inertia, and friction, must be considered and indeed may become the predominant factors.

In such studies, then, an adequate theory must be capable of treating the dynamic behavior of machines as system components. Since the analysis of a complete electromechanical system presents a complex problem, a theory of machines suitable for these purposes must be simplified as much as possible while still retaining the essential elements. The development of such a theory, based on the coupled-circuit viewpoint of Art. 3-3a, is the primary purpose of Part II. But such a simplified theory necessarily leaves out of consideration factors which should be understood for a more complete and satisfying understanding of machine theory and which may have an important bearing on machine applications. Some of these factors have already been mentioned. The purpose of Part III is to discuss some of these matters and to develop a theory based on the magnetic-field viewpoint of Art. 3-3b. Although not as adaptable to dynamic problems as the coupled-circuit viewpoint, the magnetic-field viewpoint leads to simple methods of treating steady-state problems and emphasizes physical concepts. As shown in Art. 3-3b, these viewpoints stem from the same basic ideas and are complementary to each other. Parts II and III are essentially independent treatments with somewhat different objectives. Either may be studied without the other, and they may be studied in either sequence.

PROBLEMS

3-1. The object of this problem is to illustrate how the armature windings of certain machines (i.e., d-c machines) may be approximately represented by uniform current sheets, with the degree of correspondence growing better as the winding is distributed in a greater number of slots around the armature periphery. For this purpose, consider an armature with 8 slots uniformly distributed over 360 electrical degrees or one pair of poles. The air gap is of uniform width, the slot openings are very small, and the reluctance of the iron is negligible.

Lay out 360 electrical degrees of the armature with its slots in developed form in the manner of Fig. 3-20a, and number the slots 1 to 8 from left to right. The winding consists of 8 single-turn coils, each carrying a direct current of 10 amp. Coil sides which may be placed in slots 1 to 4 carry current directed into the paper; those which may be placed in slots 5 to 8 carry current out of the paper.

a. Consider that all 8 coils are placed with one side in slot 1 and the other in slot 5. The remaining slots are empty. Draw the rectangular mmf wave produced by these coils.

b. Next consider that 4 coils have one side in slot 1 and the other in slot 5, while the remaining 4 have one side in slot 3 and the other in slot 7. Draw the component rectangular mmf waves produced by each group of coils, and superimpose the components to give the resultant mmf wave.

c. Now consider that 2 coils are placed in slots 1 and 5, 2 in 2 and 6, 2 in 3 and 7, and 2 in 4 and 8. Again superimpose the component rectangular waves to produce the resultant wave. Note that the task can be systematized and simplified by recognizing that the mmf wave is symmetrical about its axis and takes a step at each slot which is definitely related to the number of ampere-conductors in the slot.

d. Let the armature now consist of 16 slots per 360 electrical degrees with one coil side in each slot. Draw the resultant mmf wave.

e. Approximate each of the resultant waves of (*a*) to (*d*) by isosceles triangles, noting that the representation grows better as the winding is more finely distributed.

3-2. Figure 3-42 shows in cross section a machine having a rotor winding *ff* and 2 identical stator windings *aa* and *bb*. The self-inductance of each stator winding is

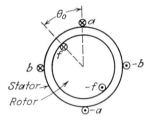

Fig. 3-42. Elementary cylindrical-rotor 2-phase synchronous machine, Prob. 3-2.

L_{aa} henrys and of the rotor winding is L_{ff} henrys. The air gap is uniform. The stator windings are in quadrature. The mutual inductance between a stator winding and the rotor winding depends on the angular position θ_o of the rotor and may be assumed to be

$$M_{af} = M \cos \theta_o \qquad M_{bf} = M \sin \theta_o$$

where M is the maximum value of the mutual inductance. The resistance of each stator winding is r_a ohms.

a. Derive a general expression for the torque T in terms of the angle θ_o, the inductance constants, and the instantaneous currents i_a, i_b, and i_f. Does this expression apply at standstill? When the rotor is revolving?

b. Suppose the rotor is stationary and constant direct currents $I_a = 5$ amp, $I_b = 5$ amp, $I_f = 10$ amp are supplied to the windings in the directions indicated by the dots and crosses in Fig. 3-42. If the rotor is allowed to move, will it rotate continuously or will it tend to come to rest? If the latter, at what value of θ_o?

c. The rotor winding is now excited by a constant direct current I_f, and the stator windings carry balanced 2-phase currents

$$i_a = \sqrt{2}\, I_a \cos \omega t \qquad i_b = \sqrt{2}\, I_a \sin \omega t$$

The rotor is revolving at synchronous speed so that its instantaneous angular position θ_o is given by $\theta_o = \omega t - \delta$, where δ is a phase angle describing the position of the rotor at $t = 0$. The machine is an elementary 2-phase synchronous machine. Derive an expression for the torque under these conditions. Describe its nature.

d. Under the conditions of part c, derive an expression for the instantaneous terminal voltages of stator phases a and b.

3-3. Figure 3-43 shows in cross section a machine having 2 identical stator windings aa and bb arranged in quadrature on a laminated steel core. The salient-pole rotor is made of steel and carries a winding f connected to slip rings. The machine is an elementary 2-phase salient-pole synchronous machine.

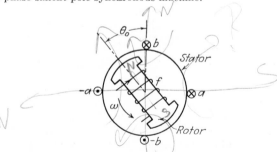

Fig. 3-43. Elementary salient-pole 2-phase synchronous machine, Prob. 3-3.

Because of the nonuniform air gap, the self- and mutual inductances of the stator windings are functions of the angular position θ_o of the rotor, as follows:

$$L_{aa} = L_0 + L_2 \cos 2\theta_o$$
$$L_{bb} = L_0 - L_2 \cos 2\theta_o$$
$$M_{ab} = L_2 \sin 2\theta_o$$

where L_0 and L_2 are positive constants. The mutual inductances between the rotor and the stator windings are functions of θ_o as follows:

$$M_{af} = M \cos \theta_o \qquad M_{bf} = M \sin \theta_o$$

where M is a positive constant. The self-inductance L_{ff} of the rotor winding is constant, independent of θ_o.

The rotor (or field) winding f is excited with direct current I_f, and the stator windings are connected to a balanced 2-phase voltage source. The currents in the stator windings are

$$i_a = \sqrt{2}\, I_a \cos \omega t \qquad i_b = \sqrt{2}\, I_a \sin \omega t$$

The rotor is revolving at synchronous speed so that its instantaneous angular position is given by

$$\theta_o = \omega t - \delta$$

where δ is a phase angle describing the position of the rotor at $t = 0$.

a. Derive an expression for the electromagnetic torque acting on the rotor. Describe its nature.

b. Can the machine be operated as a motor? As a generator? Explain.

c. Will the machine continue to run if the field current I_f is reduced to zero? If so, give an expression for the torque, and a physical explanation.

3-4. Figure 3-44 shows a 2-pole rotor revolving inside a smooth stator which carries a coil of 100 turns. The rotor produces a sinusoidal space distribution of

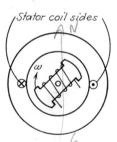

FIG. 3-44. Elementary generator, Prob. 3-4.

flux at the stator surface, the peak value of the flux-density wave being 0.80 weber/m^2 when the current in the rotor is 10 amp. The magnetic circuit is linear. The inside diameter of the stator is 0.10 m, and its axial length is 0.10 m. The rotor is driven at a speed of 60 rev/sec.

a. The rotor is excited by a direct current of 10 amp. Taking zero time as the instant when the axis of the rotor is vertical, find the expression for the instantaneous voltage generated in the open-circuited stator coil.

b. The rotor is now excited by a 60-cps sinusoidal alternating current whose rms value is 7.07 amp. Consequently, the rotor current reverses every half revolution; it is timed to go through zero whenever the axis of the rotor is vertical. Taking zero time as the instant when the axis of the rotor is vertical, find the expression for the instantaneous voltage generated in the open-circuited stator coil.

This scheme is sometimes suggested as a d-c generator without a commutator, the thought being that, if alternate half cycles of the alternating voltage generated in part *a* are reversed by reversal of the polarity of the field (rotor) winding, then a pulsating direct voltage will be generated in the stator. Explain whether this invention will work as described.

3-5. A small experimental 3-phase 4-pole alternator has the full-pitch concentrated Y-connected armature winding shown diagrammatically in Figs. 3-12*b* and 3-12*c*. Each coil (that represented by coil sides *a* and −*a*, for example) has 2 turns, and all the turns in any one phase are connected in series. The flux per pole is 25.0 megalines and is sinusoidally distributed in space. The rotor is driven at 1,800 rpm.

a. Determine the rms generated voltage to neutral.

b. Determine the rms generated voltage between lines.

c. Consider an *abc* phase order, and take zero time at the instant when the flux linkages with phase *a* are a maximum. Write a consistent set of time equations for the three phase voltages from terminals *a*, *b*, and *c* to neutral.

d. Under the conditions of (*c*), write a consistent set of time equations for the three voltages between lines *a* and *b*, *b* and *c*, and *c* and *a*.

3-6. Equation 3-42 for the instantaneous voltage generated in an N-turn coil is based on a flux wave of constant amplitude sinusoidally distributed in space and rotating at a uniform speed with respect to the coil. It applies to the normal 3-phase machine operating under balanced conditions. A different type of situation may arise in single-phase motor analysis, however. The air-gap flux density may be considered to vary sinusoidally in space around the periphery, but the wave does not rotate. Since the flux is produced by an alternating current which varies sinusoidally with time at the angular frequency ω, the amplitude of the flux wave also varies sinusoidally with time. The N-turn coil on the rotor revolves at the steady speed n.

Investigate the nature of the generated coil voltage under these conditions. In particular, show that it consists of two components, one whose amplitude is proportional to the angular velocity ω of the current in the field winding, and one whose amplitude is proportional to the speed n of the armature. The former component is called a *transformer voltage;* the latter, a *speed voltage.*

3-7. In a balanced 2-phase machine, the 2 windings are displaced 90 electrical degrees in space, and the currents in the 2 windings are phase-displaced 90 electrical degrees in time. For such a machine, carry out the process leading up to an equation such as 3-59 for the rotating mmf wave.

3-8. The following statements are made in Art. 3-4 just after deriving and discussing Eq. 3-61: "In general it may be shown that a rotating field of constant amplitude will be produced by a q-phase winding excited by balanced q-phase currents when the respective phases are wound $2\pi/q$ electrical radians apart in space. The constant amplitude will be $q/2$ times the maximum contribution of any one phase, and the speed will be $\omega = 2\pi f$ electrical radians per second."

Prove these statements.

3-9. A synchronous motor with its stator connected to a balanced polyphase source is operating at 1.00 power factor and constant load torque equal to one-half of its full-load value. State which way (in the direction of rotation or counter to the direction of rotation) the rotor will move relative to the resultant air-gap flux-density wave as the field current is increased.

3-10. A synchronous motor fed from constant-voltage mains is supplying a constant-torque load. The effects of losses and of the leakage reactance of the armature may be ignored. The field current is initially adjusted so that the motor is operating at unity power factor. Describe with reasons the effect of decreasing the field current on the following quantities:

a. The magnitude of the resultant flux wave

b. The component of armature current in phase with the voltage

c. The space-phase angle δ between the armature mmf and the resultant flux wave

3-11. Electrical power is to be supplied to a 3-phase 25-cps system from a 3-phase 60-cps system through a motor-generator set consisting of two directly coupled synchronous machines.

a. What is the minimum number of poles which the motor may have?

b. What is the minimum number of poles which the generator may have?

c. At what speed in rpm will the set specified in (a) and (b) operate?

3-12. A 3-phase induction motor runs at almost 1,200 rpm at no load and 1,140 rpm at full load when supplied with power from a 60-cps 3-phase line.

a. How many poles has the motor?

b. What is the per cent slip at full load?

c. What is the corresponding frequency of the rotor voltages?

d. What is the corresponding speed (1) of the rotor field with respect to the rotor? (2) Of the rotor field with respect to the stator? (3) Of the rotor field with respect to the stator field?

e. What speed would the rotor have at a slip of 10 per cent?

f. What is the rotor frequency at this speed?

g. Repeat part d for a slip of 10 per cent.

3-13. An Electropult[1] based on the induction-motor principle may be used for launching heavily loaded airplanes from short runways. It consists of a launching car riding on a long track. The track is a developed squirrel-cage winding, and the launching car, which is 12 ft long, $3\frac{1}{2}$ ft wide, and only $5\frac{1}{2}$ in. high, has a developed 3-phase 8-pole winding. The center-line distance between adjacent poles is $1\frac{2}{8} = 1\frac{1}{2}$ ft. Power at 60 cps is fed to the car from arms extending through slots to rails below ground level. The car develops 10,000 hp and can launch an airplane in as little as 4 sec over a 340-ft run.

a. What is the synchronous speed in miles per hour?

b. Will the car reach this speed? Explain your answer.

c. To what slip frequency does a car speed of 75 mph correspond?

d. The resistance of the bars in the squirrel-cage track winding diminishes from a maximum at the start of the runway to a minimum where the airplane leaves the runway. Explain the purpose and the effect of this construction.

e. As soon as the airplane is launched, direct current is applied to the 3-phase winding. Explain what the effect of this would be.

3-14. Describe the effect on the normal torque-speed characteristic of an induction motor produced by:

a. Halving the applied voltage with normal frequency

b. Halving both the applied voltage and frequency

Sketch the associated torque-speed characteristics in their approximate relative positions with respect to the normal one. Neglect the effects of stator resistance and leakage reactance.

3-15. The stator of an unloaded 3-phase 6-pole wound-rotor induction motor is connected to a 60-cps source; the rotor is connected to a 25-cps source.

a. Is a starting torque produced?

b. At what speed will steady-state motor action result? There are two possible answers, depending on circumstances in a particular case.

[1] See *Westinghouse Engr.*, September, 1946, p. 161.

c. What determines at which of the two speeds in (*b*) the motor will operate in a specific case?

d. Suppose now that the rotor supply frequency is varied over the range 0 to 25 cps. Sketch curves showing motor speed in rpm as a function of rotor frequency, interpreting zero frequency as direct current.

e. What changes are made in the foregoing answers if the motor is fully loaded instead of unloaded?

3-16. Figure 3-45 shows a 3-phase wound-rotor induction machine whose shaft is rigidly coupled to the shaft of a 3-phase synchronous motor. The terminals of the 3-phase rotor winding of the induction machine are brought out to slip rings as shown. The induction machine is driven by the synchronous motor at the proper speed and in the proper direction of rotation so that 3-phase 120-cps voltages are available at the slip rings. The induction machine has a 6-pole stator winding.

a. How many poles must the rotor winding of the induction machine have?

b. If the stator field in the induction machine rotates in a clockwise direction, what must be the direction of rotation of its rotor?

c. What must be the speed in rpm?

d. How many poles must the synchronous motor have?

3-17. The system shown in Fig. 3-45 is used to convert balanced 60-cps voltages to other frequencies. The synchronous motor has 2 poles and drives the interconnecting

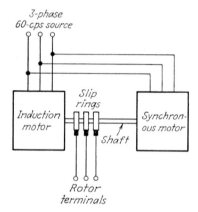

Fig. 3-45. Interconnected induction and synchronous machines, Probs. 3-16 and 3-17.

shaft in the clockwise direction. The induction machine has 12 poles, and its stator windings are connected to the lines to produce a counterclockwise rotating field (in the opposite direction to the synchronous motor). The machine has a wound rotor whose terminals are brought out through slip rings.

a. At what speed does the motor run?

b. What is the frequency of the rotor voltages in the induction machine?

3-18. *a.* Compare the effect on the speed of a d-c shunt motor of varying the line voltage with that of varying only the armature terminal voltage, so that the field current remains fixed.

b. Compare both these effects with that of varying only the shunt-field current, the armature terminal voltage remaining fixed.

3-19. State approximately how the armature current and speed of a d-c shunt motor would be affected by each of the following changes in the operating conditions:

a. Halving the armature terminal voltage, the field current and load torque remaining constant

b. Halving the armature terminal voltage, the field current and horsepower output remaining constant

c. Doubling the field flux, the armature terminal voltage and load torque remaining constant

d. Halving both the field flux and armature terminal voltage, the horsepower output remaining constant

e. Halving the armature terminal voltage, the field flux remaining constant and the load torque varying as the square of the speed

In each case, only brief quantitative statements of the order of magnitude of the changes are desired, e.g., "speed approximately doubled."

3-20. A 25-kw 250-volt d-c machine has an armature resistance of 0.10 ohm. Its magnetization curve at a constant speed of 1,200 rpm is shown in Fig. 3-46.

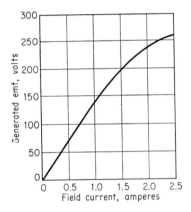

Fig. 3-46. Direct-current-machine magnetization curve at 1,200 rpm, Probs. 3-20 and 3-21.

Its field is separately excited, and it is driven by a synchronous motor at a constant speed of 1,200 rpm.

Plot a family of curves of armature terminal voltage vs. armature current for constant field currents of 2.5, 2.0, 1.5, and 1.0 amp.

3-21. The d-c machine of Prob. 3-20 is operated as a separately excited motor.

a. For a constant field current of 2.0 amp, plot a family of curves of speed in rpm versus torque in newton-meters for applied armature terminal voltages of 250, 200, 150, and 100 volts.

b. For a constant applied armature terminal voltage of 200 volts, plot a family of curves of speed vs. torque for field currents of 2.5, 2.0, 1.5, and 1.0 amp.

3-22. An eddy-current brake of the type used for load tests on motors requires a torque of 100 lb-ft to drive it at a speed of 1,000 rpm when the current in its magnetizing coils is 10.0 amp.

This brake is driven by a d-c series motor rated to deliver 20 hp at 1,000 rpm with an applied voltage of 230 volts.

a. Plot a family of five torque-speed curves for the brake at coil currents of 6, 8, 10, 12, and 14 amp, respectively. For the purposes of this problem, assume that the flux is linearly proportional to the coil current and that the magnetic effect of the eddy currents generated in the brake disk is negligible.   Also, neglect windage and friction torques.

b. On the same curve sheet plot a family of four torque-speed curves for the series motor at applied voltages of 120, 100, 80, and 60 per cent of rated voltage.   Assume that all losses are negligible, that the motor flux is linearly proportional to the motor field current, and that the resistive voltage drops in the field and armature windings are negligible.

c. Plot curves of torque and speed against brake coil current when the motor is supplied with rated voltage.

d. Plot curves of torque and speed against motor applied voltage when the brake coil current is constant at 10 amp.

PART II

The Idealized Machine

CHAPTER 4

Theory of Ideal D-C Machines

The outstanding characteristic of d-c machines is their versatility. By means of various combinations of shunt-, series-, and separately excited field windings they can be designed to have a wide variety of built-in volt-ampere or speed-torque characteristics for both dynamic and steady-state operation. Because of the ease with which they can be controlled, systems of d-c machines are often used in applications requiring a wide range of motor speeds or precise control of motor output. Often the inherent characteristics of the machines are modified by the addition of feedback circuits.

The purpose of this chapter is to develop the theory of d-c machines, with emphasis on their dynamic characteristics as electromechanical-energy-conversion system components. Included also is an elementary discussion of feedback-control theory. Because of the complexity of dynamic-system problems, a number of idealizing assumptions will be made so that the analytical techniques of linear-system theory can be applied.

4-1. The Ideal D-C Machine. In many problems involving the behavior of a d-c machine as a system component the machine can be described with satisfactory accuracy in terms of an idealized model having the following properties:

1. The stator has salient poles excited by 1 or more concentrated field coils. The air-gap flux distribution created by the field windings is symmetrical about the center line of the field poles, called the *field axis*, or *direct axis*.

2. Because the field coils are close together, it will be assumed that the resultant direct-axis field flux links all the turns of all field windings.

3. The armature has a large number of slots per pole so that the armature winding can be considered as a finely distributed winding.

4. The effect of slot openings is negligible. The designer takes these effects into account in magnetic-circuit calculations, but the details need not concern us here.

155

5. The brushes are narrow, and commutation is linear, as in Fig. 3-33. The brushes are located so that commutation occurs when the coil sides are in the neutral zone midway between the field poles. The axis of the armature-mmf wave then is fixed in space and lies along the *quadrature axis*.

6. The model is a 2-pole machine, but the results apply to a P-pole machine.

7. The armature mmf is assumed to have no effect on the total direct-axis flux, because the armature-mmf wave is perpendicular to the field axis. It will be necessary to reexamine this assumption later in Chap. 8, where the effects of magnetic saturation are investigated more thoroughly.

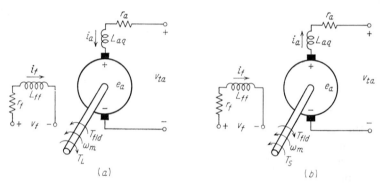

FIG. 4-1. Schematic representation of a d-c machine showing (a) motor and (b) generator reference directions.

8. For most of the problems considered in this chapter the effects of magnetic saturation will be neglected. Superposition of magnetic fields can then be used, and inductances can be considered to be independent of the currents.

The schematic representation of the model is shown in Fig. 4-1. The convention will be adopted that the arrows represent the reference directions for both current and magnetic field. A consistent set of reference directions for all the other variables can then be adopted to conform with the flux-current reference directions. For example, in Fig. 4-1a the reference direction for magnetic torque is counterclockwise, tending to align the stator and rotor fields, as shown by the arrow labeled T_{fld}. If the machine is a motor, it will turn in the counterclockwise direction against the opposing torque T_L applied to the motor by the driven mechanical load, as shown by the arrows ω_m and T_L. The upper brush will be $+$, because electrical power must be supplied to the motor. Figure 4-1b shows the reference directions for a generator, where T_S is the torque applied by the mechanical source. A consistent system of reference directions is especially important in dealing with the more complex cross-field machines discussed later in this chapter.

4-2. Dynamic Equations. The dynamic equations for a d-c machine can be derived from either the magnetic-field or the coupled-circuit viewpoint of Art. 3-3, as shown below.

a. The Magnetic-field Viewpoint. The electromechanical coupling terms are the magnetic torque T and the generated voltage e_a, which have already been derived in Art. 3-8. From Eqs. 3-68 and 3-72,

$$T = K_a \Phi_d i_a \tag{4-1}$$
$$e_a = K_a \Phi_d \omega_m \tag{4-2}$$

where
$$K_a = \frac{PZ_a}{2\pi a} \tag{4-3}$$

The symbols have been defined in Eqs. 3-68 and 3-72. These equations together with the differential equation of motion of the mechanical system, the volt-ampere equations for the armature and field circuits, and the magnetization curve describe the system performance.

Consider first the ideal d-c machine shown in Fig. 4-1 with 1 field winding and negligible magnetic saturation. The direct-axis air-gap flux Φ_d is then linearly proportional to the field current i_f, and Eqs. 4-1 and 4-2 can be expressed as

$$T = k_f i_f i_a \tag{4-4}$$
$$e_a = k_f i_f \omega_m \tag{4-5}$$

where k_f is a constant. With the brushes in the quadrature axis the mutual inductance between the field and armature circuits is zero, just as it would be for 2 coils whose axes are perpendicular. The voltage equation for the field circuit then is

$$v_f = L_{ff} p i_f + r_f i_f \tag{4-6}$$

where v_f, i_f, r_f, and L_{ff} are the terminal voltage, current, resistance, and self-inductance of the field circuit, respectively, and p is the derivative operator d/dt.

For motor reference directions (Fig. 4-1a) the voltage equation for the armature circuit is

$$v_{ta} = e_a + L_{aq} p i_a + r_a i_a \tag{4-7}$$
$$v_{ta} = k_f i_f \omega_m + L_{aq} p i_a + r_a i_a \tag{4-8}$$

where v_{ta}, i_a, r_a, and L_{aq} are the terminal voltage, current, resistance, and self-inductance of the armature circuit, respectively. The subscript q is used with the inductance because the axis of the armature mmf is along the quadrature axis. The inductance L_{aq} includes the effect of any quadrature-axis stator windings in series with the armature, such as interpoles and pole-face compensating windings used on large machines to improve commutation, as described in Chap. 8. For a motor the dynamic equation for the mechanical system is

$$T = k_f i_f i_a = Jp\omega_m + T_L \tag{4-9}$$

where J is the moment of inertia and T_L is the mechanical load torque opposing rotation.

For generator reference directions (Fig. 4-1b), the armature voltage and torque equations become

$$v_{ta} = e_a - L_{aq}pi_a - r_a i_a \tag{4-10}$$
$$v_{ta} = k_f i_f \omega_m - L_{aq}pi_a - r_a i_a \tag{4-11}$$

and
$$T_S = Jp\omega_m + T = Jp\omega_m + k_f i_f i_a \tag{4-12}$$

where T_S now is the mechanical driving torque applied to the shaft in the direction of rotation.

Equations 4-6, 4-8, and 4-9, or 4-6, 4-11, and 4-12, together with the Kirchhoff-law equations for the circuits connected to the field and armature terminals and the torque-speed characteristics of the mechanical system, determine the system performance. The equations contain product nonlinearities of the variables $i_f\omega_m$ and $i_f i_a$. Their application to specific cases will be illustrated in Arts. 4-3 and 4-4.

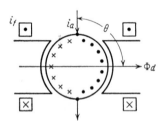

FIG. 4-2. Armature winding with leads attached to the rotor.

b. The Coupled-circuit Viewpoint. Although no new results will be obtained in this section and it may be omitted without loss of continuity, the alternative derivation of the torque and voltage equations given herein may be instructive for the further insight it gives into the role played by the commutator. This section is written primarily for the reader who is interested in looking further into the implications of dynamic-circuit theory as applied to commutator machines.

Consider the simple machine shown in Fig. 4-2, comprising a salient-pole stator with a field winding f and a cylindrical rotor with a finely distributed armature winding a. First consider what would happen if connections were made to the armature winding, *at fixed points with respect to the rotor*, through slip rings or flexible leads. With magnetic saturation neglected, the magnetic torque and induced voltages of this simple device can readily be expressed in terms of the self- and mutual inductances, as in Arts. 2-4 and 3-3a. For motor reference directions

$$T = \tfrac{1}{2}i_f^2 \frac{d\mathcal{L}_{ff}}{d\theta} + \tfrac{1}{2}i_a^2 \frac{d\mathcal{L}_{aa}}{d\theta} + i_a i_f \frac{d\mathcal{L}_{af}}{d\theta}$$ (4-13)

$$v_{ta} = r_a i_a + p(\mathcal{L}_{aa} i_a + \mathcal{L}_{af} i_f)$$ (4-14)

$$v_f = r_f i_f + p(\mathcal{L}_{ff} i_f + \mathcal{L}_{af} i_a)$$ (4-15)

if all the inductances are functions of the angular position θ of the rotor, as indicated by the script letters $\mathcal{L}$.

Inspection of Fig. 4-2 shows that the self-inductance $\mathcal{L}_{ff}$ of the field winding is constant, independent of the angular position of the rotor; i.e.,

$$\mathcal{L}_{ff} = L_{ff} = \text{const}$$ (4-16)

where the italic capital letter L denotes a constant value. The self-inductance $\mathcal{L}_{aa}$ of the rotor and the mutual inductance $\mathcal{L}_{af}$, however, are

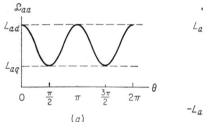
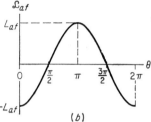

FIG. 4-3. Variation of inductances with angle. (a) Armature self-inductance. (b) Armature-to-field mutual inductance.

dependent on the angle θ between the field and armature axes. For $\theta = 0$ or π, the magnetic axis of the armature is in line with the stator poles. The self-inductance $\mathcal{L}_{aa}$ then has its maximum value, which we shall call L_{ad}, and the mutual inductance $\mathcal{L}_{af}$ also has its maximum absolute value L_{af}. But $\mathcal{L}_{af}$ is negative at $\theta = 0$ and positive at $\theta = \pi$ for the reference directions of Fig. 4-2. At $\theta = \pi/2$ or $3\pi/2$, the self-inductance $\mathcal{L}_{aa}$ has its minimum value L_{aq}, and the mutual inductance $\mathcal{L}_{af} = 0$. These inductances are periodic functions of θ, as shown in Fig. 4-3. In machine theory they are often approximated by the lowest harmonic terms in their Fourier-series expansion; thus

$$\mathcal{L}_{aa} = \frac{L_{ad} + L_{aq}}{2} + \frac{L_{ad} - L_{aq}}{2} \cos 2\theta$$ (4-17)

$$\mathcal{L}_{af} = -L_{af} \cos \theta$$ (4-18)

We shall not use the Fourier-series expansion here, however, because we can evaluate the parameters of interest in d-c machine theory by another method, as follows.

Now consider the effect of a commutator. The brushes always make contact with the coils on the armature winding which are passing through the quadrature axis. The torque and armature voltage therefore can be found from Eqs. 4-13 and 4-14 with $\theta = \pi/2$.

In Eq. 4-13, $d\mathcal{L}_{ff}/d\theta = 0$ because the field self-inductance is constant. Also, at $\theta = \pi/2$, $d\mathcal{L}_{aa}/d\theta = 0$ because $\mathcal{L}_{aa}$ is passing through its minimum value L_{aq}, as shown in Fig. 4-3a. That is, the reluctance torque is zero. Equation 4-13 then reduces to

$$T = i_a i_f \frac{d\mathcal{L}_{af}}{d\theta} \qquad \text{at } \theta = \frac{\pi}{2} \tag{4-19}$$

At $\theta = \pi/2$, the mutual inductance $\mathcal{L}_{af} = 0$, but its derivative has its maximum value. Equation 4-14 then reduces to

$$v_{ta} = r_a i_a + L_{aq} p i_a + i_f \frac{d\mathcal{L}_{af}}{d\theta} \frac{d\theta}{dt} \qquad \text{at } \theta = \frac{\pi}{2} \tag{4-20}$$

We can now evaluate the electromechanical-coupling term by finding the value of $d\mathcal{L}_{af}/d\theta$ at $\theta = \pi/2$. Consider the 2-pole model of Fig. 4-4 with fixed connections to the armature at $\theta = \pi/2$. Now give the con-

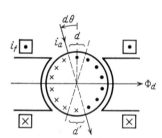

FIG. 4-4. Illustrating calculation of mutual inductance.

nection axis a virtual displacement $d\theta$. The armature conductors within the two belts d and d' (Fig. 4-4) now become the equivalent of a direct-axis armature coil linked by the direct-axis flux Φ_d produced by the field current. For a finely distributed winding with Z_a conductors, the number of conductors included in each belt of width $2\,d\theta$ is

$$\frac{Z_a}{2\pi} 2\,d\theta$$

If there are a parallel paths through the winding, the two belts taken together constitute a winding of

$$\frac{Z_a}{\pi a} d\theta = dN_{ad} \tag{4-21}$$

direct-axis series armature turns. The differential mutual inductance $d\mathcal{L}_{af}$ is the differential flux linkage with the armature per ampere in the field; i.e.,

$$d\mathcal{L}_{af} = dN_{ad} \frac{\Phi_d}{i_f} = \frac{Z_a}{\pi a} \frac{\Phi_d}{i_f} d\theta \tag{4-22}$$

or, at $\theta = \pi/2$,

$$\left. \frac{d\mathcal{L}_{af}}{d\theta} \right|_{\pi/2} = \frac{Z}{\pi a} \frac{\Phi_d}{i_f} = L'_{af} \tag{4-23}$$

With saturation neglected Φ_d is proportional to i_f, and Eq. 4-23 is a constant which we shall designate by the symbol L'_{af}. Substitution in Eq. 4-19 then gives

$$T = \frac{Z_a}{\pi a} \Phi_d i_a = K_a \Phi_d i_a \qquad (4\text{-}24)$$

The speed voltage in Eq. 4-20 is

$$e_a = i_f \frac{d\mathcal{L}_{af}}{d\theta} \frac{d\theta}{dt} = \frac{Z_a}{\pi a} \Phi_d \omega_m = K_a \Phi_d \omega_m \qquad (4\text{-}25)$$

and the armature terminal voltage is

$$v_{ta} = r_a i_a + L_{aq} p i_a + K_a \Phi_d \omega_m \qquad (4\text{-}26)$$

where $K_a = Z_a/\pi a$ and $d\theta/dt = \omega_m$. These equations are identical to Eqs. 4-1, 4-2, and 4-7 for a 2-pole machine.

From Eq. 4-15, the field terminal voltage is

$$v_f = r_f i_f + L_{ff} p i_f + p(\mathcal{L}_{af} i_a) \qquad (4\text{-}27)$$

with L_{ff} constant. This equation can be further simplified if the magnetic effect of the armature is assumed to be identical to that of a stationary coil whose magnetic axis is perpendicular to that of the field winding. For such stationary coils the mutually induced voltage would be zero, and the field voltage would be

$$v_f = r_f i_f + L_{ff} p i_f \qquad (4\text{-}28)$$

as in Eq. 4-6. This equation actually is correct. But if the machine is analyzed as a coupled-circuit device with leads attached to fixed points in the armature winding, the $p(\mathcal{L}_{af} i_a)$ term must be retained, giving

$$v_f = r_f i_f + L_{ff} p i_f + \mathcal{L}_{af} p i_a + i_a \frac{d\mathcal{L}_{af}}{d\theta} \frac{d\theta}{dt} \qquad (4\text{-}29)$$

At $\theta = \pi/2$, $\mathcal{L}_{af} = 0$, but the voltage given by the last term on the right-hand side of Eq. 4-29 is still present, indicating a speed voltage generated in the stationary field winding. What is the explanation of this apparent discrepancy?

The answer is that Eq. 4-29 is correct with leads attached to the rotor but that with brushes in the quadrature axis bearing on a commutator the effect of the currents in the coils undergoing commutation must be taken into account. The armature coils then must be considered in two groups: (1) the active coil sides carrying current i_a and producing a magnetic field along the quadrature axis, and (2) the coils undergoing commutation carrying current i_c and producing a magnetic field along the direct axis. These two groups of coils are indicated in Fig. 4-5, where 2α

is the angular width of the commutating zone (assumed to be relatively narrow). The voltage e_{fa} induced in the field by both groups of coils then is

$$e_{fa} = p(\mathcal{L}_{af}i_a) + p(\mathcal{L}_{cf}i_c)$$

$$= \mathcal{L}_{af}pi_a + i_a\frac{d\mathcal{L}_{af}}{d\theta}\frac{d\theta}{dt} + \mathcal{L}_{cf}pi_e + i_c\frac{d\mathcal{L}_{cf}}{d\theta}\frac{d\theta}{dt} \qquad (4\text{-}30)$$

where $\mathcal{L}_{cf}$ is the mutual inductance between the commutating coils and the field winding. At $\theta = \pi/2$, $\mathcal{L}_{af} = 0$, but its rate of change is a maximum and is given by L'_{af} in Eq. 4-23. In contrast, the magnetic axis of the coils undergoing commutation is along the direct axis. Their mutual inductance with the field winding is a maximum, but its rate of change is

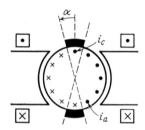

FIG. 4-5. Illustrating effect of commutated coils.

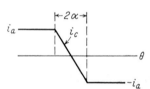

FIG. 4-6. Linear commutation.

zero. From the derivation of Eq. 4-23 it can be seen that the value of $\mathcal{L}_{cf}$ for a narrow commutating zone 2α is

$$\mathcal{L}_{cf} = L'_{af}\alpha \qquad (4\text{-}31)$$

Equation 4-30 then reduces to

$$e_{fa} = L'_{af}i_a\frac{d\theta}{dt} + L'_{af}\alpha\frac{di_c}{dt} \qquad (4\text{-}32)$$

Now assume linear commutation as shown in Fig. 4-6. From this figure

$$\frac{di_c}{d\theta} = -\frac{i_a}{\alpha} \qquad (4\text{-}33)$$

whence

$$\frac{di_c}{dt} = \frac{di_c}{d\theta}\frac{d\theta}{dt} = -\frac{i_a}{\alpha}\frac{d\theta}{dt} \qquad (4\text{-}34)$$

Substitution of Eq. 4-34 in Eq. 4-32 gives

$$e_{fa} = L'_{af}i_a\frac{d\theta}{dt} - L'_{af}i_a\frac{d\theta}{dt} = 0 \qquad (4\text{-}35)$$

Thus, with the assumptions of linear commutation and a narrow commutating zone, the rotational voltage induced in the field winding by the active part of the armature winding is canceled by the transformer voltage induced by the coils undergoing commutation. The field-voltage equation then reduces to Eq. 4-28, just as if the armature winding were a stationary coil in the quadrature axis.

A commutated armature winding with brushes attached to the stator then acts like a quasi-stationary winding—stationary with respect to the stator, but with a speed voltage induced in it by rotation. Although this conclusion may be reached intuitively, it is satisfying to see that dynamic-circuit theory also arrives at the same result when the effects of commutation are taken into account.

4-3. Transfer Functions and Block Diagrams of D-C Machines. In this article we shall consider separately excited d-c machines. In part *a* we shall be concerned primarily with the electrical transients in d-c generators resulting from changes in excitation. In part *b* attention will be focused on the dynamics of d-c motors with constant field excitation. The concepts developed in these two sections are the basis for the analysis of d-c machine systems in the rest of this chapter.

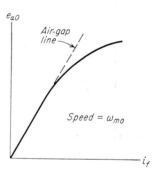

a. D-C   Generators.   Linear   Analysis. Consider the d-c generator of Fig. 4-1*b*, and assume that operation is restricted to the linear portion of the magnetization curve of Fig. 4-7. The inductance of the field winding then is constant, and the voltage equation for the field circuit is

FIG. 4-7. Magnetization curve.

$$v_f = r_f i_f + L_{ff} p i_f = r_f (1 + \tau_f p) i_f \quad (4\text{-}36)$$

where $\tau_f = L_{ff}/r_f$ is the time constant of the field circuit. The transfer function in time variables with v_f as the input and i_f as the output is

$$\frac{i_f}{v_f} = \frac{1}{r_f} \frac{1}{1 + \tau_f p} \quad (4\text{-}37)$$

At magnetization-curve speed ω_{m0} and with operation restricted to the linear range, the armature emf e_{a0} is

$$e_{a0} = K_g i_f \quad \text{or} \quad \frac{e_{a0}}{i_f} = K_g \quad (4\text{-}38)$$

where K_g is the slope of the air-gap line at ω_{m0}. The generated emf e_a at any other speed ω_m is

$$e_a = e_{a0} \frac{\omega_m}{\omega_{m0}} \quad (4\text{-}39)$$

A block-diagram representation of Eqs. 4-37 through 4-39 is shown in Fig. 4-8a with v_f and ω_m as inputs and e_a as an output. An alternative representation is shown in Fig. 4-8b. This form is suitable for use with an analog computer, because it comprises only integrators, summations, and multipliers. (See the discussion following Example 2-11.) By means of Eq. 2-125 it can readily be shown that Fig. 4-8b reduces to Fig. 4-8a.

The armature current i_a is determined by the generated emf e_a and the electrical circuits connected to the armature terminals. The magnetic torque T is then determined by the direct-axis flux and armature current,

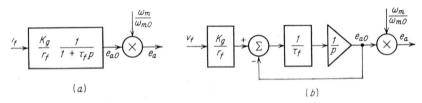

(a)   (b)

FIG. 4-8. Block diagrams representing Eqs. 4-37 to 4-39.

as in Eq. 4-1. From Eq. 3-74, the torque can be expressed in terms of the magnetization curve as

$$T = \frac{e_{a0}}{\omega_{m0}} i_a \qquad (4\text{-}40)$$

The relation between speed and torque is then given by Eq. 4-12 for a generator. The complete performance depends on the electrical and mechanical systems connected to the machine.

Example 4-1. A 200-kw 250-volt d-c generator has the following constants:

$$r_f = 33.7 \text{ ohms} \qquad r_a = 0.0125 \text{ ohm}$$
$$L_{ff} = 25 \text{ henrys} \qquad L_{aq} = 0.008 \text{ henry}$$

The slope of the air-gap line drawn on its magnetization curve at rated speed is

$$K_g = 38 \text{ volts/field amp}$$

The armature circuit is connected to a load having a resistance $R_L = 0.313$ ohm and an inductance $L_L = 1.62$ henrys.

The generator is initially unexcited but rotating at rated speed. A 230-volt d-c source of negligible impedance is suddenly connected to the field terminals. Assume that as the terminal voltage builds up and the generator takes on load its speed does not change appreciably.

Compute and plot a curve of the armature current $i_a(t)$, and investigate the possibilities of simplifying approximations.

Solution. The block diagram is shown in Fig. 4-9a in terms of time variables and in Fig. 4-9b in terms of complex-frequency variables. The first block represents the build-up of generated emf, the second the build-up of armature current, where R_a

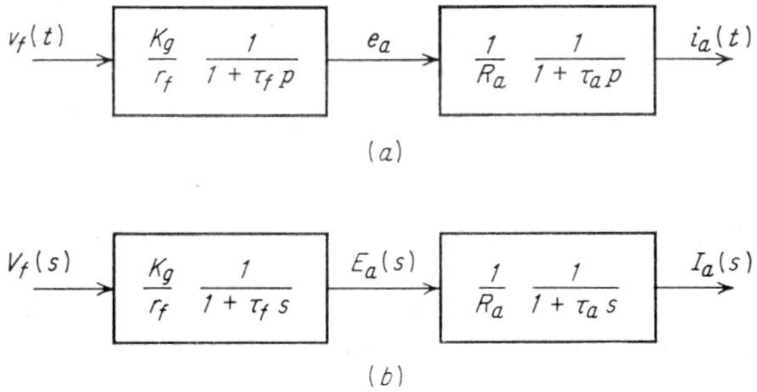

FIG. 4-9. Block diagram, Example 4-1.

and L_a are the total resistance and inductance of the armature and load in series. Because the mutual inductance between armature and field is zero, the output of the second block does not influence the behavior of the first block. Each block represents an exponential term of the form $\epsilon^{-t/\tau}$, where

$$\tau_f = \frac{L_{ff}}{r_f} = \frac{25}{33.7} = 0.74 \text{ sec} \qquad \frac{1}{\tau_f} = 1.35$$

$$\tau_a = \frac{L_a}{R_a} = \frac{L_{aq} + L_L}{r_a + R_L}$$

$$= \frac{1.63}{0.326} = 5 \text{ sec} \qquad \frac{1}{\tau_a} = 0.2$$

The final steady-state value of the generated emf is

$$E_a = \frac{(230)(38)}{33.7} = 260 \text{ volts}$$

and the final steady-state value of the armature current is

$$I_a = \frac{E_a}{R_a} = \frac{260}{0.326} = 800 \text{ amp}$$

The equation for the armature current as a function of time is

$$i_a(t) = 800 + A\epsilon^{-1.35t} + B\epsilon^{-0.2t}$$

with initial conditions

$$i_a(0) = 0 \qquad \text{and} \qquad \frac{di_a}{dt}(0) = 0$$

whence $i_a(t) = 800 + 139\epsilon^{-1.35t} - 939\epsilon^{-0.2t}$

A plot of the current build-up is shown by the solid curve in Fig. 4-10. If the smaller of the two time constants were ignored, the current build-up would be given by

$$i_a(t) = 800 - 800\epsilon^{-0.2t}$$

which is shown by the dashed curve in Fig. 4-10. Comparison of these two curves shows that the shorter of two time lags in series often may be ignored when its time constant is less than about one-quarter of the longer one.

The terminal voltage $v_{ta}(t)$ is

$$v_{ta}(t) = (R_L + L_L p)i_a(t) = 250 - 260\epsilon^{-1.35t} + 10\epsilon^{-0.2t}$$

Compare with the equation for generated emf given by

$$e_a(t) = 260 - 260\epsilon^{-1.35t}$$

An idea of the influence of armature resistance and inductance of this machine, which is typical of d-c generators used as exciters for synchronous generators, can now be gained. Obviously the influence of armature inductance is very small. The principal effect of armature resistance is to reduce the final voltage from 260 volts

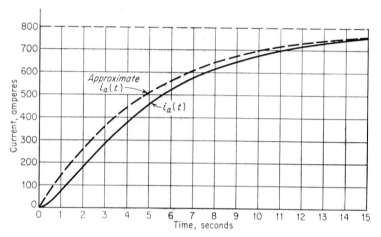

Fig. 4-10. Generator armature-current build-up and an approximation, Example 4-1.

to the 250 volts actually obtained. When this effect is taken into account in interpreting results, it is evidently possible to base many engineering analyses on the assumption of negligible armature resistance and inductance.

In Example 4-1 the generator speed is assumed to be constant. The dynamics of the mechanical drive do not enter into the problem; it is assumed that the drive is capable of delivering whatever mechanical torque is required to hold constant speed. Figure 4-11 shows schematically the components which would have to be added to the block diagram of Fig. 4-8a or b to take into account the dynamics of the mechanical drive. In Fig. 4-11, the first multiplier (reading from left to right) represents Eq. 4-40 for the magnetic torque T. Rearrangement of Eq. 4-12 gives

$$p\omega_m = \frac{T_S - T}{J} \tag{4-41}$$

as shown by the summation and the coefficient multiplier $1/J$, where J is the combined inertia of the generator and drive and T_S is obtained from the transfer function of the drive. Integration then gives ω_m, which becomes an input to the transfer function of the drive and also to the multiplier representing Eq. 4-39 for e_a. Finally i_a, obtained from the transfer function of the electrical load on the generator, is fed back into the first multiplier.

As more and more refinements are added, it can readily be appreciated that a complete system problem can soon become too complex for an analytical solution. For example, in Fig. 4-11 the transfer function of the mechanical drive may involve the transfer function of a mechanical speed governor. Fortunately simplifying approximations usually can be made. Otherwise a computer solution is necessary. The laying out of a block diagram to take into account as many refinements as desired is not especially difficult, however, because it can be constructed piece by piece.

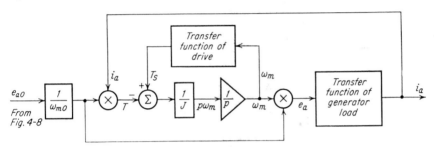

FIG. 4-11. Schematic block diagram for a d-c generator and its mechanical drive.

The block diagram is a preliminary step toward programming the problem for solution on an analog computer.

b. Separately Excited D-C Motors. Direct-current motors are often used in applications requiring precise control of speed and torque output over a wide range. One of the common ways of control is the use of a separately excited motor with constant field excitation. Control is obtained by variation of the voltage applied to the armature terminals. The analysis then involves the dynamics of the mechanical load driven by the motor.

Consider the separately excited motor shown in Fig. 4-12a. At constant field current I_f the magnetic torque and generated emf are given by

$$T = K_m i_a \qquad \text{newton-m} \qquad (4\text{-}42)$$
$$e_a = K_m \omega_m \qquad \text{volts} \qquad (4\text{-}43)$$

where
$$K_m = \frac{E_{a0}}{\omega_{m0}} \qquad (4\text{-}44)$$

with E_{a0} the generated emf corresponding to the field current I_f at the speed ω_{m0} rad/sec. In mks units the constant K_m in newton-meters per ampere (Eq. 4-42) equals the constant K_m in volt-seconds per radian

(Eqs. 4-43 and 4-44). A schematic block diagram is shown in Fig. 4-12b. The armature current i_a is determined by the electrical source connected to the armature terminals and by the generated emf e_a, as indicated by the transfer function of the source with input e_a and output i_a. Multiplication of i_a by K_m gives the motor torque T. Rearrangement of Eq. 4-9 gives

$$p\omega_m = \frac{T - T_L}{J} \tag{4-45}$$

as shown in Fig. 4-12b by the summation and the coefficient multiplier $1/J$, where J is the combined inertia of the motor and load. Integration

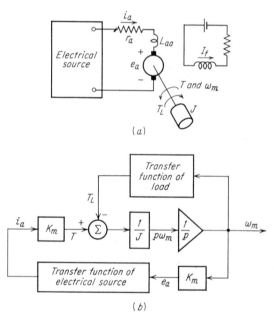

(a)

(b)

FIG. 4-12. (a) Circuit diagram and (b) block diagram of a separately excited d-c motor.

then gives the speed ω_m, which becomes an input to the transfer function (torque-speed characteristic) of the load. Multiplication of ω_m by K_m gives e_a, which is fed back as an input to the transfer function of the electrical source. In order to find the system performance, the specific details of the electrical source and mechanical load must be known.

Example 4-2. A separately excited d-c motor is directly coupled mechanically to a load. The combined inertia of the motor and load is J in mks units. The armature resistance is r_a, and armature inductance is negligible.

a. Derive the differential equation for the motor speed $\omega_m(t)$ in terms of the armature terminal voltage v_{ta} and load torque T_L as independent variables.

b. Draw the corresponding block diagram.

c. Find an equivalent electrical circuit.

d. With the motor initially at rest and $T_L = 0$, a constant d-c voltage source V_{ta} is suddenly impressed on the armature terminals. Find an expression for $\omega_m(t)$.

e. After the motor has reached its steady-state no-load speed, a constant load torque T_L is suddenly applied to its shaft. Find an expression for the change in speed $\Delta\omega_m(t)$.

f. Now consider that the motor drives a load whose torque is proportional to speed; that is, $T_L = K_L\omega_m$. The motor is initially at rest. Find the response to a suddenly applied d-c voltage V_{ta}.

g. Indicate the changes which would be made in the analysis if the load were coupled to the motor shaft through gears reducing the speed by the factor k_G. The motor armature inertia is J_m, and the load inertia is J_L. The friction and inertia of the gears themselves may be neglected.

Solution. The differential equations are

$$v_{ta} = e_a + r_a i_a = K_m\omega_m + r_a i_a \qquad (4\text{-}46)$$
$$T = K_m i_a = Jp\omega_m + T_L \qquad (4\text{-}47)$$

where all quantities are in mks units.

a. Elimination of i_a from these equations and rearrangement of the terms so as to separate the independent variables gives

$$v_{ta} - \frac{r_a}{K_m} T_L = \frac{J r_a}{K_m}\frac{d\omega_m}{dt} + K_m\omega_m \qquad (4\text{-}48)$$

or, after division by K_m,

$$\frac{v_{ta}}{K_m} - \frac{r_a}{K_m^2} T_L = \tau_m \frac{d\omega_m}{dt} + \omega_m \qquad (4\text{-}49)$$

where

$$\tau_m = \frac{J r_a}{K_m^2} \qquad (4\text{-}50)$$

The transient behavior is described by a steady state plus a decaying exponential with a *time constant* τ_m given by Eq. 4-50. The complete solution depends on the impressed voltage and load torque.

b. Equations 4-46 and 4-47 can be expressed as

$$i_a = \frac{v_{ta} - e_a}{r_a} \qquad (4\text{-}51)$$

$$p\omega_m = \frac{T - T_L}{J} \qquad (4\text{-}52)$$

with $e_a = K_m\omega_m$ and $T = K_m i_a$. The block diagram is shown in Fig. 4-13.

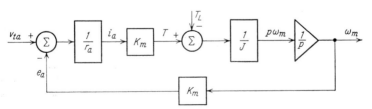

Fig. 4-13. Block diagram of a separately excited d-c motor with negligible armature inductance.

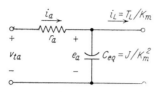

FIG. 4-14. Equivalent circuit of a separately excited d-c motor with negligible armature inductance.

c. Division of Eq. 4-47 by K_m and substitution of $\omega_m = e_a/K_m$ in the result gives

$$i_a = \frac{J}{K_m^2}\frac{de_a}{dt} + \frac{T_L}{K_m} = C_{eq}\frac{de_a}{dt} + i_L \qquad (4\text{-}53)$$

The equivalent circuit representing Eqs. 4-46 and 4-53 is shown in Fig. 4-14, where

$$C_{eq} = \frac{J}{K_m^2} \quad \text{and} \quad i_L = \frac{T_L}{K_m} \qquad (4\text{-}54)$$

Notice the similarity to the equivalent circuit of a transducer for linear incremental motion (Fig. 2-14).

d. From the equivalent circuit (Fig. 4-14), the build-up of voltage across the capacitor is

$$e_a(t) = V_{ta}(1 - \epsilon^{-t/\tau_m}) \qquad (4\text{-}55)$$

The speed is

$$\omega_m(t) = \frac{e_a(t)}{K_m} = \frac{V_{ta}}{K_m}(1 - \epsilon^{-t/\tau_m}) \qquad (4\text{-}56)$$

where

$$\frac{V_{ta}}{K_m} = \omega_m(\infty) \qquad (4\text{-}57)$$

is the final steady-state no-load speed. The same result can be obtained directly from the differential equation 4-49, with the specified initial and final conditions. It can also be found from the block diagram shown in Fig. 4-15a, obtained from Fig.

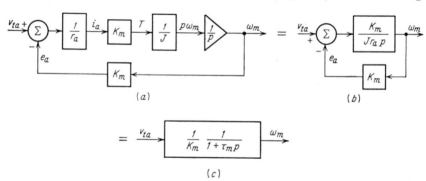

FIG. 4-15. Block diagram of a separately excited d-c motor with negligible armature inductance and load torque.

4-13 with $T_L = 0$. Successive steps in the reduction of the block diagram are shown in Fig. 4-15b and *c*. For a step input of voltage with initial rest conditions, Fig. 4-15c represents the exponential build-up given by Eq. 4-56.

e. Since the system is linear, the change in speed $\Delta\omega_m(t)$ can be found by superposition, considering the motor to be initially at rest with $v_{ta} = 0$, i.e., with the armature terminals short-circuited. From Eq. 4-49 with $v_{ta} = 0$, the final change in speed is

$$-\frac{r_a}{K_m^2}T_L$$

The complete solution is the final value plus an exponential decay, or

$$\Delta\omega_m(t) = -\frac{r_a}{K_m^2} T_L(1 - \epsilon^{-t/\tau_m}) \tag{4-58}$$

By superposition, the actual speed is the no-load speed plus the change, or

$$\omega_m(t) = \frac{V_{ta}}{K_m} - \frac{r_a T_L}{K_m^2}(1 - \epsilon^{-t/\tau_m}) \tag{4-59}$$

The same result can be obtained from the equivalent circuit (Fig. 4-14). Here a current source i_L suddenly applied in the arrow direction is equivalent to the step of load torque. The block-diagram technique with $v_{ta} = 0$ will also give the same result as Eq. 4-58.

   f. Here the load torque is not an independent variable. Substitution of $T_L = K_L\omega_m$ in Eq. 4-48 and rearrangement of the result gives

$$v_{ta} = \frac{Jr_a}{K_m}\frac{d\omega_m}{dt} + \left(K_m + \frac{K_L r_a}{K_m}\right)\omega_m \tag{4-60}$$

or

$$\frac{v_{ta}}{K_m + K_L r_a/K_m} = \frac{Jr_a}{K_m^2 + K_L r_a}\frac{d\omega_m}{dt} + \omega_m \tag{4-61}$$

For a step input V_{ta} and initial rest conditions, Eq. 4-61 can be seen to describe an exponential rise

$$\omega_m(t) = \omega_m'(\infty)(1 - \epsilon^{-t/\tau_m'}) \tag{4-\ }$$

where the final steady-state speed is

$$\omega_m'(\infty) = \frac{V_{ta}}{K_m + K_L r_a/K_m} \tag{4-63}$$

and the time constant is

$$\tau_m' = \frac{Jr_a}{K_m^2 + K_L r_a} \tag{4-64}$$

The ... dy-state speed $\omega_m'(\infty)$ is, of course, less than the no-load speed $\omega_m(\infty)$ (Eq. 4-57). The v... constant τ_m' also is less than the no-load time constant τ_m (Eq. 4-50) because of the ...ing effect of the load.

   The solution can also be found from the equivalent circuit or the block diagram. In the equivalent circuit a linear load-torque–speed characteristic is accounted for by the addition of a resistor R_L connected across the capacitor C_{eq} of Fig. 4-14. From Eqs. 4-43 and 4-54 the value of this resistor is

$$R_L = \frac{e_a}{i_L} = \frac{K_m\omega_m}{T_L/K_m} = \frac{K_m^2\omega_m}{K_L\omega_m} = \frac{K_m^2}{K_L} \tag{4-65}$$

Compare with Eq. 2-115 for a transducer. In the block diagram of Fig. 4-13 the torque-speed characteristic is accounted for by the addition of a feedback $K_L\omega_m$ from the output ω_m to the input T_L. Reduction of the circuit or the block diagram by the usual techniques will give the same result as Eq. 4-62.

   g. For the simple gear train of Fig. 4-16, the basic relations for ideal gears are

$$\omega_1 = k_G\omega_2 \quad \text{and} \quad T_1 = \frac{1}{k_G}T_2 \tag{4-66}$$

To accelerate inertia J_2 requires the torque $T_2 = J_2 p\omega_2$ on shaft 2 and hence the corresponding torque

$$T_1 = \frac{J_2}{k_G}\frac{d\omega_2}{dt} = \frac{J_2}{k_G^2}\frac{d\omega_1}{dt} \qquad (4\text{-}67)$$

on shaft 1. Consequently the system of Fig. 4-16a may be replaced by that of Fig. 4-16b without changing conditions at shaft 1 provided that

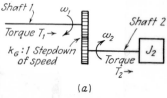

(a)

(b)

FIG. 4-16. (a) Two shafts coupled by gears and (b) the equivalent system as viewed from the first shaft.

$$J_1 = \frac{J_2}{k_G^2} \qquad (4\text{-}68)$$

Equations 4-66 and 4-68 give the load speed, torque, and inertia referred to the motor shaft, with subscript 1 indicating the motor shaft and subscript 2 the load shaft. The total inertia referred to the motor shaft is

$$J = J_m + \frac{J_L}{k_G^2} \qquad (4\text{-}69)$$

Insertion of the gear train is evidently equivalent to insertion of an ideal transformer in the equivalent circuit.

4-4. Basic Motor Speed Control Systems.

The outstanding characteristic of a d-c motor is its adaptability to control of its torque and speed. From Eqs. 3-68, 3-72, and 3-79, the steady-state output characteristics are given by

$$T = K_a \Phi_d I_a \qquad (4\text{-}70)$$

and

$$\omega_m = \frac{V_{ta} - I_a r_a}{K_a \Phi_d} \qquad (4\text{-}71)$$

where the capital letters I_a and V_{ta} are the steady-state values of the armature current and terminal voltage, respectively, and K_a is a constant fixed by the design of the armature winding. These equations, together with the magnetization curve and method of excitation of the field windings, determine the built-in torque-speed characteristics described in Art. 3-8.

When these inherent characteristics do not provide the desired result, control of the torque and speed can be obtained by variation of any of the four quantities r_a, Φ_d, I_a, and V_{ta}. In this article the first three methods will be discussed briefly. Emphasis will be given to the fourth method, because of its widespread use in control systems.

1. *Armature-resistance Control.* The speed may be reduced for a given torque by insertion of an adjustable resistance in series with the armature circuit. This method is commonly used for starting or for short-time or

intermittent slowdowns. One of its disadvantages is the power loss in the resistor. Further discussion is given in Art. 8-5.

2. *Constant Armature Voltage, Controlled Field Excitation.* This method is simple and satisfactory for speed control of a shunt or compound motor over a speed range of about 4 or 5 to 1. The field excitation is controlled by variation of the voltage applied to the field circuit or by means of an adjustable resistor in series with the shunt field. The power loss in the resistor is relatively small, because the field current is small compared with the armature current. The maximum permissible torque is limited by the permissible armature current and the maximum flux. The latter is limited by magnetic saturation or by heating of the field winding. The maximum torque occurs at the minimum speed. The maximum speed is determined by commutation and mechanical considerations. Further discussion is given in Art. 8-5.

The dynamic equations are nonlinear because they contain products of the variables. For small changes, the equations can be linearized by the techniques discussed in Art. 2-5a.

3. *Constant Armature Current, Controlled Field Excitation.* The chief obstacle to more widespread use of this method seems to be the constant armature-current source. Voltage sources are more commonly available. This method has been exploited more in Europe than in the United States.

4. *Constant Field Current, Controlled Armature Voltage.* This system is the most commonly used when manual or automatic control of speed is required over a wide range in both directions of rotation. The controlled armature voltage may be obtained from controlled rectifiers receiving input power from an a-c source, or it may come from a separately excited d-c generator. Because of its special importance, the following discussion is devoted to study of the separately excited generator-and-motor system, commonly called the *Ward Leonard system.* It is the basic scheme for a wide variety of feedback control systems.

The basic system is shown diagrammatically in Fig. 4-17a. The generator is assumed to be driven at constant speed ω_g. Its field is separately excited from a voltage source v_{fg}. The motor is separately excited with constant field current I_{fm}. The combined resistance of the generator and motor armature circuits in series is R_a. Usually the armature inductances are negligible. They are omitted in Fig. 4-17a.

A block diagram of the system is shown in Fig. 4-17b with generator-field voltage v_{fg} and motor load torque T_L as inputs and motor speed ω_m as the output. This block diagram results from combining the generator diagram (Fig. 4-8b) (at constant generator speed ω_{m0}) with the motor diagram (Fig. 4-13). In Fig. 4-17b the subscript g refers to the generator and subscript m to the motor. The generator emf e_{ag} is the input to the armature circuit comprising the combined resistance R_a of the two armatures in series. The diagram can readily be modified to take into account the variables neglected in Fig. 4-17b. For example, the speed-torque characteristics of the generator drive and the motor load can be included as indicated schematically in Figs. 4-11 and 4-12b. The armature-circuit inductance can be included by insertion of a time lag between the output of the block K_m/R_a and the input T to the torque summation.

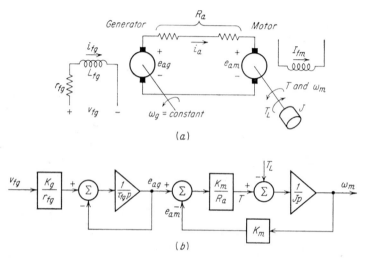

FIG. 4-17. (a) Circuit diagram and (b) block diagram of an adjustable-armature-voltage, or Ward Leonard, system of speed control.

Instead of additional complications it is often possible to make further simplifying approximations, as shown in Example 4-3.

Example 4-3. A d-c generator and a d-c motor have their armatures directly connected electrically to form a Ward Leonard system. The generator is driven at a constant speed, and the motor field is excited by a constant current. The magnetization curve of the generator is assumed to be linear. The motor is rated at 3 hp and has the following characteristics:

Armature resistance = 0.75 ohm
Inertia of motor plus load = 40 lb-ft²
Torque per unit armature current = 0.92 lb-ft/amp
Armature inductance negligible

The generator is of a size consistent with supplying the 3-hp motor and has the following characteristics:

Armature resistance = 0.25 ohm
Field resistance = 200 ohms
Field inductance = 10 henrys
Generated voltage per unit field current = 1,500 volts/amp
Armature inductance negligible

Initially the generator is running but is unexcited, and the motor is excited but stationary. The load torque is negligible.

a. A constant voltage of 36.6 volts is suddenly impressed on the generator field at $t = 0$. Find the motor speed $\omega_m(t)$ as a function of time. Approximations are permissible.

b. Find the time for the speed to reach 98 per cent of its final value.

c. After the motor has reached its final speed, a step of load torque of 8 lb-ft is suddenly applied to the motor at $t = 0$. Find the speed $\omega_m(t)$.

Solution. With $T_L = 0$, the block diagram of Fig. 4-17b reduces to Fig. 4-18a, where $\tau_m = JR_a/K_m^2$, as in Example 4-2. All quantities must be in mks units. From the data and the conversion table following Appendix C,

$$J = \frac{40}{23.7} = 1.69 \text{ kg-m}^2 \qquad R_a = 0.75 + 0.25 = 1.00 \text{ ohm}$$

$$K_m = \frac{0.92}{0.738} = 1.25 \text{ newton-m/amp or volt-sec/radian}$$

$$\tau_m = \frac{(1.69)(1.00)}{(1.25)^2} = 1.08 \text{ sec} \qquad \tau_{fg} = \frac{10}{200} = 0.05 \text{ sec}$$

a. The block diagram represents two time lags in cascade. But the generator-field time constant τ_{fg} is very much less than the motor-plus-inertia time constant τ_m.

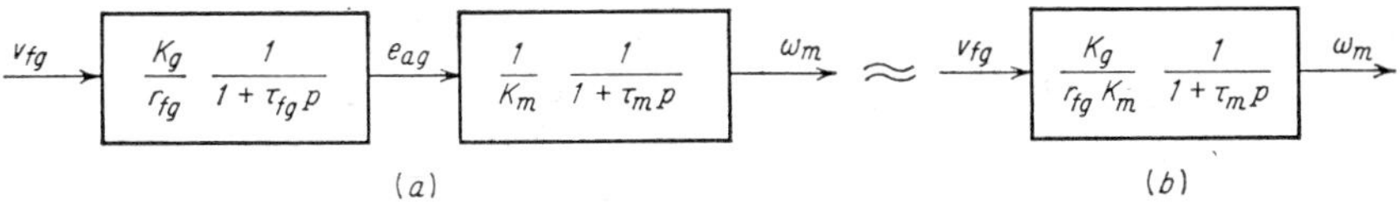

FIG. 4-18. Block diagram of Ward Leonard system with $T_L = 0$.

Therefore the generator-field time lag can be neglected with very little error; i.e., the generated emf e_{ag} builds up so rapidly that its effect in the armature circuit is almost that of a step change, and the block diagram reduces to Fig. 4-18b. For a step input $v_{fg} = 36.6$ volts, this transfer function represents an exponential build-up to a final value

$$\omega_m(\infty) = \frac{(36.6)(1,500)}{(200)(1.25)} = 219 \text{ rad/sec}$$

or

$$\omega_m(t) = 219(1 - \epsilon^{-t/1.08})$$

b. A simple exponential will decay to 0.0183, or approximately 2 per cent of its final value, in a time equal to four time constants. For the motor to come up to 98 per cent of its final speed then requires about $(4)(1.08)$, or 4.3 sec.

c. As in part *e* of Example 4-2, the decrease in speed caused by a suddenly applied step of load torque is

$$\Delta\omega_m(\infty) = \frac{T_L R_a}{K_m^2}$$

For $T_L = 8/0.738 = 10.8$ newton-m

$$\Delta\omega_m(\infty) = \frac{(10.8)(1.00)}{(1.25)^2} = 6.9 \text{ rad/sec}$$

The change is an exponential with time constant τ_m. Therefore the speed is

$$\omega_m(t) = 219 - 6.9(1 - \epsilon^{-t/1.08})$$
$$= 212 + 7\epsilon^{-t/1.08}$$

4-5. Feedback Control Systems: Introductory Aspects. As stated in the opening paragraph of this book, susceptibility to control is one of the outstanding characteristics of electrical systems. When high precision, stability, and speed of response are important specifications, the controller must be furnished with a measure of the actual performance—in other words, a feedback control system must be employed. The theory of feedback control has been developed to a high degree of accuracy, and numerous textbooks and technical papers are available covering the broad subject.[1] This article presents a brief qualitative summary of the basic principles with specific reference to control of electric-machine output.

Machine output, in the control sense, refers to more than simply the mechanical power delivered by the shaft of a motor or the electrical power delivered by a generator, although the power output is controlled in accomplishing other desired results. Among the more significant machine quantities over which control may be exercised are:

1. *Speed.* Accurate control of speed over a wide range (and sometimes coordination with the speed of other motors) is a common requirement. Papermaking machines and some steel-mill drives are examples.

2. *Torque.* An example of need for control of torque is the winding and unwinding of continuous material on reels, where a constant winding tension is required.

3. *Position.* Automatic positioning of a machine cutting tool for the next cut is an example of controlling the angular position of a shaft or the linear position of an object geared to it. The tracking of aircraft or missiles by radar and the automatic direction of defense missiles in accordance with the directions received from the radar signals are other examples.

4. *Acceleration.* Controlled acceleration may be required during the transition from one speed to another in a coordinated drive.

5. *Voltage.* Maintenance of a constant generator terminal voltage is an obvious example.

6. *Frequency.* The necessity of turbine-governor control to maintain constant frequency in electric supply systems is also an obvious one.

A certain degree of control over performance is, of course, inherent in

[1] For example, see G. S. Brown and D. P. Campbell, "Principles of Servomechanisms," John Wiley & Sons, Inc., New York, 1948; G. J. Thaler and R. G. Brown, "Analysis and Design of Feedback Control Systems," 2d ed., McGraw-Hill Book Company, Inc., New York, 1960; H. Chestnut and R. W. Mayer, "Servomechanisms and Regulating System Design," John Wiley & Sons, Inc., New York, vol. I, 2d ed., 1959, vol. II, 1955; R. A. Bruns and R. M. Saunders, "Analysis of Feedback Control Systems," McGraw-Hill Book Company, Inc., New York, 1955; J. G. Truxal, "Automatic Feedback Control System Synthesis," McGraw-Hill Book Company, Inc., New York, 1955.

the basic machine characteristics when the most suitable type of machine is chosen. A synchronous motor, for example, produces a single constant speed regardless of load without the use of external regulating devices. Or when the degree of compounding is appropriately adjusted, a d-c compound motor is capable of producing inherently a wide range of speed decreases with load. When the desired behavior becomes more complex and the performance standards more exacting, however, sufficient versatility is not provided by the machine characteristics alone: a control system must be added. Even with external control, judicious appraisal of machine characteristics is essential to minimize the duty on the controlling mechanism and to make the desired response as spontaneous as possible.

In devising an electrical control scheme, an electrical quantity must be selected whose value is a measure of the actual performance feature to be controlled, and this quantity or its deviation from an established ideal must actuate the controlling mechanism in a prescribed fashion. The type of control and its degree of reliance on inherent motor characteristics depend on the precision required. Two types of control are recognized: *open-cycle control*, in which actuation of the control mechanism is substantially independent of the actual performance of the controlled device; and *closed-cycle, closed-loop*, or *feedback control*, in which actuation of the control mechanism is affected by the performance of the controlled device.

Suppose, for example, that it is desired to maintain constant speed at any preset value and that a d-c shunt motor with fixed field excitation and adjustable armature voltage is selected. If the inherent speed regulation of a shunt motor constitutes satisfactory fulfillment of the requirements, the problem is simply one of maintaining the armature terminal voltage constant at any preset value, for this voltage is a reasonably close measure of speed at constant field current. If the inherent regulation of the motor is not good enough, armature-resistance-drop compensation may be added to the voltage regulator, an addition which means making the regulator responsive to armature current to the extent that it increases the voltage enough to compensate the increased armature-resistance drop with load. The armature induced emf is thereby kept substantially constant, resulting in closer speed regulation. So far as motor speed is concerned, however, both methods are open-cycle control schemes, for the actual motor speed is not measured, and the controller is presented with no direct information indicating whether it is performing its function properly. Accurate attainment of the specified set speed demands that the characteristics of all equipment interposed between the setting dial and the final motor shaft remain absolutely fixed at the values for which the control scheme is designed or adjusted. The effects of such disturbances as temperature changes, hysteresis, armature reaction, changing tube characteristics (if an electronic method is used), and supply voltages all may cause significant inaccuracies.

When these extraneous influences are to be circumvented and precise control of motor speed obtained, the actual speed may be measured in terms of the voltage of a pilot generator coupled to the motor shaft and the difference between this voltage and one proportional to the desired speed may be used to actuate the controller in such fashion as to tend to eliminate the error.   Closed-cycle control is thereby achieved.

The broad general features of closed-cycle control may be seen from the schematic diagram of Fig. 4-19.   The output quantity to be controlled is designated as C.   The input signal, or reference, R presents data specifying the desired performance.   The input U represents an *uncontrolled* quantity, or *upset*, such as the electrical load on a generator or the mechanical load on a motor.   The feedback link and error detector

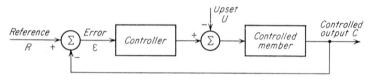

FIG. 4-19. Schematic block diagram of a feedback control system.

enable comparison of actual performance C with desired performance R; if an error ε exists, the controller acts accordingly to correct the discrepancy.   These general features may be recognized as having much in common with feedback amplifiers, and many of the analytical details will be found to be identical.   Closed-cycle control systems are sometimes subdivided into two classes.   When the input signal R remains substantially constant or is subjected to only relatively slow changes, the system is classed as a *regulator;* the main object of a regulator is to prevent extraneous effects from influencing the output quantity C.   A generator-voltage regulator is an example.   When the input signal R changes rapidly, the system is classed as a *servomechanism;* the main object of a servomechanism is to cause the output quantity C to follow R as faithfully as possible.

The controlling signal usually results from a low-power-level electrical-measurement process.   Position, for instance, may be indicated by the output of a phototube scanning the driven object or by arranging a capacitance, inductance, or resistance (such as a potentiometer) to be affected by position.   Synchros or selsyns described in Art. 6-10 are often used.   Because of the low power level of both R and the measurement of C fed back, power amplification is one essential function of the controller. The components downstream from the error signal ε must be designed to handle the power as well as the signal flow through the system.   Amplification is obtained by electronic, electromagnetic, or hydraulic means or by a combination in cascade.   The chain of events starting with the measurement of actual performance and passing through the entire cycle of amplification and control in any particular case can be followed by superposing the characteristics of each element.   This superposition must be one of dynamic characteristics, however, for stability of operation, speed of response, and freedom from oscillations are closely related problems of determining importance.

4-6. Examples of Feedback Systems Using D-C Machines.   In order to illustrate the application of feedback control to electric machines, a series of examples will be presented in this article.   For any specific

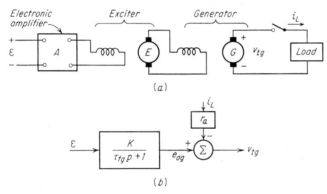

FIG. 4-20. Open-loop voltage regulation of a d-c generator.   (a) Schematic circuit diagram.   (b) Block diagram.

application, a variety of possibilities exists.   Only enough examples will be given, however, to indicate the general principles, with particular emphasis on the treatment of d-c machines as system components.[1]   Additional refinements may be necessary to achieve the desired rapidity of dynamic response with minimum error, and stabilizing arrangements may be required.   The object of this article is simply to provide an introduction to the subject.

a. An Elementary Generator-voltage Regulator.   Regulation of generator voltage is the process of controlling the voltage so that it remains at or near a particular set value.   In order to show some of the basic properties of feedback systems, a comparison of open-loop and closed-loop control will be given, with voltage regulation of a d-c generator used as a specific example.

First consider the elementary open-loop system shown in Fig. 4-20a.

[1] For a much more complete treatment, see A. Tustin, "Direct Current Machines for Control Systems," The Macmillan Company, New York, 1952.

The output voltage v_{t_g} of the generator can be controlled manually by setting the input voltage ε to the amplifier. On the assumption that all the components are linear, the internal emf e_{a_g} of the generator is proportional to the amplifier input voltage ε under steady-state conditions. Dynamically, however, the response lags the input, the most important time lag being that introduced by the generator-field inductance. On the assumption that time lags in the amplifier and exciter field are negligible, the differential equation relating amplifier input voltage ε to generator emf e_{a_g} is

$$K\varepsilon = (\tau_{f_g}p + 1)e_{a_g} \qquad (4\text{-}72)$$

where K is the over-all steady-state voltage gain and τ_{f_g} is the generator field-circuit time constant. The transfer function relating generator emf to amplifier input voltage is

$$\frac{e_{a_g}}{\varepsilon} = \frac{K}{\tau_{f_g}p + 1} \qquad (4\text{-}73)$$

On the further assumption that the generator armature inductance is negligible, the terminal voltage v_{t_g} of the generator is

$$v_{t_g} = e_{a_g} - i_L r_a \qquad (4\text{-}74)$$

where i_L is the load current and r_a is the generator armature resistance. The block diagram is shown in Fig. 4-20b with ε and i_L as inputs and v_{t_g} as the output.

Figure 4-21a shows the system of Fig. 4-20a modified by the addition of negative feedback. Here, the reference voltage E_R is obtained from a constant-voltage source and an adjustable potentiometer. The input voltage ε to the amplifier now is

$$\varepsilon = E_R - v_{t_g} \qquad (4\text{-}75)$$

The differential equation relating ε to e_{a_g} is still given by the open-loop equation 4-72 and the terminal voltage by Eq. 4-74. The block diagram is shown in Fig. 4-21b.

Now consider the responses of the two systems to changes in the inputs. Since the systems are linear, the responses can be found by considering the effect of each input by itself. By superposition, the resultant output is the sum of the initial value plus the change.

First consider the response of the open-loop system (Fig. 4-20) to a step change $\Delta\varepsilon$ of the input voltage with $i_L = 0$. From Eq. 4-72 or the block diagram, the final value of the change in terminal voltage is

$$\Delta v_{t_g}(\infty) = \Delta e_{a_g}(\infty) = K \Delta\varepsilon \qquad (4\text{-}76)$$

The transient adjustment is an exponential term Ae^{st}, where s is the

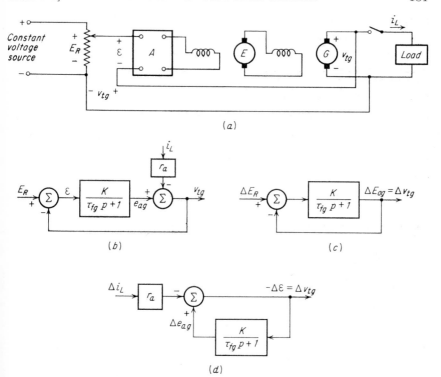

Fig. 4-21. Elementary closed-loop voltage regulation of a d-c generator. (a) Schematic circuit diagram. (b to d) Block diagrams.

natural frequency of the system found from the equation

$$0 = \tau_{fg}s + 1 \qquad (4\text{-}77)$$

or from the pole

$$\frac{1}{\tau_{fg}s + 1} = \infty \qquad (4\text{-}78)$$

of the transfer function (Eq. 4-73). From Eq. 4-77 or 4-78,

$$s = -\frac{1}{\tau_{fg}} \qquad (4\text{-}79)$$

When combined with the initial condition $\Delta e_{ag}(0+) = 0$, the result is the well-known equation

$$\Delta v_{tg} = \Delta e_{ag} = \Delta \mathcal{E} K(1 - \epsilon^{-t/\tau_{fg}}) \qquad (4\text{-}80)$$

The effect on the open-loop system of a step increase Δi_L in load current is very simple. On the assumption of negligible armature-circuit inductance and constant input voltage $\mathcal{E}$, the terminal voltage falls instantaneously by an amount

$$\Delta v_{tg} = -\Delta i_L r_a \qquad \text{or} \qquad \frac{\Delta v_{tg}}{\Delta i_L} = -r_a \tag{4-81}$$

Now consider the closed-loop system of Fig. 4-21. With $i_L = 0$, the response to a change ΔE_R in reference voltage is

$$\Delta \mathcal{E} = \Delta E_R - \Delta v_{tg} = \Delta E_R - \Delta e_{ag} \tag{4-82}$$

with $\Delta \mathcal{E}$ related to Δe_{ag} by the differential equation 4-72 or the open-loop transfer function (Eq. 4-73). Substitution of this relation in Eq. 4-82 gives

$$\frac{\tau_{fg} p + 1}{K} \Delta e_{ag} = \Delta E_R - \Delta e_{ag} \tag{4-83}$$

Algebraic manipulation then gives the differential equation

$$K \Delta E_R = (\tau_{fg} p + 1 + K) \Delta e_{ag} \tag{4-84}$$

or, after division by $1 + K$,

$$\frac{K}{1 + K} \Delta E_R = \left(\frac{\tau_{fg}}{1 + K} p + 1 \right) \Delta e_{ag} \tag{4-85}$$

The transfer function relating output Δe_{ag} (or Δv_{tg}) to input ΔE_R is

$$\frac{\Delta e_{ag}}{\Delta E_R} = \frac{\Delta v_{tg}}{\Delta E_R} = \frac{K}{1 + K} \frac{1}{[\tau_{fg}/(1 + K)]p + 1} \tag{4-86}$$

The same result can be obtained from the block diagram (Fig. 4-21c) by means of Eq. 2-125. From the differential equation 4-85, the natural frequency s is given by

$$\frac{\tau_{fg}}{1 + K} s + 1 = 0 \tag{4-87}$$

or by the pole of the transfer function

$$\frac{1}{[\tau_{fg}/(1 + K)]s + 1} = \infty \tag{4-88}$$

It is

$$s = -\frac{1}{\tau'_{fg}} \tag{4-89}$$

where

$$\tau'_{fg} = \frac{\tau_{fg}}{1 + K} \tag{4-90}$$

The response to a step input ΔE_R with initial rest conditions is

$$\Delta v_{tg} = \Delta e_{ag} = \frac{\Delta E_R K}{1 + K} (1 - \epsilon^{-t/\tau'_{fg}}) \tag{4-91}$$

The response of the closed-loop system to a change Δi_L in load current can be found by superposition with $E_R = 0$. Equation 4-75 then reduces to

$$\Delta \varepsilon = -\Delta v_{tg} = -\Delta e_{ag} + \Delta i_L \, r_a \tag{4-92}$$

Substitution of Eq. 4-72 for $\Delta \varepsilon$ gives

$$\frac{\tau_{fg}p + 1}{K} \Delta e_{ag} = -\Delta e_{ag} + \Delta i_L \, r_a \tag{4-93}$$

or, after separation of the variables and multiplication by $K/(1 + K)$,

$$\frac{\Delta i_L \, r_a K}{1 + K} = \left(\frac{\tau_{fg}}{1 + K} p + 1 \right) \Delta e_{ag} = (\tau'_{fg}p + 1) \, \Delta e_{ag} \tag{4-94}$$

where τ'_{fg} is given by Eq. 4-90. Substitution of $\Delta e_{ag} = \Delta v_{tg} + \Delta i_L \, r_a$ in Eq. 4-94 and rearrangement of the terms gives

$$(\tau_{fg}p + 1) \frac{\Delta i_L \, r_a}{1 + K} = -\left(\frac{\tau_{fg}p}{1 + K} + 1 \right) \Delta v_{tg} \tag{4-95}$$

The transfer function is

$$\frac{\Delta v_{tg}}{\Delta i_L} = -\frac{r_a}{1 + K} \frac{\tau_{fg}p + 1}{\tau'_{fg}p + 1} \tag{4-96}$$

The same result can be obtained by reduction of the block diagram (Fig. 4-21d), with $E_R = 0$.

For a step increase Δi_L in load current with E_R constant and armature inductance neglected, the terminal voltage falls instantaneously by an amount

$$\Delta v_{tg}(0+) = -\Delta i_L \, r_a \tag{4-97}$$

because e_{ag} cannot change suddenly. This initial drop applies a large corrective error voltage to the amplifier. The generated emf then builds up exponentially in accordance with the solution of Eq. 4-94; thus

$$\Delta e_{ag}(t) = \frac{\Delta i_L \, r_a K}{1 + K} (1 - \epsilon^{-t/\tau_{fg}'}) \tag{4-98}$$

The change in terminal voltage is

$$\Delta v_{tg}(t) = -\frac{\Delta i_L \, r_a}{1 + K} (1 + K\epsilon^{-t/\tau_{fg}'}) \tag{4-99}$$

Examination of the transfer functions (Eqs. 4-86 and 4-96) and comparison with the open-loop responses (Eqs. 4-73 and 4-81) show several important characteristics of feedback systems. (1) The time constant

τ'_{fg} (Eq. 4-90) of the closed-loop system is smaller than that of the open-loop system; therefore the closed-loop system recovers more rapidly from the effects of disturbances. (2) The over-all gain of the closed-loop system is reduced. In other words, the input E_R to the closed-loop system must be $1 + K$ times the input ε to the open-loop system to produce the same output e_{ag}. Note, however, that the ratio of gain to time constant is the same for both systems. (3) The closed-loop system is less sensitive to load disturbances than the open-loop system. (4) Finally, the closed-loop system is much less sensitive to changes in the characteristics of the components due to heating or other extraneous influences. Some of these features are illustrated in Example 4-4.

Example 4-4. In the elementary voltage-regulation systems of Figs. 4-20 and 4-21, the amplifier A can be considered as a linear element with a voltage amplification factor μ and plate resistance r_p, where

$$\mu = 10 \qquad r_p = 1,000 \text{ ohms}$$

The exciter E has the following constants:
  Field resistance $r_{fe} = 1,000$ ohms
  Field inductance $L_{fe} = 40$ henrys
  Generated-voltage constant $K_e = 2,000$ volts/field amp
  Armature resistance and inductance negligible
The generator G is rated at 5 kw, 240 volts, and has the following constants:
  Field resistance $r_{fg} = 200$ ohms
  Field inductance $L_{fg} = 100$ henrys
  Generated-voltage constant $K_g = 480$ volts/field amp
  Armature resistance $r_a = 0.72$ ohm
  Armature inductance negligible
  a. Compute numerical values of the over-all system voltage gain K and open-loop time constant τ_{fg}. Show that the exciter field-circuit time constant is negligible.
  b. Compute the input voltage ε to the amplifier for 240 volts output of the generator at no load.
  c. Find the corresponding value of the reference voltage E_R when the voltage v_{tg} is fed back as in Fig. 4-21.
  d. Find the response of the generator terminal voltage $v_{tg}(t)$ to a suddenly applied load current of 20.8 amp with feedback control, and compare with the open-loop response.
  e. Suppose that the open-loop gain is reduced by 10 per cent because of heating of the components. Find the change in steady-state no-load generator voltage of the closed-loop system with E_R set as in part c.
  Solution. a. The over-all system voltage gain K is

$$K = \frac{\mu K_e K_g}{(r_p + r_{fe})r_{fg}} = \frac{(10)(2,000)(480)}{(2,000)(200)} = 24 \text{ volts/volt}$$

The time constant of the generator field is

$$\tau_{fg} = {}^{100}\!/_{200} = 0.5 \text{ sec}$$

The time constant of the exciter field circuit is

$$\tau_{fe} = \frac{40}{2,000} = 0.02 \text{ sec}$$

and therefore is negligible.

b. For $e_{ag} = 240$ volts, $\varepsilon = {}^{240}\!/_{24} = 10$ volts input.

c. With $e_{ag} = 240$ and $\varepsilon = 10$, the reference voltage must be $E_R = 250$ volts.

d. For a suddenly applied load current of 20.8 amp (the rated current of the generator), the generator terminal voltage drops instantaneously by

$$\Delta i_L\, r_a = (20.8)(0.72) = 15 \text{ volts}$$

or

$$v_{tg}(0+) = 240 - 15 = 225 \text{ volts}$$

The error voltage at the amplifier input suddenly becomes $250 - 225 = 25$ volts. These numbers illustrate one of the design requirements of feedback systems: when disturbances occur, the components are subjected to much larger than normal inputs and they must not saturate under these conditions. From Eqs. 4-99 and 4-90, the final value of the voltage drop is

$$\frac{\Delta i_L\, r_a}{1 + K} = \frac{15}{25} = 0.6 \text{ volt}$$

and the time constant of the recovery is

$$\tau_{fg}' = \frac{\tau_{fg}}{1 + K} = \frac{0.5}{25} = 0.02 \text{ sec} \qquad \text{or} \qquad \frac{1}{\tau_{fg}'} = 50$$

The generator terminal voltage recovers rapidly, from a momentary drop to 225 volts to a final value of 239.4 volts. In four time constants, or 0.08 sec., all but about 2 per cent of the transient has disappeared. The equation is

$$v_{tg}(t) = 239.4 - 14.4\epsilon^{-50t}$$

Compare with the open-loop system, in which the voltage would drop to 225 volts and stay there.

e. As a result of heating, the open-loop gain K now is reduced from 24 to 21.6. With E_R held at 250 volts, the no-load voltage of the generator now is

$$\frac{K}{1 + K} E_R = \left(\frac{21.6}{22.6}\right) 250 = \left(1 - \frac{1}{22.6}\right) 250 = 239 \text{ volts}$$

A change of 10 per cent in gain K has caused only a 1-volt change in generator voltage —about 0.4 per cent. With the open-loop system, a 10 per cent change in K would cause a 10 per cent change in generator voltage.

b. *An Elementary Motor Speed Regulator.* The Ward Leonard system with feedback control is frequently used for motor speed regulation. The motor speed is measured by means of a d-c tachometer generator coupled to the motor shaft, and the voltage e_t of the tachometer is compared with a reference voltage, as shown in the schematic circuit diagram (Fig. 4-22a). The amplifier A supplies a few watts to the field of the exciter E, which gives further power amplification and supplies excitation to the generator G. The exciter may be omitted in systems requiring only a few hundred watts output and consequently only a few watts input to the generator field.   Often the exciter or the generator is a high-power-gain generator, for example, an Amplidyne (see Art. 4-10b).

The block diagram is shown in Fig. 4-22b, with E_R and load torque T_L as inputs and motor speed ω_m as the output.   In this diagram, K_1 is the combined voltage gain of the amplifier, exciter, and generator, K_t is the tachometer speed-voltage constant in volt-seconds per radian, e_t is the tachometer voltage, and e_i is the voltage input to the amplifier.   The

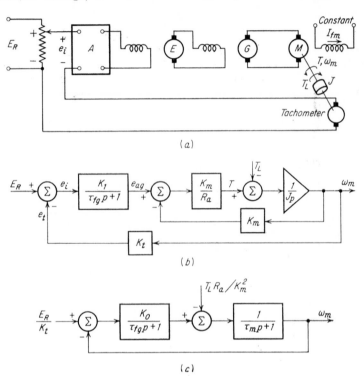

(a)

(b)

(c)

FIG. 4-22. Ward Leonard speed control system with feedback.   (a) Schematic circuit diagram.   (b) Block diagram.   (c) Simplified block diagram.

other symbols have been defined previously.   The time lag in the exciter-field circuit is ignored.   The time lags due to generator field-circuit inductance and load inertia are included.   Algebraic manipulation of the block diagram or the equations which it represents results in the simplified form shown in Fig. 4-22c, where

$$K_0 = \frac{K_1 K_t}{K_m} \tag{4-100}$$

The response to changes in reference voltage E_R and load torque T_L will now be investigated.

With $T_L = 0$, reduction of the block diagram by means of Eq. 2-125 gives the transfer function

$$\frac{\omega_m}{E_R} = \frac{K_0}{K_t} \frac{1}{(\tau_{fg}p + 1)(\tau_m p + 1) + K_0} \tag{4-101}$$

$$\frac{\omega_m}{E_R} = \frac{K_0}{K_t} \frac{1}{\tau_{fg}\tau_m p^2 + (\tau_{fg} + \tau_m)p + 1 + K_0} \tag{4-102}$$

Similarly, with $E_R = 0$

$$\frac{\omega_m}{T_L} = -\frac{R_a}{K_m^2} \frac{\tau_{fg}p + 1}{\tau_{fg}\tau_m p^2 + (\tau_{fg} + \tau_m)p + 1 + K_0} \tag{4-103}$$

In time variables, Eqs. 4-102 and 4-103 represent the second-order linear differential equations

$$\frac{K_0}{K_t} E_R = [\tau_{fg}\tau_m p^2 + (\tau_{fg} + \tau_m)p + 1 + K_0]\omega_m \tag{4-102a}$$

and

$$-\frac{R_a}{K_m^2} (\tau_{fg}p + 1)T_L = [\tau_{fg}\tau_m p^2 + (\tau_{fg} + \tau_m)p + 1 + K_0]\omega_m \tag{4-103a}$$

where p is the derivative operator d/dt. The corresponding transfer functions in complex variables are identical in form to Eqs. 4-102 and 4-103 with p replaced by complex frequency s. The variables ω_m, E_R, and T_L then are the complex amplitudes of the corresponding time variables, and the equations become algebraic equations in s. The corresponding time variables are exponentials of the form $A\epsilon^{st}$. The natural frequencies s of the system are given by the poles of the transfer function or the roots of the second-order equation

$$\tau_{fg}\tau_m s^2 + (\tau_{fg} + \tau_m)s + 1 + K_0 = 0 \tag{4-104}$$

or

$$s^2 + \left(\frac{1}{\tau_{fg}} + \frac{1}{\tau_m}\right)s + \frac{1 + K_0}{\tau_{fg}\tau_m} = 0 \tag{4-105}$$

The undamped natural frequency is

$$\omega_n = \sqrt{\frac{1 + K_0}{\tau_{fg}\tau_m}} \tag{4-106}$$

and the damping factor α is

$$\alpha = \zeta\omega_n = \frac{1}{2}\left(\frac{1}{\tau_{fg}} + \frac{1}{\tau_m}\right) \tag{4-107}$$

The *relative damping factor*, or *damping ratio*, ζ is

$$\zeta = \frac{\alpha}{\omega_n} \tag{4-108}$$

When $\zeta < 1$, the roots are conjugate complex quantities

$$s_1, s_2 = -\alpha \pm j\omega_d \qquad (4\text{-}109)$$

where

$$\omega_d = \omega_n \sqrt{1 - \zeta^2} \qquad (4\text{-}110)$$

The transient response then is a damped sinusoidal oscillation of the form

$$A\epsilon^{-\alpha t} \cos (\omega_d t + \beta)$$

where A and β are determined by the initial and final conditions.

Examination of the above equations shows several important facts concerning the transient behavior of the system and its design for satisfactory performance. For a step input ΔE_R the final steady-state response $\Delta\omega_m(\infty)$ is, from Eq. 4-102 with $p = 0$,

$$\frac{\Delta\omega_m(\infty)}{\Delta E_R} = \frac{1}{K_t}\frac{K_0}{1 + K_0} = \frac{K_1}{K_m + K_1 K_t} \qquad (4\text{-}111)$$

For initial rest conditions the step-input response is shown in normalized form by the curves in Fig. B-1. For a step input ΔT_L of load torque, from Eq. 4-103,

$$\frac{\Delta\omega_m(\infty)}{\Delta T_L} = -\frac{R_a}{K_m^2}\frac{1}{1 + K_0} = -\frac{R_a}{K_m(K_m + K_1 K_t)} \qquad (4\text{-}112)$$

For best performance, the system should be insensitive to load-torque disturbances. This requirement means that R_a should be as small as possible and K_m as large as possible; i.e., the motor should be operated at the maximum permissible flux. Also, K_1 and K_t should be as large as possible. Recall that K_1 is proportional to the amplifier gain. Increasing the amplifier gain therefore stiffens the system against the effect of load disturbances.

Increasing the amplifier gain has undesirable effects on the dynamic behavior, however. From Eqs. 4-106 and 4-108, increasing the amplifier gain increases the natural frequency ω_n and decreases the relative damping factor ζ; that is, the system oscillates rapidly and through wide extremes. The relative stability is poor. The components may wear out rapidly. In more complicated systems with three or more time lags, too much gain may lead to absolute instability, i.e., exponentially increasing oscillations. In practice it has been found that amplifier gains resulting in damping ratios lying in the range between 0.4 and 0.7 usually give satisfactory results. If straight amplification will not give a satisfactory system, various forms of compensation can be added. The techniques of compensation by use of corrective networks are discussed in texts devoted to feedback theory. Some of the possibilities for altering the machine characteristics by means of auxiliary series or shunt fields are discussed in Art. 4-9.

One other basic property of the system should be noted. Equation 4-107 shows that the damping factor α, which describes the decay of the envelope of the oscillations, is fixed entirely by the generator, motor, and load. Thus the time in seconds for the system to settle down is proportional to $1/\alpha$ and is independent of the amplifier gain; it is entirely dependent on the machines and the load.

Example 4-5. The amplifier, exciter, and generator of Example 4-4 are used in a Ward Leonard speed control system with a separately excited 5-hp 240-volt motor and load having the following constants:

Motor armature resistance r_{am} = 0.68 ohm

Motor speed at no load with 240 volts applied to its armature terminals = 1,800 rpm

Motor-plus-load inertia = 1.16 kg-m^2

The tachometer speed-voltage constant K_t = 0.1 volt/rpm. The exciter and generator constants given in Example 4-4 are:

Generator-field time constant τ_{fg} = 0.5 sec

Generator armature resistance r_{ag} = 0.72 ohm

The exciter-field time constant and the motor and generator armature inductances are negligible.

The system is required to meet the following specifications:

Relative damping factor ζ not less than 0.5

Steady-state speed drop not more than 1 per cent for a load torque T_L = 20 newton-m (approximately full load)

Can the specifications be met by selection of the amplifier gain?

Solution. The combined generator-plus-motor armature-circuit resistance R_a = 0.72 + 0.68 = 1.4 ohms. The motor speed-voltage constant in mks units is

$$K_m = \frac{240}{1,800}\frac{60}{2\pi} = 1.27 \text{ volt-sec/rad}$$

The motor-plus-load time constant is

$$\tau_m = \frac{JR_a}{K_m^2} = \frac{(1.16)(1.4)}{(1.27)^2} = 1.0 \text{ sec}$$

From Eq. 4-107

$$\alpha = \frac{1}{2}\left(\frac{1}{\tau_{fg}} + \frac{1}{\tau_m}\right) = 1.5 \text{ sec}^{-1}$$

and from Eq. 4-108 with ζ specified as 0.5

$$\omega_n = \frac{\alpha}{\zeta} = 3.0 \text{ rad/sec}$$

From Eq. 4-106

$$1 + K_0 = \omega_n^2 \tau_{fg}\tau_m = (9)(0.5)(1.0) = 4.5$$

From Eq. 4-112, the steady-state change in speed for a load torque ΔT_L = 20 newton-m is

$$\Delta\omega_m = -\frac{R_a}{K_m^2}\frac{\Delta T_L}{1 + K_0} = -\frac{1.4}{(1.27)^2}\frac{20}{4.5} = -3.85 \text{ rad/sec}$$

or

$$\frac{(3.85)(100)}{60\pi} = 2 \text{ per cent}$$

The specification of 1 per cent cannot be met without adding compensation to the system.

c. An Elementary Position-control Servo System. The Ward Leonard system is often used to control the angular position of an output shaft at high power level in accordance with an input signal at low power level. The basic system consists of a Ward Leonard arrangement with whatever

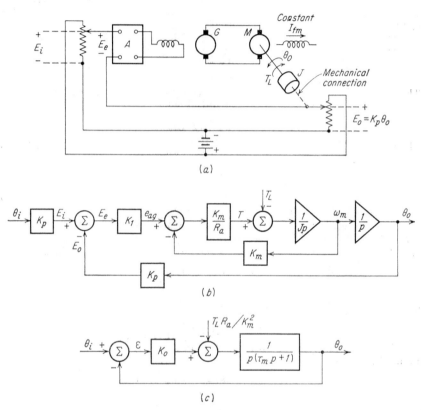

FIG. 4-23. Ward Leonard position-control servo system. (*a*) Schematic diagram. (*b*) Block diagram. (*c*) Simplified block diagram.

means for power amplification are needed to supply the generator field. The output angle θ_o is measured electrically, compared with an electrical signal proportional to the desired angle θ_i and the error voltage supplied to the amplifier input. One scheme is shown in Fig. 4-23*a*. The arm of a potentiometer is driven by the output shaft, usually through gearing not shown in the figure. The desired angle is indicated by the position of the arm of an input potentiometer. If the output and input arms are not in the same relative positions, an error signal actuates the amplifier

to correct the error.   Instead of potentiometers, synchro transformers
described in Art. 6-10 are often used.

The block diagram is shown in Fig. 4-23b.   In this diagram, E_i and E_o
are voltages proportional to the input angle θ_i and the output angle θ_o,
respectively, the constant of proportionality being K_p volts/rad.   The
error voltage $E_e = E_i - E_o$ is the input to the amplifier A.   The over-all
voltage gain of the amplifier and generator is K_1.   The time constant of
the generator field is neglected on the assumption that it is much smaller
than that due to the motor-plus-load inertia.   The block diagram giving
motor speed ω_m is the same as before.   Output angle θ_o is given by the
integral of the speed, as shown by the final integrator in Fig. 4-23b.
Algebraic manipulation results in the simplified block diagram of Fig.
4-23c, in which

$$K_0 = \frac{K_1 K_p}{K_m} \tag{4-113}$$

The transfer function relating θ_o to θ_i with $T_L = 0$ is

$$\frac{\theta_o}{\theta_i} = \frac{K_0}{\tau_m p^2 + p + K_0} \tag{4-114}$$

The error ε resulting from input θ_i is

$$\varepsilon = \theta_i - \theta_o$$

or
$$\frac{\varepsilon}{\theta_i} = 1 - \frac{\theta_o}{\theta_i} = \frac{p(\tau_m p + 1)}{\tau_m p^2 + p + K_0} \tag{4-115}$$

With $\theta_i = 0$, the transfer function relating error ε to load torque T_L is

$$\frac{\varepsilon}{T_L} = -\frac{\theta_o}{T_L} = \frac{R_a}{K_m^2} \frac{1}{\tau_m p^2 + p + K_0} \tag{4-116}$$

The differential equations corresponding to the transfer functions of Eqs.
4-114, 4-115, and 4-116 are

$$K_0 \theta_i = (\tau_m p^2 + p + K_0)\theta_o \tag{4-114a}$$
$$(\tau_m p^2 + p)\theta_i = (\tau_m p^2 + p + K_0)\varepsilon \tag{4-115a}$$

and
$$T_L \frac{R_a}{K_m^2} = (\tau_m p^2 + p + K_0)\varepsilon \tag{4-116a}$$

The natural frequencies s are given by the poles of the transfer function,
or the roots of the equation

$$\tau_m s^2 + s + K_0 = 0 \tag{4-117}$$

In normalized form, the undamped natural frequency ω_n is

$$\omega_n = \sqrt{\frac{K_0}{\tau_m}} \tag{4-118}$$

and the damping factor α is

$$\alpha = \frac{1}{2\tau_m} \tag{4-119}$$

The relative damping factor ζ is

$$\zeta = \frac{\alpha}{\omega_n} = \frac{1}{2} \sqrt{\frac{1}{K_0 \tau_m}} \tag{4-120}$$

We shall now investigate the behavior of the system for three types of disturbances, (1) a step input $\Delta\theta_i$, (2) a step of load torque ΔT_L, and (3) a constant-velocity input $d\theta_i/dt = \omega_i$.

1. For a step input $\Delta\theta_i$, the steady-state value of $\Delta\theta_o$ is

$$\Delta\theta_o(\infty) = \Delta\theta_i \tag{4-121}$$

With initial rest conditions, that is, $\Delta\theta_o(0) = 0$ and $p\,\Delta\theta_o(0) = 0$, the solution for $\Delta\theta_o(t)$ in normalized form is given by the curves in Fig. B-1 and by Eqs. B-13 through B-16. The steady-state error $\mathcal{E}(\infty) = 0$.

2. For a step input ΔT_L, the steady-state error is

$$\mathcal{E}(\infty) = \frac{R_a\,\Delta T_L}{K_m^2 K_0} = \frac{R_a\,\Delta T_L}{K_m K_1 K_p} \tag{4-122}$$

With initial rest conditions, that is, $\mathcal{E}(0) = 0$ and $p\mathcal{E}(0) = 0$, the solution for $\mathcal{E}(t)$ in normalized form is also given in Appendix B.

3. For a suddenly applied input velocity $p\theta_i = \omega_i$, that is, a ramp input, the steady-state error $\mathcal{E}(\infty)$ is

$$\mathcal{E}(\infty) = \frac{\omega_i}{K_0} \tag{4-123}$$

Note that $\mathcal{E}$ is still an error in angle, $\theta_i - \theta_o$, not an error in velocity. In the steady state the motor speed $\omega_m = \omega_i$, but the output shaft lags the angular position of the input. The constant voltage thereby applied to the amplifier is sufficient to keep the motor turning at constant speed. Here the initial conditions are $\mathcal{E}(0) = 0$ and $p\mathcal{E}(0) = \omega_i$ so that the normalized curves of Fig. B-1 do not apply.

Remarks very similar to those made in the preceding discussion of the speed control system can now be made concerning the elementary position control system. Both are second-order systems. Both are characterized by damped oscillations for $\zeta < 1$. In both, increasing the amplifier gain has the desirable effect of decreasing errors due to load torque and velocity inputs. But increasing gain increases the frequency of oscillation and decreases the relative damping ratio ζ. In both systems, the decay of the transient envelope is entirely dependent on the machine and load time constants. The settling time therefore cannot be controlled by adjustment of the gain.

Example 4-6. The following data apply to the position control system of Fig. 4-23:

Motor armature resistance r_{am} = 6 ohms
Generator armature resistance r_{ag} = 4 ohms
Motor speed-voltage constant K_m = 0.9 volt-sec/rad
Inertia of motor armature alone J_m = 0.002 kg-m²

The motor drives a load of inertia J_L = 10 kg-m² through ideal gears reducing the speed by the factor k_G.

The system is to be adjusted so that the steady-state errors for a constant-velocity input of 20°/sec or for a steady load torque of 10 newton-m are not to exceed 1°, with all quantities referred to the load shaft.

a. Find the over-all gain K_1K_p of the error detector, amplifier, and generator.

b. Find the gear ratio k_G.

c. Find the steady-state motor speed, armature voltage, and armature current for a constant-velocity input of 20°/sec with load torque T_L = 0.

d. Find the armature voltage and current at standstill with T_L = 10 newton-m.

e. Check the dynamic performance; i.e., find α, ζ, and ω_n.

f. For a step input θ_i of 20°, find the initial values of generator emf e_{ag} and armature current i_a.

Solution. Refer all quantities to the motor shaft; thus

$$\text{Angle at motor} = k_G \text{ (angle at load)}$$

$$\text{Torque at motor} = \frac{\text{torque at load}}{k_G}$$

$$\text{Load inertia referred to motor} = \frac{J_L}{k_G^2} \qquad \text{Eq. 4-69}$$

a. From Eq. 4-123, to meet the velocity-error specification with T_L = 0,

$$K_0 = \frac{\omega_i}{\varepsilon(\infty)} = \frac{20k_G}{k_G} = 20$$

From Eq. 4-113

$$K_1K_p = K_0K_m = (20)(0.9) = 18 \text{ volts/rad at motor shaft}$$

b. From Eq. 4-122 referred to the motor shaft

$$k_G\varepsilon(\infty) = \frac{R_a}{K_m^2K_0}\frac{T_L}{k_G}$$

with error and load torque given at the load shaft. To meet the load-torque specification with ω_i = 0,

$$k_G^2 = \frac{R_a}{K_m^2K_0}\frac{T_L}{\varepsilon(\infty)}$$

with $R_a = r_{ag} + r_{am}$ = 10 ohms and $\varepsilon(\infty) = \pi/180$ rad. Thus,

$$k_G^2 = \frac{(10)(10)(180)}{(0.9)^2(20)\pi} = 354 \qquad \text{or} \qquad k_G = 18.8$$

c. For ω_i = 20°/sec at load, the steady-state motor speed is

$$\omega_m = k_G\omega_i = \frac{(18.8)(20)\pi}{180} = 6.56 \text{ rad/sec} = 63 \text{ rpm}$$

The motor counter emf is

$$e_{am} = K_m\omega_m = 5.9 \text{ volts}$$

With $T_L = 0$ and $i_a = 0$, the generator emf $e_{ag} = 5.9$ volts.

d. For $T_L = 10$ newton-m at load, the steady-state motor torque is

$$T = \frac{T_L}{k_G} = \frac{10}{18.8} = 0.534 \text{ newton-m}$$

The armature current is

$$i_a = \frac{T}{K_m} = \frac{0.534}{0.9} = 0.59 \text{ amp}$$

With the motor stationary, $e_{am} = 0$, and

$$e_{ag} = i_aR_a = (0.59)(10) = 5.9 \text{ volts}$$

e. From Eq. 4-69, the motor-plus-load inertia referred to the motor is

$$J = J_m + \frac{J_L}{k_G^2} = 0.002 + \frac{10}{354} = 0.00483 \text{ kg-m}^2$$

The time constant is

$$\tau_m = \frac{JR_a}{K_m^2} = \frac{(0.00483)(10)}{0.81} = 0.06 \text{ sec}$$

From Eq. 4-119

$$\alpha = \frac{1}{2\tau_m} = \frac{1}{0.12} = 8.3 \text{ sec}^{-1}$$

From Eq. 4-118

$$\omega_n = \sqrt{\frac{K_0}{\tau_m}} = \sqrt{\frac{20}{0.06}} = 18.3 \text{ rad/sec, or 2.9 cps}$$

From Eq. 4-120

$$\zeta = \frac{\alpha}{\omega_n} = \frac{8.3}{18.3} = 0.45$$

The dynamic performance is satisfactory in so far as damping is concerned.

f. For a step input θ_i of $20°$, or 0.349 rad at the load shaft, the initial value of the generator emf is

$$e_{ag}(0+) = K_1K_pk_G\mathcal{E} = (18)(18.8)(0.349) = 118 \text{ volts}$$

With the motor stationary and armature inductances negligible, the initial armature current is

$$i_a(0+) = \frac{e_{ag}(0+)}{R_a} = 11.8 \text{ amp}$$

The initial power generated is $e_{ag}i_a = 1,390$ watts. The rotating machines must be capable of handling voltages, currents, and power surges of the magnitude just found. The signal-flow analysis alone does not show these requirements directly. Thus there is a lot more to the design of a servo system than merely the proper choice of gains, damping ratios, and so forth. The energy-conversion equipment has to be capable of doing the work required of it by the demands of the signals impressed on it.

4-7. Frequency Response of Closed-cycle Systems. Dynamic analysis of linear systems by frequency-response methods is an important complement to transient analysis and is treated thoroughly in many texts devoted to feedback theory. A brief introduction to such studies is presented in this article.

The most direct correlation between system frequency response and transient analysis occurs in systems characterized by a second-order linear differential equation. To bring out this correlation, consider the simple system of Fig. 4-23 subjected to a steady-state sinusoidal variation with time of the input $\theta_i(t)$. The response to be determined is the steady-state amplitude and phase of the output $\theta_o(t)$ over the significant frequency range.

In terms of complex frequency s, the transfer function relating the complex amplitude $\theta_o(s)$ to the complex amplitude $\theta_i(s)$ is obtained by replacing the derivative operator p in the system differential equation by the complex frequency s. For the system of Fig. 4-23, Eq. 4-114 then gives

$$\frac{\theta_o}{\theta_i}(s) = \frac{K_0}{\tau_m s^2 + s + K_0} = \frac{1}{(\tau_m/K_0)s^2 + s/K_0 + 1} \qquad (4\text{-}124)$$

By use of Eqs. 4-118 and 4-120, the result can be put in normalized form, as follows:

$$\frac{\theta_o}{\theta_i}(s) = \frac{1}{s^2/\omega_n^2 + 2\zeta s/\omega_n + 1} \qquad (4\text{-}125)$$

For steady-state sinusoidal excitation, s equals $j\omega$, where ω is the frequency of the excitation in radians per second. Equation 4-125 then yields for the steady-state complex or phasor ratio of output to input

$$\frac{\Theta_o}{\Theta_i} = \frac{1}{(1 - \omega^2/\omega_n^2) + j2\zeta(\omega/\omega_n)} \qquad (4\text{-}126)$$

The amplitude-response ratio is accordingly

$$\left|\frac{\Theta_o}{\Theta_i}\right| = \frac{1}{\sqrt{(1 - \omega^2/\omega_n^2)^2 + [2\zeta(\omega/\omega_n)]^2}} \qquad (4\text{-}127)$$

and the phase angle measured from Θ_i to Θ_o is

$$\Psi = -\tan^{-1}\frac{2\zeta(\omega/\omega_n)}{1 - (\omega^2/\omega_n^2)} \qquad (4\text{-}128)$$

Curves of amplitude-response ratio and phase angle are plotted as a function of the dimensionless variable ω/ω_n for a series of values of ζ in Figs. 4-24 and 4-25. The ideal characteristic would be a perfectly flat amplitude response and zero phase shift for all frequencies. High peaks in the amplitude-response curve evidently correspond to undesirable overshooting and undershooting in the transient response. On the other hand, a rapid falling off of the amplitude response as frequency increases corresponds to sluggish transient response. A relatively high natural frequency corresponds to a relatively low effective duration of the transient following a disturbance.

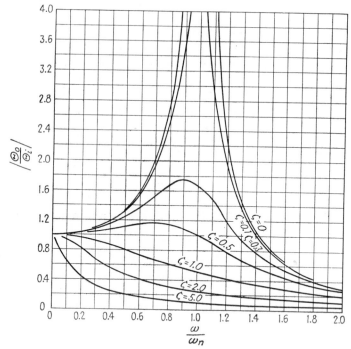

FIG. 4-24. Normalized amplitude–frequency-response curves for the second-order system of Fig. 4-23.

Interpretation of the frequency-response characteristics of more complex closed-cycle systems is, to a considerable extent, based on the correlation between frequency response and transient response for a second-order system, together with the background of experience from which one skilled in such studies views the characteristics. Response-peak values of $1\frac{1}{3}$ to $1\frac{1}{2}$, corresponding to damping ratios of 0.41 to 0.36 in a second-order system, usually are satisfactory. Of course, such a general rule is by no means made the sole basis of design, but it does afford a perspective and furnishes a valuable checking procedure for a proposed design. Moreover, plots of the appropriate frequency loci give indications of what must be done to a proposed system in the way of design changes and compensating networks to achieve the desired performance.

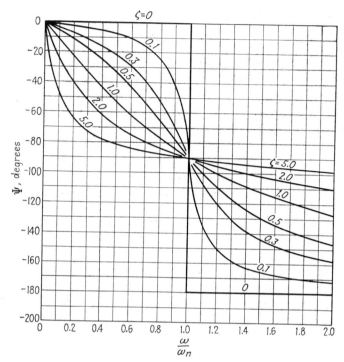

FIG. 4-25. Normalized phase-angle–frequency curves for the second-order system of Fig. 4-23. Negative angles are angles of lag of output behind input.

Consideration of these design techniques and refinements is beyond the scope of the present discussion, however.

As in any system involving feedback from the output to the input, there is always a possibility of self-excited operation—i.e., the system may undergo sustained oscillations even with no input.   Examination of this possibility involves substantially the line of thought used in studying vacuum-tube oscillators or in examining the possibility of oscillation in vac-
uum-tube amplifiers.   A brief qualitative description is given here.

Any closed-cycle system can be represented by the block diagram of Fig.

FIG. 4-26. Block diagram of a closed-cycle system.

4-26, in which $KG(j\omega)$ is the transfer
function relating the complex amplitude of the output θ_o to the complex amplitude of the error E for steady-state sinusoidal excitation.   When expressed in this way, the portion of the transfer function designated by K is the static sensitivity, or the part which is independent of ω; the portion $G(j\omega)$ is the frequency-dependent part.

In the system of Fig. 4-26, a sufficient number of energy-storage elements, with their associated time lags and phase shifts between output and input, will cause the output Θ_o to be 180° out of phase with error E at some finite frequency. In other words, the transfer function $KG(j\omega)$ will be a negative real number at this frequency. If that number is unity, self-excitation may take place; i.e., even with $\theta_i = 0$, feedback of the output around the closed loop supplies the proper input, and the system oscillates steadily at the frequency corresponding to the 180° phase shift. If that number is greater than unity, oscillations may take place at an amplitude which increases until it is limited by nonlinearities in the system. The system will not undergo sustained oscillations if the magnitude of the transfer function is less than unity at the frequency producing a 180° phase shift.

It should be noted that these conditions furnish a criterion for absolute stability. The normal closed-cycle system operates well within these limits.

4-8. Self-excited Generators. The use of shunt and series fields in conjunction with separately excited control fields opens up a wide variety of possibilities for control of d-c machine characteristics. The purpose of this article is to give a simplified explanation of the phenomena associated with self-excited generators and to describe an application of them in d-c-machine control systems. A more complete dynamic analysis is given in Art. 4-9.

Consider first the simple shunt generator shown in Fig. 4-27, driven at constant speed ω_{m0} with the field switch S open. The magnetization curve is shown in Fig. 4-28. A small residual flux is assumed

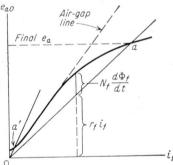

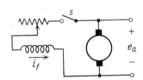

FIG. 4-27. Shunt generator.

FIG. 4-28. Magnetization curve for the generator of Fig. 4-27.

corresponding to a small generated emf at zero excitation. The resistance of the field circuit is adjustable by means of the external resistor. The straight line Oa in Fig. 4-28, called the *field-resistance line*, is a plot of the relation

$$v_f = i_f r_f \tag{4-129}$$

where v_f, i_f, and r_f are the voltage, current, and resistance of the field circuit.   The slope of line Oa is adjustable by means of the field rheostat. In Fig. 4-28, the slope of Oa is less than that of the air-gap line, and point a is the intersection of the field-resistance line with the magnetization curve.

Now let the field switch S be closed at $t = 0$. The small voltage generated in the armature by the residual flux is then applied to the shunt-field circuit, and the shunt-field current starts to build up.   If the connections of the shunt field to the armature terminals are such that the resulting field current increases the flux, positive feedback results and the voltage continues to build up until it is finally limited by magnetic saturation at point a, where the generated voltage supplies just enough field current to sustain itself.   This statement ignores the extremely small voltage drop caused by the shunt-field current in the armature-circuit resistance.   The normal operating point of a shunt generator is well up on the magnetization curve.

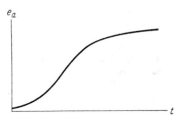

Fig. 4-29. Voltage build-up of a shunt generator.

Figure 4-29 shows a curve of the armature terminal voltage as a function of time following closure of the field switch.   This curve can be calculated by a graphical method.   Since the generated emf e_a is applied to the field circuit, the voltage equation for the field circuit is

$$v_f = e_a = r_f i_f + N_f \frac{d\Phi_f}{dt} \qquad (4\text{-}130)$$

or

$$N_f \frac{d\Phi_f}{dt} = e_a - r_f i_f \qquad (4\text{-}131)$$

where Φ_f is the field flux per pole and N_f is the number of turns in the field winding.   Thus the rate of change of field flux, and consequently of generated voltage, is proportional to the vertical difference between the magnetization curve and the field-resistance line.   The curve of Φ_f or e_a as a function of time has the shape shown in Fig. 4-29.   It can be computed by separation of the variables and graphical integration.   Notice, however, that the response is rather slow, because only relatively small voltage differences act to build up the flux.

If the field resistance is large, resulting in a field-resistance line such as Oa' in Fig. 4-28, very little voltage build-up occurs.   If the field-resistance line coincides with the magnetization-curve air-gap line, no definite intersection with the magnetization curve exists.   A slightly higher value of resistance results in essentially no voltage, a slightly lower value in build-up to a point where saturation begins.   The operating point is unstable and is very sensitive to hysteresis effects and changes in speed or temperature.   The value of r_f corresponding to the slope of the air-gap line is called the *critical field resistance*, and adjustment of r_f to this value is sometimes referred to as *tuning*.

Now consider the series generator shown in Fig. 4-30.   Here the excitation is determined by the load current and is very much influenced by the type of load.   For example, a motor load will cause the system to behave entirely differently from a static impedance load.   We shall limit ourselves to series generators with inductive impedance loads, such as the loads on exciters supplying field excitation to large generators, as shown in Fig. 4-30.

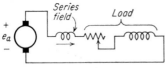

Fig. 4-30. Series generator with inductive load.

For such loads there is no basic difference between the behavior of shunt and series machines, at least from steady-state aspects.   In both, the excitation is supplied by positive feedback.   If the resistance is too large, the voltage will not build up.   If the resistance is sufficiently small, build-up will take place until the voltage is limited by saturation. Both have a critical value of resistance, and both can be tuned.   The differences show up in the magnitudes of the field currents involved and in the dynamic behavior.   In the shunt generator, the excitation is provided by a small current in a high-impedance winding of many turns, and the dynamic behavior is principally determined by the resistance and inductance of the field winding itself.   In the series generator, the excitation is provided by the much larger armature current in a low-impedance

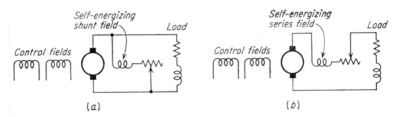

FIG. 4-31. Basic self-energizing generators.

winding of relatively few turns, and the dynamic behavior is principally determined by the impedance of the load.   The shunt generator has voltage feedback; the series generator, current feedback.   The dynamics are discussed in Art. 4-9.

One form of control-type generator is, in its most common version, a relatively simple modification of a conventional d-c generator in which are installed a series- or shunt-field winding for self-excitation and several separately excited control-field windings, as shown in Fig. 4-31.   They are commonly known by various trade names such as Rototrol, Regulex,

Magnavolt, and VSA. In the steady state, essentially all the excitation is provided by the self-excited, or *self-energizing, field.* As shown in Fig. 4-31, the self-energizing field may be either a series or a shunt winding. The outstanding feature is that the self-energizing field is *tuned* to the air-gap line, and normal operation is on the linear part of the magnetization curve.

When a change in output voltage is called for, corresponding to a change in operating conditions in the equipment being controlled, the

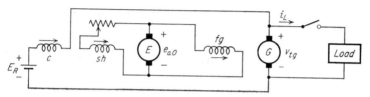

FIG. 4-32. A voltage-regulating system using a tuned shunt-field exciter.

control fields are effective in determining the new operating point. The power level in the control windings is accordingly minimized by calling upon them only to initiate changes or to stabilize steady operating conditions.

Figure 4-32 shows a voltage control system using an exciter E with a control-field winding c and a tuned shunt-field winding sh. The control-field voltage v_c is obtained by feedback comparison of the generator terminal voltage v_{tg} with a constant reference voltage E_R. The exciter is driven at constant speed ω_{m0}. For steady-state conditions, the shunt field provides all the excitation, and the error voltage v_c is zero. Operation is in the linear region, say, at point p (Fig. 4-33), where the exciter provides the generator excitation required to make the generator terminal voltage v_{tg} equal to the reference voltage E_R. Any tendency to drift from this point results in a corrective voltage v_c at the control-field

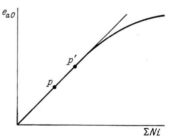

FIG. 4-33. Magnetization curve for the exciter of Fig. 4-32.

terminals. Now suppose a load is added to the generator, causing its terminal voltage to drop. An error voltage $v_c = E_R - v_{tg}$ is then applied to the control field, and the exciter voltage starts to build up. The exciter will continue to change the voltage so long as any error exists. The final operating point will shift to a new point, say, p' (Fig. 4-33), where the self-energizing shunt field alone again supplies all the excitation required by the new load conditions. At the new operating point the steady-state error again is zero. The behavior of the tuned series-excited machine is essentially the same as that of the shunt machine.

Machines of this type can be used for a variety of applications, for example, as the exciter in the Ward Leonard speed control system of Fig. 4-22a. Often they are provided with more than one control field. One field may be supplied from the reference voltage and another by negative feedback from the voltage to be controlled. Other field windings may be used to control or limit other variables.

The principal difficulties with machines of this type are that their response is slow and they are sensitive to changes in tuning caused by hysteresis and by speed and temperature changes.

4-9. Shunt and Series Feedback. In Art. 4-8 we have seen how tuned-field generators can be used in feedback control systems to increase the amplification of control-field signals. The purpose of this article is to investigate more thoroughly the effects of shunt and series feedback in d-c generator systems. Because a d-c generator is essentially a power ampli-

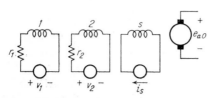

FIG. 4-34. Direct-current generator with 3 field windings.

fier, the theory of shunt or series feedback in a generator is essentially the same as the theory of voltage or current feedback in any other kind of amplifier. The differences are principally ones of details and magnitudes of the quantities involved—power levels, time constants, frequency ranges, etc.

Consider the d-c machine shown schematically in Fig. 4-34, having field windings 1, 2, and s. Windings 1 and 2 represent control or shunt fields excited from known or determinable voltage sources v_1 and v_2. We shall limit the discussion to sources containing no energy-storage elements. The combined series resistance of these sources and their windings are r_1 and r_2, respectively. Winding s represents a series field excited from a known or determinable current source i_s. The resultant direct-axis flux is produced by the combined mmf of the field windings. Because the windings are close together on a common magnetic circuit, it will be assumed that the leakage flux between them is negligible; i.e., the coefficient of coupling $k = 1$. This assumption is justified on referring back to Example 1-2, where it is shown that leakage flux between closely coupled circuits has very little effect on the main-flux transients.[1]

It will also be assumed that magnetic saturation is negligible.[1] On this assumption, the effect of each excitation can be considered separately,

[1] For a more detailed treatment, including the effects of magnetic saturation, see M. Riaz, Dynamics of D-C Machine Systems, *Trans. AIEE*, vol. 74, pt. II, pp. 365–369, 1955.

and the resultant excitation can be found by superposition. The block diagram with v_1 applied, $v_2 = 0$ (short-circuited), and $i_s = 0$ (open-circuited) is shown in Fig. 4-35a, in which e'_{a0} is the armature generated voltage due to v_1, K_1 is the steady-state generated voltage per ampere in field 1, and $\tau_1 = L_{11}/r_1$ and $\tau_2 = L_{22}/r_2$ are the time constants of field circuits 1 and 2, respectively. The only difference between this block diagram and the one shown in Fig. 4-8 is the additional time lag caused by the current induced in the short-circuited winding 2. As shown in Example 1-2, the time constant of the flux in two closely coupled circuits is very nearly $\tau_1 + \tau_2$. The block diagram with v_2 applied, $v_1 = 0$, and $i_s = 0$ is similar to Fig. 4-35a. The block diagram with i_s applied, $v_1 = 0$, and $v_2 = 0$ is shown in Fig. 4-35b. Here K_s is the steady-state

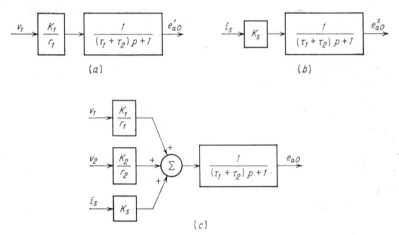

Fig. 4-35. Block diagrams for the generator of Fig. 4-34. (a) Winding 1 alone excited. (b) Winding s alone excited. (c) All 3 windings excited.

armature generated emf e^s_{a0} per ampere i_s. The time lag caused by the induced currents in windings 1 and 2 is still $\tau_1 + \tau_2$. The resultant block diagram obtained by superposition is shown in Fig. 4-35c, in which e_{a0} is the resultant generated emf.

In order to compare the effects of shunt and series excitation, two specific examples will be discussed.

Figure 4-36a shows a feedback system using an exciter E with 2 field windings. The control field c is excited from an input voltage v_c, and the shunt field sh is excited by negative voltage feedback from the output voltage v_{tg} of the main generator G. The machines are assumed to be driven at constant speed ω_{m0}. The generator supplies a resistance load R_L. The block diagram is shown in Fig. 4-36b with v_c as the input and v_{tg} as the output. In this diagram α_c and α_{sh} are the voltage gains of the exciter control and shunt fields, respectively, in exciter generated volts

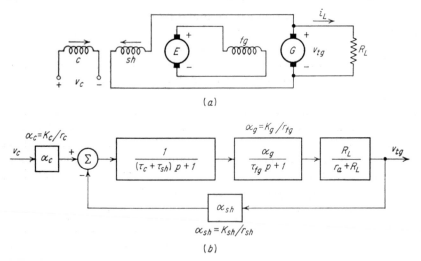

FIG. 4-36. Exciter-generator system with negative shunt feedback. (a) Circuit diagram. (b) Block diagram.

per field volt, α_g is the generator voltage gain in generated volts per field volt, and r_a is the generator armature resistance.   The time constants of the control, shunt, and generator fields are τ_c, τ_{sh}, and τ_{fg}, respectively. The generator armature inductance is neglected, and the exciter shunt-field current is entirely negligible compared with the generator load current i_L.

Now consider the system shown in Fig. 4-37a, in which the exciter has

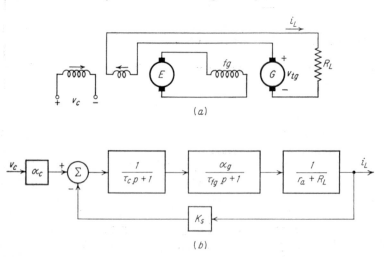

FIG. 4-37. Exciter-generator system with negative series feedback. (a) Circuit diagram. (b) Block diagram.

a differential or suppressive series field in series with the load current of the main generator. The block diagram is shown in Fig. 4-37b with i_L now as the output. Here K_s is the exciter generated emf per series-field ampere. The small voltage induced in the exciter series field by the rate of change of the exciter-field flux is neglected.

Note the similarity of the block diagrams of Figs. 4-36b and 4-37b. Both are negative-feedback systems with two time lags in cascade. Both are faster in response than the corresponding open-loop systems. Both will oscillate if the gains are high. Both tend to hold output proportional to input. Negative shunt feedback around machine systems tends to stiffen the system as a voltage source; i.e., the *shunt* system tends to hold *constant voltage* regardless of load resistance over a range of R_L larger than some minimum value where saturation sets in or windings burn out. Negative series feedback, on the other hand, tends to stiffen the system as a current source; i.e., the *series* system tends to hold *constant current* regardless of load over a range of R_L from zero up to some value where something saturates or insulation breaks down. The characteristics can be calculated from the block diagrams by the methods which are presented earlier in this chapter. The basic theory is, of course, similar to that of any other form of linear amplifier with voltage or current feedback.

One further point should be stressed regarding the basic properties of negative feedback. The improvements in system response are obtained at a sacrifice in gain, and consequently more control power is required when negative feedback is added to a system. Or if the control power level must not be increased, then the power amplification of the system must be increased and more expensive apparatus may be required. Usually several stages of power amplification are needed when negative feedback is used. At low power levels the power amplifiers may be electronic. At high power levels they may be rotating machines. Some of the possibilities for incorporating two stages of amplification in a single machine are explored in Art. 4-10.

4-10. Metadynes and Amplidynes. So far, we have considered d-c machines with a single pair of brushes located in the quadrature axis. In them, the excitation is provided by field windings located on the stator in the direct axis. We have seen that the dynamic and steady-state characteristics can be altered to a considerable extent by the design and method of excitation of the field windings.

The purpose of this article is to examine the effects of additional brushes located in the direct axis. By these means the armature mmf can be used to provide part of the excitation. Machines with more than two brush sets per pair of poles are called *metadynes*. They can be used in a wide variety of applications requiring high speed of response, or high power amplification, or some other special built-in characteristic.[1] This article is concerned with metadyne generators, with emphasis on the most commonly used form, the Amplidyne.

a. Basic Metadyne Generators. A modification of the basic d-c machine is shown in Fig. 4-38. The rotor has a 2-pole armature winding and a commutator. Brushes q, q' are located so that commutation takes place in the quadrature axis. The stator has a winding which produces a 2-pole magnetic field with an axis of symmetry along the direct axis. Do not be confused by the fact that the stator has four salient pole pieces or segmental poles. The field coils f each embrace two of the segmental pole pieces. The $\mathcal{3C}$ vector due to the field coils in Fig. 4-38a is directed radially inward in the two left-hand pole segments 1 and 2 and radially outward in the two right-hand pole segments 3 and 4. The flux lines are shown dotted in Fig. 4-38a. The voltage e_{aq} generated in the armature between the quadrature-axis brushes q, q' is given by Eq. 4-2; thus

$$e_{aq} = K_a \Phi_d \omega_m \tag{4-132}$$

where Φ_d is the total direct-axis flux per pole, i.e., the sum of the fluxes in segmental poles 1 and 2. If the machine is driven mechanically in the counterclockwise direction, the upper brush will be positive and the lower one negative, in accordance with the conventions adopted for reference directions in Art. 4-1.

Now let the quadrature-axis brushes be short-circuited. The armature current then produces a stationary magnetic field with an axis of symmetry centered on the quadrature axis. The magnetic torque is clockwise, opposing rotation. The magnetic field of the armature is directed upward, and the currents in the armature coils are in the directions indicated by the dots and crosses in Fig. 4-38b, in which the direct-axis field coils have been omitted so as to simplify the drawing. The magnetic field due to the armature currents is indicated by the dashed lines in Fig. 4-38b. It is in the same direction as the direct-axis flux in segmental poles 2 and 4 and in the opposite direction in segmental poles 1 and 3. With saturation neglected, the total direct-axis flux is unchanged, however.

Because the magnetic field due to the quadrature-axis armature current is stationary, its effect is similar to that of a winding on the stator producing a quadrature-axis flux. If brushes d, d' are now placed on the

[1] For a thorough discussion of the steady-state theory of metadynes and descriptions of a number of applications see J. M. Pestarini, "Metadyne Statics," Technology Press and John Wiley & Sons, Inc., New York, 1952. For discussions of the transient theory, see M. Riaz, Transient Analysis of the Metadyne Generator, *Trans. AIEE*, vol. 72, pt. III, pp. 52–62, 1953; K. A. Fegley, Metadyne Transients, *Trans. AIEE*, vol. 74, pt. III, pp. 1179–1188, 1955.

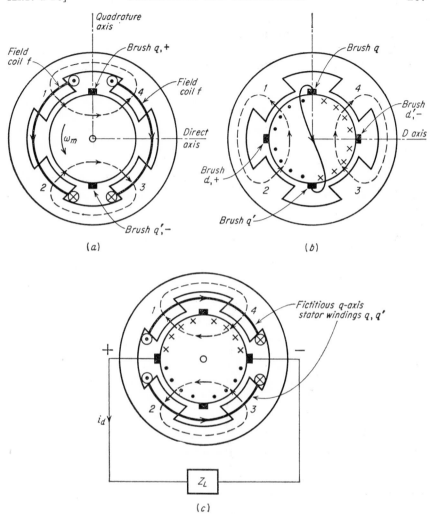

FIG. 4-38. Currents and magnetic fields in a metadyne generator. (*a*) Direct-axis field current and flux. (*b*) Quadrature-axis armature current and flux. (*c*) Direct-axis armature current and flux.

commutator in the direct axis, the emf e_{ad} generated in the armature by its rotation in the quadrature-axis flux Φ_q will appear across these brushes. By direct similarity to Eq. 4-132, this voltage is

$$e_{ad} = K_a \Phi_q \omega_m \qquad (4\text{-}133)$$

The polarity of the direct-axis brushes is shown in Fig. 4-38*b*, in agreement with the reference directions adopted in Art. 4-1.

Now connect a load $Z_L(p)$ to the direct-axis brushes as shown in Fig.

4-38c, in which the direct-axis field coils are omitted and the effect of the quadrature-axis armature current is replaced by a fictitious quadrature-axis stator winding q, q' which produces the same quadrature-axis flux Φ_q. For generator action, the magnetic torque opposes rotation. The direction of the component direct-axis current in the armature coils is shown by the dots and crosses, and its magnetic field is indicated by the dashed lines in Fig. 4-38c. Comparison of Figs. 4-38b and 4-38c shows that the direct- and quadrature-axis armature currents are in the same direction in the armature coils under segmental poles 2 and 4 and in opposite directions in the coils under segmental poles 1 and 3.

Comparison of Figs. 4-38a and 4-38c shows the highly significant fact that the direct-axis armature mmf opposes the mmf of the direct-axis

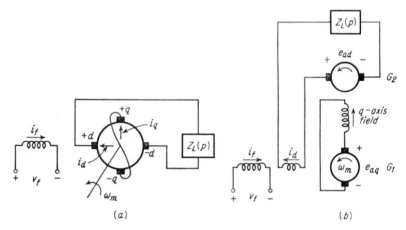

FIG. 4-39. (a) Schematic diagram of a metadyne generator and (b) the equivalent cascade system.

field coils f. Each stage of voltage generation results in a current whose magnetic field is in space quadrature with the flux producing the voltage. With two stages of voltage generation, the mmf of the direct-axis output current in a metadyne generator is shifted 90° twice and therefore opposes the original field excitation.

The metadyne generator of Fig. 4-38, therefore, is a two-stage power amplifier with strong negative current feedback from the final output stage to the input. Figure 4-39a shows a simplified schematic diagram of the metadyne, and Fig. 4-39b shows an equivalent system comprising two generators in cascade with negative series feedback.

The first stage of the metadyne, from the resultant direct-axis flux to the quadrature-axis armature circuit, is represented by the generator G_1 in Fig. 4-39b. The differential equations for this stage, in transfer-function form, are

$$e_{aq} = \frac{K_{qf}v_f/r_f - K_{qd}i_d}{\tau_f p + 1}\frac{\omega_m}{\omega_{m0}} \tag{4-134}$$

$$i_q = \frac{e_{aq}}{r_{aq}}\frac{1}{\tau_{aq}p + 1} \tag{4-135}$$

In Eq. 4-134, K_{qf} is the quadrature-axis generated voltage per ampere of field current i_f at speed ω_{m0}, K_{qd} is the quadrature-axis generated voltage per ampere of direct-axis armature current i_d, r_f is the field resistance, and τ_f is the field-circuit time constant. In Eq. 4-135, i_q, r_{aq}, and τ_{aq} are the quadrature-axis armature current, resistance, and time constant, respectively. The equations for the second stage are

$$e_{ad} = K_{dq}i_q\frac{\omega_m}{\omega_{m0}} \tag{4-136}$$

$$i_d = \frac{e_{ad}}{Z_L(p)} \tag{4-137}$$

where K_{dq} is the direct-axis generated voltage per ampere of quadrature-axis armature current and $Z_L(p)$ is the load impedance. In these equations, the effects of magnetic saturation and of magnetic leakage between

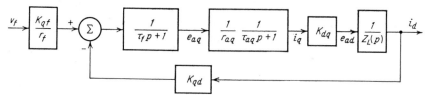

Fig. 4-40. Block diagram of a metadyne generator.

the field circuit and the direct-axis armature circuit are neglected, the transformer voltage induced in the direct-axis armature circuit by the time rate of change of the resultant direct-axis flux is neglected, and the direct-axis armature impedance is assumed to be negligible compared with the load impedance. The block diagram corresponding to Eqs. 4-134 through 4-137 is shown in Fig. 4-40 with v_f as the input and i_d as the output. The speed is assumed to be equal to ω_{m0}. Except for changes in notation, the block diagram of Fig. 4-40 is the same as that of Fig. 4-37.

The simple metadyne of Fig. 4-39 has the characteristics of a two-stage negative-current-feedback amplifier. It is rapid in response and maintains nearly constant output current i_d over a wide range of load impedance. Its power amplification, however, is reduced by the effect of the negative feedback. By the addition of more field windings on either axis of the stator, a wide variety of characteristics can be obtained.

b. Amplidynes.   The commonest form of metadyne is the Amplidyne.
It consists of the basic metadyne plus a cumulative winding on the direct
axis in series with the direct-axis load current, as shown by the winding
labeled *Comp* in the schematic diagram of Fig. 4-41.   This winding,
called a *compensating* winding, is very carefully designed to produce a
flux as nearly as possible equal and opposite to the flux produced by the
direct-axis armature current.   The negative-feedback effect of the load
current is thereby canceled, and the field winding has almost complete
control over the direct-axis flux.   The block diagram then reduces to
that shown in Fig. 4-42, comprising
two stages of amplification and two
time lags in cascade, with no internal
feedback.   Very little control-field
power input is required to produce
a large current in the short-circuited
quadrature axis of the armature.
The quadrature-axis current then

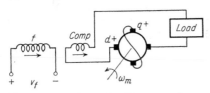

FIG. 4-41.   Schematic diagram of an
Amplidyne.

produces the principal magnetic field.   The power required to sustain
the quadrature-axis current is supplied mechanically by the motor driving
the Amplidyne.   Power amplification of the order of 20,000:1 can easily
be obtained.   This amplification ratio may be compared with values in
the range from about 20:1 to 100:1 for conventional generators.   The
response, however, is slower than that of the metadyne.   The principal
time lag in the Amplidyne is that due to the quadrature-axis time constant τ_{aq} and is in the range from 0.02 to 0.25 second.   Another contrast
between the metadyne and the Amplidyne is that the former is basically
a current source, while the Amplidyne is a voltage source.

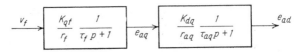

FIG. 4-42.   Block diagram of an Amplidyne.

Amplidynes are frequently used to provide the power amplification in a
variety of feedback control systems requiring controlled power output in
the range from a few hundred to a few thousand watts.   For example,
the exciter in the regulating systems of Figs. 4-21a and 4-22a may be an
Amplidyne.   The electronic amplifier may be omitted if the control
circuitry is capable of supplying a few watts to the Amplidyne control
field.   An Amplidyne may also be used as the generator in a Ward
Leonard speed or position control system (Fig. 4-22a or Fig. 4-23a) if the
power requirements of the regulated motor do not exceed a few kilowatts.
Various auxiliary or control-field windings may be added to either axis

of an Amplidyne to provide desirable performance characteristics. For example, a cumulative series field may be wound on the quadrature axis and connected in series with the quadrature-axis current. The quadrature-axis series field increases the gain factor K_{dq} and therefore decreases the quadrature-axis current for a specified direct-axis voltage output. Quadrature-axis commutation is thereby improved. The quadrature-axis series field increases the quadrature-axis time constant, however, because the inductance increases more than the resistance. The over-all amplification may be slightly reduced by the addition to the quadrature-axis resistance r_{aq}.

An example of the versatility of an Amplidyne for control purposes is shown in Fig. 4-43. Here the Amplidyne is the exciter for the field of a

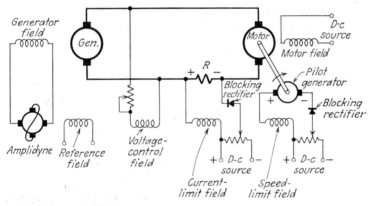

FIG. 4-43. Circuit using an Amplidyne to maintain constant motor-impressed voltage and to limit motor armature current and speed to predetermined values.

large generator in a Ward Leonard system. (The compensating winding of the Amplidyne is often not explicitly shown in schematic diagrams of Amplidyne circuits. It has been omitted in Fig. 4-43.) The objects are to maintain the motor terminal voltage constant at a preset value and at the same time to limit both the motor armature current and speed to predetermined, safe values. Four control fields are required in the Amplidyne. The reference field and the voltage control field, connected to produce opposing mmfs, maintain constant generator output voltage; the value of the generator voltage is adjusted by means of the rheostat in the voltage control field. Current limitation is provided by connecting the current-limit field so that its mmf opposes the reference-field mmf when the current in the motor armature is excessive, an action which lowers the generator voltage and so restores the current to safe values. Armature current is measured in terms of the voltage drop across a low resistance R (such as an ammeter shunt) in the armature circuit. If this voltage is greater than the opposing voltage picked off a d-c source, a current appears in the current-limit field. If this voltage is smaller, however, no current appears because of the presence of the blocking rectifier (a selenium or copper oxide rectifier); thus the current-limit field cannot aid the reference field and increase the armature current. Speed limitation is provided by the speed-limit field in an essentially identical manner, the measurement of speed being made by a pilot generator connected to the motor shaft. The values of current limit and speed limit may be set by the drop-wire rheostats across the d-c sources in the respective control-field circuits. The entire drive is thereby protected against severe electrical and mechanical strains, and at the same time changes in operating conditions may be brought about as rapidly as these limits permit.

4-11. The Metadyne as a Generalized Machine. In Chaps. 5 and 6 it is shown that the currents in a synchronous or induction machine can

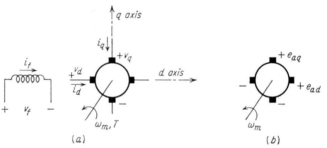

FIG. 4-44. (a) Schematic diagram of a metadyne with voltages impressed on both axes. (b) Illustrating reference directions for speed voltages.

be resolved into components which produce component magnetic fields in the air gap centered along two perpendicular axes of symmetry, like the direct and quadrature axes of the two-axis metadyne of Art. 4-10a. When this is done, the voltages can be expressed as the algebraic sum of speed and transformer voltages and the torque as the algebraic sum of the torques due to the interacting perpendicular fields. The basic equations of all machines then are similar to those of a metadyne. The two-axis metadyne may accordingly be regarded as a basic prototype, or *generalized machine*. The purpose of this article is to express the equations of a metadyne in a form which is similar to the equations of synchronous and induction machines.

Consider the simple metadyne shown in Fig. 4-44a. Let v_d and v_q be the voltages applied to the direct- and quadrature-axis brushes, respectively, and v_f be the voltage applied to the direct-axis stator field circuit. Also, let i_d, i_q, and i_f be the currents supplied to the respective circuits, as shown in Fig. 4-44. Note that the reference directions for the currents here are opposite to those in Figs. 4-38 and 4-39. For these reference directions, the mmfs of the field current and of the direct-axis armature current are in the same direction, and the mutual inductance L_{fd} between the field winding and the direct axis of the armature is a positive quantity. The flux linkages λ_f, λ_d, and λ_q with the field winding, the direct-axis armature winding, and the quadrature-axis armature winding can then be expressed in matrix form as

$$\begin{bmatrix} \lambda_f \\ \lambda_d \\ \lambda_q \end{bmatrix} = \begin{bmatrix} L_{ff} & L_{fd} & 0 \\ L_{fd} & L_{ad} & 0 \\ 0 & 0 & L_{aq} \end{bmatrix} \begin{bmatrix} i_f \\ i_d \\ i_q \end{bmatrix} \tag{4-138}$$

where L_{ff}, L_{ad}, and L_{aq} are the self-inductances of the field winding, the direct-axis armature winding, and the quadrature-axis armature winding, respectively. (More stator windings on either axis can easily be taken into account in the matrix.)

The voltages applied to the 3 windings are the algebraic sums of the resistance voltage drops ri, the transformer voltages $p\lambda$, and, in the armature, the speed voltages e_{ad} and e_{aq}. These speed voltages are given by Eqs. 4-133 and 4-132, respectively, with Φ_d and Φ_q the resultant direct- and quadrature-axis fluxes. The reference direction for direct-axis flux in Fig. 4-44 is the same as in Fig. 4-38a, and therefore the polarity of e_{aq} is the same in both cases, as indicated by the $+$ and $-$ signs with e_{aq} in Fig. 4-44b. The reference direction for quadrature-axis current and flux in Fig. 4-44 is opposite to that in Fig. 4-38b, and therefore the polarity of e_{ad} is opposite, as shown in Fig. 4-44b. The voltage equations can now be written in accordance with the reference directions of Fig. 4-44 as follows,

$$v_f = r_f i_f + p\lambda_f \tag{4-139}$$
$$v_d = r_{ad} i_d + p\lambda_d - e_{ad} \tag{4-140}$$
$$v_q = r_{aq} i_q + p\lambda_q + e_{aq} \tag{4-141}$$

where r_f, r_{ad}, and r_{aq} are the resistances of the respective windings.

With saturation neglected, Φ_q is proportional to i_q, and Eq. 4-133 becomes

$$e_{ad} = \omega_m G_{aq} i_q \tag{4-142}$$

where G_{aq} is a constant. Similarly Eq. 4-132 becomes

$$e_{aq} = \omega_m (G_{af} i_f + G_{ad} i_d) \tag{4-143}$$

where G_{af} and G_{ad} are constants. (For a 2-pole machine with sinusoidally distributed windings it can be shown that the speed-voltage coefficients equal the corresponding inductances; that is, $G_{aq} = L_{aq}$, $G_{ad} = L_{ad}$, and $G_{af} = L_{af}$.)

Substitution of Eqs. 4-138, 4-142, and 4-143 in Eqs. 4-139, 4-140, and 4-141 gives

$$\begin{bmatrix} v_f \\ v_d \\ v_q \end{bmatrix} = \begin{bmatrix} r_f + L_{ff}p & L_{fd}p & 0 \\ L_{fd}p & r_{ad} + L_{ad}p & -\omega_m G_{aq} \\ \omega_m G_{af} & \omega_m G_{ad} & r_{aq} + L_{aq}p \end{bmatrix} \begin{bmatrix} i_f \\ i_d \\ i_q \end{bmatrix} \qquad (4\text{-}144)$$

The magnetic torque in the positive direction of rotation (Fig. 4-44a) is the power input corresponding to the speed voltages divided by ω_m, or

$$T = \frac{e_{aq}i_q - e_{ad}i_d}{\omega_m} = G_{af}i_f i_q + (G_{ad} - G_{aq})i_d i_q \qquad (4\text{-}145)$$

Equations 4-144 and 4-145 express the terminal voltages and torque of the metadyne in terms of constant inductance and speed-voltage coefficients, the currents, and the speed. Similar equations will be found to apply to synchronous and induction machines when their currents and voltages are resolved into equivalent direct- and quadrature-axis components.

4-12. Résumé. Our primary objective in this chapter is to construct and analyze mathematical models of the idealized d-c machine. From these models we wish to find the dynamic performance not only of the machine itself as either a generator or motor but also of combinations of d-c machines and simple control elements forming systems capable of a variety of responses to control signals. These systems may be of the open-loop type, or they may involve feedback in external loops or in loops which include the magnetic circuit of a machine.

For the basic d-c machine, the dynamic equations are relatively simple and are easily established. They are given in Art. 4-2a. Accordingly, that article is the basic one in the chapter. The articles which follow it are devoted to examples of applying the equations, to the development of techniques for solving them, and to illustrating the adaptability and versatility of d-c machines as control devices.

When the d-c machine comprises a single field winding and an armature circuit, the basic equations show that there are three sources of time lag in the dynamic response of the machine. One is created by the field inductance, one by the armature-circuit inductance, and one by the mechanical equipment connected to the machine shaft, including the inertia of the armature itself. Analysis may often be simplified, however, by virtue of one or more time constants being small compared with others. Armature-circuit time constants, for example, may frequently be neglected in comparison with field time constants or inertia time constants. Thus, the build-up of a separately excited d-c generator operating at constant speed may often be characterized by a single exponential determined by the field time constant. Or the acceleration and deceleration of a motor operating with constant field current may similarly be described with sufficient accuracy in terms of the inertia time constant. Such simplification is of especial value when one is concerned with analysis of a system of machines rather than a single machine.

Since the more important and more interesting problems do deal with systems of machines, we have illustrated the use of several techniques for expediting their analysis, with emphasis on the effects of feedback on system performance. Among the problems are generator voltage control, motor speed control, and position control. A common system of machines for wide-range and precise control of speed, shaft position, and other motor performance features is based on a d-c motor whose armature is supplied from an adjustable-voltage d-c generator (the so-called Ward Leonard system). Among the techniques of analysis, in addition to the classical solution of differential equations, are the use of block diagrams, transfer functions, equivalent circuits, and frequency-response methods. These techniques, of course, are broadly applicable to system problems in general. They are applied more generously here than in other chapters because the idealized d-c machine provides an excellent vehicle for illustrating their use. Conversely, their application to the d-c machine brings out more fully its valuable potentialities as a control-system element.

One result of using these techniques is to view the machine as more than simply a brute-force energy-conversion device. The separately excited generator, for example, is looked upon as a power amplifier—a gain and one or more time constants, together with an increase in power level. The introduction of a shunt or series field is regarded as obtaining performance control through feedback. The shunt generator is seen to be similar to a feedback oscillator. From such broader viewpoints one can more fully assess the control possibilities of more complex d-c machines. The additions to the basic machine may include multiple field windings, series or shunt self-excited fields "tuned" so that the field-resistance line lies along the air-gap line (as in the Rototrol, Regulex, etc.), or brushes and multiple field windings in the direct as well as in the quadrature axis (as in the Amplidyne and metadyne). When these windings are combined with feedback through external circuits, much can be done to "tailor" the system characteristics to meet performance specifications. Ideally, the objectives are to increase the sensitivity or gain, to decrease the effective time constants or response time, and to decrease the sensitivity of the system to uncontrolled external disturbances. Not all these ideals are compatible. For example, the addition of negative feedback to a system has the beneficial effect of decreasing the response time and stiffening the system against the effects of disturbances; but the gain is decreased. To obtain the same power output with the same control power input, the power amplification must accordingly be increased. The cost of equipment with the increased power amplification must be balanced against the improvements in system performance.

Throughout all these analyses, then, it should always be borne in mind that the machines must have adequate capability to handle the voltage, current, and power surges demanded by the control signals. In other words, the signal-flow characteristics of the ideal machine must be coordinated with the limitations imposed by the properties of the materials making up the realistic machine and the cost of equipment to give the required power amplification.

PROBLEMS

4-1. A separately excited d-c generator has the following constants:
Field-winding resistance $r_f = 100$ ohms
Field-winding inductance $L_{ff} = 50$ henrys
Armature resistance $r_a = 0.05$ ohm
Armature inductance $L_a = 0.5$ mh
Generated emf constant $K_g = 100$ volts/field amp at 1,200 rpm
The generator is driven at a constant speed of 1,200 rpm. Its field and armature circuits are initially open.

a. At $t = 0$ a constant-voltage source of 250 volts is suddenly applied to the terminals of its field winding. Find the equation for the armature terminal voltage as a function of time, and sketch the curve.

b. After steady-state conditions have been established in (a), the armature is suddenly connected to a load of resistance 1.20 ohms and inductance 1.5 mh in series. Find the equations for (1) the armature current and (2) the armature terminal voltage as functions of time. Include the effect of the armature inductance and resistance. Sketch the curves.

c. Find the magnetic torque as a function of time.

4-2. A d-c motor M has its armature permanently connected to a source S as shown in Fig. 4-45a. The volt-ampere characteristic of the source is shown in Fig. 4-45b.

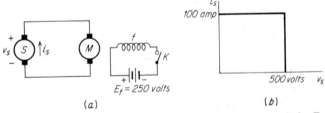

FIG. 4-45. (a) Circuit diagram and (b) idealized source characteristic, Prob. 4-2.

The motor field f is separately excited from a voltage source E_f as shown.
Motor armature resistance $r_a = 0.5$ ohm
Motor armature inductance negligible
Motor field resistance $r_f = 50$ ohms
Motor field inductance $L_{ff} = 50$ henrys

Motor torque at 5 amp field current and 100 amp armature current = 200 newton-m

Motor load = pure inertia. Total moment of inertia J of load and armature = 10 kg-m²

Neglect magnetic-saturation effects in the motor

The motor field switch K is closed at $t = 0$.

Derive an expression, with numerical values, for the speed in radians per second as a function of time in seconds. Sketch this curve roughly to scale. Indicate on it the final steady-state speed and the speed and time at which the break point in the source characteristic is reached. Compute the time required for the motor to reach approximately 96 per cent of its final speed.

4-3. A separately excited d-c motor drives a pure inertia load. The combined inertia of motor and load is J kg-m². The armature resistance is r_a ohms. Neglect armature inductance. The motor torque constant is K_m newton-m/amp.

With the motor initially at standstill and the field excited in the steady state, a constant voltage V_t is suddenly applied to the armature. Find the total heat dissipated in the motor armature in bringing the motor up to its final steady-state speed. Compare with the kinetic energy stored in the rotating masses.

4-4. Figure 4-46 shows a d-c generator and motor in a Ward Leonard connection with the generator excitation furnished by a push-pull Class A amplifier. It is part

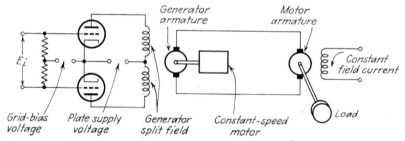

FIG. 4-46. Ward Leonard connection of a d-c motor and generator with generator excitation furnished by a vacuum-tube amplifier, Prob. 4-4.

of a scheme for obtaining automatic speed control of the motor. The motor drives a pure-inertia load. Linearized analysis of motor and generator performance is to be used. Armature reaction and all rotational losses are to be ignored.

The motor is rated at 3 hp and has the following characteristics:

Armature resistance = 0.75 ohm

Wk^2 (including load) = 40 lb-ft²

Torque per unit armature current = 1.25 newton-m/amp

Armature inductance negligible

The generator is of a size consistent with supplying the 3-hp motor and has the following characteristics:

Armature resistance = 0.25 ohm

Field resistance = 200 ohms (each section)

Field inductance = 10 henrys (each section)

Coefficient of coupling between field sections = 1.0

Generated voltage = 1,500 volts/amp difference in the split fields

Armature inductance negligible

The two tubes are identical and have an amplification factor $\mu = 10$ and plate resistance $r_p = 800$ ohms.

At an instant when the generator has zero net excitation and the motor is stationary, a constant voltage $E_i = 15.3$ volts is impressed at the amplifier input.

a. Give the numerical equation for motor speed in rpm as a function of time.

b. Sketch the curve of speed as a function of time.

c. Determine the time required for the speed to attain 98 per cent of its final value.

4-5. A d-c shunt motor is driving a pure-inertia load. The armature and field are supplied from a source of constant direct voltage. The motor is initially operating in the steady state. Neglect all rotational losses and armature reaction. Assume that the flux is directly proportional to the field current and that armature inductance is negligible.

The field rheostat is suddenly short-circuited. Develop the differential equation for the speed of the motor following this disturbance, using the ordinary symbols for the various quantities. Indicate all initial conditions. It is not necessary to solve the equation.

4-6. In modern continuous rolling mills the stands, or rolls, through which the bar passes in the rolling process are arranged in tandem, with the majority of the stands driven by separate motors. It is common to use d-c motors supplied with power from one or several generators. The transient changes of the motor speed under suddenly applied loads as the bar enters one stand after another may seriously affect the quality of the product. In particular, the *impact speed drop* which occurs at the maximum of the transient oscillation is of major importance.

Consider a single motor M supplied by a generator G, each with separate and constant field excitation. The internal voltage E of the generator may be considered constant, and the armature reaction of both machines may be considered negligible. With the motor running without external load and the system in the steady state, a bar enters the stand at $t = 0$, causing the load torque to be increased suddenly from zero to T. The following numerical values apply:

Internal voltage of G, $E = 387$ volts

Motor-plus-generator armature inductance, $L = 0.00768$ henry

Motor-plus-generator armature resistance, $R = 0.0353$ ohm

Moment of inertia of motor armature and connected rolls, all referred to motor speed, $J = 42.2$ kg-m^2

Electromechanical conversion constant for motor, $K_m = 4.23$ newton-m/amp

No-load armature current, $i_o = 35$ amp

Suddenly applied torque, $T = 2,040$ newton-m

Determine the following quantities:

a. The undamped angular frequency of the transient speed oscillations

b. The damping ratio of the system

c. The time constant of the system, in seconds

d. The initial speed, in rpm

e. The initial acceleration, in rpm per second

f. The ultimate speed drop, in rpm

g. The impact speed drop, in rpm

4-7. Figure 4-47 shows a d-c generator whose field current is supplied from an exciter. The generator and exciter are driven at constant speed. The machine constants are:

Exciter:

Field inductance $L_1 = 125$ henrys

Field resistance $R_1 = 250$ ohms

Generated voltage $= 1,000$ volts/field amp

Armature resistance negligible

Main generator:

Field inductance L_2 = 100 henrys
Field resistance R_2 = 100 ohms
Generated voltage = 250 volts/field amp
Armature resistance R_a = 1.0 ohm
Armature inductance negligible

Neglect the effect of the exciter-field current on the voltage drop in the armature of the main generator.

a. With switch S closed the reference voltage E_R is adjusted until v_t = 250 volts with R_L = 10 ohms. Find E_R.

b. With the system in the steady state as in part *a*, switch S is opened at $t = 0$. Find $v_t(t)$.

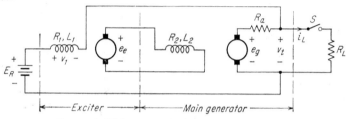

Fig. 4-47. Voltage-regulating system, Prob. 4-7.

4-8. For the speed control system of Example 4-5, Fig. 4-22, find the gain factor K_1 if the steady-state speed drop is 1.0 per cent for a load torque T_L = 20 newton-m. Find the corresponding values of the damping factor α, the undamped natural frequency ω_n, and the relative damping factor ζ.

4-9. The speed control system of Example 4-5 is adjusted for 1,800 rpm at no load. The amplifier gain is adjusted to meet the conditions described in Prob. 4-8. Find:

a. The initial field current of the generator
b. The initial field current of the exciter
c. The value of the reference voltage E_R

With the system initially in the steady state at no load, a step of load torque T_L = 20 newton-m is suddenly applied to the motor shaft.

d. Find the final steady-state values of (1) the motor armature current, (2) the motor terminal voltage, and (3) the generator internal emf e_{ag}.

e. Find the initial values ($t = 0+$) of (1) the armature current, (2) the generator emf e_{ag}, (3) the motor counter emf e_{am}, and (4) the motor speed.

f. Find the initial rates of change of the variables in (*e*).

g. Find the equations for (1) the armature current $i_a(t)$ and (2) the motor speed $\omega_m(t)$ as functions of time. Sketch the curves. Estimate the maximum instantaneous armature current and the minimum instantaneous speed.

4-10. The positional servo system of Fig. 4-23 has the following constants in mks units:

Load inertia = 1.25
Motor inertia = 0.5 × 10⁻³
Gear ratio = 50:1
Motor torque/amp = 0.3
Motor armature resistance = 20
Generator armature resistance = 10
Generator emf = 1,000 volts/field amp

The amplifier can be considered to be a current source with an output of 1 ma/volt input. The amplifier saturates at 50 ma output.

The output of the potentiometer system is 1.0 volt/rad at the motor shaft.

a. Find the natural frequency ω_n, the damping factor α, and the damping ratio ζ.

b. Find the steady-state load torque for a steady-state error of 0.1 rad, both measured at the load shaft. Find the corresponding values of amplifier input voltage, generator emf, and armature current.

c. Repeat (b) for a constant velocity of 0.1 rad/sec with load torque $T_L = 0$.

d. Find the maximum steady-state speed at the load shaft.

4-11. A servomechanism is described by the differential equation

$$2\frac{d^2\theta_o}{dt^2} + 10\frac{d\theta_o}{dt} = 50\varepsilon$$

a. Determine the open-loop transfer function θ_o/ε.

b. Determine the closed-loop transfer function θ_o/θ_i.

c. Compute the natural frequency ω_n and damping ratio ζ.

d. Compute the steady-state velocity-lag error for a constant-velocity input $\omega_i = 1.0$ rad/sec.

4-12. The terminal voltage v_t of the d-c generator shown in Fig. 4-48a responds to a step change in field voltage E_f with a time constant τ_f and a power gain

$$A_p = \frac{V_t^2/R_L}{I_f^2 R_f}$$

where V_t is the terminal voltage and I_f is the field current in the steady-state condition. Assume that the generator is driven at constant speed and that the magnetic circuit is linear.

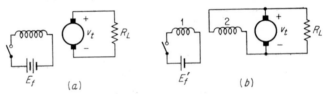

FIG. 4-48. (a) Separately excited generator and (b) the same generator with field winding in two parts for shunt and separate excitation, Prob. 4-12.

The single field winding on the machine shown in Fig. 4-48a is divided into 2 field windings as shown in Fig. 4-48b. The 2 field windings occupy the same winding space and have the same total copper cross-sectional area as the original winding. The steady-state current density in the field windings is to remain unchanged. The coupling between the 2 windings can be assumed unity. For the same steady-state terminal voltage V_t as for Fig. 4-48a (a new value E_f' of excitation voltage for Fig. 4-48b), winding 2 supplies 75 per cent and winding 1 supplies the rest of the required ampere-turns in the same direction. What are the new value of power gain and the new time constant of the d-c generator?

4-13. The following data are given for the voltage-regulating system shown in Fig. 4-32 and described in Art. 4-8:

Regulex exciter E:
    Shunt-field turns per pole = 1,000
    Shunt-field resistance = 300 ohms, not including tuning resistor

Shunt-field inductance = 100 henrys
Control-field turns per pole = 500
Control-field resistance = 500 ohms
Coefficient of coupling between field windings = 1.0
Generated emf = 0.40 volts/amp-turn in either field
Armature resistance and inductance negligible
Saturation negligible

Main generator G, 50 kw, 250 volts:
 Field resistance = 20 ohms
 Field inductance = 15 henrys
 Generated emf = 50 volts/field amp
 Armature resistance = 0.075 ohm
 Armature inductance negligible

The machines are driven at constant speed, the tuning resistor is adjusted so that the shunt field of the exciter provides all the steady-state excitation, and the reference voltage E_R is adjusted so that the terminal voltage v_{tg} of the generator is 250 volts at no load.

 a. Find the resistance of the tuning resistor.

 b. With no load initially, find the response of the terminal voltage $v_{tg}(t)$ as a function of time following the sudden application of a step of load current $i_L = 200$ amp.

4-14. Consider a voltage-regulating system similar to that of Fig. 4-32 except that a series self-energizing field is used on the exciter instead of the tuned shunt field (see Fig. 4-31). Data for the exciter and generator are the same as given in Prob. 4-13 except that the exciter shunt field is replaced by a series field of 75 turns per pole. Neglect the resistance and inductance of the series field. The series field is tuned to provide all the steady-state excitation. The initial settings are the same as described in Prob. 4-13.

Find the results required in (*a*) and (*b*) of Prob. 4-13.

4-15. A 2-kw 200-volt metadyne generator of the type shown in Fig. 4-39 is driven by a synchronous motor at 1,800 rpm and has the following constants:
 Control-field resistance $r_f = 20$ ohms
 Control-field inductance $L_{ff} = 2$ henrys
 Voltage constant $K_{qf} = 240$ volts/field amp
 Armature resistances $r_{aq} = r_{ad} = 4$ ohms
 Armature inductance $L_{aq} = 1.0$ henry
 Voltage constants $K_{dq} = K_{qd} = 120$ volts/amp

The metadyne supplies a 20-ohm resistive load at a voltage of 200 volts. Find the power input to the control field and the power amplification.

4-16. The voltage applied to the field winding of the metadyne generator described in Prob. 4-15 is held constant at 60 volts, and the load resistance is varied from 0 to 25 ohms. Plot the steady-state output volt-ampere characteristic.

4-17. The metadyne generator of Prob. 4-15 supplies power to a 40-ohm load. The field current is 2.0 amp, and the system is in the steady state initially.

At $t = 0$, the voltage applied to the field terminals is suddenly doubled. Find the output current $i_d(t)$ as a function of time. Sketch the curve. Neglect the direct-axis armature inductance.

4-18. The metadyne generator of Prob. 4-15 is initially operating in the steady state as described in Prob. 4-15.

At $t = 0$ the load resistance is suddenly increased to 40 ohms. Find the output current $i_d(t)$ as a function of time. Sketch the curve. Neglect the direct-axis armature inductance. Also neglect saturation.

4-19. A compensating winding is added to the metadyne of Prob. 4-15, thereby converting it into an Amplidyne. The Amplidyne supplies 200 volts to a 20-ohm load. Find the power input to the control field, and compare with the result of Prob. 4-15. Neglect the resistance of the compensating winding.

4-20. An Amplidyne exciter supplies field current to a 10-kw 125-volt d-c generator.

Amplidyne data:
  Control-field turns $N_c = 400$
  Control-field resistance $r_c = 40$ ohms
  Control-field inductance $L_c = 1.6$ henrys
  Quadrature-axis time constant $\tau_q = 0.10$ sec
  Direct-axis generated voltage = 5.0 volts/control-field amp-turn
  Armature resistance = 5.0 ohms

Generator data:
  Field resistance $r_{fg} = 35$ ohms
  Field inductance $L_{fg} = 10$ henrys
  Generated voltage constant = 50 volts/field amp
  Armature resistance = 0.075 ohm

  a. Compute the open-loop transfer function $KG(j\omega)$ relating generator output voltage at no load and Amplidyne control-field voltage.

  b. Compute the complex value of $KG(j\omega)$ at $\omega = 20$ rad/sec. Sketch the complete locus for positive values of ω.

  c. The system is now connected as a closed-loop voltage-regulating system. Will the system be stable without any antihunt feedback?

  d. Assume that the system is inherently stable or has been stabilized by an antihunt feedback circuit. What must be the value of the constant reference voltage to give a generator output voltage of 125 volts at no load?

  e. With the reference voltage held constant as in (*d*), what will be the generator terminal voltage when it is delivering an armature current of 80 amp?

4-21. A metadyne having no stator windings is driven at a constant speed. Its armature resistance $r_a = 0.10$ ohm measured between either pair of brushes. Its armature inductance $L_a = 0.01$ henry measured between either pair of brushes. A test taken with the direct axis open and a constant voltage of 20 volts applied to the quadrature-axis brushes gives a steady-state direct-axis open-circuit voltage of 600 volts. A similar test with the direct and quadrature axes interchanged gives similar results. Magnetic saturation is negligible.

This machine is used as a constant-voltage to constant-current transformer to supply substantially constant current to a variable-resistance load. The constant source voltage of 600 volts is applied to the quadrature-axis brushes, and the resistive load is connected to the direct-axis brushes.

  a. Compute the steady-state load current and source current when the load voltage is 600 volts.

  b. Compute the transient load current and source current when the load of (*a*) is suddenly short-circuited.

CHAPTER 5

Theory of Ideal Synchronous Machines

We have seen that a synchronous machine is one in which alternating currents are impressed on or obtained from one set of windings (the armature) and direct current is impressed on the other (the field). The armature winding, normally located on the stator, produces a rotating magnetic field like that described in Art. 3-4. The stator field rotates at synchronous speed, given by Eq. 3-61. Ability to produce a steady torque results from interaction of the stator and rotor fields when the rotor is also revolving at synchronous speed. Electromechanical energy conversion in either direction may then be achieved.

Analytical methods of examining the performance of polyphase synchronous machines will be developed in this chapter. In order to permit immediate emphasis on dynamic and transient aspects as well as on steady-state behavior, the machine will be idealized. It will be regarded as a group of coils with time-varying self- and mutual inductances, the general viewpoint being that of Arts. 2-3 and 3-3. The concept of dividing mmfs into direct- and quadrature-axis components will be found to be a great convenience, just as in certain of the d-c machine considerations of Chap. 4.

5-1. The Ideal Synchronous Machine. The bare, essential features of a 3-phase synchronous machine from the analytical viewpoint are shown in Fig. 5-1. On the stator are the 3 distributed windings a, b, and c, one in each phase. They are symbolized by the correspondingly labeled concentrated coils, the magnetic axes of the phase windings coinciding with the coil axes. On the rotor is the d-c field winding f. The possibility of other electrical circuits on the rotor formed by the damper bars in a practical machine will be ignored for the present to permit concentration on the most important events.

A salient-pole rotor is shown in Fig. 5-1. The rotor has two axes of symmetry, the polar, or *direct*, *axis d* and the interpolar, or *quadrature*, *axis q*. Obviously the magnetic flux paths have different permeances in the two axes. Even in a cylindrical-rotor machine there are differences

223

in the two axes, differences created mostly by the relatively large slots for the field winding. The d and q axes, of course, revolve with the rotor, while the magnetic axes of the three stator phases remain fixed. At the instant of time in Fig. 5-1, θ is the angle from the axis of phase a to the d axis. The corresponding angle from the phase b axis to the d axis is $\theta + 240°$ or, what amounts to the same thing, $\theta - 120°$. The angle from the phase c axis is $\theta + 120°$. As the rotor turns, θ varies with time. With a constant rotor angular velocity ω,

$$\theta = \omega t \tag{5-1}$$

(subject to θ being zero at $t = 0$).

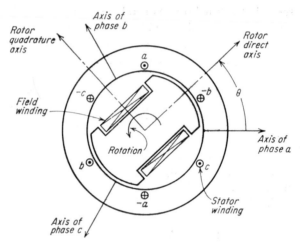

FIG. 5-1. Idealized synchronous machine.

To expedite analysis, the machine is idealized by ignoring saturation, hysteresis, and eddy currents. Linear coupled circuits are then being dealt with, and superposition is applicable. As will be seen in Art. 5-2, it will also be assumed that the space mmf and flux waves are sinusoidally distributed.

All the circuits a, b, c, and f have their own resistance and their own self-inductance and mutual inductances with respect to every other circuit. Moreover, the self- and mutual inductances associated with the stator circuits are functions of rotor position, varying periodically as the rotor revolves. The script letter $\mathcal{L}$ with the appropriate subscripts will be used to denote these inductances for any value of θ.

For analysis of the idealized machine, voltage-current relations are written in accordance with the methods of Art. 1-5. For any one of the windings, typified by Fig. 5-2, the relation in terms of the applied voltage and input current is

$$v = ri + \frac{d\lambda}{dt} = ri + p\lambda \tag{5-2}$$

where v is the applied voltage, i the input current, r the winding resistance, λ the flux linkages with the winding, and p the differential operator d/dt. With the subscript a, b, c, or f attached, this equation is written for each of the 4 windings. In terms of the self- and mutual inductances $\mathcal{L}$, the flux linkages are

$$\lambda_a = \mathcal{L}_{aa}i_a + \mathcal{L}_{ab}i_b + \mathcal{L}_{ac}i_c + \mathcal{L}_{af}i_f \tag{5-3}$$
$$\lambda_b = \mathcal{L}_{ba}i_a + \mathcal{L}_{bb}i_b + \mathcal{L}_{bc}i_c + \mathcal{L}_{bf}i_f \tag{5-4}$$
$$\lambda_c = \mathcal{L}_{ca}i_a + \mathcal{L}_{cb}i_b + \mathcal{L}_{cc}i_c + \mathcal{L}_{cf}i_f \tag{5-5}$$
$$\lambda_f = \mathcal{L}_{fa}i_a + \mathcal{L}_{fb}i_b + \mathcal{L}_{fc}i_c + \mathcal{L}_{ff}i_f \tag{5-6}$$

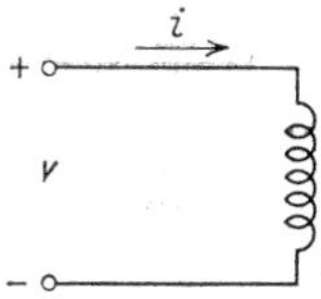

As usual, two like subscripts on $\mathcal{L}$ denote a self-inductance and two unlike subscripts denote a mutual inductance between the 2 windings concerned. In matrix form, Eqs. 5-3 through 5-6 become

Fig. 5-2. Typical winding.

$$\begin{bmatrix} \lambda_a \\ \lambda_b \\ \lambda_c \\ \lambda_f \end{bmatrix} = \begin{bmatrix} \mathcal{L}_{aa} & \mathcal{L}_{ab} & \mathcal{L}_{ac} & \mathcal{L}_{af} \\ \mathcal{L}_{ba} & \mathcal{L}_{bb} & \mathcal{L}_{bc} & \mathcal{L}_{bf} \\ \mathcal{L}_{ca} & \mathcal{L}_{cb} & \mathcal{L}_{cc} & \mathcal{L}_{cf} \\ \mathcal{L}_{fa} & \mathcal{L}_{fb} & \mathcal{L}_{fc} & \mathcal{L}_{ff} \end{bmatrix} \begin{bmatrix} i_a \\ i_b \\ i_c \\ i_f \end{bmatrix} \tag{5-7}$$

In these equations, all inductances except $\mathcal{L}_{ff}$ are functions of θ and are thus time-varying. Before proceeding further, therefore, it is desirable to examine the nature of these inductances.

5-2. Synchronous-machine Inductances. The nature of the inductance terms in Eqs. 5-3 to 5-7 can be determined from inspection of the machine geometry in Fig. 5-1 together with application of some of the idealizing assumptions.

a. Rotor Self-inductance and Stator-Rotor Mutual Inductances. Since the stator is a cylindrical structure, the self-inductance of the field winding f will not depend on rotor position (in the absence of stator slot effects). Hence

$$\mathcal{L}_{ff} = L_{ff} \tag{5-8}$$

The stator-to-rotor mutual inductances will vary periodically with θ. Between phase a and the field winding, for example, the mutual will be a maximum L_{af} at $\theta = 0$, zero at $\theta = 90°$, a negative maximum $-L_{af}$ at $\theta = 180°$, and zero again at $\theta = 270°$. Accordingly, with space mmf and flux distributions assumed sinusoidal,

$$\mathcal{L}_{af} = \mathcal{L}_{fa} = L_{af} \cos \theta \tag{5-9}$$

with similar expressions for phases b and c except that θ is replaced by $\theta - 120°$ and $\theta + 120°$, respectively.

b. Stator Self-inductances. The self-inductance of any stator phase will always have a positive value, but there will be a second-harmonic variation because of the different air-gap geometries in the d and q axes. The inductance $\mathcal{L}_{aa}$, for example, will be a maximum for $\theta = 0$, a minimum for $\theta = 90°$, a maximum again for $\theta = 180°$, and so on. For more complete investigation, consider the flux linkages with phase a when only it is excited.

With space harmonics ignored, the mmf of phase a is a cosine wave centered on the phase a axis. The wave is shown in Fig. 5-3, which is a developed sketch of the stator of Fig. 5-1 with only the phase a winding retained. The peak amplitude is

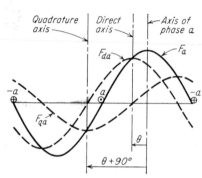

FIG. 5-3. Phase a mmf wave and its d- and q-axis components.

$$F_a = N_a i_a \qquad (5\text{-}10)$$

where N_a symbolizes the effective turns per phase and includes any factor required to relate actual turns in a distributed winding to equivalent turns in a concentrated winding. Now let this mmf wave be resolved into two component sinusoidal space distributions, one centered on the d axis and one on the q axis. The component waves are also shown in Fig. 5-3. Their peak amplitudes are

$$F_{da} = F_a \cos \theta \qquad (5\text{-}11)$$

and
$$F_{qa} = F_a \cos (\theta + 90°) = -F_a \sin \theta \qquad (5\text{-}12)$$

The advantage of so resolving the mmf wave is that the two component mmfs act on specific air-gap geometries in their respective axes. Thus, the permeance coefficient $\mathcal{P}_{gd}$ can be ascribed to the d axis and the coefficient $\mathcal{P}_{gq}$ to the q axis. These coefficients give the space-fundamental flux per pole produced by unit-amplitude fundamental mmf wave centered on the associated axis. They include not only the true permeance but also the constant factors required to relate flux per pole with the peak value of the sinusoidal mmf wave. They are here regarded as known, constant quantities, and their values can be found by flux plots for a specific machine geometry. The fundamental air-gap fluxes per pole along the two axes are accordingly

$$\varphi_{gda} = F_{da}\mathcal{P}_{gd} = F_a\mathcal{P}_{gd} \cos \theta \qquad (5\text{-}13)$$

and
$$\varphi_{gqa} = F_{qa}\mathcal{P}_{gq} = -F_a\mathcal{P}_{gq} \sin \theta \qquad (5\text{-}14)$$

The air-gap flux linking phase a is then

$$\varphi_{gaa} = \varphi_{gda} \cos \theta - \varphi_{gqa} \sin \theta \tag{5-15}$$
$$\varphi_{gaa} = F_a(\mathcal{P}_{gd} \cos^2 \theta + \mathcal{P}_{gq} \sin^2 \theta) \tag{5-16}$$
$$\varphi_{gaa} = N_a i_a \left(\frac{\mathcal{P}_{gd} + \mathcal{P}_{gq}}{2} + \frac{\mathcal{P}_{gd} - \mathcal{P}_{gq}}{2} \cos 2\theta \right) \tag{5-17}$$

Since inductance is the proportionality factor relating flux linkages to current, the self-inductance $\mathcal{L}_{gaa}$ of phase a due to air-gap flux is

$$\mathcal{L}_{gaa} = \frac{N_a \varphi_{gaa}}{i_a} = N_a^2 \left(\frac{\mathcal{P}_{gd} + \mathcal{P}_{gq}}{2} + \frac{\mathcal{P}_{gd} - \mathcal{P}_{gq}}{2} \cos 2\theta \right) \tag{5-18}$$
$$\mathcal{L}_{gaa} = L_{g0} + L_{g2} \cos 2\theta \tag{5-19}$$

L_{g0} being the constant term and L_{g2} the amplitude of the second-harmonic variation. To get the total self-inductance $\mathcal{L}_{aa}$, the leakage inductance L_{al}, representing flux which does not cross the gap to the rotor, must be added. That is,

$$\mathcal{L}_{aa} = L_{al} + \mathcal{L}_{gaa} \tag{5-20}$$
$$\mathcal{L}_{aa} = L_{aa0} + L_{g2} \cos 2\theta \tag{5-21}$$

where

$$L_{aa0} = L_{al} + L_{g0} \tag{5-22}$$

This variation of $\mathcal{L}_{aa}$ with θ is shown in Fig. 5-4. The corresponding expressions for $\mathcal{L}_{bb}$ and $\mathcal{L}_{cc}$ may be written by replacing θ in Eq. 5-21 by $\theta - 120°$ and $\theta + 120°$, respectively.

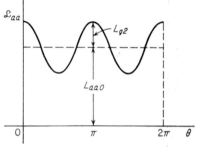

FIG. 5-4. Variation of self-inductance of stator phase.

c. *Stator Mutual Inductances.* The mutual inductances between stator phases will also exhibit a second-harmonic variation with θ because of the rotor shape. The mutual inductance $\mathcal{L}_{ba} = \mathcal{L}_{ab}$ between phases a and b can be found by evaluating the air-gap flux φ_{gba} linking phase b when only phase a is excited. From Eq. 5-15 with θ replaced by $\theta - 120°$ because we now wish to evaluate the flux linking phase b,

$$\varphi_{gba} = \varphi_{gda} \cos (\theta - 120°) - \varphi_{gqa} \sin (\theta - 120°) \tag{5-23}$$

With φ_{gda} and φ_{gqa} replaced by their values from Eqs. 5-13 and 5-14,

$$\varphi_{gba} = F_a[\mathcal{P}_{gd} \cos \theta \cos (\theta - 120°) + \mathcal{P}_{gq} \sin \theta \sin (\theta - 120°)] \tag{5-24}$$

By trigonometric transformations and use of Eq. 5-10 for F_a, this expression reduces to

$$\varphi_{gba} = N_a i_a \left[-\frac{\mathcal{P}_{gd} + \mathcal{P}_{gq}}{4} + \frac{\mathcal{P}_{gd} - \mathcal{P}_{gq}}{2} \cos (2\theta - 120°) \right] \tag{5-25}$$

The mutual inductance between phases a and b due to air-gap flux is then

$$\mathcal{L}_{gba} = \frac{N_a \varphi_{gba}}{i_a} = -0.5L_{g0} + L_{g2} \cos (2\theta - 120°) \qquad (5\text{-}26)$$

where L_{g0} and L_{g2} have the same meaning as in Eq. 5-19. There is also a very small amount of mutual flux which does not cross the air gap (e.g., flux around the ends of the windings). With this flux neglected, the desired mutual inductance is then

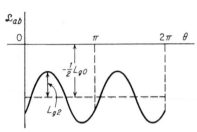

FIG. 5-5. Variation of mutual inductance between stator phases.

$$\mathcal{L}_{ab} = \mathcal{L}_{ba} = -0.5L_{g0}$$
$$+ L_{g2} \cos (2\theta - 120°) \qquad (5\text{-}27)$$

The variation with θ is illustrated in Fig. 5-5. Note that the amplitude of the second-harmonic variation is the same as for the stator self-inductance (Eq. 5-21). As in part b of this article, the mutual inductances between other stator phases can be found by appropriately replacing θ in Eq. 5-27.

d. *Summary of Inductances.* It will be helpful to summarize the results of this article by listing the expressions for the various inductances entering into Eqs. 5-3 to 5-7.

For the stator self-inductances,

$$\begin{aligned}
\mathcal{L}_{aa} &= L_{aa0} + L_{g2} \cos 2\theta \\
\mathcal{L}_{bb} &= L_{aa0} + L_{g2} \cos (2\theta + 120°) \\
\mathcal{L}_{cc} &= L_{aa0} + L_{g2} \cos (2\theta - 120°)
\end{aligned} \qquad (5\text{-}28)$$

For the stator-to-stator mutual inductances,

$$\begin{aligned}
\mathcal{L}_{ab} &= \mathcal{L}_{ba} = -0.5L_{g0} + L_{g2} \cos (2\theta - 120°) \\
\mathcal{L}_{bc} &= \mathcal{L}_{cb} = -0.5L_{g0} + L_{g2} \cos 2\theta \\
\mathcal{L}_{ca} &= \mathcal{L}_{ac} = -0.5L_{g0} + L_{g2} \cos (2\theta + 120°)
\end{aligned} \qquad (5\text{-}29)$$

For the rotor self-inductance,

$$\mathcal{L}_{ff} = L_{ff} \qquad (5\text{-}30)$$

For the stator-to-rotor mutual inductances,

$$\begin{aligned}
\mathcal{L}_{af} &= \mathcal{L}_{fa} = L_{af} \cos \theta \\
\mathcal{L}_{bf} &= \mathcal{L}_{fb} = L_{af} \cos (\theta - 120°) \\
\mathcal{L}_{cf} &= \mathcal{L}_{fc} = L_{af} \cos (\theta + 120°)
\end{aligned} \qquad (5\text{-}31)$$

The important feature of this array of equations is that they show the variations of the inductances $\mathcal{L}$ in terms of θ and constants symbolized by L with the appropriate subscripts. The L quantities will now be regarded as known machine constants, either determined by test or calculated by the designer from physical dimensions and properties of materials. We wish to express the performance of the machine in terms of these known constants and the appropriate dependent and independent variables.

5-3. Transformation to Direct- and Quadrature-axis Variables. Substitution of Eqs. 5-28 to 5-31 in the flux-linkage equations 5-3 to 5-6, followed by substitution of the flux-linkage expressions in the four voltage-current relations typified by Eq. 5-2, will yield a set of simultaneous equations which must be satisfied by the synchronous machine. This process yields equations which are algebraically very complicated, however, and their solution would be a most unwieldy task. The analysis is greatly simplified by a change of variables for current, voltage, and flux linkage.

The general idea underlying the transformation is not unlike that in Eqs. 5-11 and 5-12, where the mmf of phase a alone is divided into components along the direct and quadrature axes. When this is done with all three phases excited, the total stator mmfs along the two axes are

$$F_{ds} = N_a[i_a \cos \theta + i_b \cos (\theta - 120°) + i_c \cos (\theta + 120°)] \quad (5\text{-}32)$$
$$F_{qs} = N_a[-i_a \sin \theta - i_b \sin (\theta - 120°) - i_c \sin (\theta + 120°)] \quad (5\text{-}33)$$

These equations suggest that new current variables i_d and i_q be defined in terms of the bracketed quantities. Arbitrary constants k_d and k_q can also be included. Thus,

$$i_d = k_d[i_a \cos \theta + i_b \cos (\theta - 120°) + i_c \cos (\theta + 120°)] \quad (5\text{-}34)$$
$$i_q = k_q[-i_a \sin \theta - i_b \sin (\theta - 120°) - i_c \sin (\theta + 120°)] \quad (5\text{-}35)$$

Equations 5-32 and 5-33 then simplify to

$$F_{ds} = \frac{N_a}{k_d} i_d \quad (5\text{-}36)$$

$$F_{qs} = \frac{N_a}{k_q} i_q \quad (5\text{-}37)$$

The relative simplicity of Eqs. 5-36 and 5-37 compared with Eqs. 5-32 and 5-33 is representative of the simplification achieved by the change of variable.

The constants k_d and k_q may be chosen so as to simplify the numerical coefficients in performance equations to be derived in the next article.

In most of the machinery literature, both k_d and k_q are taken as $\frac{2}{3}$. This choice will also be followed here, so that

$$i_d = \frac{2}{3}[i_a \cos \theta + i_b \cos (\theta - 120°) + i_c \cos (\theta + 120°)] \qquad (5\text{-}38)$$
$$i_q = \frac{2}{3}[-i_a \sin \theta - i_b \cos (\theta - 120°) - i_c \cos (\theta + 120°)] \qquad (5\text{-}39)$$

These equations define currents which produce the same magnetic fields as the actual phase currents. The idea behind the transformation is an old one stemming from the work of André Blondel in France, and the technique is sometimes referred to as the *Blondel two-reaction method*. Much of the development in the form used here was carried out by R. E. Doherty, C. A. Nickle, R. H. Park, and their associates in the United States. Since the stator mmfs are resolved along axes which turn with the rotor, the magnetic fields of i_d and i_q are obviously stationary with respect to the rotor. The currents i_d and i_q are equivalent to the brush currents in a two-axis sinusoidally distributed commutated winding on the stator whose brushes are attached to the d and q axes of the rotor.

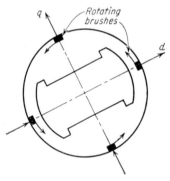

FIG. 5-6. Brush currents in commutated stator winding. They are the equivalents of i_d and i_q.

This equivalence may be visualized with the aid of Fig. 5-6 and by comparison with the discussion in Art. 4-11.

Three variables are present in the original set of phase currents i_a, i_b, and i_c. In the general case, therefore, three current variables must also appear in the new set. Since the two currents i_d and i_q produce the correct magnetic field, the third variable must produce no space fundamental field in the air gap. It can be shown that this condition is met by the variable

$$i_0 = \frac{1}{3}(i_a + i_b + i_c) \qquad (5\text{-}40)$$

where the factor $\frac{1}{3}$ is chosen arbitrarily as were k_d and k_q in Eqs. 5-38 and 5-39. Those who are familiar with the method of symmetrical components will recognize i_0 as the *zero-sequence current*. Since i_0 produces no flux linking the rotor, it is associated with the stator leakage inductance L_{al}. When the phase currents are constrained so that their sum is zero (as in an ungrounded Y connection or under balanced 3-phase conditions in any connection), i_0 must also be zero. This is the case with any problems that we are concerned with in this book.

The relations between the new and the phase variables are thus given by Eqs. 5-38 through 5-40. The reverse relations by which the phase variables are obtained when the $dq0$ variables are known can be found by

simultaneous solution of these three equations.   To summarize, the two
sets of relations, written in matrix form, are as follows:

$$\begin{bmatrix} i_d \\ i_q \\ i_0 \end{bmatrix} = \frac{2}{3} \begin{bmatrix} \cos \theta & \cos (\theta - 120°) & \cos (\theta + 120°) \\ - \sin \theta & - \sin (\theta - 120°) & - \sin (\theta + 120°) \\ \frac{1}{2} & \frac{1}{2} & \frac{1}{2} \end{bmatrix} \begin{bmatrix} i_a \\ i_b \\ i_c \end{bmatrix}$$

$$(5\text{-}41)$$

$$\begin{bmatrix} i_a \\ i_b \\ i_c \end{bmatrix} = \begin{bmatrix} \cos \theta & - \sin \theta & 1 \\ \cos (\theta - 120°) & - \sin (\theta - 120°) & 1 \\ \cos (\theta + 120°) & - \sin (\theta + 120°) & 1 \end{bmatrix} \begin{bmatrix} i_d \\ i_q \\ i_0 \end{bmatrix} \quad (5\text{-}42)$$

Exactly the same transformations are made for the flux linkages λ and
the applied armature voltages v.   Thus, Eqs. 5-41 and 5-42 can be rewritten twice, once with λ replacing i and then with v replacing i.   The
results are, respectively, the relations between the phase linkages (λ_a, λ_b,
λ_c) and the $dq0$ linkages (λ_d, λ_q, λ_0) and between the phase voltages
(v_a, v_b, v_c) and the $dq0$ voltages (v_d, v_q, v_0).

At this point, let us look back and see where we are.   The basic relations to be analyzed are still those in Eqs. 5-2 to 5-7.   The variations of
the inductances in these relations are given by Eqs. 5-28 to 5-31.   Now we
have digressed to examine a transformation of variable which will greatly
simplify the analysis of the basic relations.   The next step is to carry
out the transformations in Eqs. 5-2 to 5-7 to find the relations among the
new variables.

5-4. Basic Machine Relations in $dq0$ Variables.   The flux-linkage
relations (Eqs. 5-3 to 5-6) become much simpler when expressed in terms
of the new variables.   They are obtained by substituting Eqs. 5-28 to
5-31 in 5-3 to 5-6 and using the $dq0$ transformations for both flux linkages
and currents.   The manipulations are somewhat laborious and will be
omitted here because they are simply algebraic in nature.   (These
manipulations, incidentally, can be systematized by carrying them out in
matrix form.)   The results are

$$\lambda_f = L_{ff}i_f + \tfrac{3}{2}L_{af}i_d \qquad (5\text{-}43)$$
$$\lambda_d = L_{af}i_f + L_d i_d \qquad (5\text{-}44)$$
$$\lambda_q = L_q i_q \qquad (5\text{-}45)$$
$$\lambda_0 = L_0 i_0 \qquad (5\text{-}46)$$

In these equations, certain inductance terms have been given new
symbols.   They are

$$L_d = L_{al} + \tfrac{3}{2}(L_{g0} + L_{g2}) \qquad (5\text{-}47)$$
$$L_q = L_{al} + \tfrac{3}{2}(L_{g0} - L_{g2}) \qquad (5\text{-}48)$$
$$L_0 = L_{al} \qquad (5\text{-}49)$$

The quantities L_d, L_q, and L_0 are called, respectively, the *direct-axis synchronous inductance*, the *quadrature-axis synchronous inductance*, and the *zero-sequence inductance*. As we shall see in later articles, L_d and L_q are particularly important machine constants which can readily be determined from simple tests. In $dq0$ terms, the voltage-current relations typified by Eq. 5-2, when written for the field winding and for each of the 3 stator phases, become

$$v_f = r_f i_f + p\lambda_f \qquad (5\text{-}50)$$
$$v_d = r_a i_d + p\lambda_d - \lambda_q \omega \qquad (5\text{-}51)$$
$$v_q = r_a i_q + p\lambda_q + \lambda_d \omega \qquad (5\text{-}52)$$
$$v_0 = r_a i_0 + p\lambda_0 \qquad (5\text{-}53)$$

where $\omega = p\theta = d\theta/dt$ is the electrical angular velocity. Again the details of algebraic manipulation are omitted. Equations 5-50 and 5-53 are self-evident, however. Equations 5-51 and 5-52 are obtained by writing the transformation equations 5-41 for v_d and v_q, substituting Eq. 5-2 written for v_a, v_b, and v_c, and recognizing combinations of terms as λ_d, λ_q, $p\lambda_d$, and $p\lambda_q$.

We now have the basic relations for analysis of the idealized synchronous machine. They consist of the flux-linkage equations 5-43 to 5-46, the voltage equations 5-50 to 5-53, and the transformation equations 5-41 and 5-42. A common procedure is the substitution of Eqs. 5-43 to 5-46 in Eqs. 5-50 to 5-53, the solution of the resulting differential equations (subject to the conditions of the specific problem and in conjunction with other relations prescribed by that problem), and substitution in Eq. 5-42 to determine phase quantities. When the machine speed ω is constant, the differential equations are linear with constant coefficients. This fact, together with the relative simplicity of the equations, constitutes one of the principal advantages of the dq transformation. The analytical procedure will be illustrated by a number of applications in the following articles of this chapter. We shall then be in a position to note some of the physical interpretations resulting from the dq transformation.

In Eqs. 5-51 and 5-52, the terms $\lambda_q\omega$ and $\lambda_d\omega$ are speed voltages. The terms $p\lambda_d$ and $p\lambda_q$ are transformer voltages. In many problems the transformer voltages are small compared with the speed voltages, and the $p\lambda_d$ and $p\lambda_q$ terms may be neglected, providing further simplification. As will be illustrated later, omission of these terms corresponds to neglect of the harmonics and d-c component in the transient solution for stator voltages and currents.

In using these equations and the corresponding relations in the machinery literature, careful note should be made of the sign conventions and units employed. Here, applied voltage and current into the armature windings are positive (i.e., motor conditions are positive; see Eq. 5-2 and Fig. 5-2), and positive armature current produces positive armature and field linkages. In many references,[1] generator conditions are positive: armature voltages are generated voltages, and positive armature current is out of the winding and produces negative armature and field linkages. Under the latter convention, the signs of the i_d, i_q, and i_0 terms in Eqs. 5-43 through 5-46 and 5-51 through 5-53 become negative. Also, normal mks units—volts, amperes, ohms, henrys, etc.—are used here; often in the literature one of several per-unit systems is used to provide numerical simplification.[2]

To complete the basic array, relations for power and torque are needed. The instantaneous power input to the 3-phase stator is

$$p_s = v_a i_a + v_b i_b + v_c i_c \tag{5-54}$$

Phase quantities may be eliminated from Eq. 5-54 by using Eq. 5-42 written for voltages and currents. The result is

$$p_s = \tfrac{3}{2}(v_d i_d + v_q i_q + 2v_0 i_0) \tag{5-55}$$

The electromagnetic torque developed is readily obtained as the power input corresponding to the speed voltages divided by the shaft speed (in mechanical radians per second). From Eq. 5-55 with the speed-voltage terms from 5-51 and 5-52, and by recognizing ω as the speed in electrical radians per second,

$$T = \frac{3}{2} \frac{\text{poles}}{2} (\lambda_d i_q - \lambda_q i_d) \tag{5-56}$$

The torque of Eq. 5-56 is positive for motor action. It can be seen that this result is in general conformity with torque production from interacting magnetic fields as expressed in Eq. 3-34. In Eq. 5-56, we are superimposing the interaction of components: d-axis magnetic field with q-axis mmf, and q-axis magnetic field with d-axis mmf. For both interactions the sine of the space-displacement angle has unity magnitude. Again the use of the dq transformation leads to a compact result which can be related to our earlier work.

This torque is available to overcome the counter torque of the load and to provide acceleration. The inertia torque required to accelerate the rotating mass is given by

$$T_{\text{inertia}} = J\left(\frac{2}{\text{poles}}\right)\frac{d\omega}{dt} = J\left(\frac{2}{\text{poles}}\right)\frac{d^2\theta}{dt^2} \tag{5-57}$$

[1] See, for example, Charles Concordia, "Synchronous Machines," John Wiley & Sons, Inc., New York, 1951.

[2] See A. W. Rankin, Per-unit Impedances of Synchronous Machines, *Trans. AIEE*, vol. 64, pt. I, pp. 569-573, pt. II, pp. 839-841, 1945.

where J is the moment of inertia of the rotor and the mechanical equipment coupled to it. The factor 2/poles is required because the angular measurement in θ and ω is electrical radians rather than mechanical radians. Further consideration of dynamic aspects is given in Art. 5-11.

5-5. Steady-state Analysis. The performance of synchronous motors and generators under balanced steady-state conditions may readily be analyzed by applying the equations of the preceding article.

a. Voltage Equations. With the machine operating at synchronous speed and time $t = 0$ when the d axis is lined up with the phase a axis, the angle θ (Fig. 5-1) is given by

$$\theta = \omega t \tag{5-58}$$

where ω is the stator angular frequency. Let the three stator currents be

$$i_a = \sqrt{2}\, I \cos (\omega t + \alpha) \tag{5-59}$$
$$i_b = \sqrt{2}\, I \cos (\omega t + \alpha - 120°) \tag{5-60}$$
$$i_c = \sqrt{2}\, I \cos (\omega t + \alpha + 120°) \tag{5-61}$$

where α is the phase angle of i_a with respect to the time origin. Substitution of Eqs. 5-58 to 5-61 in 5-41, followed by reduction of the resulting expressions, yields for the $dq0$-component currents

$$i_d = \sqrt{2}\, I \cos \alpha \tag{5-62}$$
$$i_q = \sqrt{2}\, I \sin \alpha \tag{5-63}$$
$$i_0 = 0 \tag{5-64}$$

The currents i_d and i_q are constant. This result is what would be expected from looking at the dq transformation physically. As shown in Art. 3-4, the three phase currents produce a rotating field in the air gap. To an observer on the rotor, the field appears stationary. In applying the dq transformation, we are simply resolving this stationary field into components along the two rotor axes. The components themselves are then naturally steady fields fixed with respect to the rotor, just as though they had been produced by direct currents in windings on the two rotor axes. In the balanced steady state, therefore, the stator alternating currents appear as components which are steady direct currents when viewed from the dq axes.

The linkages λ_d and λ_q (Eqs. 5-44 and 5-45) are also constant. The $p\lambda_d$ and $p\lambda_q$ terms therefore drop out of the voltage equations 5-51 and 5-52. After substitution of Eqs. 5-44 and 5-45, these two voltage equations become

$$v_d = r_a i_d - \omega L_q i_q \tag{5-65}$$
$$v_q = r_a i_q + \omega L_{af} i_f + \omega L_d i_d \tag{5-66}$$

The quantities ωL_d and ωL_q are known as the *direct-* and *quadrature-axis synchronous reactances*, respectively, and are symbolized by x_d and x_q. They enable us to account for the inductive effects created by the armature mmf wave by separately computing the effects for the d- and q-axis components of the wave. The component voltages are then

$$v_d = r_a i_d - x_q i_q \tag{5-67}$$
$$v_q = \omega L_{af} i_f + r_a i_q + x_d i_d \tag{5-68}$$

By substitution in Eq. 5-42 written for voltages, the phase a voltage becomes

$$v_{ta} = (r_a i_d - x_q i_q) \cos \omega t - (\omega L_{af} i_f + r_a i_q + x_d i_d) \sin \omega t \tag{5-69}$$

Because flux linkages are constant, the field voltage is given by the simple Ohm's law relation

$$v_f = r_f i_f \tag{5-70}$$

b. Phasor Diagrams. In steady-state investigations, we are usually interested in rms values and phase displacements rather than in instantaneous values as in Eq. 5-69. The relation between rms phase currents and the dq components can be found from the reverse transformation (Eq. 5-42). Thus, with θ as in Eq. 5-58,

$$i_a = i_d \cos \omega t - i_q \sin \omega t$$
$$= i_d \cos \omega t + i_q \cos (\omega t + 90°) \tag{5-71}$$

In phasor form with the dq axes as reference, the rms phase current I_a may then be written

$$I_a = I_d + j I_q \tag{5-72}$$

where $\qquad I_d = \dfrac{i_d}{\sqrt{2}} \qquad$ and $\qquad I_q = \dfrac{i_q}{\sqrt{2}}$

Similarly, $\qquad V_{ta} = V_d + j V_q \tag{5-73}$

where $\qquad V_d = \dfrac{v_d}{\sqrt{2}} \qquad$ and $\qquad V_q = \dfrac{v_q}{\sqrt{2}}$

In Eqs. 5-68 and 5-69, the quantity $\omega L_{af} i_f$ is the peak value of the phase voltage when i_f alone is acting ($i_d = i_q = 0$). The rms value

$$E_f = \frac{\omega L_{af} i_f}{\sqrt{2}} \tag{5-74}$$

is called the *excitation emf*, or *excitation voltage*. In terms of these newly defined quantities, Eqs. 5-67 and 5-68 may be written

$$V_d = r_a I_d - x_q I_q \tag{5-75}$$
$$V_q = E_f + r_a I_q + x_d I_d \tag{5-76}$$

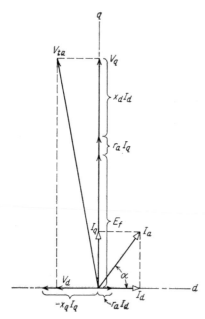

FIG. 5-7. Phasor representation of dq currents and voltages.

The combining of terms in Eqs. 5-75 and 5-76 to yield the phase voltage of Eq. 5-73 can be carried out diagrammatically as shown in Fig. 5-7. Here the d axis is taken horizontally and the q axis vertically. This diagram is redrawn in Fig. 5-8 with the axes rotated $-90°$ to be more conveniently located. Figure 5-8 is the phasor diagram for a synchronous motor. The phase displacements and relations between motor currents and voltages can be determined from the geometry of the phasor diagram. The angle ϕ is the power-factor angle of the motor. The terminal voltage can now be written in phasor form as

$$V_t = E_f + r_a I_a + j x_d I_d + j x_q I_q \quad (5\text{-}77)$$

Phasor diagrams for a synchronous generator are more conveniently drawn in terms of generated voltages and current output from the machine. A diagram drawn for generator conditions is shown in Fig. 5-9. The phasor voltage relation is then

$$E_f = V_t + r_a I_a + j x_d I_d + j x_q I_q \quad (5\text{-}78)$$

For both generators and motors, the reactance x_d is greater than the reactance x_q because the permeance of the air gap is greater in the direct axis (see Eqs. 5-47 and 5-48 and Art. 5-2). Usually x_q is between 0.6 and 0.7 of x_d. Typical values are given in Table 5-1 for the principal types

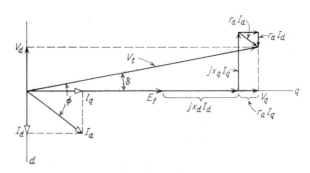

FIG. 5-8. Phasor diagram for synchronous motor.

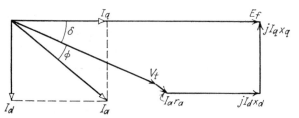

FIG. 5-9. Phasor diagram for synchronous generator.

of synchronous machines.[1] Note that a small salient-pole effect is present in turbine-generators, even though they are cylindrical-rotor machines, because of the effect of the rotor slots on the quadrature-axis permeance.

Table 5-1
Typical Per-unit Values of Machine Reactances
(Machine kva rating as base)

	Synchronous motors		Synchronous condensers	Water-wheel generators	Turbine-generators
	High-speed	Low-speed			
x_d	0.65 (min)	0.80	....	0.60	
	0.80 (av)	1.10	1.60	1.00	1.15
	0.90 (max)	1.50	....	1.25	
x_q	0.50 (min)	0.60	....	0.40	
	0.65 (av)	0.80	1.00	0.65	1.00
	0.70 (max)	1.10	....	0.80	

In using the phasor diagram of Fig. 5-9, the armature current must be resolved into its d- and q-axis components. This resolution assumes that the phase angle $\phi + \delta$ of the armature current with respect to the excitation voltage is known. Often, however, the power-factor angle ϕ at the machine terminals is explicitly known, rather than the internal power-factor angle $\phi + \delta$. The phasor diagram of Fig. 5-9 is repeated by the solid-line phasors in Fig. 5-10. Study of this phasor diagram shows that the dashed phasor $o'a'$, perpendicular to I_a, equals jI_ax_q. This result follows geometrically from the fact that triangles $o'a'b'$ and oab are similar, because their corresponding sides are perpendicular. Thus

$$\frac{o'a'}{oa} = \frac{b'a'}{ba} \tag{5-79}$$

or

$$o'a' = \frac{b'a'}{ba} oa = \frac{jI_qx_q}{I_q} I_a = jI_ax_q \tag{5-80}$$

[1] The method of expressing a-c quantities in per unit is described in Appendix A. One advantage of the method, illustrated in Table 5-1, is that the constants of normal machines lie in a narrow numerical range regardless of machine size.

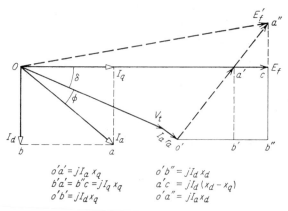

$$o'a' = jI_a x_q \qquad o'b'' = jI_d x_d$$
$$b'a' = b''c = jI_q x_q \qquad a'c = jI_d (x_d - x_q)$$
$$o'b' = jI_d x_q \qquad o'a'' = jI_a x_d$$

FIG. 5-10. Relations among component voltages in phasor diagram.

The phasor sum $V_t + I_a r_a + jI_a x_q$ then locates the angular position of the excitation voltage E_f and therefore the d and q axes. Physically this must be so, because all the field excitation in a normal machine is in the direct axis. One use of these relations in determining the excitation require-ments for specified operating conditions at the terminals of a salient-pole machine is illustrated in Example 5-1.

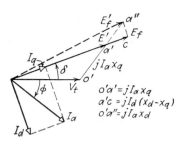

$$o'a' = jI_a x_q$$
$$a'c = jI_d (x_d - x_q)$$
$$o'a'' = jI_a x_d$$

FIG. 5-11. Generator phasor dia-gram, Example 5-1.

Example 5-1. The reactances x_d and x_q of a salient-pole synchronous generator are 1.00 and 0.60 per unit, respectively. The armature resistance is negligible.

Compute the excitation voltage when the generator delivers rated kva at 0.80 power fac-tor, lagging current, and rated terminal voltage.

Solution. First, the phase of E_f must be found so that I_a can be resolved into its d- and q-axis components. The phasor diagram is shown in Fig. 5-11.

$$I_a = 0.80 - j0.60 = 1.00\underline{/-36.9°}$$
$$jI_a x_q = j(0.80 - j0.60)(0.60) = 0.36 + j0.48$$
$$V_t = \text{reference phasor} = 1.00 + j0$$
$$\text{Phasor sum} = E' = \overline{1.36 + j0.48} = 1.44\underline{/19.4°}$$

The angle $\delta = 19.4°$, and the phase angle between E_f and I_a is $36.9° + 19.4° = 56.3°$.

The armature current can now be resolved into its d- and q-axis components. Their magnitudes are

$$I_d = 1.00 \sin 56.3° = 0.832$$
$$I_q = 1.00 \cos 56.3° = 0.555$$

As phasors,
$$I_d = 0.832\underline{/-90°} + 19.4° = 0.832\underline{/-70.6°}$$
$$I_q = 0.555\underline{/19.4°}$$

We could now find E_f from Eq. 5-78. A shorter method, however, is to add numerically the length $a'c = I_d(x_d - x_q)$ to the magnitude of E'; thus, the magnitude of the excitation voltage is the algebraic sum

$$E_f = E' + I_d(x_d - x_q)$$
$$= 1.44 + (0.832)(0.40) = 1.77 \text{ per unit}$$

As a phasor, $E_f = 1.77\underline{/19.4°}$

c. Simplifications for Cylindrical-rotor Machines. When the rotor of a synchronous machine is a smooth cylinder, as is substantially the case in turbine-generators, the permeances in the d and q axes are equal and

$$x_d = x_q = x_s \tag{5-81}$$

where x_s is the *synchronous reactance.* The impedance $r_a + jx_s$ is called the *synchronous impedance* Z_s. Equation 5-78 reduces to

$$E_f = V_t + (r_a + jx_s)I_a \tag{5-82}$$

and the phasor diagram for generator conditions becomes that of Fig. 5-12.

The cylindrical-rotor synchronous machine in the balanced steady state can thus be represented by a single impedance as in the simple equivalent

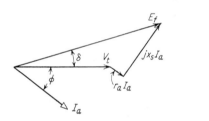

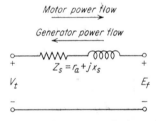

FIG. 5-12. Phasor diagram for cylindrical-rotor generator.   FIG. 5-13. Steady-state equivalent circuit for cylindrical-rotor machine.

circuit of Fig. 5-13. The synchronous reactance x_s takes into account all the flux produced by the stator currents, while the excitation voltage accounts for that produced by the field current. As in the salient-pole machine, the excitation voltage is proportional to the field current and equals the voltage which would appear at the terminals if the armature were open-circuited, the speed and field current being held constant. Bear in mind, however, that one of the important idealizing assumptions in Art. 5-1 is neglect of saturation. As shown in Chap. 9, saturation affects both x_s and the proportionality between E_f and i_f.

The question naturally arises as to how serious an approximation is involved if a salient-pole machine is treated in this simple fashion. Suppose the salient-pole machine of Figs. 5-10 and 5-11 were treated by cylindrical-rotor theory as if it had a single synchronous reactance equal to its direct-axis value x_d. For the same conditions at its terminals, the synchronous-reactance drop jI_ax_d would be the phasor $o'a''$, and the equivalent excitation voltage would be E'_f as shown in these figures. Because ca'' is perpendicular to E_f, there is little difference in magnitude between the correct value E_f and the approximate value E'_f for a normally excited machine. Recomputation of the excitation voltage on this basis for Example 5-1 gives a value of $1.79\underline{/26.6°}$.

In so far as the interrelations among terminal voltage, armature current, power, and excitation over the normal operating range are concerned, the effects of salient poles usually are of minor importance, and such characteristics of a salient-pole machine usually can be computed with satisfactory accuracy by the simple cylindrical-rotor theory. Only at small excitations will the differences between cylindrical-rotor and salient-pole theory become important.

There is, however, considerable difference in the phase angles of E_f and E'_f in Figs. 5-10 and 5-11. This difference is caused by the reluctance torque in a salient-pole machine. Its effect is investigated in the following article.

5-6. Steady-state Power-angle Characteristics. The maximum short-time overload which a synchronous machine can deliver is determined by

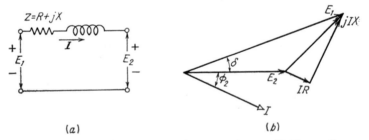

Fig. 5-14. (a) Impedance interconnecting two voltages. (b) Phasor diagram.

the maximum torque which can be applied without loss of synchronism. The purpose of this article is to derive expressions for the steady-state power limits of simple systems with gradually applied loads. The heretofore neglected effects of external impedance will also be included.

a. Cylindrical-rotor Machines. Since the machine can be represented by a simple impedance, the study of power limits becomes merely a special case of the more general problem of the limitations on power flow through an inductive impedance. The impedance can include that of a line and transformer bank as well as the synchronous impedance of the machine.

Consider the simple circuit of Fig. 5-14a comprising two a-c voltages E_1 and E_2 connected by an impedance Z through which the current is I. The phasor diagram is shown in Fig. 5-14b. The power P_2 delivered through the impedance to the load end E_2 is

$$P_2 = E_2 I \cos \phi_2 \qquad (5\text{-}83)$$

where ϕ_2 is the phase angle of I with respect to E_2. The phasor current is

$$I = \frac{E_1 - E_2}{Z} \qquad (5\text{-}84)$$

If the phasor voltages and the impedance are expressed in polar form,

$$I = \frac{E_1\underline{/\delta} - E_2\underline{/0°}}{Z\underline{/\phi_Z}} = \frac{E_1}{Z}\underline{/\delta - \phi_Z} - \frac{E_2}{Z}\underline{/-\phi_Z} \qquad (5\text{-}85)$$

wherein E_1 and E_2 are the magnitudes of the voltages, δ is the phase angle by which E_1 leads E_2, Z is the magnitude of the impedance, and ϕ_Z is its angle in polar form. The real part of the phasor equation 5-85 is the component of I in phase in E_2, whence

$$I \cos \phi_2 = \frac{E_1}{Z} \cos (\delta - \phi_Z) - \frac{E_2}{Z} \cos (-\phi_Z) \qquad (5\text{-}86)$$

Substitution of Eq. 5-86 in Eq. 5-83, it being noted that

$$\cos (-\phi_Z) = \cos \phi_Z = R/Z$$

gives

$$P_2 = \frac{E_1 E_2}{Z} \cos (\delta - \phi_Z) - \frac{E_2^2 R}{Z^2} \qquad (5\text{-}87)$$

$$P_2 = \frac{E_1 E_2}{Z} \sin (\delta + \alpha_Z) - \frac{E_2^2 R}{Z^2} \qquad (5\text{-}88)$$

where

$$\alpha_Z = 90° - \phi_Z = \tan^{-1} \frac{R}{X} \qquad (5\text{-}89)$$

and usually is a small angle.

Similarly the power P_1 at source end E_1 of the impedance can be expressed as

$$P_1 = \frac{E_1 E_2}{Z} \sin (\delta - \alpha_Z) + \frac{E_1^2 R}{Z^2} \qquad (5\text{-}90)$$

If, as is frequently the case, the resistance is negligible,

$$P_1 = P_2 = \frac{E_1 E_2}{X} \sin \delta \qquad (5\text{-}91)$$

If the resistance is negligible and the voltages are constant, the maximum power is

$$P_{1 \text{ max}} = P_{2 \text{ max}} = \frac{E_1 E_2}{X} \qquad (5\text{-}92)$$

and occurs when $\delta = 90°$.

When Eq. 5-91 is compared with Eq. 3-37 for torque in terms of interacting flux and mmf waves, it is seen that they are of the same form. This is no coincidence. First remember that torque and power are linearly proportional when, as here, speed is constant. Then what we are really saying is that Eq. 3-37, when applied specifically to the idealized cylindrical-rotor machine and translated to circuit terms, becomes Eq. 5-91. A quick mental review of the background of each relation should show that they stem from the same fundamental considerations.

Example 5-2. A 2,000-hp 1.0-power-factor 3-phase Y-connected 2,300-volt 30-pole 60-cps synchronous motor has a synchronous reactance of 1.95 ohms per phase. For the purposes of this problem all losses may be neglected.

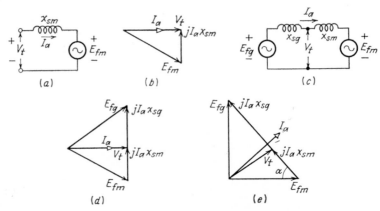

Fig. 5-15. Equivalent circuits and phasor diagrams, Example 5-2.

a. Compute the maximum torque in pound-feet which this motor can deliver if it is supplied with power from a constant-voltage constant-frequency source, commonly called an *infinite bus*, and if its field excitation is constant at the value which would result in 1.00 power factor at rated load.

b. Instead of the infinite bus of part *a*, suppose that the motor were supplied with power from a 3-phase Y-connected 2,300-volt 1,750-kva 2-pole 3,600-rpm turbine-generator whose synchronous reactance is 2.65 ohms per phase. The generator is driven at rated speed, and the field excitations of generator and motor are adjusted so that the motor runs at 1.00 power factor and rated terminal voltage at full load. The field excitations of both machines are then held constant, and the mechanical load on the synchronous motor is gradually increased. Compute the maximum motor torque under these conditions. Also compute the terminal voltage when the motor is delivering its maximum torque.

Solution. Although this machine is undoubtedly of the salient-pole type, we shall solve the problem by simple cylindrical-rotor theory. The solution accordingly neglects reluctance torque. The machine actually would develop a maximum torque somewhat greater than our computed value.

a. The equivalent circuit is shown in Fig. 5-15a and the phasor diagram at full load in Fig. 5-15b, wherein E_{fm} is the excitation voltage of the motor and x_{sm} is its synchronous reactance.   From the motor rating with losses neglected,

Rated kva $= 2,000 \times 0.746 = 1,492$ kva, 3-phase $= 497$ kva per phase

Rated voltage $= \dfrac{2,300}{\sqrt{3}} = 1,330$ volts to neutral

Rated current $= \dfrac{497,000}{1,330} = 374$ amp per phase Y

$$I_a x_{sm} = 374 \times 1.95 = 730 \text{ volts per phase}$$

From the phasor diagram at full load

$$E_{fm} = \sqrt{V_t^2 + (I_a x_{sm})^2} = 1,515 \text{ volts}$$

When the power source is an infinite bus and the field excitation is constant, V_t and E_{fm} are constant.   Substitution of V_t for E_1, E_{fm} for E_2, and x_{sm} for X in Eq. 5-92 then gives

$$
\begin{aligned}
P_{\max} &= \frac{V_t E_{fm}}{x_{sm}} \\
&= \frac{1,330 \times 1,515}{1.95} = 1,030 \times 10^3 \text{ watts per phase} \\
&= 3,090 \text{ kw for 3 phases}
\end{aligned}
$$

(In per unit, $P_{\max} = 3,090/1,492 = 2.07$.)   With 30 poles at 60 cps, synchronous speed $= 4$ rev/sec.

$$
\begin{aligned}
T_{\max} &= \frac{P_{\max}}{\omega_s} = \frac{3,090 \times 10^3}{2\pi \times 4} = 123 \times 10^3 \text{ newton-m} \\
&= 0.738(123 \times 10^3) = 90,600 \text{ lb-ft}
\end{aligned}
$$

b. When the power source is the turbine-generator, the equivalent circuit becomes that shown in Fig. 5-15c, wherein E_{fg} is the excitation voltage of the generator and x_{sg} is its synchronous reactance.   The phasor diagram at full motor load, 1.00 power factor, is shown in Fig. 5-15d.   As before,

$$V_t = 1,330 \text{ volts at full load}$$
$$E_{fm} = 1,515 \text{ volts}$$

The synchronous-reactance drop in the generator is

$$I_a x_{sg} = 374 \times 2.65 = 991 \text{ volts}$$

and from the phasor diagram

$$E_{fg} = \sqrt{V_t^2 + (I_a x_{sg})^2} = 1,655 \text{ volts}$$

Since the field excitations and speeds of both machines are constant, E_{fg} and E_{fm} are constant.   Substitution of E_{fg} for E_1, E_{fm} for E_2, and $x_{sg} + x_{sm}$ for X in Eq. 5-92 then gives

$$
\begin{aligned}
P_{\max} &= \frac{E_{fg} E_{fm}}{x_{sg} + x_{sm}} \\
&= \frac{1,655 \times 1,515}{4.60} = 545 \times 10^3 \text{ watts per phase} \\
&= 1,635 \text{ kw for 3 phases}
\end{aligned}
$$

(In per unit, $P_{\text{max}} = 1,635/1,492 = 1.095$.)

$$T_{\text{max}} = \frac{P_{\text{max}}}{\omega_s} = \frac{1,635 \times 10^3}{2\pi \times 4} = 65 \times 10^3 \text{ newton-m}$$
$$= 48,000 \text{ lb-ft}$$

Synchronism would be lost if a load torque greater than this value were applied to the motor shaft. The motor would stall, the generator would tend to overspeed, and the circuit would be opened by circuit-breaker action.

With fixed excitations, maximum power occurs when E_{fg} leads E_{fm} by 90°, as shown in Fig. 5-15e. From this phasor diagram

$$I_a(x_{sg} + x_{sm}) = \sqrt{E_{fg}^2 + E_{fm}^2} = 2,240 \text{ volts}$$

$$I_a = \frac{2,240}{4.60} = 488 \text{ amp}$$

$$I_a x_{sm} = 488 \times 1.95 = 951 \text{ volts}$$

$$\cos \alpha = \frac{E_{fm}}{I_a(x_{sg} + x_{sm})} = \frac{1,515}{2,240} = 0.676$$

$$\sin \alpha = \frac{E_{fg}}{I_a(x_{sg} + x_{sm})} = \frac{1,655}{2,240} = 0.739$$

The phasor equation for the terminal voltage is

$$V_t = E_{fm} + jI_a x_{sm} = E_{fm} - I_a x_{sm} \cos \alpha + jI_a x_{sm} \sin \alpha$$
$$= 1,515 - 643 + j703 = 872 + j703$$

The magnitude of V_t is

$$V_t = 1,120 \text{ volts to neutral}$$
$$= 1,940 \text{ volts, line to line}$$

When the source is the turbine-generator, as in part b, the effect of its impedance causes the terminal voltage to decrease with increasing load, thereby reducing the maximum power from 3,090 kw in part a to 1,635 kw in part b.

$b.$ *Salient-pole Machines.* We shall limit the discussion to the simple system shown in the schematic diagram of Fig. 5-16a comprising a salient-pole synchronous machine SM connected to an infinite bus of voltage E_e through a series impedance of reactance x_e per phase. Resistance will be neglected because it usually is small. Consider that the

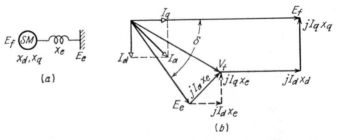

FIG. 5-16. Salient-pole synchronous machine and series impedance. (a) Single-line diagram. (b) Phasor diagram.

synchronous machine is acting as a generator. The phasor diagram is shown by the solid-line phasors in Fig. 5-16b. The dashed phasors show the external reactance drop resolved into components due to I_d and I_q. The effect of the external impedance is merely to add its reactance to the reactances of the machine; i.e., the total values of reactance interposed between the excitation voltage E_f and the bus voltage E_e are

$$X_d = x_d + x_e \tag{5-93}$$
$$X_q = x_q + x_e \tag{5-94}$$

If the bus voltage E_e is resolved into components $E_e \sin \delta$ and $E_e \cos \delta$ in phase with I_d and I_q, respectively, the power P delivered to the bus per phase is

$$P = I_d E_e \sin \delta + I_q E_e \cos \delta \tag{5-95}$$

Also, from Fig. 5-16b,

$$I_d = \frac{E_f - E_e \cos \delta}{X_d} \tag{5-96}$$

$$I_q = \frac{E_e \sin \delta}{X_q} \tag{5-97}$$

Substitution of Eqs. 5-96 and 5-97 in Eq. 5-95 gives

$$P = \frac{E_f E_e}{X_d} \sin \delta + E_e^2 \frac{X_d - X_q}{2 X_d X_q} \sin 2\delta \tag{5-98}$$

This power-angle characteristic is shown in Fig. 5-17. The first term is the same as the expression obtained for a cylindrical-rotor machine.

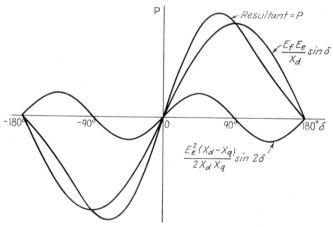

FIG. 5-17. Power-angle characteristic of a salient-pole synchronous machine showing fundamental component due to field excitation and second-harmonic component due to reluctance torque.

This term is merely an extension of the basic concepts of Chap. 3 to include the effects of series reactance. The second term introduces the effect of salient poles. It represents the fact that the air-gap flux wave creates torque tending to align the field poles in the position of minimum reluctance. This term is the power corresponding to the *reluctance torque* and is of the same general nature as the reluctance torque discussed in Art. 2-2. Note that the reluctance torque is independent of field excitation. Note, also, that if $X_d = X_q$, as in a uniform-air-gap machine,

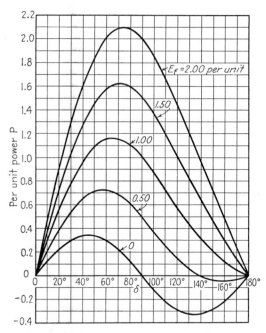

FIG. 5-18. Family of power-angle characteristics for system of Fig. 5-16a with $E_e = 1.00$, $R = 0$, $X_d = 1.00$, $X_q = 0.60$.

there is no preferential direction of magnetization, the reluctance torque is zero, and Eq. 5-98 reduces to the power-angle equation for a cylindrical-rotor machine whose synchronous reactance is X_d.

Figure 5-18 shows a family of power-angle characteristics at various values of excitation and constant terminal voltage. Only positive values of δ are shown. The curves for negative values of δ are the same except for a reversal in the sign of P. That is, the generator and motor regions are alike if the effects of resistance are negligible. For generator action E_f leads E_e; for motor action E_f lags E_e. Steady-state operation is stable over the range where the slope of the power-angle characteristic is positive. Because of the reluctance torque, a salient-pole machine is stiffer than one with a cylindrical rotor—i.e., for equal voltages and equal values of X_d, a salient-pole machine develops a given torque at a smaller value of δ, and the maximum torque which can be developed is somewhat greater.

c. *Normalized Power-angle Curves.* Equation 5-98 contains six quantities—the two variables P and δ, and the four parameters E_f, E_e, X_d, and X_q. To simplify the notation, let the maximum power due to the field excitation be designated by $P_{f\,max}$ and the maximum power due to the

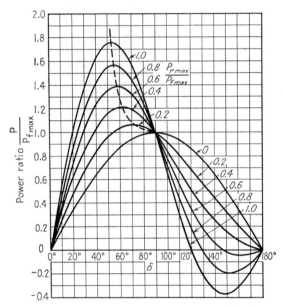

FIG. 5-19. Normalized power-angle curves for system of Fig. 5-16a with $R = 0$.

reluctance torque be designated by $P_{r\,max}$. Then Eq. 5-98 can be expressed as

$$P = P_{f\,max} \sin \delta + P_{r\,max} \sin 2\delta \qquad (5\text{-}99)$$

A further reduction of the number of parameters can be obtained if Eq. 5-99 is divided by $P_{f\,max}$; thus

$$\frac{P}{P_{f\,max}} = \sin \delta + \frac{P_{r\,max}}{P_{f\,max}} \sin 2\delta \qquad (5\text{-}100)$$

Equation 5-100 is in normalized form. It applies to all possible combinations of a synchronous machine and an external system, as in Fig. 5-16a, so long as the resistance is negligible. A family of curves can be plotted from Eq. 5-100, as shown in Fig. 5-19. The maximum value $P_{max}/P_{f\,max}$ of the power ratio and the angle $\delta_{max\,P}$ at which maximum power occurs are shown as functions of the reluctance-power ratio $P_{r\ max}/P_{f\ max}$ in Fig. 5-20. These curves correspond to the dashed locus of the maximum points on the curves of Fig. 5-19. Use of these curves for computing steady-state power limits is illustrated in Example 5-3.

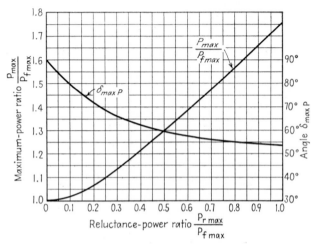

Fig. 5-20. Normalized curves showing effects of reluctance torque on steady-state power limits.

Example 5-3. The 2,000-hp 1.0-power-factor 3-phase Y-connected 2,300-volt synchronous motor of Example 5-2 has reactances of $x_d = 1.95$ and $x_q = 1.40$ ohms per phase. All losses may be neglected.

Compute the maximum mechanical power in kilowatts which this motor can deliver if it is supplied with electrical power from an infinite bus (Fig. 5-21a) at rated voltage and frequency, and if its field excitation is constant at the value which would

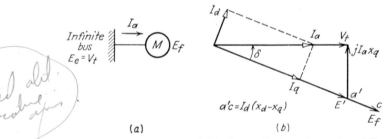

Fig. 5-21. (a) Single-line diagram and (b) phasor diagram for motor of Example 5-3.

result in 1.00 power factor at rated load. The shaft load is assumed to be increased gradually so that transient swings are negligible and the steady-state power limit applies. Include the effects of salient poles.

Solution. The first step is to compute the synchronous-motor excitation at rated voltage, full load, 1.0 power factor. As in Example 5-2, the full-load terminal voltage and current are 1,330 volts to neutral and 374 amp per phase Y. The phasor diagram for the specified full-load conditions is shown in Fig. 5-21b. The only essential difference between this phasor diagram and the generator phasor diagram of Fig. 5-11 is that I_a in Fig. 5-21 represents motor *input* current. The phasor voltage equation then becomes

$$E_f = V_t - jI_d x_d - jI_q x_q$$

In Fig. 5-21b,

$$E' = V_t - jI_a x_q$$
$$= 1,330 + j0 - j(374)(1.40) = 1,429 \underline{/-21.5°}$$

That is, the angle δ is 21.5°, with E_f lagging V_t. The magnitude of I_d is

$$I_d = {}^1I_a \sin \delta = (374)(0.367) = 137 \text{ amp}$$

The magnitude of E_f can now be found by adding numerically the length $a'c = I_d(x_d - x_q)$ to the magnitude of E'; thus

$$E_f = E' + I_d(x_d - x_q)$$
$$= 1,429 + (137)(0.55) = 1,504 \text{ volts to neutral}$$

The maximum values of the field-excitation and reluctance-torque components of the power can now be computed. From Eqs. 5-99 and 5-100,

$$P_{f\,\text{max}} = \frac{(1,504)(1,330)}{1.95} = 1,025 \times 10^3 \text{ watts per phase}$$

$$P_{r\,\text{max}} = \frac{(1,330)^2(0.55)}{2(1.95)(1.40)} = 178 \times 10^3 \text{ watts per phase}$$

whence

$$\frac{P_{r\,\text{max}}}{P_{f\,\text{max}}} = 0.174$$

From Fig. 5-20, the corresponding value of the maximum-power ratio is

$$\frac{P_{\text{max}}}{P_{f\,\text{max}}} = 1.05$$

whence the maximum power is

$$P_{\text{max}} = 1.05 P_{f\,\text{max}} = (1.05)(1,025 \times 10^3) = 1,080 \text{ kw per phase}$$
$$= 3,240 \text{ kw for 3 phases}$$

Compare with $P_{\text{max}} = 3,090$ kw found in Example 5-2, where the effects of salient poles were neglected. The error caused by neglecting saliency is slightly less than 5 per cent.

The effect of salient poles on the power limits increases as the reluctance-power ratio $P_{r\,\text{max}}/P_{f\,\text{max}}$ increases, as shown in Fig. 5-20. For a normally excited machine the effect of salient poles usually amounts to a few per cent at most. Only at small excitations does the reluctance torque become important. Except at small excitations or when exceptionally accurate results are required, a salient-pole machine usually can be treated by simple cylindrical-rotor theory.

5-7. Transient Analysis—Three-phase Short Circuits. The general procedure of applying the basic relations of Art. 5-4 to the solution of transient problems can be illustrated by examining the currents resulting from a balanced 3-phase short circuit at the machine terminals. The machine is assumed to be initially unloaded and to continue operating at synchronous speed ω after the short circuit occurs. Zero-sequence quantities do not appear.

To avoid lengthy algebra, we shall examine three special cases which permit some of the terms in Eqs. 5-50 to 5-52 to be omitted. Our object is to arrive at admissible approximations leading to relatively simple representation of the machine in transient and dynamic problems.

a. Armature and Field Resistances Neglected. The basic machine equations under these conditions become

$$\lambda_f = L_{ff}i_f + \tfrac{3}{2}L_{af}i_d \tag{5-101}$$
$$\lambda_d = L_{af}i_f + L_d i_d \tag{5-102}$$
$$\lambda_q = L_q i_q \tag{5-103}$$
$$v_d = p\lambda_d - \lambda_q\omega \tag{5-104}$$
$$v_q = p\lambda_q + \lambda_d\omega \tag{5-105}$$
$$v_f = p\lambda_f \tag{5-106}$$

The currents i_d and i_q are initially zero, and i_f is initially i_{f0}.

It is now necessary to represent the short circuit in mathematical form. This can be done by noting its effect on the machine voltages. Both before and after the short circuit,

$$v_d = 0 \tag{5-107}$$

Hence the short circuit has no effect on v_d. The voltage v_q, however, is $\omega L_{af}i_{f0}$ before the short circuit and zero afterward. Since the short circuit causes v_q to vanish suddenly, its effect can be found by suddenly impressing on the machine the voltage

$$v_q = -\omega L_{af}i_{f0} \tag{5-108}$$

The currents found in this way must be added to the initial values of the currents existing before the short circuit in order to obtain the resultant currents after the short circuit.

The response to the voltage of Eq. 5-108 must be the response for this voltage alone, not the combined effect of this voltage and the initial excitation. Accordingly, the response must be evaluated with the field winding considered to be closed and initially unexcited, i.e., with

$$v_f = 0 \tag{5-109}$$

The subscript t (for transient) will be added to the symbols i_f, λ_f, λ_d, and λ_q to denote the values under these conditions. Then the true initial values are added, as in

$$i_f = i_{f0} + i_{ft} \tag{5-110}$$

to find the resultant quantities after the short circuit, thereby superimposing the effect of the true initial excitation. No added subscripts are necessary for i_d and i_q because their initial values are obviously zero for an unloaded machine.

From Eqs. 5-106 and 5-109 it can be seen that the field linkages λ_{ft} must be zero. In other words, with r_f neglected, the flux linkages λ_f with the field winding cannot change. This is a specific case of what is sometimes called the *principle of constant flux linkages*, which simply states that the flux linkages with a closed circuit having zero resistance and no voltage source cannot change. To maintain field linkages constant, a current must be induced in the field winding to counteract the magnetic effects of i_d. From Eq. 5-101 with $\lambda_f = 0$, this current is

$$i_{ft} = -\frac{3}{2}\frac{L_{af}}{L_{ff}}i_d \tag{5-111}$$

Upon substitution of Eq. 5-111 in 5-102,

$$\lambda_{dt} = \left(L_d - \frac{3}{2}\frac{L_{af}^2}{L_{ff}}\right)i_d \tag{5-112}$$

$$= L_d' i_d \tag{5-113}$$

where

$$L_d' = L_d - \frac{3}{2}\frac{L_{af}^2}{L_{ff}} \tag{5-114}$$

is the *direct-axis transient inductance*. As we shall see, it is an important constant in machine-transient theory.

The specific values of the voltages v_d and v_q are now introduced. From Eqs. 5-103 and 5-104 with $v_d = 0$,

$$0 = p\lambda_{dt} - \omega L_q i_q \tag{5-115}$$

or, after using Eq. 5-113 to obtain $p\lambda_{dt}$,

$$0 = L_d' p i_d - \omega L_q i_q \tag{5-116}$$

Similarly, from Eqs. 5-105 and 5-108,

$$-\omega L_{af} i_{f0} = p\lambda_q + \lambda_d \omega \tag{5-117}$$

which, with Eqs. 5-103 and 5-113, becomes

$$-\omega L_{af} i_{f0} = L_q p i_q + \omega L_d' i_d \tag{5-118}$$

Equations 5-116 and 5-118 are two simultaneous equations in i_d and i_q. With i_q eliminated and the resulting equation written in differential-equation form,

$$\frac{d^2 i_d}{dt^2} + \omega^2 i_d = -\frac{\omega^2}{L_d'} L_{af} i_{f0} \tag{5-119}$$

Had the work been carried out in Laplace-transform notation, the comparable expression would have been

$$i_d(s) = -\frac{\omega^2 L_{af} i_{f0}}{L'_d} \frac{1}{s(s^2 + \omega^2)} \tag{5-120}$$

The solution of Eq. 5-119 or the transform of 5-120 is

$$i_d = -\frac{L_{af} i_{f0}}{L'_d}(1 - \cos \omega t) \tag{5-121}$$

From Eq. 5-116,

$$i_q = \frac{L'_d}{\omega L_q}\frac{di_d}{dt} = -\frac{L_{af} i_{f0}}{L_q}\sin \omega t \tag{5-122}$$

From Eqs. 5-110 and 5-111,

$$i_f = i_{f0} + \frac{3}{2}\frac{L_{af}}{L_{ff}}\frac{L_{af} i_{f0}}{L'_d}(1 - \cos \omega t) \tag{5-123}$$

The waveforms of i_d, i_q, and i_f as given by these results are sketched in Fig. 5-22.

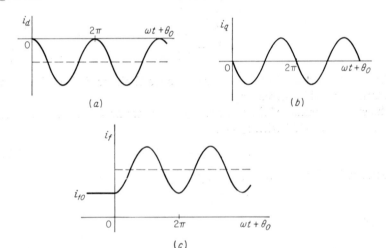

FIG. 5-22. Waveforms of (a) i_d, (b) i_q, and (c) i_f following short circuit.   Machine resistances are ignored.

Upon substitution in the dq transformation (Eq. 5-42), with θ taken as $\omega t + \theta_0$, the phase current is

$$i_a = -\frac{L_{af} i_{f0}}{L'_d}\cos(\omega t + \theta_0) + \frac{L_{af} i_{f0}}{2}\left(\frac{1}{L'_d} + \frac{1}{L_q}\right)\cos \theta_0$$
$$+ \frac{L_{af} i_{f0}}{2}\left(\frac{1}{L'_d} - \frac{1}{L_q}\right)\cos(2\omega t + \theta_0) \tag{5-124}$$

By recognizing, as in Eq. 5-74, that $\omega L_{af} i_{f0}$ is the peak value of the pre-fault excitation voltage $\sqrt{2}\, E_{f0}$, Eq. 5-124 can be rewritten

$$i_a = -\frac{\sqrt{2}\, E_{f0}}{x_d'} \cos(\omega t + \theta_0) + \frac{\sqrt{2}\, E_{f0}}{2}\left(\frac{1}{x_d'} + \frac{1}{x_q}\right) \cos \theta_0$$

$$+ \frac{\sqrt{2}\, E_{f0}}{2}\left(\frac{1}{x_d'} - \frac{1}{x_q}\right) \cos(2\omega t + \theta_0) \quad (5\text{-}125)$$

where
$$x_d' = \omega L_d' \quad (5\text{-}126)$$

is the *direct-axis transient reactance*.

The phase current is seen to consist of a fundamental-frequency term, a d-c component, and a second harmonic. The fundamental is much the most important item. Its magnitude depends on the prefault excitation and the transient reactance. It has a negative sign in Eq. 5-125 because we have adopted motor conventions (i.e., current into the stator is taken as positive, whereas under short-circuit conditions the actual current is out of the stator). The d-c term depends on θ_0 and hence on the instant when the short circuit appears. If, for example, the fault occurs at the instant when the d axis is 90° from the axis of phase a, no d-c component appears in the phase a current. Even then, d-c components do appear in the phase b and phase c currents because of the 120° displacement between phases. The second-harmonic term depends on so-called *transient saliency*—the differences in transient circuitry in the two rotor axes as represented by the quantity $1/x_d' - 1/x_q$. The second-harmonic amplitude is usually small and very often neglected.

Because of the neglect of field and armature resistances none of the terms in Eqs. 5-121 to 5-125 dies away with time. Actually, exponential decays are encountered, as they are in any inductive circuit when resistance is present. This fact is illustrated in Fig. 5-23, which shows the phase currents with their d-c component after a short circuit. Before investigating the rates of decay, however, we wish to simplify our basic relations somewhat further. This will be done now by showing that neglect of the transformer-voltage terms $p\lambda_d$ and $p\lambda_q$ in Eqs. 5-104 and 5-105 corresponds to dropping out the d-c and second-harmonic terms in the above solutions.

b. Resistances and Transformer Voltages Neglected. When the $p\lambda_d$ and $p\lambda_q$ terms are omitted from Eqs. 5-104 and 5-105, very simple expressions for the machine currents are obtained. They are

$$i_d = -\frac{L_{af} i_{f0}}{L_d'} \quad (5\text{-}127)$$

$$i_q = 0 \quad (5\text{-}128)$$

$$i_f = i_{f0} + i_{ft} = i_{f0} + \frac{3}{2}\frac{L_{af}}{L_{ff}}\frac{L_{af} i_{f0}}{L_d'} \quad (5\text{-}129)$$

By substitution in the dq transformation (Eq. 5-42) and use of Eq. 5-126,

$$i_a = - \frac{\sqrt{2}\, E_{f0}}{x_d'} \cos (\omega t + \theta_0) \qquad (5\text{-}130)$$

The d-c and second-harmonic terms have now dropped out of the phase current, as have the fundamental-frequency terms in i_d, i_q, and i_f. The

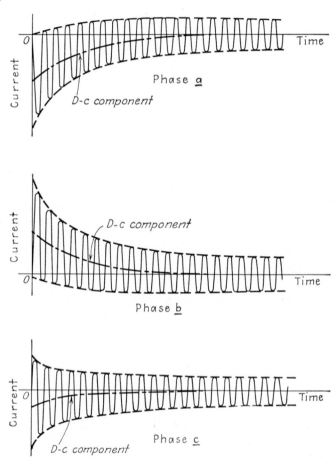

FIG. 5-23. Short-circuit currents in the 3 phases of a synchronous machine.

currents i_d and i_f now follow the dashed lines in Fig. 5-22a and c; they have a sudden step at $t = 0$.

Neglect of the second-harmonic and d-c components in the phase currents is very common in machine analysis. The former is usually quite small, and the latter dies away very rapidly. Neither has a significant influence on the average torque of the machine for an appreciable time, so that their influence on dynamic performance is relatively small. Accordingly, many machine analyses are carried out with the $p\lambda_d$ and $p\lambda_q$ terms omitted. The advantage is that the resulting equations are much simpler.

c. *Field Resistance Included, Transformer Voltages Neglected.* We now wish to investigate the decay of the currents i_d and i_{ft} of Eqs. 5-127 and 5-129. To do so, we follow substantially the approach of part a of this article except that the $p\lambda_d$ and $p\lambda_q$ terms are omitted but the $r_f i_f$ term is retained in Eq. 5-50. Again,

$$i_q = 0 \tag{5-131}$$

The equation followed by the induced field current i_{ft} becomes

$$\frac{L_{ff}}{L_d}\left(L_d - \frac{3}{2}\frac{L_{af}^2}{L_{ff}}\right)\frac{di_{ft}}{dt} + r_f i_{ft} = 0 \tag{5-132}$$

or, by using Eq. 5-114 and dividing through by r_f,

$$\frac{L_{ff}}{r_f}\frac{L_d'}{L_d}\frac{di_{ft}}{dt} + i_{ft} = 0 \tag{5-133}$$

Now the fraction

$$\frac{L_{ff}}{r_f} = T_{do}' \tag{5-134}$$

is the time constant of the field winding. (The symbol T is used for time constant in this and the next chapter to conform with standard notation. Unlike Chap. 4, where τ is used, there is practically no possibility of confusion with torque here.) It is called the *direct-axis open-circuit transient time constant.* It characterizes the decay of transients with the armature open-circuited. With the armature short-circuited, however, the apparent field inductance is lower because of coupling to the armature winding. From Eq. 5-133, the time constant is then

$$T_d' = T_{do}'\frac{L_d'}{L_d} = T_{do}'\frac{x_d'}{x_d} \tag{5-135}$$

and is called the *direct-axis short-circuit transient time constant.* Both T_{do}' and T_d' are important constants of the synchronous machine. Typical values for large machines are about 5 sec for T_{do}' and 1 to 2 sec for T_d'.

Equation 5-132 may then be written

$$T_d'\frac{di_{ft}}{dt} + i_{ft} = 0 \tag{5-136}$$

Similarly, for the current i_d one obtains

$$T_d'\frac{di_d}{dt} + i_d = -\frac{L_{af}i_{f0}}{L_d} \tag{5-137}$$

The currents i_d and i_f become, subject to their being given by Eqs. 5-127 and 5-129 at $t = 0+$,

$$i_d = -\frac{L_{af}i_{f0}}{L_d} - L_{af}i_{f0}\left(\frac{1}{L_d'} - \frac{1}{L_d}\right)\epsilon^{-t/T_d'} \qquad (5\text{-}138)$$

$$i_f = i_{f0} + \frac{3}{2}\frac{L_{af}}{L_{ff}}\frac{L_{af}i_{f0}}{L_d'}\epsilon^{-t/T_d'} \qquad (5\text{-}139)$$

Finally, the phase current is

$$i_a = -\frac{\sqrt{2}\,E_{f0}}{x_d}\cos(\omega t + \theta_0)$$

$$\qquad\qquad - \sqrt{2}\,E_{f0}\left(\frac{1}{x_d'} - \frac{1}{x_d}\right)\epsilon^{-t/T_d'}\cos(\omega t + \theta_0) \qquad (5\text{-}140)$$

The first term on the right in Eq. 5-140 is the steady-state short-circuit current. It might, of course, have been written down immediately from the considerations of Art. 5-5. The second is the transient term. The phase current is a damped sinusoid. Its initial amplitude is limited by the transient reactance x_d' and its final amplitude by the synchronous reactance x_d. It passes from one to the other exponentially as determined by the time constant T_d'.

The machine-current solutions obtained in this article can readily be adapted to include external reactance x_e between the machine terminals and the short circuit. Such external reactance merely plays the same role as the armature leakage reactance ωL_{al}, which is a component of x_d, x_d', and x_q. All that need be done is to add x_e to x_d, x_d', and x_q wherever they appear (or the corresponding inductance L_e to L_d, L_d', and L_q). The results are thus made more widely applicable.

To summarize the results of this article, note first that we avoid a frontal attack on the basic machine equations with all terms retained. We do so to avoid complex and cumbersome analysis in which it would be difficult to distinguish between the important and the unimportant. By comparison of the results of parts a and b of the article, we find neglect of the $p\lambda_d$ and $p\lambda_q$ terms to be an admissible approximation in most cases. In part c we adopt this approximation and investigate how the transients die away. The results are quite simple, and we have established valuable guides to the conduct of other machine-transient analyses. At no time should it be forgotten, however, that comparison with experiment can be the only ultimate guide.

5-8. Voltage-regulation Studies; Block-diagram Representation. Two important groups of problems involving the synchronous machine as a dynamic system element are voltage-regulation studies and analyses of motional transients. The former will be discussed in this article and the latter in later articles.

In almost all applications of synchronous generators, it is desirable that the terminal voltage remain substantially constant regardless of load (or in some cases increase somewhat with load to compensate partially for increased voltage drop in associated lines and transformers). When the generator is operated at constant field current, the performance falls considerably short of this goal because of the voltage drop in the internal reactance.

Example 5-4. Particularly severe dips in generator terminal voltage are produced by the application of inductive loads at or close to zero power factor. The starting inrush to a large motor is one such type of load.

Consider that a synchronous generator is operating initially unloaded at normal terminal voltage. A balanced inductive load x_L is suddenly applied to its terminals. The field voltage is not changed, and the generator continues to operate at synchronous speed. Ignore saturation.

a. Study the variation of terminal voltage with time after load application.

b. Give per-unit voltage magnitudes when $x_d = 1.10$, $x'_d = 0.20$, $x_L = 1.25$, and $T'_{do} = 5.0$ sec. The reactances are per-unit values. Those for the machine are typical of large turbine-generators. That for x_L will, at normal voltage, load the generator to about its continuous reactive capability at zero power factor.

Solution. *a.* The suddenly applied load x_L is equivalent to a short circuit through external reactance equal to x_L. From Eq. 5-140 with x_L added to the machine reactances, the rms phase current is

$$I_a = \frac{E_{f0}}{x_d + x_L} + \left(\frac{E_{f0}}{x'_d + x_L} - \frac{E_{f0}}{x_d + x_L} \right) \epsilon^{-t/T_d'} \tag{5-141}$$

where, in accordance with Eq. 5-135,

$$T'_d = T'_{do} \frac{x'_d + x_L}{x_d + x_L} \tag{5-142}$$

The terminal voltage is then

$$V_t = E_{f0} \frac{x_L}{x_d + x_L} + E_{f0} \left(\frac{x_L}{x_d + x_L} - \frac{x_L}{x'_d + x_L} \right) \epsilon^{-t/T_d'} \tag{5-143}$$

Just after load application, it is $E_{f0}[x_L/(x'_d + x_L)]$. In the final steady state, it decreases to $E_{f0}[x_L/(x_d + x_L)]$.

b. Before load application, $V_t = 1.00$. At $t = 0+$, its value is 0.862. In the final steady state, it decreases to 0.532. The time constant of the exponential change is 3.1 sec. The voltage at $t = 0+$ is higher than the final value because of the induced field current to maintain constant field linkages in the face of the mmf of i_d. As the induced current dies away, the voltage sags very appreciably.[1]

A simplified schematic diagram of a typical automatic voltage-regulation scheme for an alternator is shown in Fig. 5-24. The reference quantity, or datum, may be of an electrical nature, such as a constant voltage

---

[1] For an analysis including load resistance and build-up of field voltage, see H. C. Anderson, Voltage Variation of Suddenly Loaded Generators, *Gen. Elec. Rev.*, vol. 48, pp. 25-33, August, 1945.

obtained from an independent source or the balance point of a voltage-sensitive bridge, or it may be of a mechanical nature, such as the tension of a spring or the balance point of a lever.   The values of terminal voltage and reference quantity are compared to determine the error ε, which is amplified and made to determine the excitation of the generator so that V_t behaves in the desired manner.

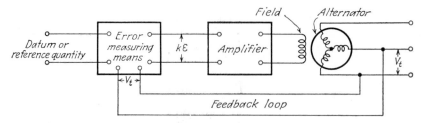

FIG. 5-24. Block diagram for automatic voltage regulation of an alternator.

In analyzing such a control system it is desirable to have a block-diagram representation of the alternator.   The simplest one, shown in Fig. 5-25, recognizes that the predominant time constant is that of the generator field.   It therefore ignores all self- and mutual inductances involving the armature and reflects only the open-circuit time constant T'_{do}.   (An adjusted value, such as that in Example 5-4, may also be used.)   The terminal voltage is related to the field voltage in the steady state by the constant k_V.   For a more comprehensive and accurate representation, the block must be obtained from the basic relations of Art. 5-4.   The process is illustrated in the following example.[1]

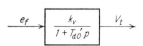

FIG. 5-25. Simplified block diagram of alternator.

Example 5-5.   Develop a block diagram for the representation of a 3-phase generator in studies of voltage-regulating systems.   For present purposes, saturation, as well as the transformer voltages ($p\lambda_d$ and $p\lambda_q$ terms) and armature resistances in the machine equations, may be ignored.

Solution.   The basic machine relations involved are given by Eqs. 5-43 to 5-45 and 5-50 to 5-52, both inclusive.   Because we are dealing specifically with generator operation, simpler visualization is obtained if we rewrite these equations with generator rather than motor conditions taken as positive (i.e., armature voltages are generated voltages, and positive armature current is out of the winding and produces negative armature and field linkages).   With the neglected terms omitted, the rela-

[1] For analysis of a similar problem including the effects of both saturation and additional rotor circuits, see M. Riaz, Analogue Computer Representations of Synchronous Generators in Voltage-regulation Studies, *Trans. AIEE*, vol. 75, pp. 1178–1182, 1956.   A comprehensive presentation of the analytical background for such studies is given in D. B. Breedon and R. W. Ferguson, Fundamental Equations for Analogue Studies of Synchronous Machines, *Trans. AIEE*, vol. 75, pp. 297–306, 1956.

tions become

$$\lambda_f = L_{ff}i_f - \tfrac{3}{2}L_{af}i_d$$
$$\lambda_d = L_{af}i_f - L_{d}i_d$$
$$\lambda_q = -L_q i_q$$
$$v_f = r_f i_f + p\lambda_f$$
$$v_d = -\omega\lambda_q$$
$$v_q = \omega\lambda_d$$

The block diagram is given in Fig. 5-26. The first of the above equations is represented around the adder in the center. The second is represented at the right-hand adder and the fourth at the left-hand adder. The third, fifth, and sixth equations appear in obtaining v_d and v_q. The v_f signal is obtained from the excitation system. The velocity ω either is a constant, corresponding to no speed change, or is obtained from a representation of the prime mover and mechanical characteristics.

With the $p\lambda_d$ and $p\lambda_q$ terms omitted, the only coupling between the d and q axes is through the load. The v_d and v_q signals are fed to the load, and the i_d and i_q signals

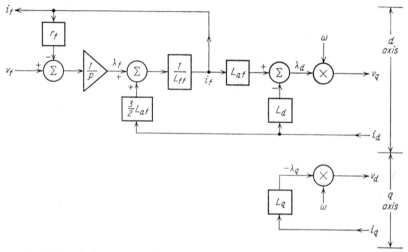

Fig. 5-26. Block diagram of salient-pole synchronous generator, Example 5-5.

are returned from it. To illustrate more specifically, consider that the load is approximated by a balanced 3-phase Y-connected circuit having resistance r_L and inductance L_L in each phase. The load equations are then

$$v_d = r_L i_d + L_L p i_d - \omega L_L i_q$$
$$v_q = r_L i_q + L_L p i_q + \omega L_L i_d$$

(The development of these relations is the subject of Prob. 5-3.)

Now the $L p i_d$ and $L p i_q$ terms may often be neglected in these relations, just as the $p\lambda_d$ and $p\lambda_q$ terms are often neglected in the machine equations. On this basis, the currents i_d and i_q become

$$i_d = \frac{r_L}{r_L^2 + (\omega L_L)^2}v_d + \frac{\omega L_L}{r_L^2 + (\omega L_L)^2}v_q = \frac{r_L}{z_L^2}v_d + \frac{\omega L_L}{z_L^2}v_q$$

$$i_q = \frac{-\omega L_L}{r_L^2 + (\omega L_L)^2}v_d + \frac{r_L}{r_L^2 + (\omega L_L)^2}v_q = \frac{-\omega L_L}{z_L^2}v_d + \frac{r_L}{z_L^2}v_q$$

Even though the variation of ω determined by the prime-mover and inertia characteristics is included in the machine representation, as in Fig. 5-26, it is common to consider ω constant at the normal frequency in this load representation. This assumption is an empiricism adopted because it usually gives closer simulation of the actual load characteristics. The block diagram then becomes that of Fig. 5-27. The representation would, of course, become more complex with ω variable but could readily be constructed.

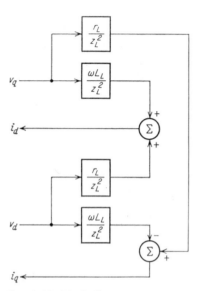

FIG. 5-27. Block-diagram representation of generator load, Example 5-5.

5-9. Transient Power-angle Characteristics.

It can be seen from Art. 5-7 that, in the first instant following a transient disturbance in the armature circuit of a synchronous machine, the total field linkage λ_f remains constant at its value before the disturbance. Thereafter, in the absence of voltage-regulator action, λ_f decays to a new steady-state value. The time constant of the decay is an appropriately adjusted value of T'_{do}, as in Eq. 5-142. For periods of time which are short compared with the time constant (or, alternatively, on the assumption of a moderate amount of voltage-regulator action sufficient to keep λ_f approximately constant), the decrement in field linkages may be neglected. This approximation leads to a simplified representation of the machine which is especially useful in investigating dynamic problems.

The field and d-axis armature linkages are, from Eqs. 5-43 and 5-44,

$$\lambda_f = L_{ff}i_f + \tfrac{3}{2}L_{af}i_d \qquad (5\text{-}144)$$
$$\lambda_d = L_{af}i_f + L_d i_d \qquad (5\text{-}145)$$

Upon solving 5-145 for i_f and substituting in 5-144,

$$\lambda_f = \frac{L_{ff}}{L_{af}}(\lambda_d - L_d i_d) + \tfrac{3}{2}L_{af}i_d \qquad (5\text{-}146)$$

or

$$\frac{L_{af}}{L_{ff}}\lambda_f = \lambda_d - \left(L_d - \frac{3}{2}\frac{L_{af}^2}{L_{ff}}\right)i_d \qquad (5\text{-}147)$$

$$\frac{L_{af}}{L_{ff}}\lambda_f = \lambda_d - L'_d i_d \qquad (5\text{-}148)$$

where Eq. 5-114 is used for the transient inductance L'_d. When both sides of Eq. 5-148 are multiplied by ω,

$$\omega \frac{L_{af}}{L_{ff}} \lambda_f = \omega \lambda_d - x'_d i_d \tag{5-149}$$

In terms of rms values as in Art. 5-5 (see, for instance, Eqs. 5-75 and 5-76),

$$E'_q = V_q - x'_d i_d \tag{5-150}$$

where
$$E'_q = \omega \frac{L_{af}}{L_{ff}} \frac{\lambda_f}{\sqrt{2}} \tag{5-151}$$

and V_q is written by virtue of Eq. 5-52 with resistance omitted and the $p\lambda_q$ term ignored.

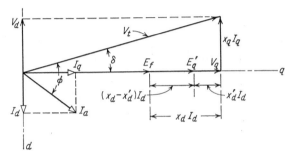

Fig. 5-28. Synchronous-motor phasor diagram showing the voltage E'_q.

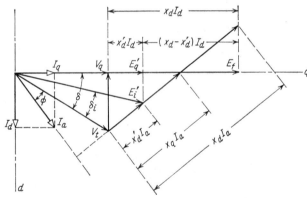

Fig. 5-29. Synchronous-generator phasor diagram showing the voltages E'_q and E'_i.

The voltage E'_q, being directly proportional to λ_f, is constant whenever field flux linkages may be considered constant. Its magnitude and position on a phasor diagram are shown in Fig. 5-28, which is in other respects a repetition of the synchronous-motor phasor diagram of Fig. 5-8 with armature resistance ignored. Its location in a synchronous-generator phasor diagram is given in Fig. 5-29. The latter diagram is more fully dimensioned to make evident the geometric relations involving E'_q. If, now, the analysis in Art. 5-6b leading to Eqs. 5-98 is repeated with E'_q and X'_d replacing E_f and X_d, the result is

$$P = \frac{E'_q E_e}{X'_d} \sin \delta + E^2_e \frac{X'_d - X_q}{2X'_d X_q} \sin 2\delta \qquad (5\text{-}152)$$

where $$X'_d = x'_d + x_e \qquad (5\text{-}153)$$
and $$X_q = x_q + x_e \qquad (5\text{-}154)$$

We now have in Eq. 5-152 a power-angle expression which is useful in the analysis of sudden disturbances or of sudden load application. It is applicable only over a period of time short compared with the adjusted

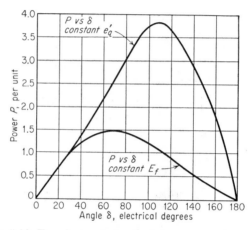

FIG. 5-30. Transient and steady-state power-angle curves.

time constant T'_d (or, as mentioned above, on the assumption of suffi-cient voltage-regulator action to keep λ_f substantially constant), but this covers the critical period in many dynamic analyses. On the other hand, the steady-state power-angle expression (Eq. 5-98) is applicable during changes which are sufficiently slow so that the machine is always in the steady state. Note that the coefficient of the second term on the right of Eq. 5-152 is numerically negative because x_q for a normal machine is greater than x'_d.

The transient power-angle curve will have an amplitude significantly greater than that of the steady-state curve. The relative amplitudes in a specific instance may be seen in Fig. 5-30. The suddenly induced com-ponent of field current following a disturbance is the physical reason for the greater transient amplitude. The practical consequence is that the machine is a stiffer system element in the transient state—for example, it can withstand a large, suddenly applied power or torque overload pro-vided that the duration of the overload is relatively short.

A further simplification of transient-power-angle representation is often made, one not unlike that in Art. 5-6 when cylindrical-rotor rather than salient-pole theory is used. Transient saliency is ignored by dropping the last term in Eq. 5-152. Not infrequently the simplification is carried one step further by using the equivalent circuit of Fig. 5-31 for the machine. The voltage E_i' in this circuit is called the *voltage behind transient reactance* and is shown on the phasor diagram of Fig. 5-29.
The simplicity of this approximate representation is a valuable feature when transients and dynamics are to be investigated in complex multimachine networks, even when comprehensive analog or digital computers are used.[1]

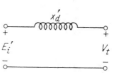

FIG. 5-31. Approximate transient equivalent circuit for synchronous machine.

5-10. Effects of Additional Rotor Circuits. Up to this point we have considered that there is only one effective circuit on the rotor of the synchronous machine, namely, the main-field winding in the direct axis. As a result, we have been able to concentrate on the most important aspects of machine performance without distracting algebraic complication. In many actual synchronous machines, however, there are additional circuits called *damper*, or *amortisseur*, *circuits*. (See, for instance, Fig. 3-31.) In many salient-pole machines, they are formed by bar or cage windings embedded in the pole faces and connected at their ends by short-circuiting end rings. An additional equivalent rotor circuit may be formed by the bolts and iron of the rotor structure. Cylindrical-rotor machines may likewise have rotor circuits other than the main-field winding, especially in the quadrature axis, where the rotor iron may form an equivalent circuit almost as effective as the main field for induced currents.

a. Effects on Power and Torque. Damper bars form the starting winding for synchronous motors. The principal reason for installing them in generators is, as their name implies, to produce torques which help to damp out oscillations of the machine rotor about its equilibrium position. When the speed of the rotor departs from synchronous speed, the damper circuits produce induction-motor torques. These torques will be studied in some detail in the next chapter. It is sufficient for present purposes to state that their magnitude is approximately proportional to the departure of rotor speed from synchronous speed as long as that departure is small. Motor torques (i.e., in the direction of rotation) are produced when the speed is below synchronous and generator torques when the speed is above. Strictly speaking, the torques are also a function of the power angle δ, but this dependence will be ignored. As illustrated in the

---

[1] For quantitative examinations and comparisons illustrating the applicability of this approximation, see S. B. Crary, "Power System Stability," vol. II, Transient Stability, John Wiley & Sons, Inc., New York, 1947.

following article, inclusion of damping torque and power is desirable in many dynamic analyses.

b. Effects on Current-Voltage Relations.   The damper circuits, of course, have their own resistances and their own self-inductances and mutual inductances with respect to every other machine circuit.   They therefore have an influence on the current-voltage performance of the machine following a disturbance.   To reduce the complexity of the problem somewhat, analyses are usually confined to machines having but one effective rotor circuit other than the main field in the direct axis and one effective

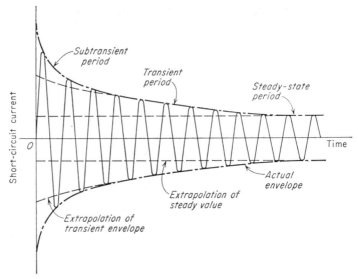

FIG. 5-32. Symmetrical trace of armature short-circuit current in synchronous machine.

rotor circuit in the quadrature axis—in other words, one equivalent damper circuit in each axis.

If the analysis in Art. 5-7*a* were repeated but with the damper circuits included, two additional equations would appear to express the damper linkages and two further equations would be needed to indicate that the damper-circuit voltages are zero (i.e., the damper circuits closed on themselves).   Additional terms would, of course, appear in the armature- and field-linkage relations to reflect the contributions from the damper circuits.   The resulting phase current would be the same as in Eq. 5-125 except that x_d' and x_q would be replaced by the constants x_d'' and x_q'', respectively, representing new self- and mutual-inductance combinations including damper-circuit values.   The reactance x_d'' is called the *direct-axis subtransient reactance*, and x_q'' is the *quadrature-axis subtransient* *reactance.* They are both lower than the respective reactances which they replace. In effect, the initial short-circuit current is higher because induced damper currents appear as well as an induced field current.[1]

Further investigation shows that, because the damper circuits have relatively high resistance, the induced damper currents die out rapidly. After very few cycles, the phase current becomes that given by the methods of Art. 5-7. This is illustrated in Fig. 5-32, which shows a symmetrical trace of a short-circuit current wave (d-c component absent or taken out) such as might be obtained oscillographically. The wave, whose envelope is shown in Fig. 5-33, may be divided into three periods, or time regimes: the *subtransient period*, lasting only for the first few cycles, during which the current decrement is very rapid; the *transient*

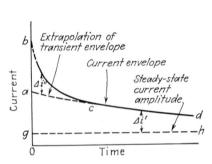

FIG. 5-33. Envelope of synchronous-machine symmetrical short-circuit current.

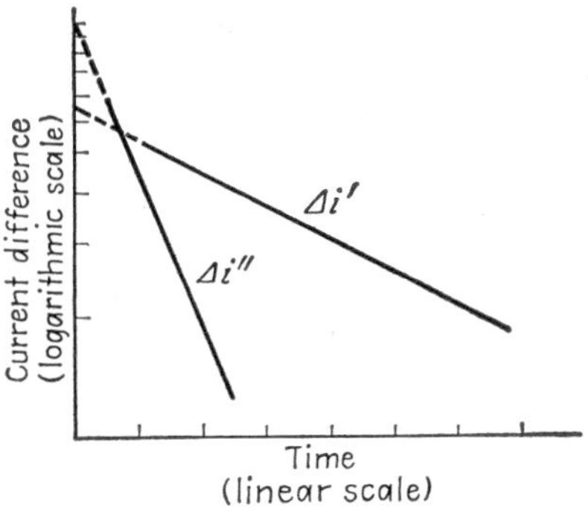

FIG. 5-34. Current differences plotted to semilogarithmic coordinates.

period, covering a relatively longer time, during which the current decrement is more moderate; and finally the *steady-state period*. That the three successive periods merge through the medium of nearly exponential envelope decays can be shown by appropriate semilogarithmic plots. The difference $\Delta i'$ (Fig. 5-33) between the transient envelope and the steady-state amplitude is plotted to a logarithmic scale as a function of time in Fig. 5-34. In similar fashion the difference $\Delta i''$ between the subtransient envelope and an extrapolation of the transient envelope is also plotted in Fig. 5-34. When the work is done carefully, both plots closely approximate straight lines, illustrating the essentially exponential nature of the decrement.

The subtransient reactance x_d'' determines the initial value Ob of the symmetrical subtransient envelope bc (Fig. 5-33); it is equal to the rms value of the prefault open-circuit phase voltage divided by $Ob/\sqrt{2}$, the

---

[1] For a detailed analysis including damper circuits, see Concordia, *op. cit.*

factor $\sqrt{2}$ appearing because bc is the envelope of peak current values. The *direct-axis short-circuit subtransient time constant* T_d'' determines the decay of the subtransient envelope bc; it is equal to the time required for the envelope to decay to the point where the difference between it and the transient envelope acd is $1/\epsilon$, or 0.368 of the initial difference ab.

Under the assumption of negligible transformer voltages, the short-circuit oscillogram (Fig. 5-32) of an unloaded machine involves only d-axis quantities. In a more general case, such as that of a machine with an initial active-power loading, a comparable set of q-axis constants must be available. These include, in addition to x_q and x_q'', the following: T_q'', the *quadrature-axis short-circuit subtransient time constant;* x_q', the *quadrature-axis transient reactance;* and T_q', the *quadrature-axis short-circuit transient time constant.* These constants enter into the initial magnitude and decay of quadrature current i_q in the same manner as the d-axis constants do for i_d. When x_q, x_q', and x_q'' all have different values, the implication is that there are two equivalent q-axis rotor circuits. The induced currents in one are decremented at an appreciably slower rate than in the other.

Greater insight into the effects of damper circuits will be gained during the study of induction machines in the next chapter.

5-11. Synchronous-machine Dynamics. Important dynamic problems arise in synchronous-machine systems because successful operation of the machines demands equality of the mechanical speed of the rotor and the speed of the stator field, and because synchronizing forces tending to maintain this equality are brought into play whenever the relationship is disturbed. If the instantaneous speed of a synchronous machine in a system containing other synchronous equipment should decrease slightly, the decrease would be associated with a decrease in torque angle if the machine were a generator or an increase if it were a motor. For example, if a large load is suddenly applied to the shaft of a synchronous motor, the motor must slow down at least momentarily in order that the torque angle may assume the increased value necessary to supply the added load. In fact, until the new angle is reached, an appreciable portion of the energy furnished to the load comes from stored energy in the rotating mass as it slows down. When the newly required value of angle is first reached, equilibrium is not yet attained, for the mechanical speed is then below synchronous speed. The angle must momentarily increase further in order to permit replacing the deficit of stored energy in the rotating mass. The ensuing processes involve a series of oscillations about the final position even when equilibrium is ultimately restored. Exact description of such events can be given only in terms of the associated electromechanical differential equation, and decisions on restoration of equilibrium can be based only on the solution of the equation.

Similar oscillations or hunting, with the accompanying power and current pulsations, may be particularly troublesome in synchronous motors driving loads whose torque requirements vary cyclically at a fairly rapid frequency, as in motors driving reciprocating air or ammonia compressors. If the natural frequency of mechanical oscillation of the synchronous motor approximates the frequency of an important torque harmonic in the compressor cycle, intolerable oscillations result. Electrodynamic transients of a very complicated form but of the same basic nature occur in electric power systems. Unless they are carefully investigated during system planning, they may result in complete shutdowns over wide areas.

a. The Basic Electromechanical Equation. As in all other types of machines, the electromechanical equation for a synchronous machine follows from recognition of the three classes of torque acting on the rotating members. They are an inertia torque, an electromagnetic torque T_e resulting from energy conversion, and a mechanical shaft torque T_{sh} representing input from the prime mover or output to turn the load. Thus,

$$T_{\text{inertia}} + T_e = T_{sh} \qquad (5\text{-}155)$$

This equation, like those to follow, is written with a generator specifically in mind. The same equations may be applied to a motor by following an appropriate sign convention. The convention used will be stated below after the final form of the equation is given.

The electromagnetic term in Eq. 5-155, and often the shaft input or output as well, can be obtained more conveniently as a power than as a torque. Hence the equation is usually rewritten in power form as

$$P_{\text{inertia}} + P_e = P_{sh} \qquad (5\text{-}156)$$

The inertia power is, of course, found from the angular acceleration. The angular position of the shaft at any instant is taken as the electrical angle δ between a point on it and a reference which is rotating at synchronous speed. Often in simple problems the angle δ is taken identical with the power angle of the machine. The inertia power is then

$$P_{\text{inertia}} = P_j \frac{d^2\delta}{dt^2} \qquad (5\text{-}157)$$

where P_j is the inertia power per unit acceleration. When δ is measured in electrical radians,

$$P_j = J \frac{2}{\text{poles}} \frac{2\pi n}{60} \qquad (5\text{-}158)$$

where J is the moment of inertia and n the speed in rpm. The factor 2/poles changes electrical to mechanical angle, and the factor $2\pi n/60$

changes torque to power. The coefficient P_j is usually considered a constant and evaluated with n equal to synchronous speed. This procedure is justified by the fact that the angular oscillations become intolerable before the speed departs more than 1 or 2 per cent from synchronous speed.

The electromagnetic power P_e has two components. One component is the *damping power*, introduced in Art. 5-10a. As stated there, it is often considered to vary linearly with the departure $d\delta/dt$ from synchronous speed. The second component is the *synchronous power* resulting from synchronous-machine action and characterized by Eqs. 5-90, 5-98, and 5-152 for a single machine on an infinite bus. The electromechanical equation 5-156 then becomes

$$P_j \frac{d^2\delta}{dt^2} + P_d \frac{d\delta}{dt} + P(\delta) = P_{sh} \qquad (5\text{-}159)$$

where P_d is the damping power per unit departure in speed from synchronous and the term $P(\delta)$ indicates that synchronous power is a function of angle δ.

The specific nature of the external network must be known before the function $P(\delta)$ can be identified. When consideration is restricted to one machine connected directly to the terminals of a very large system (see Arts. 5-6 and 5-9) and saliency is ignored, the function is $P_m \sin \delta$, where P_m is the amplitude of the sinusoidal power-angle curve. Equation 5-159 becomes

$$P_j \frac{d^2\delta}{dt^2} + P_d \frac{d\delta}{dt} + P_m \sin \delta = P_{sh} \qquad (5\text{-}160)$$

Positive values of δ denote generator action and therefore energy conversion from mechanical to electrical form, positive values of P_{sh} denote mechanical power input to the shaft, positive values of $d\delta/dt$ denote speeds above synchronous speed, and positive values of $d^2\delta/dt^2$ denote acceleration. Alternatively, the reverse convention may be used. That is, positive values of δ may denote motor action, positive values of P_{sh} mechanical power output from the shaft, positive values of $d\delta/dt$ speeds below synchronous speed, and positive values of $d^2\delta/dt^2$ deceleration.

Both Eqs. 5-159 and 5-160 are nonlinear. One method of analysis, applicable for small oscillations and illustrated below, is to linearize the power-angle expression. It is simply a special case of linearization about an operating point, introduced in Art. 2-5.

b. Linearized Analysis. When a single machine connected to a large system is under study, only a single differential equation rather than a group of such equations is involved. If, in addition, the variations of δ

are small, the term $P(\delta)$ in Eq. 5-159 may be replaced by the equation for the slope of the power-angle curve at the operating point.

When δ varies between about $+\pi/6$ and $-\pi/6$ electrical radians, the sine of the angle is closely equal to the angle in radians. The term $P_m \sin \delta$ in Eq. 5-160 may then be replaced by the term $P_s \delta$, where P_s is the *synchronizing power*, or slope, of the power-angle curve evaluated at the origin. Equation 5-160 becomes

$$P_j \frac{d^2\delta}{dt^2} + P_d \frac{d\delta}{dt} + P_s \delta = P_{sh} \qquad (5\text{-}161)$$

Since the equation is now linear, its solution in a particular case may be obtained by the methods of Appendix B.

Example 5-6. A 200-hp 2,300-volt 3-phase 60-cps 28-pole 257-rpm synchronous motor is directly connected to a large power system. The motor has the following characteristics:

$Wk^2 = 10,500$ lb-ft² (motor plus load)

Synchronizing power $P_s = 11.0$ kw/elec deg

Damping torque $= 1,770$ lb-ft/mech rad/sec

a. Investigate the mode of electrodynamic oscillation of the machine.

b. Rated mechanical load is suddenly thrown on the motor shaft at a time when it is operating in the steady state, but unloaded. Study the electrodynamic transient which will ensue.

Solution. Throughout this solution, the angle δ will be measured in electrical degrees rather than radians. This fact must be recognized in obtaining P_j, P_d, and P_s from the given data.

The inertia is given as Wk^2 (weight times square of radius of gyration) in English units, a common practice for large machines. In mks units (see table of conversion factors at end of book),

$$J = \frac{Wk^2}{23.7} = \frac{10,500}{23.7} = 444 \text{ kg-m}^2$$

From Eq. 5-158 with the factor $\pi/180$ inserted to convert angular measurement to degrees,

$$P_j = 444 \times \frac{2}{28} \times \frac{2\pi(257)}{60} \times \frac{\pi}{180} = 14.9 \text{ watts/elec deg/sec}^2$$

The remaining motor constants in the appropriate units are

$$P_d = 2\pi \times 257 \times 1,770 \times \frac{746}{33,000} \times \frac{\pi}{180} \times \frac{2}{28} = 80.6 \text{ watts/elec deg/sec}$$

$$P_s = 11.0 \times 1,000 = 11,000 \text{ watts/elec deg}$$

The force-free equation which determines the mode of oscillation is then

$$14.9 \frac{d^2\delta}{dt^2} + 80.6 \frac{d\delta}{dt} + 11,000\delta = 0$$

which is the form of Eq. B-2. From Eqs. B-4 and B-5, the undamped angular frequency and damping ratio are, respectively,

$$\omega_n = \sqrt{\frac{11,000}{14.9}} = 27 \text{ rad/sec}$$

$$\zeta = \frac{80.6}{2 \sqrt{14.9 \times 11,000}} = 0.10$$

The magnitude of ζ places the transient response decidedly in the oscillatory region' as it does for all synchronous machines. Any operating disturbance will be followed by a relatively slowly damped oscillation, or swing, of the rotor before steady operation at synchronous speed is resumed. A large disturbance may, of course, be followed by complete loss of synchronism. The damped angular velocity of the motor is, from Eq. B-18,

$$\omega_d = 27 \sqrt{1 - (0.10)^2} = 26.9 \text{ rad/sec}$$

corresponding to a damped oscillation frequency of

$$f_d = \frac{26.9}{2\pi} = 4.3 \text{ cps}$$

b. The full load of 200 hp is equivalent to $200 \times 746 = 149,200$ watts. The steady-state operating angle is

$$\delta_\infty = \frac{149,200}{11,000} = 13.6 \text{ elec deg}$$

In accordance with Eqs. B-13 and B-14, the angular excursions are characterized by the equation

$$\delta = 13.6°[1 - 1.004\epsilon^{-2.7t} \sin (26.9t + 84.3°)]$$

The oscillation is depicted graphically by the curve for $\zeta = 0.1$ in Fig. B-1 when one unit on the vertical scale is taken as 13.6°.

c. *Nonlinear Analysis. Equal-area Methods.* In most of the serious dynamic problems, the oscillations are of such magnitude that the foregoing linearization is not permissible. The equations of motion must be retained in nonlinear form. Analog or digital computers are then often used to aid the analysis. For hand computation or for programming the study on a digital computer, use is made of numerical methods of solving sets of differential equations.[1] The object of the study is usually to find whether or not synchronism is maintained—i.e., whether or not the angle δ settles down to a steady operating value after the machine has been subjected to a sizeable disturbance.

For simple synchronous-machine systems with negligible damping, use

[1] See, for instance, F. B. Hildebrand, "Introduction to Numerical Analysis," chap. 6, McGraw-Hill Book Company, Inc., New York, 1956. For a typical approach using the Runge-Kutta method of numerical integration, see G. W. Stagg, A. F. Gabrielle, D. R. Moore, and J. F. Hohenstein, Calculation of Transient Stability Problems Using a High-speed Digital Computer, *Trans. AIEE*, vol. 78, pt. III, pp. 566–572, August, 1959.

may be made of graphical interpretation of the energy stored in the rotating mass as an aid to determining the maximum angle of swing and to settling the question of maintenance of synchronism. Because of the physical insight which it gives to the dynamic process, application of the method to analysis of a single machine connected to a large system will be discussed.

Consider specifically a synchronous motor having the power-angle curve of Fig. 5-35. With the motor initially unloaded, the operating point is at the origin of the curve. When a mechanical load P_{sh} is suddenly applied, the operating point travels along the sinusoid ABC and, if synchronism is maintained, finally comes to rest at point B with a new torque angle δ_∞. To reach this new operating point, the motor must decelerate at least momentarily under the influence of the difference

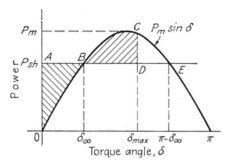

FIG. 5-35. Synchronous-motor power-angle curve and power required by load.

$P_{sh} - P_m \sin \delta$ between the power required by the load and that resulting from electromechanical energy conversion. Now recall from the thought process leading to Eq. 5-160 that both P_{sh} and $P_m \sin \delta$ are proportional to the corresponding torques. Recall also that the integral $\int T\, d\delta$ of torque with respect to angle is energy. The area OAB in Fig. 5-35 is then seen to be proportional to the energy abstracted from the rotating mass during the initial period when electromagnetic energy conversion is insufficient to supply the shaft load. When point B is reached on the first excursion, therefore, the rotor has a momentum in the direction of deceleration. Acting under this momentum, the rotor must swing past point B until an equal amount of energy is recovered by the rotating mass. The result is that the rotor swings to point C and the angle $\delta_{\max}$, at which point

$$\text{Area } BCD = \text{area } OAB \qquad (5\text{-}162)$$

Thereafter, in the absence of damping, the rotor continues to oscillate between points O and C at its natural frequency. The damping present in any physical machine causes successive oscillations to be of decreasing amplitude and finally results in dynamic equilibrium at point B.   The analogy to the oscillations of a pendulum may be noted.

This *equal-area method* provides a ready means of finding the maximum angle of swing.   It also provides a simple indication of whether synchronism is maintained and a rough measure of the margin of stability.   Thus,

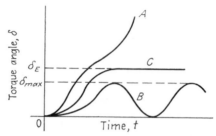

FIG. 5-36. Simple synchronous-machine swing curves showing instability (curve A), stability (curve B), and marginal or critical case (curve C).

if area $BCED$ in Fig. 5-35 is less than area OAB, the decelerating momentum can never be overcome, the angle-time curve follows the course of curve A in Fig. 5-36, and synchronism is lost.   On the other hand, if area $BCED$ is greater than area OAB, synchronism is maintained with a margin indicated by the difference in areas and the angle-time curve follows curve B of Fig. 5-36.   Equality of areas $BCED$ and OAB yields a borderline solution of unstable equilibrium for which curve C is followed.

Example 5-7.   Determine the maximum shaft load which may be suddenly applied to the motor of Example 5-6 when it is initially operating unloaded.   The synchroniz-

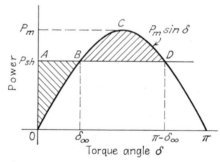

FIG. 5-37. Graphical application of equal-area criterion, Example 5-7.

ing power of 11.0 kw per electrical degree quoted in that example is the initial slope of the power-angle curve followed under these conditions.   Damping is to be ignored.

Solution.   The initial slope of the sinusoidal power-angle curve expressed in kilowatts per radian is equal to the amplitude of the curve in kilowatts.   Hence

$$P_m = 11.0 \times \frac{180}{\pi} = 630 \text{ kw}$$

The load P_{sh} (Fig. 5-37) must be adjusted so that

$$\text{Area } OAB = \text{area } BCD$$

or
$$P_{sh}\delta_\infty - \int_0^{\delta_\infty} 630 \sin \delta \, d\delta = \int_{\delta_\infty}^{\pi - \delta_\infty} 630 \sin \delta \, d\delta - P_{sh}(\pi - 2\delta_\infty)$$

Also
$$P_{sh} = 630 \sin \delta_\infty$$

Trial-and-error solution yields

$$P_{sh} = 455 \text{ kw} = 610 \text{ hp}$$

Notice that the result is independent of inertia when damping is neglected. Under these circumstances, inertia determines the period of oscillation but does not influence its amplitude.

5-12. Résumé. In treating the synchronous machine, we have followed a procedure which is very common in modern engineering. We have established a mathematical model of the device, and, on the basis of this model, we have carried out typical analyses of the steady-state, transient, and dynamic performance.

The elemental properties of the model form the subject of the first two articles. The machine is idealized to the point where linear coupled-circuit theory may be applied. The nature of the self- and mutual inductances is specified as a logical consequence of the machine geometry and the idealizing assumptions. Then the basic electric-circuit relations may be applied.

Straightforward application of the circuit approach leads to a complex set of simultaneous equations which would be very cumbersome to deal with. The $dq0$ transformation of variables, typified by Eq. 5-41, is introduced at this point. From the mathematical viewpoint, the $dq0$ transformation is merely a linear change of variables which simplifies the circuit relations and expedites their solution. Of equal importance is the physical significance. When armature currents are resolved into d- and q-axis components, for example, the associated mmf wave is split into components along the polar and interpolar axes. Such interpretations enable us to make use of the physical views of the energy-conversion process in terms of the interaction of magnetic fields described in earlier chapters. Moreover, we can observe correlation of the operation of the d-c machines in Chap. 4 with that of the synchronous machine. In this manner we can often pass judgment on the reasonableness of analytical results.

The mathematical model is completed when the flux-linkage relations (Eqs. 5-43 to 5-46), voltage-current relations (Eqs. 5-50 to 5-53), and power and torque expressions (Eqs. 5-55 and 5-56) are obtained. The electrical performance of the ideal machine is fully characterized by these equations. For analysis of a specific problem, one needs to supplement these basic machine relations by the equations characterizing the particular circuitry and equipment connected to the armature terminals as well as those determined by the excitation system connected to the field terminals and the mechanical equipment connected to the shaft. Carrying out this process, together with obtaining solutions in readily usable form, may be no small task, however, so that some illustrations of procedure are in order.

The remainder of the chapter is devoted to such illustrations. At the same time, the specific situations chosen for investigation are ones concerned with the more important performance features of the machine. They include the behavior under steady-state conditions, the response to 3-phase short circuits in the a-c system, and relatively simple dynamic problems. During these investigations we sometimes run into the desirability of additional minor simplifications. Neglect of the $p\lambda_d$ and $p\lambda_q$ terms in the voltage relations during transient analyses is an example. These simplifications are empirical in nature, but note that they are generally no more so than the original empiricisms which make up the definition of the idealized machine. The need for continual checks with experiment and experience is therefore underlined.

A very simple approximate picture of the synchronous machine as a circuit element emerges from these considerations. The machine is simply a reactance behind which a readily determined voltage exists. In the steady state, the reactance is the synchronous reactance, and the internal voltage is the excitation voltage. Under transient conditions, the reactance decreases and becomes the transient reactance; the associated internal voltage is one dependent on the field flux linkages. No refinements or subtleties are included in this picture, but it can be very valuable in roughing out the strategy prior to the detailed investigation.

Finally, and with reference to detailed investigation, it should be noted that we have dealt only with relatively simple problems here. For example, we have made no mention of the effects of unbalance in the 3-phase system. In fact, as shown by the discussion in Art. 5-10, our mathematical model is not sufficiently comprehensive to handle all the important problems. The economic importance of synchronous machines and of systems containing them is so great that an extensive body of literature has been built up around their analysis and application. This chapter is simply an introduction to that literature.

PROBLEMS

5-1. An idealized 3-phase 2-pole synchronous machine has the field winding f on the salient-pole rotor. The stator phases a, b, and c are identical windings with their magnetic axes spaced 120° apart around the stator. As in Fig. 5-1, θ is the angle from the axis of phase a to the d axis.

The values of some of the inductances are as follows:

Field self-inductance, $L_{ff} = 100$ henrys

Phase a self-inductance, $\mathcal{L}_{aa} = 1.1 + 0.4 \cos 2\theta$

Mutual between a and f, $\mathcal{L}_{af} = 10 \cos \theta$

Mutual between b and c, $\mathcal{L}_{bc} = -0.5 + 0.4 \cos 2\theta$

a. Write expressions for all self- and mutual inductances associated with windings a, b, c, and f as functions of θ.

b. Summarize the results in part a by writing a 4×4 inductance matrix $[\mathcal{L}_{abcf}]$.

c. Determine the d- and q-axis synchronous inductances L_d and L_q.

d. Determine the d-axis transient inductance L_d'.

5-2. Show that, when only zero-sequence current is present in a 3-phase synchronous machine, i_a, i_b, and i_c must all be equal and hence no flux will link the rotor.

5-3. The dq transformation is obviously correlated closely with the physical structure of the synchronous machine. As a linear transformation of variable, however, it can be applied to static circuits as well as to machines. Consider a balanced 3-phase Y-connected impedance load having resistance r_L and inductance L_L in each phase. Show that the relations between the impressed voltages v_d and v_q and the currents i_d and i_q taken by the load are

$$v_d = r_L i_d + L_L p i_d - L_L i_q \omega$$
$$v_q = r_L i_q + L_L p i_q + L_L i_d \omega$$

5-4. In some types of problems involving unbalance on the stator side of the synchronous machine, it may be convenient to use a different transformation of variable resolving along axes other than the dq axes. Consider that, as an alternative, two axes fixed in the stator structure are to be used. The α axis coincides with the axis of phase a. The β axis is 90° ahead of the α axis in the direction of rotation. The zero-sequence component remains the same as before. Such a transformation corresponds to using equivalent 2-phase currents which produce the same mmf at the air gap as do the actual 3-phase currents.

a. Show that the relations between phase variables and $\alpha\beta$ variables are typified by

$$i_\alpha = \tfrac{2}{3}(i_a - \tfrac{1}{2}i_b - \tfrac{1}{2}i_c)$$

$$i_\beta = -\frac{1}{\sqrt{3}}(i_b - i_c)$$

$$i_0 = \tfrac{1}{3}(i_a + i_b + i_c)$$
$$i_a = i_\alpha + i_0$$

$$i_b = -\tfrac{1}{2}i_\alpha + \frac{\sqrt{3}}{2}i_\beta + i_0$$

$$i_c = -\tfrac{1}{2}i_\alpha - \frac{\sqrt{3}}{2}i_\beta + i_0$$

b. Show that the relations between the dq variables and the $\alpha\beta$ variables are typified by

$$i_\alpha = i_d \cos \theta - i_q \sin \theta$$
$$i_\beta = i_d \sin \theta + i_q \cos \theta$$

c. Show that the voltage-current relations expressed in $\alpha\beta$ variables are

$$v_\alpha = r_a i_\alpha + p\lambda_\alpha$$
$$v_\beta = r_a i_\beta + p\lambda_\beta$$
$$v_0 = r_a i_0 + p\lambda_0$$

5-5. *a.* By carrying out the manipulations described at the beginning of Art. 5-4, show that Eqs. 5-43 to 5-46 are correct.

b. Similarly, show that Eqs. 5-50 to 5-53 are correct.

5-6. This problem is concerned with analysis of a 2-phase synchronous machine instead of the 3-phase machine of the text. Consider that the machine is idealized as in Art. 5-1 except that there are 2 distributed windings *a* and *b* on the stator, 1 in each phase, with magnetic axes 90° apart. The salient-pole rotor has only the main-field winding *f* in the *d* axis and no winding in the *q* axis. The angle from the axis of phase *a* to the *d* axis is θ. That from the phase *b* axis to the *d* axis is $\theta + 270°$ or, what amounts to the same thing, $\theta - 90°$. The same general assumptions, conventions, and notation as in Arts. 5-1 through 5-4 apply.

a. Write the flux-linkage equations in matrix form corresponding to Eq. 5-7.

b. In the manner of Art. 5-2, show that the inductance matrix $[\mathcal{L}_{abf}]$ is given by

$$\begin{bmatrix} L_{aa0} + L_{g2}\cos 2\theta & L_{g2}\sin 2\theta & L_{af}\cos \theta \\ L_{g2}\sin 2\theta & L_{aa0} - L_{g2}\cos 2\theta & L_{af}\sin \theta \\ L_{af}\cos \theta & L_{af}\sin \theta & L_{ff} \end{bmatrix}$$

c. Show that the appropriate *dq* transformation of variables is typified by

$$\begin{bmatrix} i_d \\ i_q \end{bmatrix} = \begin{bmatrix} \cos \theta & \sin \theta \\ -\sin \theta & \cos \theta \end{bmatrix} \begin{bmatrix} i_a \\ i_b \end{bmatrix}$$

Also write the relations for i_a and i_b in terms of i_d, i_q, and θ.

d. Show that the flux linkages are given by

$$\lambda_f = L_{ff}i_f + L_{af}i_d$$
$$\lambda_d = L_{af}i_f + L_d i_d$$
$$\lambda_q = L_q i_q$$

Also identify the *d*- and *q*-axis synchronous inductances L_d and L_q in terms of L_{aa0} and L_{g2}.

e. Show that Eqs. 5-50 to 5-52 are correct for the voltages v_f, v_d, and v_q in this case.

f. Show that the instantaneous power input to the 2-phase stator is

$$p_s = v_d i_d + v_q i_q$$

g. Show that the motor torque is given by

$$T = \frac{\text{poles}}{2}(\lambda_d i_q - \lambda_q i_d)$$

5-7. A 2-pole synchronous machine with a uniform air gap has a Y-connected 3-phase stator winding. The stator windings have a synchronous inductance of 0.01 henry per phase and negligible resistance. The rotor winding has an inductance of 20 henrys and a resistance of 10 ohms. It is connected to a d-c voltage source of 100 volts. The mutual inductance between the rotor and a stator phase when their magnetic axes are aligned is 0.4 henry.

The machine is operating as a generator under steady-state conditions delivering power to a balanced 3-phase system at 1.0 power factor and 500 radians/sec angular frequency. The terminal voltage of each phase is 1,000 volts rms. What is the electrical power output of the generator in kilowatts?

5-8. Draw the steady-state *dq* phasor diagram for an overexcited synchronous motor (i.e., one whose field current is sufficiently high so that lagging reactive kva is delivered to the supply system). From this phasor diagram show that the torque angle δ between the excitation- and terminal-voltage phasors is given by

$$\tan \delta = \frac{I_a x_q \cos \phi + I_a r_a \sin \phi}{V_t + I_a x_q \sin \phi - I_a r_a \cos \phi}$$

5-9. A d-c shunt motor is mechanically coupled to a 3-phase cylindrical-rotor synchronous generator. The d-c motor is connected to a 230-volt constant-potential d-c supply, and the a-c generator is connected to a 230-volt (line to line) constant-potential constant-frequency 3-phase supply. The 4-pole Y-connected synchronous machine is rated 25 kva, 230 volts, and has a synchronous reactance of 1.60 ohms per phase. The 4-pole d-c machine is rated 25 kw, 230 volts. All losses are to be neglected.

a. If the two machines act as a motor-generator set receiving power from the d-c mains and delivering power to the a-c mains, what is the excitation voltage of the a-c machine in volts per phase (line to neutral) when it delivers rated kva at 1.00 power factor?

b. Leaving the field current of the a-c machine as in part a, what adjustment can be made to reduce the power transfer (between a-c and d-c) to zero? Under this condition of zero power transfer what is the armature current of the d-c machine? What is the armature current of the a-c machine?

c. Leaving the field current of the a-c machine as in parts a and b, what adjustment can be made to cause 25 kw to be taken from the a-c mains and delivered to the d-c mains? Under these conditions, what is the armature current of the d-c machine? What are the magnitude and phase of the current of the a-c machine?

5-10. A synchronous generator is connected to an infinite bus through two parallel 3-phase transmission circuits each having a reactance of 0.60 per unit including step-up and step-down transformers at each end. The synchronous reactance of the generator (which may be handled on a cylindrical-rotor basis) is 0.90 per unit. All resistances are negligible, and reactances are expressed on the generator rating as a base. The infinite-bus voltage is 1.00 per unit.

a. The power output and excitation of the generator are adjusted so that it delivers rated current at 1.0 power factor at its terminals in the steady state. Compute the generator terminal and excitation voltages, the power output, and the reactive power delivered to the infinite bus.

b. The throttle of the prime mover is now adjusted so that there is no power transfer between the generator and the infinite bus. The field current of the generator is adjusted until 0.50-per-unit lagging reactive kva is delivered to the infinite bus. Under these conditions, compute the terminal and excitation voltages of the generator.

c. The system is then returned to the operating conditions of part a. One of the two parallel transmission circuits is disconnected by tripping the circuit breakers at its ends. The generator excitation is kept constant. Will the generator remain in synchronism? After comparing the desired power transfer with the maximum under these conditions, give an opinion regarding the adequacy of the transmission system.

5-11. A 1,000-hp 2,300-volt Y-connected 3-phase 60-cps 20-pole synchronous motor has a synchronous reactance of 4.00 ohms per phase. In this problem cylindrical-rotor theory may be used, and all losses may be neglected.

a. This motor is operated from an infinite bus supplying rated voltage at rated frequency, and its field excitation is adjusted so that the power factor is unity when the shaft load is such as to require an input of 800 kw. If the shaft load is slowly increased, with the field excitation held constant, determine the maximum torque (in pound-feet) that the motor can deliver.

b. Instead of the infinite bus of part a, suppose that the power supply is a 1,000-kva

2,300-volt Y-connected synchronous generator whose synchronous reactance is also 4.00 ohms per phase. The frequency is held constant by a governor, and the field excitations of motor and generator are held constant at the values which result in rated terminal voltage when the motor absorbs 800 kw at unity power factor. If the shaft load on the synchronous motor is slowly increased, determine the maximum torque (in pound-feet). Also determine the armature current, terminal voltage, and power factor at the terminals corresponding to this maximum load.

c. Determine the maximum motor torque if, instead of remaining constant as in part b, the field currents of the generator and motor are slowly increased so as always to maintain rated terminal voltage and unity power factor while the shaft load is increased.

5-12. What per cent of its rated output will a salient-pole synchronous motor deliver without loss of synchronism when the applied voltage is normal and the field excitation is zero, if $x_d = 0.80$ per unit and $x_q = 0.50$ per unit? Compute the per-unit armature current at maximum power.

5-13. A salient-pole synchronous motor has $x_d = 0.80$ and $x_q = 0.50$ per unit. It is running from an infinite bus of $V_t = 1.00$ per unit. Neglect all losses. What is the minimum per-unit excitation for which the machine will stay in synchronism with full-load torque?

5-14. A 2-pole synchronous motor has a 2-phase winding with negligible resistance on the rotor. Its stator has salient poles with a field winding on the d axis having the resistance r_f and excited by a direct voltage V_f. There is a short-circuited stator winding in the q axis.

The motor is running in the steady state with balanced 2-phase voltages given by

$$v_a = -V \sin \omega t \quad \text{and} \quad v_b = -V \cos \omega t$$

applied to the rotor windings. The angle from the d axis to the magnetic axis of rotor phase a is

$$\theta = \omega t + \delta$$

That between the phase b axis and the d axis is 90° greater than this.

(The statement or solution of Prob. 5-6 may be used as a guide in the solution of this problem. Note very carefully the conditions stated here, however, in order to ensure the correct signs.)

a. Show that the d- and q-axis rotor currents into the motor are given by

$$i_d = \frac{-\omega L_{ff} I_f + V \cos \delta}{\omega L_d} \quad \text{and} \quad i_q = \frac{V \sin \delta}{\omega L_q}$$

b. Show that the motor torque is given by

$$T = -\frac{L_{ff} V_f V}{\omega L_d r_f} \sin \delta - \frac{V^2 (L_d - L_q)}{2 \omega^2 L_d L_q} \sin 2\delta$$

c. Show that the phase a rotor current is

$$i_a = i_d \cos \theta + i_q \sin \theta$$

5-15. In Prob. 5-6 the development of the basic theory of a 2-phase synchronous machine is outlined as an alternative to the 3-phase machine of the text. Answer the following questions for this 2-phase machine.

a. What modifications, if any, must be made in Art. 5-5 to be applicable to the 2-phase machine? Specifically, do the phasor diagrams of Figs. 5-8, 5-9, 5-10, and 5-12 still apply? Is the simple equivalent circuit of Fig. 5-13 still correct?

b. What modifications, if any, must be made in Art. 5-6? Are the power-angle expressions (Eqs. 5-88, 5-90, and 5-98) still correct? May the normalized power-angle curves of Fig. 5-19 be used?

c. What modifications, if any, must be made in the transient analyses of Art. 5-7? What are the expressions for L_d and T_{do} which correspond to Eqs. 5-114 and 5-134?

5-16. An idealized 2-pole 3-phase synchronous machine like that of Arts. 5-1 and 5-2 is being driven at synchronous speed so that the angle from the axis of phase *a* to the *d* axis is $\omega t + \alpha$. Use the conventions on which Eqs. 5-43 to 5-53 are based, and express results in terms of machine constants appearing in these equations.

a. The armature terminals are open-circuited, and the field is excited by a step-function voltage V_f. Find the expressions for the instantaneous voltages of the armature phases and their *d* and *q* components.

b. Reduce these expressions to those obtaining when the transformer voltages $p\lambda_d$ and $p\lambda_q$ are ignored.

c. Now consider that the field circuit is closed and unexcited ($v_f = 0$), the initial field and armature currents are zero, and $v_d = 0$. Neglect all resistances. At $t = 0$, a step-function voltage $v_q(t)$ of magnitude V_q is applied to the armature terminals. Find expressions for the armature currents i_d and i_q and the field current i_f. Introduce the transient inductance L_d where appropriate.

5-17. A 3-phase turbine-generator is rated 13.8 kv (line to line), 110,000 kva. Its constants, with reactances expressed in per unit on the machine rating as a base, are

$$x_d = 1.10 \qquad x'_d = 0.20 \qquad T'_d = 1.0 \text{ sec}$$

It is operating unloaded at a terminal voltage of 1.00 per unit when a 3-phase short circuit occurs at it terminals. Ignore the second harmonic and, except in part *g*, the d-c component in the short-circuit current. Express numerical answers both in per unit and in amperes.

a. What is the rms steady-state short-circuit current? Does it make sense physically for the steady-state short-circuit current to be lower than rated current as it is here? Explain.

b. Write the numerical equation for the instantaneous phase *a* current as a function of time. Consider the fault to occur when $\theta_0 = 90°$. Because of the neglect of the d-c component, this is the *symmetrical* short-circuit current.

c. Write the numerical equation for the envelope of the short-circuit current wave as a function of time.

d. Using the results of part *c*, write the numerical equation showing how the rms value of short-circuit current varies with time.

e. What value is given by the expression in (*d*) at $t = 0$? This is known as the *initial symmetrical* rms short-circuit current.

f. Generalize the result in (*d*) by writing the equation for rms symmetrical short-circuit current as a function of time, initial voltage behind transient reactance, and the machine constants.

g. In part *b*, suppose the fault occurs when the magnitude of θ_0 is other than 90°. The value of i_a at $t = 0$ from Eq. 5-140 would then be nonzero. But since the phase *a* winding is a resistance-inductance circuit, the complete phase *a* current cannot change instantaneously from zero. Hence a d-c component must be present in i_a to reconcile the situation. This component dies away rapidly. Give the maximum possible initial magnitude of the d-c component.

5-18. The rotors of turbine-generators usually consist of solid forgings, which means that there is a large mass of iron in the *q* axis. Under transient conditions this iron mass may provide an effective closed path for induced *q*-axis rotor currents. For purposes of analysis, assume that it may be represented by an equivalent q-axis rotor winding which is closed on itself and has the resistance r_{1q}, self-inductance L_{11}, and mutual inductance L_{a1} with a stator phase when the q axis is aligned with the magnetic axis of that phase.

a. Show that this winding can be reflected in the basic machine relations of Art. 5-4 by adding the following two equations

$$\lambda_{1q} = L_{11}i_{1q} + \tfrac{3}{2}L_{a1}i_q$$
$$v_{1q} = r_{1q}i_{1q} + p\lambda_{1q} = 0$$

and changing the λ_q relation to

$$\lambda_q = L_{a1}i_{1q} + L_q i_q$$

The quantities λ_{1q} and i_{1q} are the linkages with and current in the equivalent winding.

b. In the transient analysis of Art. 5-7a, show that the end results as given by Eqs. 5-121 to 5-124 remain the same with the equivalent winding present except that L_q is replaced by

$$L_q' = L_q - \frac{3}{2}\frac{L_{a1}^2}{L_{11}}$$

the q-axis transient inductance. Similarly in Eq. 5-125, x_q is replaced by x_q', the q-axis transient reactance. Ignore the resistance r_{1q} here.

c. How does the presence of the equivalent winding affect the analyses in Art. 5-7b and c?

5-19. Using the assumptions of Art. 5-7a, derive an expression for the instantaneous electromagnetic torque as a function of time after the occurrence of a 3-phase short circuit at the terminals of an unloaded machine. Express the result in terms of the initial field current i_{f0} and machine constants such as L_d' and L_q. (Because of the underlying assumptions, the solution does not contain a unidirectional term which may be of great importance in studying shaft stresses.)

5-20. Draw the block diagram for the generator of Example 5-5 connected to a zero-power-factor lagging load. Consider for these purposes that the load may be represented by a constant reactance x_L. (This may approximate the starting of a large motor, for example.)

5-21. Equations 5-43 to 5-45 and 5-50 to 5-52, both inclusive, constitute the basic electrical relations for a synchronous machine with no zero-sequence currents present. On the basis of these equations, set up a block diagram in the style of Fig. 5-26 to represent the electrical performance of the machine. The voltage v_f is a signal to be received from the excitation system, v_d and v_q are signals to be received from the representation of the external system connected to the a-c windings, and $\omega = p\theta$ is either constant or a signal to be received from a representation of the mechanics of the machine and the equipment coupled to its shaft. Signals for i_f, i_d, and i_q are to flow out from the block diagram.

5-22. The relations in the block diagram of Prob. 5-21 are based on motor conditions as positive. Show the block diagram with generator conditions taken as positive in the equations.

5-23. A proposed scheme for regulating the output voltage of a 500-kva alternator is shown diagrammatically in Fig. 5-38. In addition to the alternator, the system includes a d-c exciter whose field excitation is obtained from the output of an amplifier. The input to the amplifier is the difference between the set value of voltage θ_i and the actual output voltage θ_o. The resistance and inductance of the exciter-field circuit (including the output impedance of the amplifier) are r_1 and L_1. The generated voltage of the exciter is k_1 volts/amp in its field. The resistance and inductance of the alternator-field circuit (including the exciter armature) are r_2 and L_2. The alternator voltage is k_2 volts/amp in its field. For simplicity, the linear rectifier required to change the alternating voltage θ_o to a direct voltage for comparison with θ_i may be assumed to produce 1.0 volt d-c output per volt a-c input. (Alternatively, θ_o may be considered the output voltage of the rectifier, and any transfer constant associated with the rectifier may be considered as part of the constant k_2.)

To examine the stability of the system, consider that the alternator and exciter are rotating at rated speed but that initially their fields are unexcited and $\theta_i = 0$. The alternator is unloaded.

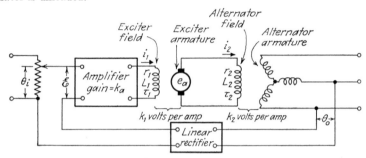

FIG. 5-38. Circuit for voltage regulation of an alternator, Probs. 5-23 and 5-25.

a. Show that the response of the system to a suddenly impressed value of θ_i is characterized by the differential equation

$$\tau_1 \tau_2 \frac{d^2\theta_o}{dt^2} + (\tau_1 + \tau_2) \frac{d\theta_o}{dt} + (1 + K)\theta_o = K\theta_i$$

Identify the time constants τ_1 and τ_2 and the static sensitivity K in terms of the system constants.

b. For a particular alternator and its excitation system, $\tau_1 = 0.4$ sec, and $\tau_2 = 1.0$ sec. The system is to regulate within 0.5 per cent; i.e., the steady-state error in θ_o is not to exceed 0.5 per cent of the set value θ_i. Determine the damping constant ζ, the undamped natural angular frequency ω_n, and sketch the curve of the response θ_o/θ_i as a function of time. Appendix B should be consulted for the meanings of ζ and ω_n and for guidance in sketching the curve.

c. Indicate whether or not the performance of the system is satisfactory.

5-24. Because insufficient damping is found to be present in the voltage-regulating system of Fig. 5-38, Prob. 5-23, an additional feedback loop is to be introduced to improve system performance. As shown in Fig. 5-39, a circuit r_3C_3 is connected across the exciter output, and the fraction x of the voltage across r_3 is fed back in series with the error ε to the input of the amplifier. For purposes of analysis, the voltage across r_3C_3 is to be taken as e_a, so that the resistance and inductance of the exciter armature are neglected in this respect. Otherwise the system is as described in Prob. 5-23.

a. Explain physically why this addition may be expected to improve the dynamic performance of the system. Is the steady-state performance affected?

b. To analyze the dynamic response of the system to a suddenly impressed value of θ_i under initial-rest conditions (the exciter and alternator are, of course, rotating at rated speed), write the differential equations of the system in operator form with the differential operator d/dt replaced by p and the integral operator $\int dt$ replaced by $1/p$.

Then, by treating the resulting equations as though they were algebraic equations, show that the response to a suddenly impressed value of θ_i is characterized by the equation

$$\theta_o = \frac{K\theta_i}{(1 + \tau_1 p)(1 + \tau_2 p) + \dfrac{(1 + \tau_2 p)p}{1 + \tau_3 p} K \dfrac{r_2}{k_2} x\tau_3 + K}$$

Identify the time constants τ_1, τ_2, and τ_3 and the static sensitivity K in terms of the system constants.

c. For the special case of $\tau_3 = \tau_2$ and with initial-rest conditions, it is permissible to cancel $1 + \tau_2 p$ and $1 + \tau_3 p$ in the middle term of the denominator of the equation in (b). Equality of τ_3 and τ_2 does not imply optimum operating conditions; it merely permits

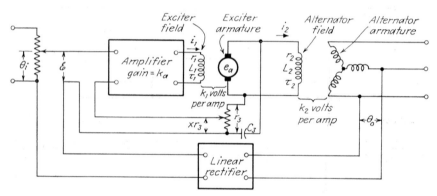

FIG. 5-39. Circuit for voltage regulation of an alternator with stabilizing loop added, Probs. 5-24 and 5-26.

evaluation of the effect of the added loop without analyzing anything more than a simple second-order equation. Show that this equation becomes

$$\tau_1 \tau_2 \frac{d^2\theta_o}{dt^2} + \left(\tau_1 + \tau_2 + K \frac{r_2}{k_2} \tau_2 x\right) \frac{d\theta_o}{dt} + (1 + K)\theta_o = K\theta_i$$

Compare this equation with that given in part a of Prob. 5-23.

d. As in Prob. 5-23, take $\tau_1 = 0.4$ sec and $\tau_2 = \tau_3 = 1.0$ sec, and consider that the system is to regulate within 0.5 per cent. In addition consider that $k_2/r_2 = 20$ and $x = 0.75$. Determine the damping constant ζ, the undamped natural angular frequency ω_n, and sketch the curve of the response θ_o/θ_i as a function of time. Compare the results with those of part b of Prob. 5-23.

5-25. The scheme shown in Fig. 5-38 and described in Prob. 5-23 is to be analyzed by frequency-response rather than transient-response techniques.

a. Using the values given in part b of Prob. 5-23, obtain a numerical expression for the phasor ratio θ_o/θ_i of output to input as a function of frequency. Sketch the curve of the amplitude of this ratio as a function of frequency, and evaluate the maximum amplitude.

b. Compare the conclusions reached from this study with those indicated by the transient study of Prob. 5-23.

PROBLEMS 283

5-26. Because the frequency response of the voltage-regulating system of Prob. 5-25 is found to be unsatisfactory, an additional feedback loop is to be introduced to improve system performance. The revised system is shown in Fig. 5-39 and described in Prob. 5-24.

a. Consider the special case of $\tau_3 = \tau_2$ as in Prob. 5-24. Using the numerical values given in part *d* of Prob. 5-24, obtain a numerical expression for the phasor ratio Θ_o/Θ_i of output to input as a function of frequency. Sketch the curve of the amplitude of this ratio as a function of frequency, and evaluate the maximum amplitude.

b. Compare the conclusions reached from this study with those indicated by the transient study of Prob. 5-24.

5-27. A 3-phase salient-pole generator has the following constants in per unit on the machine kva rating as a base:

$$x_d = 1.0 \qquad x_q = 0.6 \qquad x_d' = 0.3$$

a. The machine is connected to an infinite bus at its terminals with rated voltage and power output at 1.0 power factor. Compute and plot the transient power-angle curve of the machine. Consider E_q' constant, and retain the true angle δ.

b. Repeat (*a*), using the approximate simplified representation of Fig. 5-31 for the machine.

c. Instead of being at the terminals of the machine, the infinite bus is supplied from the generator over a line having negligible resistance and a reactance of 0.7 per unit. The generator continues to operate at rated terminal voltage, unity power factor at its terminals, and 1.00 power output.

After determining the new value of the infinite-bus voltage, repeat (*a*) and (*b*) for the combination of machine and external reactance.

5-28. The machine in Prob. 5-17 has the constants

$$x_d'' = 0.10 \qquad T_d'' = 0.035 \text{ sec}$$

in addition to those given there. Work Prob. 5-17, except for part *b*, with the subtransient effects included as well as the transient effects. In part *f*, the initial voltage behind subtransient reactance must also be reflected. In part *g*, the principle still holds that the d-c component must preserve continuity of instantaneous phase current just before and just after the short circuit.

5-29. Reciprocating air and ammonia compressors require a torque which fluctuates periodically about a steady average value. For a 2-cycle unit, the torque harmonics have frequencies in cycles per second which are multiples of the speed in revolutions per second. When, as is commonly the case, the compressors are driven by synchronous motors, the torque harmonics cause periodic fluctuation of the torque angle δ and may result in undesirably high pulsations of power and current to the motor. It is therefore essential that, for the significant harmonics, the electrodynamic response of the motor be held to a minimum.

a. To investigate the response of the motor to torque harmonics, use a linearized analysis as in Eq. 5-161. Let

$$P_{sh} = P_{shm} \sin \omega t$$

where P_{shm} corresponds to the amplitude of the harmonic-torque pulsation whose angular frequency is ω. Then show that the differential equation can be written

$$\frac{d^2\delta}{dt^2} + 2\zeta\omega_n \frac{d\delta}{dt} + \omega_n^2\delta = \frac{P_{shm}}{P_i} \sin \omega t$$

where ζ and ω_n are as in Appendix B. Identify these quantities in terms of P_s, P_d, and P_j.

b. Show that the phasor expression for the steady-state solution is

$$\Delta = \frac{P_{shm}/P_j}{(\omega_n^2 - \omega^2) + j2\zeta\omega_n\omega}$$

c. The motor driving the compressor is that of Example 5-6. The compressor has a first-order torque harmonic with an amplitude of 580 lb-ft and a frequency of 4.3 cps. Determine the maximum deviation in power angle δ and the corresponding pulsation of synchronous power.

d. Consider that a flywheel is added to bring the total Wk^2 up to 16,500 lb-ft^2. Repeat the computation of (c), and compare the results.

5-30. The ideal conditions for synchronizing an alternator with an electric power system are that the alternator voltage be the same as that of the system bus in magnitude, phase, and frequency. Departure from these conditions results in undesirable current and power surges accompanying electromechanical oscillation of the alternator rotor. As long as the oscillations are not too violent, they may be investigated by a linearized analysis.

Consider that a 2,500-kw 0.80-power-factor 25-cps 26-pole oil-engine-driven alternator is to be synchronized with a 25-cps system large enough to be considered an infinite bus. The Wk^2 of the alternator, engine, and associated flywheel is 750,000 lb-ft^2. The damping-power coefficient P_d is 3,600 watts per electrical degree per second, and the synchronizing-power coefficient P_s is 1.21 × 10^5 watts per electrical degree. Both P_d and P_s may be assumed to remain constant. In all cases below, the terminal voltage is adjusted to its correct magnitude. The engine governor is sufficiently insensitive so that it does not act during the synchronizing period.

a. Consider that the alternator is initially adjusted to the correct speed but that it is synchronized out of phase by 20 electrical degrees, with the alternator leading the bus. Obtain a numerical expression for the ensuing electromechanical oscillations. Also give the largest value of torque exerted on the rotor during the synchronizing period. Ignore losses, and express this torque as a percentage of that corresponding to the nameplate rating.

b. Repeat (a) with the alternator synchronized at the proper angle but with its speed initially adjusted 1.0 cps fast.

c. Repeat (a) with the alternator initially leading the bus by 20 electrical degrees and its speed initially adjusted 1.0 cps fast.

5-31. A synchronous motor whose input under rated operating conditions is 10,000 kva is connected to an infinite bus over a short feeder whose impedance is purely reactive. The motor is rated at 60 cps, 600 rpm, and has a total Wk^2 of 500,000 lb-ft^2 (including the shaft load). The power-angle curve under transient conditions is 2.00 sin δ, where the amplitude is in per unit on a 10,000-kva base.

a. With the motor operating initially unloaded, a 10,000-kw shaft load is suddenly applied. Does the motor remain in synchronism?

b. How large a shaft load may be suddenly applied without loss of synchronism?

c. Consider now that the suddenly applied load is on for only 0.2 sec, after which a comparatively long time elapses before any load is again applied. Determine the maximum value of such a load which will still allow synchronism to be maintained. Use the equal-area criterion as an aid in the process. For purposes of computing the angle δ at 0.2 sec, ignore damping, and use a linearized analysis in which the power-angle curve is approximated by a straight line through the origin and the 60° point.

CHAPTER 6

Theory of Ideal Polyphase
Induction Machines

In the induction machine, alternating currents are present in both the stator and the rotor windings, those in the rotor usually being the result of electromagnetic induction from the stator.   The rotor- and stator-mmf waves and associated flux waves rotate around the air gap at synchronous speed in the manner described in Art. 3-4.   The rotor structure itself, however, normally rotates at a different speed—a slower speed for motor action, giving rise to the term *slip* and its definition in Eq. 3-63.

The operation of the induction machine is discussed qualitatively in Art. 3-6.   We now wish to develop analytical methods for studying its performance under dynamic, transient, and steady conditions.   The general procedure closely parallels that for synchronous machines in the preceding chapter.   First, the machine is idealized; then, with the help of the dq transformation of variables, the basic equations are developed; and finally, these relations are applied to a variety of important specific cases. The similarity to synchronous-machine analysis will be obvious to those who study both chapters.   Nevertheless, reading of the previous chapter is not a prerequisite to this one.

6-1. The Ideal Induction Machine.   A schematic representation of an ideal 3-phase induction motor is given in Fig. 6-1.   On the stator are the 3 distributed windings a, b, and c, 1 in each phase and symbolized by the correspondingly labeled concentrated coils.   On the rotor are 3 other distributed windings A, B, and C.   The stator and rotor phases are balanced and may be connected in Y or Δ.   In Fig. 6-2 they are each shown Y-connected.   The rotor may be a squirrel-cage structure short-circuited on itself by end rings, or it may be a wound rotor with terminals brought to slip rings on the shaft so that it may be connected to an external circuit. In the former case, the terminals A, B, and C in Fig. 6-2 are short-circuited, and the rotor voltages v_A, v_B, and v_C are zero.   For greater generality, we shall retain the identity of the rotor terminal voltages in our study.

285

The magnetic axes of the individual stator and rotor phases are marked in Fig. 6-1. The axis of a rotor phase is displaced by the angle θ_2 from the axis of the corresponding stator phase. As the rotor turns, the angle

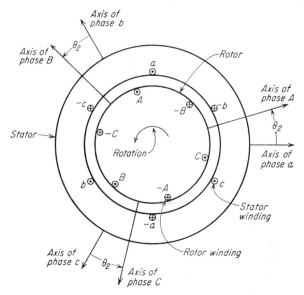

FIG. 6-1. Idealized 3-phase induction machine.

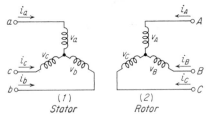

FIG. 6-2. Connections and current conventions for 3-phase induction machine.

θ_2 varies with time. When the rotor angular velocity is constant at the value ω_2,

$$\theta_2 = \omega_2 t \tag{6-1}$$

or, for a constant slip s,

$$\theta_2 = (1 - s)\omega t \tag{6-2}$$

where ω is the stator electrical angular velocity.

As in many of our earlier analyses, saturation, hysteresis, and eddy currents will be ignored, permitting superposition to be applied. Space mmf and flux waves are considered to be sinusoidally distributed, implying negligible effects of teeth and slots. The machine is regarded as a group of linear coupled circuits.

The voltage-current relations for the 6 windings are

Stator:

$$v_a = r_1 i_a + p\lambda_a \tag{6-3}$$
$$v_b = r_1 i_b + p\lambda_b \tag{6-4}$$
$$v_c = r_1 i_c + p\lambda_c \tag{6-5}$$

Rotor:

$$v_A = r_2 i_A + p\lambda_A \tag{6-6}$$
$$v_B = r_2 i_B + p\lambda_B \tag{6-7}$$
$$v_C = r_2 i_C + p\lambda_C \tag{6-8}$$

Here r_1 is the stator phase resistance, r_2 the rotor phase resistance, λ the flux linkages with the winding denoted by the subscript, and p the differential operator d/dt. Voltage symbols denote voltages applied to the windings, and positive currents are directed into the windings.

All 6 of the windings have their own self-inductances and mutual inductances with respect to every other winding. Because the rotor is a smooth cylinder, however, the situation is simpler than in the salient-pole synchronous machine. Only the mutual inductances between stator and rotor phases change as the rotor revolves, and only they are functions of the rotor position angle θ_2. Let L_{aa} be the self-inductance of the stator windings, L_{AA} the self-inductance of the rotor windings, L_{ab} the mutual inductance between stator phases, and L_{AB} the mutual inductance between rotor phases. All these values are constant. Let the peak value of the stator-to-rotor mutual inductance be L_{aA}. This value obtains when the axes of the 2 phases concerned coincide. Otherwise the instantaneous value is proportional to the cosine of the instantaneous angle between the axes.

The phase-linkage equations then are

Stator:

$$\lambda_a = L_{aa} i_a + L_{ab}(i_b + i_c)$$
$$+ L_{aA}[i_A \cos \theta_2 + i_B \cos (\theta_2 + 120°) + i_C \cos (\theta_2 - 120°)] \tag{6-9}$$
$$\lambda_b = L_{aa} i_b + L_{ab}(i_a + i_c)$$
$$+ L_{aA}[i_A \cos (\theta_2 - 120°) + i_B \cos \theta_2 + i_C \cos (\theta_2 + 120°)] \tag{6-10}$$
$$\lambda_c = L_{aa} i_c + L_{ab}(i_a + i_b)$$
$$+ L_{aA}[i_A \cos (\theta_2 + 120°) + i_B \cos (\theta_2 - 120°) + i_C \cos \theta_2] \tag{6-11}$$

Rotor:

$$\lambda_A = L_{AA} i_A + L_{AB}(i_B + i_c)$$
$$+ L_{aA}[i_a \cos \theta_2 + i_b \cos (\theta_2 - 120°) + i_c \cos (\theta_2 + 120°)] \tag{6-12}$$
$$\lambda_B = L_{AA} i_B + L_{AB}(i_A + i_c)$$
$$+ L_{aA}[i_a \cos (\theta_2 + 120°) + i_b \cos \theta_2 + i_c \cos (\theta_2 - 120°)] \tag{6-13}$$
$$\lambda_C = L_{AA} i_C + L_{AB}(i_A + i_B)$$
$$+ L_{aA}[i_a \cos (\theta_2 - 120°) + i_b \cos (\theta_2 + 120°) + i_c \cos \theta_2] \tag{6-14}$$

Now we shall consider that

$$i_a + i_b + i_c = 0 \qquad (6\text{-}15)$$
$$i_A + i_B + i_C = 0 \qquad (6\text{-}16)$$

These conditions are equivalent to stating that there is no neutral connection (which is true of the great majority of induction machines) or that, in any event, the external circuitry is such that these conditions are imposed—in other words, there are no zero-sequence currents. Terms such as $L_{aa}i_a + L_{ab}(i_b + i_c)$ in Eqs. 6-9 to 6-14 then reduce to expressions like $(L_{aa} - L_{ab})i_a$. Let

$$L_{11} = L_{aa} - L_{ab} \qquad (6\text{-}17)$$
$$L_{22} = L_{AA} - L_{AB} \qquad (6\text{-}18)$$

Then the phase-linkage equations become

Stator:

$$\lambda_a = L_{11}i_a + L_{aA}[i_A \cos \theta_2 + i_B \cos (\theta_2 + 120°) + i_C \cos (\theta_2 - 120°)] \qquad (6\text{-}19)$$

$$\lambda_b = L_{11}i_b + L_{aA}[i_A \cos (\theta_2 - 120°) + i_B \cos \theta_2 + i_C \cos (\theta_2 + 120°)] \qquad (6\text{-}20)$$

$$\lambda_c = L_{11}i_c + L_{aA}[i_A \cos (\theta_2 + 120°) + i_B \cos (\theta_2 - 120°) + i_C \cos \theta_2] \qquad (6\text{-}21)$$

Rotor:

$$\lambda_A = L_{22}i_A + L_{aA}[i_a \cos \theta_2 + i_b \cos (\theta_2 - 120°) + i_c \cos (\theta_2 + 120°)] \qquad (6\text{-}22)$$

$$\lambda_B = L_{22}i_B + L_{aA}[i_a \cos (\theta_2 + 120°) + i_b \cos \theta_2 + i_c \cos (\theta_2 - 120°)] \qquad (6\text{-}23)$$

$$\lambda_C = L_{22}i_C + L_{aA}[i_a \cos (\theta_2 - 120°) + i_b \cos (\theta_2 + 120°) + i_c \cos \theta_2] \qquad (6\text{-}24)$$

The straightforward procedure would now be to substitute the linkage expressions in the voltage-current relations of Eqs. 6-3 to 6-8. The result would be an algebraically complicated set of nonlinear differential equations, the nonlinearity being introduced by the trigonometric terms in Eqs. 6-19 to 6-24 because θ_2 is a time function. By the appropriate transformation of variable, however, the algebra can be greatly simplified and the resulting equations made linear for all constant-speed cases.

6-2. Transformations to dq Variables. The appropriate changes of variable for simplification of induction-motor analysis may again be suggested by splitting the air-gap mmfs into components along two perpendicular axes as is done for d-c and synchronous machines. There is now no obvious geometric feature of the machine, such as brushes or salient poles, to dictate the specific choice.   We shall choose d and q axes 90° apart in space and rotating at synchronous speed as determined by the electrical angular velocity ω of the impressed stator voltages—in other words, synchronously rotating axes.[1]   The q axis is 90° ahead of the d axis in the direction of rotation.

When the d axis is so placed that it coincides with the phase a axis at $t = 0$, its displacement from the phase a axis at any time t is ωt.   Its corresponding displacements from the phase b and c axes are $\omega t - 120°$ and $\omega t + 120°$.   The respective q-axis displacements are 90° greater than those of the d axis.   With all 3 stator phases excited, the component mmfs along the d and q axes are then

$$F_{1d} = N_a[i_a \cos \omega t + i_b \cos (\omega t - 120°) + i_c \cos (\omega t + 120°)] \quad (6\text{-}25)$$
$$F_{1q} = N_a[-i_a \sin \omega t - i_b \sin (\omega t - 120°) - i_c \sin (\omega t + 120°)] \quad (6\text{-}26)$$

where N_a represents the effective turns per stator phase.   New stator current variables i_{1d} and i_{1q} may now be defined in terms of the bracketed quantities with arbitrary constant multipliers k_d and k_q.   Thus,

$$i_{1d} = k_d[i_a \cos \omega t + i_b \cos (\omega t - 120°) + i_c \cos (\omega t + 120°)] \quad (6\text{-}27)$$
$$i_{1q} = -k_q[i_a \sin \omega t + i_b \sin (\omega t - 120°) + i_c \sin (\omega t + 120°)] \quad (6\text{-}28)$$

The mmf components then become simply

$$F_{1d} = \frac{N_a}{k_d} i_{1d} \quad (6\text{-}29)$$

$$F_{1q} = \frac{N_a}{k_q} i_{1q} \quad (6\text{-}30)$$

The constants k_d and k_q will each be taken as $\frac{2}{3}$ in order to simplify the numerical coefficients in later equations.   The stator d- and q-axis currents are then

$$i_{1d} = \frac{2}{3}[i_a \cos \omega t + i_b \cos (\omega t - 120°) + i_c \cos (\omega t + 120°)] \quad (6\text{-}31)$$
$$i_{1q} = -\frac{2}{3}[i_a \sin \omega t + i_b \sin (\omega t - 120°) + i_c \sin (\omega t + 120°)] \quad (6\text{-}32)$$

[1] This choice is followed in D. S. Brereton, D. G. Lewis, and C. C. Young, Representation of Induction-motor Loads during Power-system Stability Studies, *Trans. AIEE*, vol. 76, pt. III, pp. 451–460, 1957.   A slight modification may be found in K. G. Black and R. J. Noorda, Analog Computer Study of Wind-tunnel Drives, *Trans. AIEE*, vol. 76, pt. I, pp. 745–750, 1957.

Synchronously rotating axes are not the only possible choice, however.   The axes may be fixed in the rotor, or they may be fixed in the stator.   For examples of the latter, see H. C. Stanley, An Analysis of the Induction Machine, *Trans. AIEE*, vol. 57, pp. 751–755, 1938; and F. J. Maginnis and N. R. Schultz, Transient Performance of Induction Motors, *Trans. AIEE*, vol. 63, pp. 641–646, 1944.

The reverse relations, obtained by simultaneous solution of Eqs. 6-31 and 6-32 in conjunction with 6-15, are

$$i_a = i_{1d} \cos \omega t - i_{1q} \sin \omega t \tag{6-33}$$
$$i_b = i_{1d} \cos (\omega t - 120°) - i_{1q} \sin (\omega t - 120°) \tag{6-34}$$
$$i_c = i_{1d} \cos (\omega t + 120°) - i_{1q} \sin (\omega t + 120°) \tag{6-35}$$

Exactly the same transformations are made for the stator flux linkages λ_a, λ_b, and λ_c in terms of λ_{1d} and λ_{1q} and for the stator phase voltages v_a, v_b, and v_c in terms of v_{1d} and v_{1q}. Equations 6-31 through 6-35 can accordingly be written twice more, once with λ replacing i and once with v replacing i. The similarity to the procedure in Art. 5-3 for synchronous machines will be obvious upon comparison. In both machines, the component currents produce the same magnetic fields as the actual phase currents, and the flux-linkage and voltage transformations are patterned on the current transformations. The similarity to the brush currents in a commutated winding with brushes in the d and q axes will again be noted by comparison with Art. 4-11.

We now need corresponding transformations for rotor quantities in relation to the same synchronously rotating dq axes. Let θ_s be the angle from the rotor phase A axis to the d axis. If the rotor is revolving at the slip s, the d axis is advancing continuously with respect to a point on the rotor at the rate

$$\frac{d\theta_s}{dt} = p\theta_s = s\omega \tag{6-36}$$

Accordingly, the subscript s on the angle θ_s stands for *slip*. The rotor-mmf components are then

$$F_{2d} = N_A[i_A \cos \theta_s + i_B \cos (\theta_s - 120°) + i_C \cos (\theta_s + 120°)] \tag{6-37}$$
$$F_{2q} = N_A[-i_A \sin \theta_s - i_B \sin (\theta_s - 120°) - i_C \sin (\theta_s + 120°)] \tag{6-38}$$

where N_A represents the effective turns per rotor phase. With the same arbitrary $\frac{2}{3}$ factor as used for the stator, the rotor dq component currents are

$$i_{2d} = \frac{2}{3}[i_A \cos \theta_s + i_B \cos (\theta_s - 120°) + i_C \cos (\theta_s + 120°)] \tag{6-39}$$
$$i_{2q} = -\frac{2}{3}[i_A \sin \theta_s + i_B \sin (\theta_s - 120°) + i_C \sin (\theta_s + 120°)] \tag{6-40}$$

and the reverse relations are

$$i_A = i_{2d} \cos \theta_s - i_{2q} \sin \theta_s \tag{6-41}$$
$$i_B = i_{2d} \cos (\theta_s - 120°) - i_{2q} \sin (\theta_s - 120°) \tag{6-42}$$
$$i_C = i_{2d} \cos (\theta_s + 120°) - i_{2q} \sin (\theta_s + 120°) \tag{6-43}$$

Once more exactly the same transformations are made for the rotor linkages λ_A, λ_B, and λ_C in terms of λ_{2d} and λ_{2q} and for the rotor voltages v_A, v_B, and v_C in terms of v_{2d} and v_{2q}. Equations 6-31 to 6-35 and 6-39 to 6-43 now define the transformation of variables to be used in association with the voltage-current equations (Eqs. 6-3 to 6-8) and the flux-linkage relations (Eqs. 6-19 to 6-24).

6-3. Basic Machine Relations in dq Variables. Now we wish to proceed with the main analysis by first obtaining expressions for the dq component linkages in terms of dq currents. The process for the stator is to write Eqs. 6-31 and 6-32 for λ_{1d} and λ_{1q}. Then recognize that in Eqs. 6-19 to 6-24 the angle θ_2 may be replaced by

$$\theta_2 = \omega t - \theta_s \qquad (6\text{-}44)$$

With this replacement, substitute Eqs. 6-19, 6-20, and 6-21 in the λ_{1d} and λ_{1q} equations, and simplify the result by the use of trigonometric reduction formulas. A similar process applies to the rotor. The resulting flux-linkage relations are

Stator:

$$\lambda_{1d} = L_{11}i_{1d} + L_{12}i_{2d} \qquad (6\text{-}45)$$
$$\lambda_{1q} = L_{11}i_{1q} + L_{12}i_{2q} \qquad (6\text{-}46)$$

Rotor:

$$\lambda_{2d} = L_{22}i_{2d} + L_{12}i_{1d} \qquad (6\text{-}47)$$
$$\lambda_{2q} = L_{22}i_{2q} + L_{12}i_{1q} \qquad (6\text{-}48)$$

where

$$L_{12} = \tfrac{3}{2}L_{aA} \qquad (6\text{-}49)$$

Next we wish to obtain expressions for the dq component voltages in terms of these linkages. For the stator, this is accomplished by writing Eqs. 6-31 and 6-32 for v_{1d} and v_{1q}. Then Eqs. 6-3, 6-4, and 6-5 are substituted and the result simplified by recognizing combinations of terms which may be replaced by λ_{1d} and λ_{1q}. A similar process is used for rotor voltages. The final results are

Stator:

$$v_{1d} = r_1 i_{1d} + p\lambda_{1d} - \omega\lambda_{1q} \qquad (6\text{-}50)$$
$$v_{1q} = r_1 i_{1q} + p\lambda_{1q} + \omega\lambda_{1d} \qquad (6\text{-}51)$$

Rotor:

$$v_{2d} = r_2 i_{2d} + p\lambda_{2d} - \lambda_{2q}(p\theta_s) \qquad (6\text{-}52)$$
$$v_{2q} = r_2 i_{2q} + p\lambda_{2q} + \lambda_{2d}(p\theta_s) \qquad (6\text{-}53)$$

Equations 6-45 to 6-48 and 6-50 to 6-53 constitute the basic relations for analysis of the idealized induction machine. Note that the quantity $p\theta_s$ in the speed-voltage contributions in Eqs. 6-52 and 6-53 is the slip angular velocity and is given by

$$p\theta_s = s\omega \qquad (6\text{-}54)$$

It is the relative angular velocity of the synchronously rotating dq axes with respect to the rotor. When s is positive, corresponding to motor action, $p\theta_s$ is positive. When s is negative, corresponding to generator action, $p\theta_s$ is negative. When the rotor speed is constant, $p\theta_s$ is constant and Eqs. 6-50 to 6-53 are linear differential equations with constant coefficients. The $p\lambda_{1d}$ and $p\lambda_{1q}$ terms in Eqs. 6-50 and 6-51 are usually small compared with $\omega\lambda_{1q}$ and $\omega\lambda_{1d}$ and are often neglected. As in the synchronous machine, this neglect corresponds to ignoring the d-c component in the stator winding following a transient. The r_1 terms are frequently neglected in transient analyses but usually included in steady-state analyses.

The common analytical procedure is to substitute the linkage relations (Eqs. 6-45 to 6-48) in the voltage relations (Eqs. 6-50 to 6-53), the particular conditions of the specific problem being taken into account. Solution of the resulting differential equations leads to expressions for the dq voltages and currents. These in turn, substituted into the transformation equations, yield actual phase quantities. A number of such applications to important induction-motor problems are given in the remaining articles of this chapter.

When power and torque are required, they may readily be determined from the dq variables. The instantaneous power input to the 3-phase stator is

$$p_1 = v_a i_a + v_b i_b + v_c i_c \tag{6-55}$$

By use of Eqs. 6-33 to 6-35 written for voltages as well as for currents, phase quantities in Eq. 6-55 can be replaced by dq quantities to yield

$$p_1 = \tfrac{3}{2}(v_{1d} i_{1d} + v_{1q} i_{1q}) \tag{6-56}$$

A similar expression may be written for the rotor. As in the machine types studied earlier, electromagnetic torque can be obtained as the power associated with the speed voltages divided by the corresponding speed in mechanical radians per second. The speed-voltage terms in Eqs. 6-52 and 6-53 are $-\lambda_{2q}(p\theta_s)$ and $\lambda_{2d}(p\theta_s)$. The associated power, as in Eq. 6-56 written for rotor quantities, is

$$\tfrac{3}{2}[-\lambda_{2q} i_{2d}(p\theta_s) + \lambda_{2d} i_{2q}(p\theta_s)]$$

If $p\theta_s$ is positive, the rotor is going backward with respect to the dq axes. The corresponding speed is therefore

$$-(p\theta_s)\,\frac{2}{\text{poles}}$$

expressed in mechanical radians per second. The torque (positive for motor action) is accordingly

$$T = \frac{3}{2} \frac{\text{poles}}{2} (\lambda_{2q} i_{2d} - \lambda_{2d} i_{2q}) \qquad (6\text{-}57)$$

Once more the result is compatible with the concept of torque production from interacting magnetic fields as described in Art. 3-3.   In Eq. 6-57 we are superimposing the interaction of components: d-axis magnetic field with q-axis mmf, and q-axis magnetic field with d-axis mmf.   The sine of the space-displacement angle has unity magnitude for both interactions. The result is also consistent with that for the synchronous machine (Eq. 5-56).

This torque is available to drive the load (plus furnishing rotational losses) and provide acceleration.   The inertia torque required to accelerate the rotating mass is given by

$$T_{\text{inertia}} = J \frac{d\omega_o}{dt} = J \frac{d^2\theta_o}{dt^2} \qquad (6\text{-}58)$$

where J is the moment of inertia of the rotor and the mechanical equipment coupled to it, θ_o the shaft position angle, and ω_o the shaft angular velocity, angular measurements being in mechanical radians.

6-4. Steady-state Analysis.   Consider that the motor is operating at a constant slip s with balance voltages applied to the stator and with the rotor windings short-circuited.   Let the three stator currents be

$$i_a = \sqrt{2}\,I_1 \cos (\omega t + \alpha) \qquad (6\text{-}59)$$
$$i_b = \sqrt{2}\,I_1 \cos (\omega t + \alpha - 120°) \qquad (6\text{-}60)$$
$$i_c = \sqrt{2}\,I_1 \cos (\omega t + \alpha + 120°) \qquad (6\text{-}61)$$

where α is an arbitrary phase angle.   From the dq transformation (Eqs. 6-31 and 6-32) the component currents are

$$i_{1d} = \sqrt{2}\,I_1 \cos \alpha \qquad (6\text{-}62)$$
$$i_{1q} = \sqrt{2}\,I_1 \sin \alpha \qquad (6\text{-}63)$$

Similar results may be obtained for the stator voltages and rotor currents. We see, therefore, that the stator and rotor currents and voltages appear as steady d-c quantities when viewed from the synchronously rotating dq axes.   This is naturally to be expected, for we are viewing rotating fields from a set of axes rotating with the fields.

In steady-state analyses we are usually interested in relations involving rms currents and voltages rather than instantaneous values.   A convenient link between the dq variables and the rms phase variables is furnished by Eq. 6-33 for stator quantities. Bear in mind that, as stated early in Art. 6-2, the d axis is so placed that it coincides with the axis of phase a at $t = 0$. Thus, when i_{1d} and i_{1q} have been evaluated, the stator phase current is

$$i_1 = i_a = i_{1d} \cos \omega t - i_{1q} \sin \omega t \qquad (6\text{-}64)$$

or

$$i_1 = i_{1d} \cos \omega t + i_{1q} \cos (\omega t + 90°) \qquad (6\text{-}65)$$

The latter equation can evidently be written in phasor form as

$$I_1 = I_{1d} + jI_{1q} \qquad (6\text{-}66)$$

where

$$I_{1d} = \frac{i_{1d}}{\sqrt{2}} \quad \text{and} \quad I_{1q} = \frac{i_{1q}}{\sqrt{2}} \qquad (6\text{-}67)$$

In similar fashion it can be seen that the stator phase voltage and rotor phase current are, respectively,

$$V_1 = V_{1d} + jV_{1q} \qquad (6\text{-}68)$$

$$I_2 = I_{2d} + jI_{2q} \qquad (6\text{-}69)$$

where

$$V_{1d} = \frac{v_{1d}}{\sqrt{2}} \quad V_{1q} = \frac{v_{1q}}{\sqrt{2}} \qquad (6\text{-}70)$$

$$I_{2d} = \frac{i_{2d}}{\sqrt{2}} \quad I_{2q} = \frac{i_{2q}}{\sqrt{2}} \qquad (6\text{-}71)$$

The flux linkages λ_{1d}, λ_{1q}, λ_{2d}, and λ_{2q} are constant in the steady state, so that the $p\lambda$ terms drop out of the voltage relations (Eqs. 6-50 to 6-53). When the linkage expressions (Eqs. 6-45 to 6-48) are substituted in these voltage relations and it is recognized that $p\theta_s = s\omega$, the results are

Stator:

$$v_{1d} = r_1 i_{1d} - \omega L_{11} i_{1q} - \omega L_{12} i_{2q} \qquad (6\text{-}72)$$

$$v_{1q} = r_1 i_{1q} + \omega L_{11} i_{1d} + \omega L_{12} i_{2d} \qquad (6\text{-}73)$$

Rotor:

$$v_{2d} = 0 = r_2 i_{2d} - s\omega L_{22} i_{2q} - s\omega L_{12} i_{1q} \qquad (6\text{-}74)$$

$$v_{2q} = 0 = r_2 i_{2q} + s\omega L_{22} i_{2d} + s\omega L_{12} i_{1d} \qquad (6\text{-}75)$$

By combining Eqs. 6-72 and 6-73 in accordance with Eqs. 6-66 to 6-71,

$$V_{1d} + jV_{1q} = r_1(I_{1d} + jI_{1q}) + j\omega L_{11}(I_{1d} + jI_{1q}) + j\omega L_{12}(I_{2d} + jI_{2q}) \quad (6\text{-}76)$$

Similarly, by combining Eqs. 6-74 and 6-75,

$$0 = \frac{r_2}{s}(I_{2d} + jI_{2q}) + j\omega L_{22}(I_{2d} + jI_{2q}) + j\omega L_{12}(I_{1d} + jI_{1q}) \quad (6\text{-}77)$$

These last two equations can be rewritten

$$V_1 = r_1 I_1 + j\omega L_{11} I_1 + j\omega L_{12} I_2 \qquad (6\text{-}78)$$

$$0 = \frac{r_2}{s} I_2 + j\omega L_{22} I_2 + j\omega L_{12} I_1 \qquad (6\text{-}79)$$

or

$$V_1 = r_1 I_1 + j\omega(L_{11} - L_{12}) I_1 + j\omega L_{12}(I_1 + I_2) \qquad (6\text{-}80)$$

$$0 = \frac{r_2}{s} I_2 + j\omega(L_{22} - L_{12}) I_2 + j\omega L_{12}(I_1 + I_2) \qquad (6\text{-}81)$$

and finally

$$V_1 = r_1 I_1 + j x_1 I_1 + j x_\varphi(I_1 + I_2) \qquad (6\text{-}82)$$

$$0 = \frac{r_2}{s} I_2 + j x_2 I_2 + j x_\varphi(I_1 + I_2) \qquad (6\text{-}83)$$

In the last two equations,

$$x_1 = \omega(L_{11} - L_{12}) \qquad (6\text{-}84)$$
$$x_2 = \omega(L_{22} - L_{12}) \qquad (6\text{-}85)$$
$$x_\varphi = \omega L_{12} \qquad (6\text{-}86)$$

The reactance x_1 is the *stator leakage reactance*, x_2 the *rotor leakage reactance*, and x_φ the *magnetizing reactance*, all per phase.   When all quantities are referred to the stator, the circuit of Fig. 6-3 satisfies Eqs. 6-82 and 6-83 and hence becomes an equivalent circuit for the induction machine under balanced steady-state conditions.   It is a valuable aid in determining both the effect of the motor on its supply circuits and the characteristics of the motor itself.   Because of the similarity of the induction machine and the transformer, the two equivalent circuits are similar.

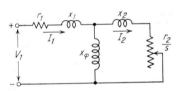

FIG. 6-3. Equivalent circuit of polyphase induction motor.

The torque can also be computed readily with the aid of the equivalent circuit.   From Eqs. 6-52 to 6-54 with v_{2d}, v_{2q}, $p\lambda_{2d}$, and $p\lambda_{2q}$ all equal to zero,

$$\lambda_{2d} = -\frac{r_2 i_{2q}}{s\omega} \qquad (6\text{-}87)$$

$$\lambda_{2q} = \frac{r_2 i_{2d}}{s\omega} \qquad (6\text{-}88)$$

Substitution of these values in Eq. 6-57 yields for the internal electromagnetic torque

$$T = \frac{3}{2} \frac{\text{poles}}{2} \frac{1}{\omega} (i_{2d}^2 + i_{2q}^2) \frac{r_2}{s} \qquad (6\text{-}89)$$

$$T = 3 \frac{\text{poles}}{2} \frac{1}{\omega} I_2^2 \frac{r_2}{s} \qquad (6\text{-}90)$$

This expression is for a 3-phase machine.   More generally, the torque for a machine with q_1 stator phases is

$$T = q_1 \frac{1}{\omega_s} I_2^2 \frac{r_2}{s} \tag{6-91}$$

where ω_s is the synchronous angular velocity in mechanical radians per second, given by

$$\omega_s = \omega \frac{2}{\text{poles}} = \frac{4\pi f}{\text{poles}} \tag{6-92}$$

6-5. Steady-state Characteristics.   Among the important performance aspects in the steady state are the variations of current, speed, and losses as the load-torque requirements change, the starting torque, and the maximum torque.   All these characteristics can be determined from the equivalent circuit.

a. Analysis of the Equivalent Circuit.   Since mechanical power equals torque times angular velocity, the internal mechanical power P developed by the motor is

$$P = (1 - s)\omega_s T = q_1 I_2^2 r_2 \frac{1 - s}{s} \tag{6-93}$$

The total rotor copper loss is evidently

$$\text{Rotor copper loss} = q_1 I_2^2 r_2 \tag{6-94}$$

The total power transferred across the air gap from the stator is

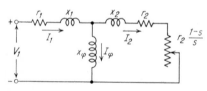

$$P_{g1} = q_1 I_2^2 \frac{r_2}{s} \tag{6-95}$$

We see, therefore, that of the total power delivered to the rotor the fraction $1 - s$ is converted to mechanical power and the fraction s is dissipated as rotor-circuit copper loss.   From this it is evident that

FIG. 6-4. Alternative form of equivalent circuit.

an induction motor running at high slip is inherently an inefficient means for producing torque.

When power aspects are to be emphasized, the equivalent circuit is frequently redrawn in the manner of Fig. 6-4.   (The positive direction of I_2 has also been changed.   This simply means that the exciting current I_φ is $I_1 - I_2$ in Fig. 6-4 instead of $I_1 + I_2$ as in Fig. 6-3.)   The internal mechanical power per stator phase is the power absorbed by the resistance $r_2(1 - s)/s$.   The torque T and power P are not the output values available at the shaft, because core losses, friction, and windage remain to be

accounted for.   They are often taken into account by simply deducting
them from T or P as computed from Eqs. 6-91 and 6-93.

Example 6-1.   A 3-phase Y-connected 220-volt (line to line) 10-hp 60-cps 6-pole
induction motor has the following constants in ohms per phase referred to the stator:

$$r_1 = 0.294 \qquad r_2 = 0.144$$
$$x_1 = 0.503 \qquad x_2 = 0.209 \qquad x_\varphi = 13.25$$

The total friction, windage, and core losses may be assumed to be constant at 403
watts, independent of load.

For a slip of 2.00 per cent, compute the speed, output torque and power, stator
current, power factor, and efficiency when the motor is operated at rated voltage
and frequency.

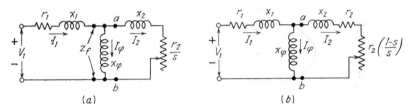

(a)   (b)

FIG. 6-5. Equivalent circuits.

Solution.   The impedance Z_f (Fig. 6-5a) represents physically the per-phase impedance presented to the stator by the air-gap field, both the reflected effect of the rotor
and the effect of the exciting current being included therein.   From Fig. 6-5a,

$$Z_f = R_f + jX_f = \frac{r_2}{s} + jx_2 \qquad \text{in parallel with } jx_\varphi$$

Substitution of numerical values gives, for $s = 0.0200$,

$$R_f + jX_f = 5.41 + j3.11$$
$$r_1 + jx_1 = 0.29 + j0.50$$
$$\text{Sum} = 5.70 + j3.61 = 6.75\underline{/32.4°} \text{ ohms}$$

$$\text{Applied voltage to neutral} = \frac{220}{\sqrt{3}} = 127 \text{ volts}$$

$$\text{Stator current } I_1 = \frac{127}{6.75} = 18.8 \text{ amp}$$

$$\text{Power factor} = \cos 32.4° = 0.844$$

$$\text{Synchronous speed} = \frac{2f}{p} = \frac{120}{6} = 20 \text{ rev/sec, or 1,200 rpm}$$

$$\omega_s = 2\pi(20) = 125.6 \text{ rad/sec}$$
$$\text{Rotor speed} = (1 - s) \times \text{(synchronous speed)}$$
$$= (0.98)(1,200) = 1,176 \text{ rpm}$$

From Eq. 6-95,

$$P_{g1} = q_1 I_2^2 \frac{r_2}{s} = q_1 I_1^2 R_f$$

$$= (3)(18.8)^2(5.41) = 5,740 \text{ watts}$$

From Eqs. 6-93 and 6-95, the internal mechanical power is

$$P = (0.98)(5,740) = 5,630 \text{ watts}$$

Deducting losses of 403 watts gives

Output power $= 5,630 - 403 = 5,230$ watts, or 7.00 hp

$$\text{Output torque} = \frac{\text{output power}}{\omega_{\text{rotor}}} = \frac{5,230}{(0.98)(125.6)}$$

$$= 42.5 \text{ newton-m, or } 31.4 \text{ lb-ft}$$

The efficiency is calculated from the losses.

Total stator copper loss $= (3)(18.8)^2(0.294)$	$=$	312 watts
Rotor copper loss (from Eq. 6-94) $= (0.0200)(5,740)$	$=$	115
Friction, windage, and core losses	$=$	403
Total losses	$=$	830 watts
Output		$= 5,230$
Input		$= 6,060$ watts

$$\frac{\text{Losses}}{\text{Input}} = \frac{830}{6,060} = 0.137 \qquad \text{Efficiency} = 1.000 - 0.137 = 0.863$$

The complete performance characteristics of the motor can be determined by repeating these calculations for other assumed values of slip.

b. Thévenin's Theorem Applied to Equivalent Circuit. When torque and power relations are to be emphasized, considerable simplication

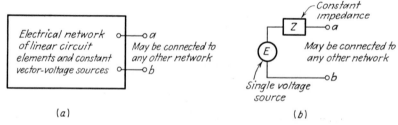

(a)   (b)

FIG. 6-6. (a) General linear network and (b) its equivalent at terminals ab by Thévenin's theorem.

results from application of Thévenin's network theorem to the induction-motor equivalent circuit.

In its general form, Thévenin's theorem permits the replacement of any network of linear circuit elements and constant phasor voltage sources, as viewed from two terminals a and b in Fig. 6-6a, by a single phasor voltage source E in series with a single impedance Z (Fig. 6-6b). The voltage E is that appearing across terminals a and b of the original network when these terminals are open-circuited; the impedance Z is that viewed from the same terminals when all voltage sources within the network are short-circuited. For application to the induction-motor equivalent circuit, points a and b are taken as those so designated in Fig. 6-5a and b.   The equivalent circuit then assumes the forms given in Fig. 6-7.   So far as phenomena to the right of points a and b are concerned, the circuits of Figs. 6-5 and 6-7 are identical when the voltage V_{1a} and the impedance $R_1 + jX_1$ have the proper values.   According to Thévenin's theorem, the

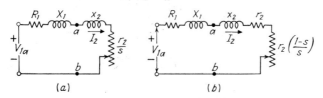

FIG. 6-7. Induction-motor equivalent circuits simplified by Thévenin's theorem.

equivalent source voltage V_{1a} is the voltage that would appear across terminals a and b of Fig. 6-5 with the rotor circuits open and is

$$V_{1a} = V_1 - I_0(r_1 + jx_1) = V_1 \frac{jx_\varphi}{r_1 + jx_{11}} \qquad (6\text{-}96)$$

where I_0 is the zero-load exciting current and

$$x_{11} = x_1 + x_\varphi \qquad (6\text{-}97)$$

is the self-reactance of the stator per phase and very nearly equals the reactive component of the zero-load motor impedance.   For most induction motors, negligible error results from neglecting the stator resistance in Eq. 6-96.   The Thévenin equivalent stator impedance $R_1 + jX_1$ is the impedance between terminals a and b of Fig. 6-5, viewed toward the source with the source voltage short-circuited, and therefore is

$$R_1 + jX_1 = r_1 + jx_1 \qquad \text{in parallel with } jx_\varphi \qquad (6\text{-}98)$$

c. *Torque-Slip Characteristics.*   From the Thévenin equivalent circuit (Fig. 6-7) and the torque expression (Eq. 6-91) it can be seen that

$$T = \frac{1}{\omega_s} \frac{q_1 V_{1a}^2 (r_2/s)}{(R_1 + r_2/s)^2 + (X_1 + x_2)^2} \qquad (6\text{-}99)$$

The general shape of the torque-speed or torque-slip curve is that shown in Fig. 6-8.   Both the motor region ($s > 0$) and the generator region ($s < 0$) are shown for completeness.

Curves of stator load-component current I_2, internal torque T, and internal power P as functions of slip s are shown in Fig. 6-9.   Data for these curves are computed in Example 6-2.   Starting conditions are those for $s = 1$.   In order physically to obtain operation in the region of s greater than 1, the motor must be driven backward, against the direction

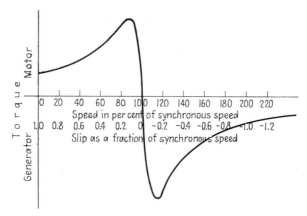

Fig. 6-8. Induction-machine torque-slip curve in both motor and generator region.

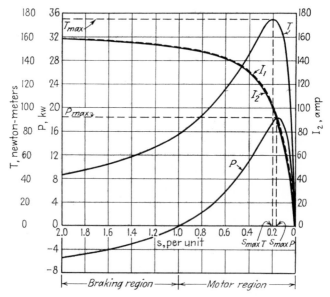

Fig. 6-9. Computed torque, power, and current curves for 10-hp induction motor, Examples 6-1 and 6-2.

of rotation of its magnetic field, by a source of mechanical power capable of counteracting the internal torque T. The chief practical usefulness of this region is in bringing motors to a quick stop by a method called *plugging*. By interchange of two stator leads in a 3-phase motor, the phase sequence, and hence the direction of rotation of the magnetic field, is reversed suddenly; the motor comes to a stop under the influence of the torque T and is disconnected from the line before it can start in the other direction. Accordingly, the region from $s = 1.0$ to $s = 2.0$ is labeled *Braking region* in Fig. 6-9.

The maximum internal, or breakdown, torque T_{max} and the maximum internal power P_{max}, indicated in Fig. 6-9, can be obtained readily from circuit considerations. Note that maximum torque and maximum power do not occur at the same speed. Internal torque is a maximum when the power delivered to r_2/s in Fig. 6-7a is a maximum. Now by the familiar impedance-matching principle in circuit theory, this power will be greatest when the impedance of r_2/s equals the magnitude of the impedance between it and the constant voltage V_{1a}, or at a value $s_{max\ T}$ of slip for which

$$\frac{r_2}{s_{max\ T}} = \sqrt{R_1^2 + (X_1 + x_2)^2} \qquad (6\text{-}100)$$

The slip $s_{max\ T}$ at maximum torque is therefore

$$s_{max\ T} = \frac{r_2}{\sqrt{R_1^2 + (X_1 + x_2)^2}} \qquad (6\text{-}101)$$

and the corresponding torque is, from Eq. 6-99,

$$T_{max} = \frac{1}{\omega_s} \frac{0.5 q_1 V_{1a}^2}{R_1 + \sqrt{R_1^2 + (X_1 + x_2)^2}} \qquad (6\text{-}102)$$

Example 6-2. For the motor of Example 6-1, determine:

a. The load component I_2 of the stator current, the internal torque T, and the internal power P for a slip $s = 0.03$

b. The maximum internal torque and the corresponding speed

c. The internal starting torque and the corresponding stator-load current I_2

Solution. First reduce the circuit to its Thévenin-theorem form. From Eq. 6-96, $V_{1a} = 122.3$; and from Eq. 6-98, $R_1 + jX_1 = 0.273 + j0.490$.

a. At $s = 0.03$, $r_2/s = 4.80$. Then from Fig. 6-7a,

$$I_2 = \frac{122.3}{\sqrt{(5.07)^2 + (0.699)^2}} = 23.9 \text{ amp}$$

From Eq. 6-91,

$$T = \frac{1}{125.6} (3)(23.9)^2(4.80) = 65.5 \text{ newton-m}$$

From Eq. 6-93,

$$P = (3)(23.9)^2(4.80)(0.97) = 7,970 \text{ watts}$$

Data for the curves of Fig. 6-9 were computed by repeating these calculations for a number of assumed values of s.

b. At the maximum-torque point, from Eq. 6-101,

$$s_{max\ T} = \frac{0.144}{\sqrt{(0.273)^2 + (0.699)^2}} = \frac{0.144}{0.750} = 0.192$$

Speed at $T_{max} = (1 - 0.192)(1,200) = 970 \text{ rpm}$

From Eq. 6-102,

$$T_{\text{max}} = \frac{1}{125.6} \frac{(0.5)(3)(122.3)^2}{0.273 + 0.750} = 175 \text{ newton-m}$$

c. At starting, $s = 1$, and r_2 will be assumed constant. Therefore,

$$\frac{r_2}{s} = r_2 = 0.144 \qquad R_1 + \frac{r_2}{s} = 0.417$$

$$I_{2 \text{ start}} = \frac{122.3}{\sqrt{(0.417)^2 + (0.699)^2}} = 150.5 \text{ amp}$$

From Eq. 6-91,

$$T_{\text{start}} = \frac{1}{125.6} (3)(150.5)^2(0.144)$$

$$= 78.0 \text{ newton-m}$$

It is thus seen that the conventional induction motor with a squirrel-cage rotor is substantially a constant-speed motor having about 5 per cent

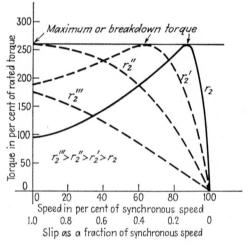

FIG. 6-10. Induction-motor torque-slip curves showing effect of changing rotor-circuit resistance.

drop in speed from no load to full load. Speed variation may be obtained by using a wound-rotor motor and inserting external resistance in the rotor circuit. In the normal operating range, the external resistance simply increases the rotor impedance, necessitating a higher slip for a desired rotor mmf and torque. The influence of increased rotor resistance on the torque-speed characteristic is shown by the dashed curves in Fig. 6-10. Variation of starting torque with rotor resistance may be seen from these curves by noting the variation of the zero-speed ordinates.

Notice from Eqs. 6-101 and 6-102 that the slip at maximum torque is directly proportional to rotor resistance r_2 but the value of the maximum torque is independent of r_2. When r_2 is increased by inserting external resistance in the rotor of a wound-rotor motor, the maximum internal torque is therefore unaffected but the speed at which it occurs may be directly controlled.

In applying the induction-motor equivalent circuit, the idealizations on which it is based should be kept in mind. This is particularly necessary when investigations are carried out over a wide speed range, as in motor-starting problems. Saturation under the heavy inrush currents associated with starting has a significant effect on the motor reactances. Moreover, the rotor currents are at slip frequency, which, of course, varies from stator frequency at zero speed to a low value at full-load speed. The current distribution in the rotor conductors and hence the rotor resistance may vary very significantly over this range. Errors from these causes may be kept to a minimum by using equivalent-circuit constants determined by simulating the proposed operating conditions as closely as possible.[1]

6-6. Electrical Transients in Induction Machines. In examining the electrical-transient behavior of induction machines, we shall follow substantially the same course as in Art. 5-7 for synchronous machines. Although the following investigation is self-contained, it will take advantage of a few simplifications without as complete an examination as for the synchronous machine. The results will be very similar to those in the synchronous case.

a. Initial Current for Three-phase Short Circuit. Consider that the machine is acting as either a motor or a generator when a 3-phase short circuit takes place at its terminals. In either case, the machine will feed current into the fault because of the "trapped" flux linkages with the rotor circuits. This current will, in time, decay to zero. To determine its initial magnitude, we shall neglect stator resistance r_1 and the $p\lambda_{1d}$ and $p\lambda_{1q}$ terms in the stator voltage relations (Eqs. 6-50 and 6-51). As with synchronous machines, this neglect corresponds to ignoring the d-c component in the short-circuit current, permitting concentration on the fundamental component alone. In addition, we shall consider the machine to be operating at small values of slip so that the speed-voltage terms $\lambda_{2q}(p\theta_s)$ and $\lambda_{2d}(p\theta_s)$ in the rotor-voltage equations 6-52 and 6-53 may be ignored. In a practical case, this last assumption is justifiable for two reasons: (1) the normal machine usually operates at small values of slip, and (2) the short-circuit current dies out rapidly enough (as we shall see) so that the machine does not have time to change speed appreciably.

[1] See, for instance, R. F. Horrell and W. E. Wood, A Method of Determining Induction Motor Speed-Torque-Current Curves from Reduced Voltage Tests, *Trans. AIEE*, vol. 73, pt. III, pp. 670–674, 1954.

The voltage-current relations (Eqs. 6-50 to 6-53) then become

Stator:

$$v_{1d} = -\omega\lambda_{1q} \tag{6-103}$$

$$v_{1q} = \omega\lambda_{1d} \tag{6-104}$$

Rotor:

$$v_{2d} = r_2 i_{2d} + p\lambda_{2d} = 0 \tag{6-105}$$

$$v_{2q} = r_2 i_{2q} + p\lambda_{2q} = 0 \tag{6-106}$$

The voltages in Eqs. 6-105 and 6-106 are equated to zero to indicate a squirrel-cage rotor or short-circuited slip rings on a wound-rotor motor; in the latter case, rotor external impedance can ultimately be included with the rotor constants.

The rotor currents will now be eliminated from the stator linkage relations (Eqs. 6-45 and 6-46). Thus, from Eq. 6-47,

$$i_{2d} = \frac{\lambda_{2d} - L_{12}i_{1d}}{L_{22}} \tag{6-107}$$

and, upon substitution in Eq. 6-45,

$$\lambda_{1d} = \left(L_{11} - \frac{L_{12}^2}{L_{22}}\right) i_{1d} + \frac{L_{12}}{L_{22}} \lambda_{2d} \tag{6-108}$$

$$\lambda_{1d} = L' i_{1d} + \frac{L_{12}}{L_{22}} \lambda_{2d} \tag{6-109}$$

where

$$L' = L_{11} - \frac{L_{12}^2}{L_{22}} \tag{6-110}$$

Similarly, from Eqs. 6-46 and 6-48,

$$\lambda_{1q} = L' i_{1q} + \frac{L_{12}}{L_{22}} \lambda_{2q} \tag{6-111}$$

The quantity L' is the *transient inductance* of the induction machine. It is comparable with the direct-axis transient inductance L'_d (Eq. 5-114) of the synchronous machine.

When the short circuit appears, the voltages v_{1d} and v_{1q} go to zero. From Eqs. 6-103 and 6-104, the stator linkages λ_{1d} and λ_{1q} must also go to zero. (Bear in mind that the d-c component of stator current, which physically prevents λ_{1d} and λ_{1q} from changing suddenly, is being ignored because of neglect of the $p\lambda_{1d}$ and $p\lambda_{1q}$ terms.) Under these circumstances, maintenance of the rotor linkages constant at their initial prefault values λ_{2d0} and λ_{2q0} requires that the stator component currents become (from Eqs. 6-109 and 6-111 with $\lambda_{1d} = \lambda_{1q} = 0$)

$$i_{1d} = -\frac{(L_{12}/L_{22})\lambda_{2d0}}{L'} \tag{6-112}$$

$$i_{1q} = -\frac{(L_{12}/L_{22})\lambda_{2q0}}{L'} \tag{6-113}$$

These are the initial values immediately after occurrence of the short-circuit (i.e., at $t = 0+$). They are also the values which would continue to exist if there were no machine resistance to cause their decay. In the latter case, they can be combined in accordance with Eqs. 6-33 to 6-35 to yield the instantaneous phase currents. The corresponding rms stator current, written in accordance with Eqs. 6-66 and 6-67, is

$$I_1 = -\frac{1}{x'}\,\omega\,\frac{L_{12}}{L_{22}}\left(\frac{\lambda_{2d0}}{\sqrt{2}} + j\,\frac{\lambda_{2q0}}{\sqrt{2}}\right) \tag{6-114}$$

where

$$x' = \omega L' \tag{6-115}$$

is the *transient reactance*. We are primarily interested in the rms magnitude of I_1, which is

$$I_1 = \frac{1}{x'}\,\omega\,\frac{L_{12}}{L_{22}}\,\frac{1}{\sqrt{2}}\,\sqrt{\lambda_{2d0}^2 + \lambda_{2q0}^2} \tag{6-116}$$

This value of I_1 is the *initial symmetrical short-circuit current*.

The decay of this short-circuit current is examined in the next part of this article, and the evaluation from prefault conditions of the parenthetic term in Eq. 6-114 is given in the third part.

b. Decrement of Short-circuit Current. The short-circuit current whose initial magnitude is given by Eq. 6-116 will die away to zero because of the presence of rotor resistance r_2. As with synchronous machines, the decrement can be found by examining the decay of rotor currents i_{2d} and i_{2q}. To do so, substitute in Eq. 6-105 the value of λ_{2d} from Eq. 6-47, yielding

$$r_2 i_{2d} + L_{22} p i_{2d} + L_{12} p i_{1d} = 0 \tag{6-117}$$

From Eq. 6-45 with $\lambda_{1d} = 0$,

$$i_{1d} = -\frac{L_{12}}{L_{11}}\,i_{2d} \tag{6-118}$$

Then, by substitution of Eq. 6-118 in 6-117 and algebraic reduction,

$$r_2 i_{2d} + \frac{1}{L_{11}}\left(L_{11} - \frac{L_{12}^2}{L_{22}}\right)L_{22} p i_{2d} = 0$$

or

$$i_{2d} + \frac{L'}{L_{11}}\,\frac{L_{22}}{r_2}\,\frac{di_{2d}}{dt} = 0 \tag{6-119}$$

In Eq. 6-119, the fraction

$$\frac{L_{22}}{r_2} = T_o' \tag{6-120}$$

is the time constant of the rotor circuit alone. It is the *open-circuit time constant* of the induction machine and characterizes the decay of rotor transients when the stator is open-circuited. With the stator short-circuited, however, the apparent inductance is lower because of the coupling to the stator winding. From Eq. 6-119, the time constant is then

$$T' = T'_o \frac{L'}{L_{11}} = T'_o \frac{x'}{x_{11}} \qquad (6\text{-}121)$$

and is called the *short-circuit time constant*. Identical results are obtained if, instead of starting with Eq. 6-105, one starts with Eq. 6-106.

The time constant T' characterizes the exponential decay of the transient current whose initial rms magnitude is given by Eq. 6-116. Note the parallelism between the treatment here and that in Art. 5-7c for the transient time constant of the synchronous machine. The results are substantially the same except that the short-circuit current decays to zero in the induction machine. The short-circuit current as a function of time then decays in the manner of Fig. 6-11. Recall that the d-c component of this short-circuit current has been neglected.

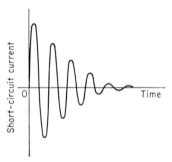

FIG. 6-11. Waveform of symmetrical short-circuit current in induction machine.

c. *Transient Equivalent Circuit.* To complete the investigation, we need to evaluate the flux linkages λ_{2d0} and λ_{2q0} in Eqs. 6-114 and 6-116 from the prefault operating conditions of the machine. As a by-product of this evaluation, a transient equivalent circuit is obtained.

Consider that before the short circuit each phase of the stator of the induction machine carries the rms current I_{10}. Let the dq components be i_{1d0} and i_{1q0}, and let I_{1d0} and I_{1q0}, respectively, be these components divided by $\sqrt{2}$. Then, from Eq. 6-109 written for prefault conditions and multiplied by ω,

$$\omega \frac{L_{12}}{L_2} \lambda_{2d0} = \omega\lambda_{1d0} - x'i_{1d0} \qquad (6\text{-}122)$$

or

$$\omega \frac{L_{12}}{L_2} \frac{\lambda_{2d0}}{\sqrt{2}} = V_{1q0} - x'I_{1d0} \qquad (6\text{-}123)$$

In Eq. 6-123,

$$V_{1q0} = \frac{v_{1q0}}{\sqrt{2}} \qquad (6\text{-}124)$$

and the replacement of $\omega\lambda_{1d0}$ by v_{1q0} follows from Eq. 6-104. In similar fashion from Eq. 6-111,

$$\omega \frac{L_{12}}{L_2} \frac{\lambda_{2q0}}{\sqrt{2}} = -V_{1d0} - x'I_{1q0} \qquad (6\text{-}125)$$

By combining Eqs. 6-123 and 6-125,

$$\omega \frac{L_{12}}{L_{22}} \left(\frac{\lambda_{2d0}}{\sqrt{2}} + j \frac{\lambda_{2q0}}{\sqrt{2}} \right) = \frac{1}{j} [(V_{1d0} + jV_{1q0}) - jx'(I_{1d0} + jI_{1q0})]$$

$$= \frac{1}{j} (V_{10} - jx'I_{10}) = \frac{1}{j} E_1' \quad (6\text{-}126)$$

In Eq. 6-126, V_{10} is the prefault rms terminal voltage, and E_1' is given by

$$E_1' = V_{10} - jx'I_{10} \qquad (6\text{-}127)$$

It is called the initial *voltage behind the transient reactance* of the induction machine. In the circuit of Fig. 6-12 it is the voltage behind the reactance x' when the terminal voltage and current are the prefault values V_{10} and I_{10}. The rms magnitude of the initial symmetrical short-circuit current (Eq. 6-116) then becomes

$$I_1 = \frac{E_1'}{x'} \qquad (6\text{-}128)$$

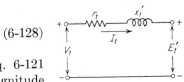

With the decrement determined by Eq. 6-121 applied, the rms short-circuit-current magnitude at any time t after the fault is

$$I_1' = \frac{E_1'}{x'} \epsilon^{-t/T'} \qquad (6\text{-}129)$$

FIG. 6-12. Simplified transient equivalent circuit of induction machine.

From the foregoing development, it is evident that the induction machine can be represented by the simple transient equivalent circuit of Fig. 6-12. The reactance is the transient reactance x', defined by Eqs. 6-110 and 6-115. Although it has been ignored in this article, the stator resistance r_1 can also be added if somewhat greater precision is desired. The voltage E_1' behind transient reactance is a voltage proportional to rotor linkages (see Eq. 6-126). It changes with these linkages and, for a 3-phase short circuit, decreases to zero at a rate determined by the time constant T' (Eq. 6-121). Adjustment of the time constant for external reactance between the machine terminals and the fault can readily be carried out by adding that reactance to the numerator and denominator of the fraction in Eq. 6-121.

Thus we once more have results very similar to those obtained for the synchronous machine. Compare, for example, the circuit of Fig. 6-12 with that of Fig. 5-13 for the synchronous machine.

Example 6-3. A 400-hp 440-volt (line to line) 60-cps Y-connected 6-pole squirrel-cage induction motor has a full-load efficiency of 93 per cent and power factor of 90 per cent. The motor constants in ohms per phase referred to the stator are as follows:

$$x_1 = 0.060 \qquad x_2 = 0.060 \qquad x_\varphi = 2.50$$
$$r_1 = 0.0073 \qquad r_2 = 0.0064$$

While the motor is operating in the steady state under rated conditions, a 3-phase short circuit occurs on its supply line near the motor terminals. Determine the motor rms short-circuit current.

Solution. From Eqs. 6-84 to 6-86 and 6-110, the motor transient reactance is seen to be

$$x' = x_1 + x_\varphi - \frac{x_\varphi^2}{x_2 + x_\varphi}$$

$$= 0.060 + 2.50 - \frac{(2.50)^2}{0.06 + 2.50} = 0.12 \text{ ohm per phase}$$

The prefault stator current is

$$I_1 = \frac{400 \times 746}{0.90 \times 0.93 \times 440 \sqrt{3}} = 467 \text{ amp}$$

With terminal voltage as the reference phasor, the prefault voltage behind transient reactance is then

$$E_1' = \frac{440}{\sqrt{3}} - (0.0073 + j0.12)(467\underline{/-\cos^{-1} 0.90})$$

$$= 232\underline{/-12.2°}$$

From Eq. 6-128, the initial rms short-circuit current is

$$\frac{240}{0.12} = 1,940 \text{ amp}$$

The open-circuit time constant (Eq. 6-120) is

$$T_o' = \frac{2.50 + 0.060}{2\pi \times 60 \times 0.0064} = 1.06 \text{ sec}$$

and the short-circuit time constant (Eq. 6-121) is

$$T'' = 1.06 \times \frac{0.12}{2.56} = 0.050 \text{ sec}$$

The rms short-circuit current is therefore

$$I_1 = 1,940\epsilon^{-t/0.050} \qquad \text{amp}$$

The short-circuit time constant is 3 cycles on a 60-cycle base. Accordingly, in 3 cycles the short-circuit current decreases to 36.8 per cent of its initial value. It has substantially disappeared in about 10 cycles. It is thus seen that, while the initial short-circuit current of an induction machine is relatively high compared with its normal current, the transient usually disappears rapidly. Because of this fact, the electrical transients in induction machines are not infrequently neglected.

Those who have studied Art. 5-10 on the effect of additional rotor circuits in synchronous machines will recognize that, as might be expected, these effects are very like the superposition of induction-machine action on synchronous-machine action. The usual damper circuits in synchronous machines are essentially equivalent to squirrel-cage rotors.　Damper torques are induction-machine torques; to a fair approximation, both vary linearly with slip in the neighborhood of synchronous speed.　Under short-circuit conditions, the induced damper currents in the synchronous machine are comparable with the induced rotor currents required to maintain constant rotor linkages at the first instant in the induction machine; both die away very rapidly.　In effect, then, during the short subtransient period following a synchronous-machine disturbance we have induction and synchronous effects combined; when the subtransient period is over, synchronous transient effects remain.

6-7. Induction-machine Dynamics.　Among integral-horsepower induction motors (i.e., those used primarily for power purposes), the most common dynamic problems are associated with starting and stopping and with the ability of the motor to continue operation during serious disturbances of the supply system.　For example, a typical problem in an industrial plant may concern the ability to start a large motor without causing other parallel motors to cease normal operation because of the voltage reduction caused by the heavy inrush current to the motor being started.

One category of induction motor operates almost continuously in the dynamic state, being rarely called upon to settle down to steady conditions.　This is the 2-phase control motor considered in the next article.

The methods of induction-motor representation in dynamic analyses depend to a considerable extent on the nature and complexity of the problem and the associated precision requirements.　When the electrical transients in the motor are to be included as well as the motional transients (and especially when the motor is an important element in a complex network), the equivalent circuit of Fig. 6-12 may be used.[1]　In many problems, however, the electrical transients in the induction machine may be ignored.　This simplification is possible because, as illustrated in Example 6-3, the electrical transient subsides so rapidly—most commonly in a time short compared with the duration of the motional transient. (Among the principal exceptions to this statement are large 3,600-rpm motors.)　We shall confine ourselves here to this type of problem.

Representation of the machine under these conditions may be based on steady-state theory, including the equivalent circuits of Figs. 6-4 and 6-7, the torque-slip curve of Fig. 6-8, and the torque-slip relation (Eq. 6-99). The problem then becomes one of arriving at a sufficiently simple yet reasonably realistic representation which will not unduly complicate the dynamic analysis, particularly through the introduction of nonlinearities.

[1] See J. L. Gabbard, Jr., and J. E. Rowe, Digital Computation of Induction Motor Transient Stability, *Trans. AIEE*, vol. 76, pp. 970–975, 1957; and Brereton, Lewis, and Young, *op. cit.*

One approach applicable to relatively simple problems is a graphical one. Both the torque produced by the motor and the torque required to turn the load are considered to be nonlinear functions of speed for which data are given in the form of curves. The procedure is illustrated in the following example.

Example 6-4. A polyphase induction motor has the torque-speed curve for rated impressed voltage shown in Fig. 6-13. A curve of the torque required to maintain

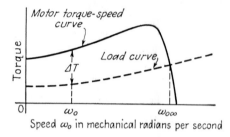

FIG. 6-13. Induction-motor torque-speed curve and curve of load torque.

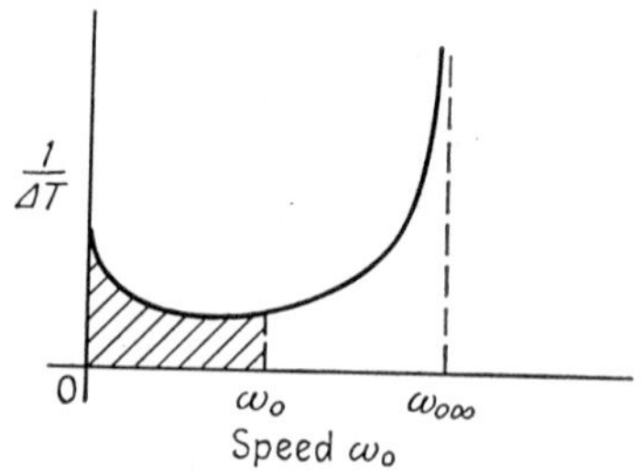

FIG. 6-14. Graphical analysis of induction-motor starting.

rotation of the load is also given in Fig. 6-13. The inertia of the load and rotor is J mks units.

Consider that across-the-line starting at rated voltage is used and that the steady-state torque-speed curve represents the performance under transient conditions with sufficient accuracy. Show how a curve of speed as a function of time may be obtained.

Solution. At any motor speed ω_o mechanical radians per second, the torque differential ΔT between that produced by the motor and that required to turn the load is available to accelerate the rotating mass. Consequently,

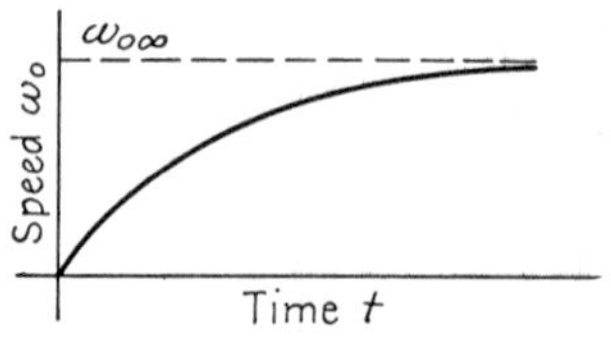

$$J \frac{d\omega_o}{dt} = \Delta T \qquad (6\text{-}130)$$

The time required to attain the speed ω_o is therefore

$$t = J \int_0^{\omega_o} \frac{1}{\Delta T} \, d\omega_o \qquad (6\text{-}131)$$

FIG. 6-15. Speed-time curve of induction motor during starting.

The integral in Eq. 6-131 can be evaluated graphically by plotting a curve of $1/\Delta T$ as a function of ω_o and finding the area between the curve and the ω_o axis up to the value corresponding to the upper limit of the integral, a procedure illustrated in Fig. 6-14. The area can be found by planimeter, by counting small squares on the curve sheet, or by dividing it into uniform segments and using the average ordinate for each section. This area in units of radians per second per newton-meter times the inertia J in mks units gives the time t in seconds. The computations can be carried out conveniently in tabular form to yield a result of the type shown in Fig. 6-15.

Analytical methods are often based on piecewise linear representations of the torque-slip curve or the pertinent portion of it. For example, the curve is close to linear in the normal operating region of small slips. In this region, the relation

$$T = ks \qquad (6\text{-}132)$$

may be used, where k is a constant. Or if terminal voltage is variable, the relation

$$T = k'V_1^2 s \qquad (6\text{-}133)$$

may be substituted to incorporate the fact that, according to Eq. 6-99, the electromagnetic torque varies as the square of the voltage. When a wider region of the torque-slip curve is involved, a number of straight lines may be required. Alternatively, it is shown in Art. 10-3 that a reasonably good representation of the torque-slip relation in accordance with Eq. 6-99 is given by the equation

$$\frac{T}{T_{\max}} = \frac{2}{s/s_{\max\,T} + s_{\max\,T}/s} \qquad (6\text{-}134)$$

where $T_{\max}$ is the maximum torque and $s_{\max\,T}$ is the slip at maximum torque.

Example 6-5. The period of heavy current inrush to an induction motor during starting usually lasts for about the time required to reach the slip $s_{\max\,T}$ at maximum torque, after which it decreases to the normal running value. Develop an expression for the time t required to reach the speed corresponding to $s_{\max\,T}$ for an induction motor being started at full voltage.

The combined inertia of the rotor and the connected mechanical equipment is J. The motor is unloaded at starting, and rotational losses are to be neglected. Consider that the torque-slip curve may be represented by Eq. 6-134.

Solution. Let all quantities except time t be expressed in per unit. The base for torque T may be the rated torque of the motor. Unit speed is synchronous speed for the motor, and s, of course, is given in per unit by the usual expression 3-63. The inertia J will then have the dimensions

$$\frac{\text{Per-unit torque}}{\text{Per-unit change in speed per second}}$$

With n representing motor speed, the basic differential equation is then

$$J\frac{dn}{dt} = -J\frac{ds}{dt} = \frac{2T_{\max}}{s/s_{\max\,T} + s_{\max\,T}/s}$$

Upon integration,

$$t = -\frac{J}{2T_{\max}}\left(\frac{1}{s_{\max\,T}}\int_1^{s_{\max\,T}} s\,ds + s_{\max\,T}\int_1^{s_{\max\,T}}\frac{ds}{s}\right)$$

$$= \frac{J}{2T_{\max}}\left(\frac{1 - s_{\max\,T}^2}{2s_{\max\,T}} + s_{\max\,T}\ln\frac{1}{s_{\max\,T}}\right)$$

Neglect of rotational losses tends to make this result optimistic. A significant breakaway torque may be required to turn the motor over at very low speeds, for example, especially if the bearings are cold.

6-8. Two-phase Control Motors.   As already pointed out in discussing d-c machines, electric motors find widespread use in positioning and driving shafts in control systems.   In small-power control systems, where the maximum outputs required from the motor range from a fraction of a watt up to a few hundred watts, 2-phase induction motors are often used. The 2-phase induction motor usually consists of a stator with 2 windings displaced 90 electrical degrees from each other and a squirrel-cage rotor or the equivalent.   The operation of the 2-phase motor is, of course, in accord with the general theory presented in this chapter.   For example, the steady-state torque-slip relation with balanced applied voltages is given by Eq. 6-99 with $q_1 = 2$.

A schematic diagram of a 2-phase control motor is given in Fig. 6-16. Phase m of the motor is the *fixed*, or *reference, phase*.   The voltage V_m is a fixed voltage applied from a constant-voltage constant-frequency source.

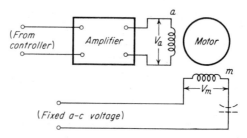

FIG. 6-16. Schematic diagram of 2-phase control motor.

Phase a is the *control phase*.   The voltage V_a is supplied from the controller, usually from an amplifier at the controller output.   Its magnitude is a function of the degree of action required of the motor; for example, it may be proportional to angular error of shaft position in a position control system.   The voltages V_m and V_a must be in synchronism, which means that they must be derived from the same ultimate a-c source. They must also be made to be approximately in time quadrature either by introducing a 90° phase shift in the amplifier or by connecting a suitable capacitor in series with the reference phase m.   When V_a has a nonzero value leading V_m by approximately 90°, rotation in one direction is obtained; when V_a lags V_m, rotation in the other direction results.   Since the torque is a function of both V_m and V_a, changing the magnitude of V_a changes the developed torque of the motor.

Typical torque-speed curves for a 2-phase control motor are given in Fig. 6-17 for a series of values of control voltage and unity reference voltage.   They are based on the motor having identical 2-phase stator windings and on negligible source impedances.   (Sample computations of points on these curves are given in Example 11-3.)

The requirements of a control system very nearly specify the shape of the torque-speed characteristic of a 2-phase induction motor suitable for such use. As with any motor for such service, the torque should be high at speeds near zero, and the slope of the torque-speed characteristic should be negative in the normal operating range around zero speed in order to provide a stabilizing feature for the control system. Both these requirements can be met by use of a high-resistance rotor designed so that maximum torque is developed at a reverse speed of approximately one-half synchronous speed, as shown by the torque-speed characteristic labeled $V_a = 1.0$ in Fig. 6-17. Normal operation near zero speed is then in the

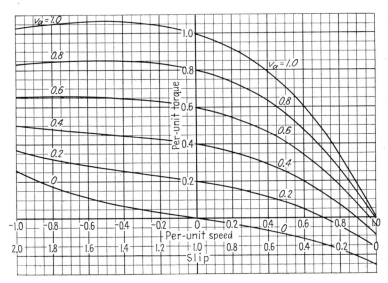

FIG. 6-17. Typical torque-speed curves of 2-phase control motor.

stable region to the right of the maximum-torque points. A further requirement is that the motor must not tend to run as a single-phase motor when the error signal is zero. It can be shown that this requirement also is met by use of a high-resistance rotor.

Although the squirrel-cage induction motor prefers to run at a small slip and therefore is most readily adaptable to constant-speed drives, nevertheless this type of motor has other features which are sufficiently attractive so that it is used extensively in low-power control systems. The ruggedness and simplicity of the cage rotor are a great advantage, for both economic and technical reasons. There are no brushes riding on sliding contacts and requiring inspection and maintenance as in other types of motors. Because the rotor windings do not require insulation, the rotor temperature is limited only by mechanical considerations and indirectly by its effect on the stator-winding temperature. If suitable means are provided for cooling the stator windings, higher rotor losses can be tolerated than in other types of motors. Because there is relatively little inactive material, the inertia of a squirrel-cage motor can be made less than that of a correspondingly rated d-c motor. When the maximum power output is below a few watts, inertia can be minimized by using a thin metallic cup as the rotor. As shown in the simplified sketch of Fig. 6-18, the rotating member is then like a can with one end removed. A stationary iron core, like a plug inside the cup, completes the magnetic circuit. The construction is known as a *drag-cup rotor*.

The principal disadvantage of the 2-phase control motor is the inherent inefficiency of a squirrel-cage induction motor running at a large slip. As pointed out in Art. 6-5, the efficiency of a polyphase induction motor with short-circuited rotor windings is like that of a slipping mechanical clutch; the slip is a direct measure of the rotor losses. The inherent limit on efficiency will be even lower in a speed control scheme which involves unbalancing the applied voltages, because of the decrease in output and increase in rotor losses. Speed-regulating schemes involving slip control of a squirrel-cage motor are not practicable for large motors because the difficulties associated with cooling and with power supply increase with size, as does the economic importance of the losses.

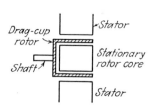

Fig. 6-18. Cross section of drag-cup rotor.

Example 6-6. It may be noted from Fig. 6-17 that, in the low-speed range, the torque of a 2-phase control motor is linearly proportional to the rms control-winding voltage. In this range, the torque-speed curves have a negative slope which is approximately constant and substantially the same for the lower values of control voltage. Under these conditions, the torque-speed curves may be represented empirically by the relation

$$T = k_1 V_a - k_2 \omega_o$$

where ω_o is the shaft mechanical angular velocity and k_1 and k_2 are constants determined from the curves and the units involved.[1]

The motor is driving a load requiring a viscous-friction torque $f_v \omega_o$ proportional to speed. The combined inertia of rotor and load is J. Determine the transfer functions relating:

a. Motor shaft position and control voltage
b. Motor shaft velocity and control voltage
Show the corresponding block-diagram representation.

[1] For a more comprehensive treatment, see A. M. Hopkin, Transient Response of Small Two-phase Servomotors, *Trans. AIEE*, vol. 70, pp. 881–886, 1951. The theoretical fundamentals underlying the motor performance on unbalanced voltages are presented in Chap. 11.

Solution. *a.* The signal to the motor consists of variation of the rms value V_a of the control-winding voltage. Let the value of this voltage at any time t be v_s. The electrodynamic differential equation in terms of the shaft position angle θ_o is then

$$J \frac{d^2\theta_o}{dt^2} + f_v \frac{d\theta_o}{dt} = k_1 v_s - k_2 \frac{d\theta_o}{dt}$$

In terms of the phasor amplitudes Θ_o and V_s of sinusoidal variations at the angular frequency ω, this equation becomes

$$(j\omega)^2 J\Theta_o + j\omega(f_v + k_2)\Theta_o = k_1 V_s$$

which yields the transfer function

$$\frac{\Theta_o}{V_s} = \frac{k_1}{(j\omega)^2 J + j\omega(f_v + k_2)}$$

The associated block diagram is shown in Fig. 6-19a.

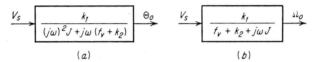

(a)   (b)

Fig. 6-19. Block-diagram representations, Example 6-6.

b. The differential equation in terms of shaft angular velocity ω_o is

$$J \frac{d\omega_o}{dt} + f_v\omega_o = k_1 v_s - k_2\omega_o$$

Then

$$j\omega J\Omega_o + (f_v + k_2)\Omega_o = k_1 V_s$$

or the transfer function is

$$\frac{\Omega_o}{V_s} = \frac{k_1}{f_v + k_2 + (j\omega)J}$$

The block diagram is that of Fig. 6-19b.

6-9. Self-synchronous Systems.

Among the more exacting of modern control requirements is that of position control, or causing the angular position of one shaft to follow that of another as closely as possible. A group of induction machines called *self-synchronous devices* are valuable adjuncts for such control systems. They are also known by various other names, such as *selsyn*, *synchro*, and *autosyn*. In the following discussion, the specific word *selsyn* will frequently be used.

There are three general types of systems involving selsyn devices, (1) 3-phase power selsyns for heavy torque transmission, (2) single-phase instrument or indicator selsyns for only very light torque transmission, and (3) generator-transformer systems for indicating shaft misalignment in terms of a voltage magnitude and polarity. The first two will be described here; the last will be discussed in Art. 6-10.

a. Three-phase Power Types.   In integral-horsepower sizes, the selsyn systems consist of 3-phase wound-rotor induction machines with their primary windings excited from the same 3-phase source and their secondary windings connected together, as shown in Fig. 6-20.   If one of these machines is driven mechanically, the other will follow in synchronism with it, much as if the two shafts were connected mechanically.   Such systems have been applied to maintain synchronism between the hoist motors raising the two ends of large lift bridges, to maintain synchronism between parts of printing presses, and for many similar applications requiring speed coordination between parts of complex apparatus.   In Fig. 6-20, suppose that the two machines are standing still with their stators excited.   Voltages are induced in the rotor windings whose time phases depend on the angular positions of the two rotors.   Corresponding phases are shown schematically by the coil sides aa in Fig. 6-21a, the angle between the two rotors being δ measured from A to B in the direction of rotation of the magnetic field.   The rotor voltage in machine B then lags that in machine A by the time-phase angle δ, as shown in the phasor diagram of Fig. 6-21b.   The equivalent circuit for one phase of the rotors is shown in Fig. 6-21c.   Because of the phase difference between

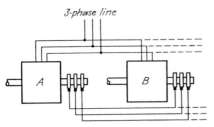

FIG. 6-20. Self-synchronous system.

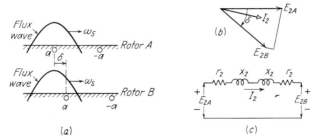

FIG. 6-21. Flux waves, phasor diagram, and equivalent circuit for system of Fig. 6-20 at zero speed.

the two voltages there is current in the rotor circuits, and power flows from the rotor of machine A to that of machine B.   The situation is like that of a synchronous generator supplying power to a synchronous motor, and torque is created in each machine by the interaction of its air-gap flux and rotor-mmf waves.   These torques act in directions to tend to reduce the angle δ—that is, to advance the rotor of A and retard that of B until the two rotors are in line.   The induced voltages then balance each other,

and the current is reduced to zero.   Typical torque-angle characteristics
at standstill are shown in Fig. 6-22.

Now suppose one of the machines is driven mechanically at a speed corresponding to a slip s.   The other will run in synchronism with it, the
displacement angle between the two rotors being a function of the

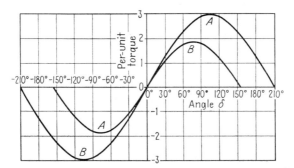

Fig. 6-22. Typical torque-angle characteristics of system of Fig. 6-20 at zero speed.

mechanical load on the follower unit.   The only difference between this
situation and that at standstill is that an observer on the rotor now sees
the air-gap flux wave traveling past him at slip speed.   The induced
voltages and rotor leakage reactances become s times their stator-frequency values.

Typical curves of maximum torque as a function of slip are shown in
Fig. 6-23.   Because of rotor resistance, the maximum torque falls off

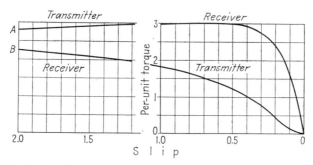

Fig. 6-23. Typical maximum-torque curves for system of Fig. 6-20 under running
conditions.

rapidly if the slip is decreased below about 0.3.   Machines which are
required to run in only one direction usually are connected to rotate in the
opposite direction to their magnetic fields.

b. Single-phase Instrument Types.   Substantially the same type of
action is obtained when the 3-phase system is replaced by the single-phase

system shown diagrammatically in Fig. 6-24.   In most respects, the construction of the *selsyn generator*, or *transmitter*, is similar to that of the *selsyn motor*, or *receiver*.   Both have a single-phase winding (usually on the rotor) connected to a common a-c voltage source.   On the other member (usually the stator), both have 3 windings with axes 120° apart and connected in Y; these windings on the generator and motor have their

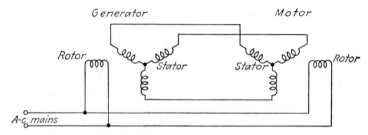

FIG. 6-24. Single-phase selsyn generator-motor system.

corresponding terminals connected together.   When the single-phase rotor windings are excited, voltages are induced by transformer action in the Y-connected stator windings.   If the two rotors are in the same space position relative to their stator windings, the generator and motor stator-winding voltages are equal, no current circulates in these windings, and no torque is transmitted.   If, however, the two rotor space positions do not

FIG. 6-25. Typical high-accuracy selsyns.   (*Courtesy of General Electric Company.*)

correspond, the stator-winding voltages are unequal and currents circulate in the stator winding.   These currents, in conjunction with the air-gap magnetic fields, produce torques tending to align the two rotors.

Mechanically, selsyns have the same general construction features as small motors.   The external appearance of typical selsyns is shown in Fig. 6-25.   The rotor structure of a selsyn motor may be seen in Fig. 6-26.

The rotor and stator are laminated, and ball bearings are used to minimize friction. Both the generator and the motor have 2-pole windings with a salient-pole rotor structure.

As in 3-phase systems, the motor torque at standstill or for slow rotation may be shown to depend closely upon the sine of the relative angular

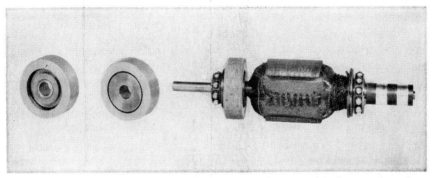

FIG. 6-26. Two dampers (front and rear) and wound rotor, with damper, for selsyn motor. (*Courtesy of General Electric Company.*)

difference in position of the generator and motor shafts. Torque gradients developed by electrically identical generators and motors interconnected as in Fig. 6-24 range from 0.07 in.-oz per degree for the smaller units to 1.75 in.-oz per degree for the larger units.

A modification of the selsyn system of Fig. 6-24 may be introduced by including a *differential selsyn*, thereby permitting the rotation of a shaft to be a function of the sum or difference of the rotation of two other shafts. In Fig. 6-27, the differential selsyn acts as a differential generator. The

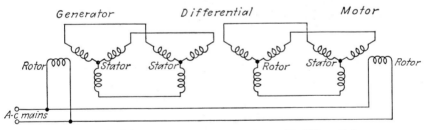

FIG. 6-27. Selsyn generator-motor system with differential.

voltages impressed on its stator windings induce corresponding voltages in the rotor windings. The relative magnitudes of the three rotor voltages are the same as would exist if the differential were removed and the generator turned through an angle equal to the sum or difference of the generator and differential angles. Such differential generators usually have a bank of three capacitors connected across the primary terminals to improve power factor and hence minimize the possibility of overheating in the system. Alternatively, the differential may be used as a motor supplied from two separate selsyn generators and producing a rotation dependent upon the sum or difference of the two generator rotations. The connections in this case are the same as in Fig. 6-27 except that the differential is relabeled *Differential motor* and the motor on the right is relabeled *Generator*.

These single-phase selsyn systems are used primarily for instrumentation and data transmission in cases where the data can be translated into the angular position of a shaft. Remote indication of the height of water in a reservoir or of the position of control surfaces on aircraft are examples. They may also be used for such purposes as opening or closing a valve to correct discrepancies revealed in terms of the angular position transmitted to the shaft of the receiver selsyn. One generator may drive several motors, the number depending on the relative size of generator and motor units and on the error which may be tolerated. In instrument systems it may be feasible to incorporate unity-voltage-gain electronic power amplifiers between the generator and motors to increase the power level and permit the use of more motors. The maximum static error for a system consisting of a generator and a single motor of the same size is of the order of 1° and is caused largely by friction in the motor bearings. The error increases as additional selsyns are added or as the line impedance between generator and motor becomes appreciable.

Dynamic errors, created by mechanical oscillation of the motor shaft about the correct position, may be two or three times the static errors. To minimize dynamic errors, mechanical dampers are built into the rotors of motor units. Dampers are shown in Fig. 6-26. A common form of inertia-friction damper consists of two disks driven by the shaft, one driven directly and the other through a friction pad. When the shaft is running at a steady speed, both disks rotate at the same speed and no damping is produced. When the speed is changing, however, one disk is free to move against the friction pad with respect to the other disk and damping is produced.

When the motor is called upon to supply significant torque, the error increases because of the need of a definite angular displacement between generator and motor shafts for torque transmission. This fact, together with heating of the selsyn equipment, definitely limits the torque magnitudes.

6-10. Synchro Control Transformers. Very commonly the process of controlling with reasonable exactness the instant-by-instant angular position of a shaft calls for the exertion of large torques. When selsyn equipment must exert these torques directly, a very considerable and intolerable sacrifice in the faithfulness of position reproduction may result. For such control purposes, it is common to apply the self-synchronous principle in such a manner that a voltage is produced whose magnitude is a function of the angular displacement between the positions of two shafts. Such a voltage is an *error voltage*, for its presence indicates a discrepancy in the position of the shaft being controlled. The error voltage may then be fed into other devices to instigate correction of the discrepancy causing it. The selsyns themselves thus do not have to supply mechanical power. The error voltage may be referred to as an *error-modulated signal*—a carrier wave whose amplitude is proportional to the error and whose instantaneous polarity is determined by the sign of the error.

The basic method of producing the error voltage is shown by the circuit of Fig. 6-28. Two interconnected selsyns are again involved, one a

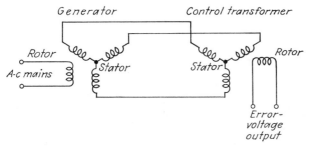

FIG. 6-28. Selsyn generator-transformer system.

generator and the other a very similar unit called a *selsyn* (or *synchro*) *control transformer*. The rotor of the selsyn generator is excited from a single-phase source, producing a magnetic field in the generator and voltages in the stator windings of both the generator and the control transformer. If the voltage drops caused by exciting current are neglected, the induced voltages in the 2 stator windings must be equal. Therefore the distribution of flux about the control-transformer stator must be similar to that about the generator stator. The effect is consequently the same as if the 2 rotor windings were on the same magnetic circuit and arranged so that their axes could be given any arbitrary displacement angle in space. The arrangement is thus the equivalent of an adjustable mutual inductance between the 2 rotor windings, but with the added feature that geographical separation of the 2 windings is possible. When the angle is 90 electrical degrees, corresponding to a 90-electrical-degree displacement of the two shafts, no voltage is induced in the transformer rotor; this displacement is the equilibrium position of the two shafts. When the angle has any value except 90° and 270°, a voltage is induced in the transformer rotor. As shown in Fig. 6-29, the magnitude of the voltage is a function of the angular discrepancy between the two shafts, and the instantaneous polarity depends on the direction of the displacement. The function is essentially a sinusoid. Differential selsyns may also be incorporated between the generators and control transformers of these systems.

This qualitative picture of the combined operation of generator and control transformer may be made more specific by a brief analysis in outline form for an idealized system as illustrated in Fig. 6-30. Consider that the two selsyns have cylindrical-rotor structures and that they, together with the interconnecting lines, are lossless. Let E_1 be the rms

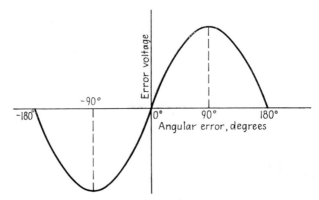

FIG. 6-29. Variation of error voltage with angular error.

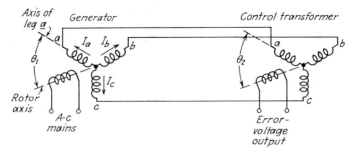

FIG. 6-30. Selsyn generator-transformer system for evaluation of error voltage. (Positive values of θ_1 and θ_2 are measured clockwise from the axis of phase a.)

voltage induced in one leg of the generator stator winding when the axis of that leg coincides with the rotor-winding axis, and assume that the induced voltage varies as the cosine of the angle between the leg and rotor-winding axes. Consider that the rotors are stationary or revolving slowly enough so that speed voltages are negligible. When θ_1 is the angle between the leg a and rotor-winding axes, the rms voltages in the three legs are

$$E_a = E_1 \cos \theta_1 \qquad (6\text{-}135)$$
$$E_b = E_1 \cos (\theta_1 - 120°) \qquad (6\text{-}136)$$
and
$$E_c = E_1 \cos (\theta_1 - 240°) \qquad (6\text{-}137)$$

Notice that these are single-phase voltages of different magnitudes and do not form a 3-phase system.

Now consider that the iron is unsaturated, so that the self- and mutual inductances of the stator windings are constant. Let L be the total self-inductance of one leg of the generator stator, one leg of the transformer stator, and the interconnecting line. Let M be the sum of the mutual inductance between generator stator legs plus that between transformer stator legs. (Because the windings are 120° apart in space, M is numerically a negative quantity.) Phasor equations involving the three leg currents I_a, I_b, and I_c may then be written by noting that the voltage between stator junctions is the same regardless of the path followed. Accordingly,

$$E_1 \cos \theta_1 - j\omega L I_a - j\omega M (I_b + I_c)$$
$$= E_1 \cos (\theta_1 - 120°) - j\omega L I_b - j\omega M (I_a + I_c)$$
$$= E_1 \cos (\theta_1 - 240°) - j\omega L I_c - j\omega M (I_a + I_b) \qquad (6\text{-}138)$$

Moreover, $\qquad\qquad I_a + I_b + I_c = 0 \qquad\qquad (6\text{-}139)$

Simultaneous solution of these equations yields

$$j\omega I_a = \frac{E_1}{L - M} \cos \theta_1 \qquad\qquad (6\text{-}140)$$

$$j\omega I_b = \frac{E_1}{L - M} \cos (\theta_1 - 120°) \qquad\qquad (6\text{-}141)$$

and $\qquad j\omega I_c = \dfrac{E_1}{L - M} \cos (\theta_1 - 240°) \qquad\qquad (6\text{-}142)$

Lastly, assume that the mutual inductance between a transformer stator leg and the transformer rotor winding has the maximum value M_t and varies as the cosine of the angle between that leg and the rotor axis. When θ_2 is the angle between leg a and the rotor winding, the rms error voltage induced in the rotor is

$$E_e = j\omega I_a M_t \cos \theta_2 + j\omega I_b M_t \cos (\theta_2 - 120°) + j\omega I_c M_t \cos (\theta_2 - 240°)$$
$$(6\text{-}143)$$

Upon substitution of Eqs. 6-140 to 6-142 and reduction to its simplest form, Eq. 6-143 becomes

$$E_e = \tfrac{3}{2} E_1 \frac{M_t}{L - M} \cos (\theta_2 - \theta_1) \qquad\qquad (6\text{-}144)$$

This result confirms the physical conclusion that the error voltage is zero when the shaft displacement is 90°; it also shows that, under idealized circumstances, the magnitude of the error voltage varies sinusoidally with the departure from this equilibrium displacement.

The selsyn control transformer has essentially a cylindrical-rotor structure and accordingly conforms quite well with the foregoing assumptions. It also has high-impedance stator windings to minimize the current drain on the generator and its associated effects. The generator has a salient-pole rotor structure, which represents a departure from the idealizing assumptions. The principal static errors are caused by unbalanced reactances and resistances in the stator-winding legs and interconnecting lines and unbalanced mutual reactances between rotor winding and stator legs. The static error for the generator-transformer system is of the order of $\pm 0.3°$. Velocity errors, caused by the appearance of speed voltages, are introduced when the selsyns rotate at significant speeds. These errors are of the order of $1°/320$ rpm for 60-cps selsyns. For a fixed value

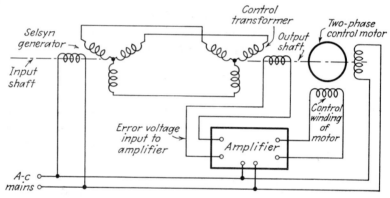

FIG. 6-31. Application of selsyn generator and transformer to angular-position control.

of rotational speed, velocity errors decrease as the excitation frequency increases, so that the errors are definitely smaller for 400-cps selsyns.[1]

The rotor of a selsyn control transformer normally is connected to the terminals of high-input-impedance electronic equipment, so that the current drain on the transformer is very low. Figure 6-31, for example, illustrates an application to control of the angular position of an output shaft. The object is to cause the output shaft to follow the angular variations of the input shaft. The rotor of the selsyn generator is mechanically connected to the input shaft. The rotor of the control transformer is mechanically connected to the output shaft and electrically connected to the input of a power amplifier. Mechanical power to turn the output shaft and its associated load is furnished by a 2-phase control motor. The

[1] Orders of magnitude cited here are taken from Harold Chestnut, Electrical Accuracy of Selsyn Generator–Control Transformer System, *Trans. AIEE*, vol. 65, pp. 570–576, 1946. This paper contains quantitative analyses including saliency, resistances, and speed voltages.

input to the control winding of the motor is supplied by the amplifier, which includes phase-splitting capacitors in its circuitry. When the output shaft is in the correct position, the voltage input to the amplifier and hence the power input to the control winding of the motor is zero and the motor does not turn. When an angular discrepancy exists, a definite error voltage appears at the amplifier input. Its relative polarity is such that the motor is caused to turn in the direction to correct the angular discrepancy.

6-11. Résumé. Our analysis of the polyphase induction machine has followed, step by step, a pattern almost identical with that of Chap. 5 for the synchronous machine. The steps are five in number:

1. Set up an idealized model of the machine.

2. Write the linkage equations in terms of self- and mutual inductances, together with the Kirchhoff-law voltage-current relations.

3. Introduce a transformation of variables in order to simplify the equations and their solutions, noting the advantages of a transformation which can be given a simple physical interpretation.

4. Establish the basic relations which the model must obey in the new system of variables.

5. Illustrate the application of these relations to important performance problems. In doing this, make combinations of constants, where possible, to lead to resulting constants which can be visualized simply and measured easily.

At the end of the fourth step (i.e., at the end of Art. 6-3), we have the essential machine relations (Eqs. 6-45 to 6-57). When the constraints imposed by the external stator and rotor circuitry and the mechanical shaft equipment are expressed, solution of the simultaneous equations yields the desired performance analysis.

From these performance analyses—and especially from the steady-state analyses of Arts. 6-4 and 6-5—it is evident that the induction machine is a valuable energy-conversion device. In fact, it is the most common type of electric motor. Structural simplicity, ruggedness, and relatively light maintenance requirements are contributing factors here. It is widely used, not only for heavy power drives, but also, in the form of 2-phase control motors (Art. 6-8) and selsyns or synchros (Arts. 6-9 and 6-10), as a control-system auxiliary. The single-phase version of this motor is commonly applied in the fractional-horsepower range (see Chap. 11).

The induction-motor equivalent circuit (Figs. 6-4 and 6-7) is the most important single result in the chapter. From it the steady-state performance features of the motor can readily be derived. Moreover, as shown in Art. 6-6, the electrical transients in the typical motor often subside rapidly in comparison with the duration of mechanical transients. Hence for many purposes the steady-state equivalent circuit can be used as well for dynamic analyses.

Both the principal features and the limitation of the induction motor can be seen from the equivalent circuit and the steady-state analysis associated with it. Thus, the motor operates at a substantially constant speed unless provisions are made to insert a high or an adjustable rotor-circuit resistance. It has a definite maximum torque (Eq. 6-102) which occurs at the slip for which r_2/s matches the impedance in series with it in Fig. 6-7a. For the induction motor with short-circuited rotor windings, the fraction s of the power absorbed from the stator is dissipated as heat in the resistances of the rotor circuits. In this respect, the induction machine is like a slipping mechanical clutch or any other power-transmission device operating with slip between its input and output members. An induction motor with short-circuited rotor is inherently inefficient when running at high values of slip.

In looking back upon the three chapters making up Part II of the book, we see that the process of analysis is essentially the same for d-c, synchronous, and induction machines. This sameness could have been inferred from the underlying material in Part I. The analytical process is the one introduced in Art. 3-3a using the coupled-circuit viewpoint. In carrying out the process, we have always found it convenient to deal in components of fields taken along perpendicular axes in space (just as in mechanics, for example, we often find it convenient to resolve a force at an odd angle into its horizontal and vertical components). Accordingly, we have used current, voltage, and flux-linkage variables consistent with these components. After a preliminary result has been obtained, it has often been possible for us to change back to true phase or winding variables while still retaining reasonable simplicity in the final result.

In Part III we return to Art. 3-3 and develop the magnetic-field viewpoint outlined in Art. 3-3b. Closer association with the properties of iron, copper, and insulation can be brought about. As a result, it becomes possible to examine a number of factors either ignored or brushed aside in studying idealized machines.

PROBLEMS

6-1. The dq transformation developed in the text uses synchronously rotating axes. An alternative approach to induction-motor analysis is to use axes which are fixed in the stator structure. Since these axes are often called the α and β axes, we shall use the subscripts α and β here instead of d and q, respectively. Also, let θ be the angle between the axes of correspondingly lettered rotor and stator phases (e.g., phase a on the stator and phase A on the rotor).

a. Write the transformation equations relating phase currents and $\alpha\beta$ currents for the stator by replacing ωt by zero in Eqs. 6-31 through 6-35 and simplifying the results.

(Similar equations hold, of course, for stator voltages and linkages.) By physical interpretation, show that the results correspond to axes fixed in the stator.

b. Repeat (*a*) except for rotor currents, obtaining the relations by replacing θ_s by $-\theta$ in Eqs. 6-39 through 6-43.

c. Show that the component flux-linkage relations are the same as in Eqs. 6-45 through 6-48 except for replacing *d* and *q* by α and β.

d. Show that the voltage relations are

Stator:

$$e_{1\alpha} = r_1 i_{1\alpha} + p\lambda_{1\alpha}$$
$$i_{1\beta} = r_1 i_{1\beta} + p\lambda_{1\beta}$$

Rotor:

$$e_{2\alpha} = r_2 i_{2\alpha} + p\lambda_{2\alpha} + \lambda_{2\beta}(p\theta)$$
$$e_{2\beta} = r_2 i_{2\beta} + p\lambda_{2\beta} - \lambda_{2\alpha}(p\theta)$$

e. Show that, in the steady state, the component currents and voltages are stator-frequency quantities.

6-2. Another alternative to the use of synchronously rotating axes is to use axes fixed in the rotor. For these axes we shall continue to use the subscripts *d* and *q*. Also, let θ be the angle between the axes of correspondingly lettered rotor and stator phases (e.g., phase *a* on the stator and phase *A* on the rotor).

a. Write the transformation equations relating phase currents and these new *dq* currents by replacing ωt by θ in Eqs. 6-31 through 6-35. By physical interpretation, show that the results correspond to axes fixed in the rotor.

b. Repeat (*a*) except for rotor currents, obtaining the relations by replacing θ_s by zero in Eqs. 6-39 through 6-43 and simplifying.

c. Show that the component flux-linkage relations are the same as in Eqs. 6-45 through 6-48.

d. Show that the voltage relations are

Stator:

$$e_{1d} = r_1 i_{1d} + p\lambda_{1d} - \lambda_{1q}(p\theta)$$
$$e_{1q} = r_1 i_{1q} + p\lambda_{1q} + \lambda_{1d}(p\theta)$$

Rotor:

$$e_{2d} = r_2 i_{2d} + p\lambda_{2d}$$
$$e_{2q} = r_2 i_{2q} + p\lambda_{2q}$$

e. Show that, in the steady state, the component currents and voltages are slip-frequency quantities.

6-3. *a.* By carrying out the manipulations described at the beginning of Art. 6-3, show that Eqs. 6-45 to 6-48 are correct.

b. Similarly, show that Eqs. 6-50 to 6-53 are correct.

6-4. This problem is concerned with analysis of a 2-phase induction machine instead of the 3-phase machine of the text. Synchronously rotating *dq* axes are still used. Consider that the machine is idealized as in Art. 6-1. There are, however, 2 distributed windings *a* and *b* on the stator, 1 in each phase, with the magnetic axis of phase *b* 90° ahead of the phase *a* axis in the direction of rotation. There are also 2 corresponding windings *A* and *B* on the rotor, also with axes 90° apart. At any instant of time, the axis of a rotor phase is displaced by the angle θ_2 from the axis of the correspondingly lettered stator phase. The same general assumptions, conventions, and notation as in Arts. 6-1 through 6-3 apply.

   a. Write the phase-linkage equations corresponding to Eqs. 6-19 to 6-24.

   b. Show that the appropriate dq transformation of variables is typified by the following:

Stator:

$$i_{1d} = i_a \cos \omega t + i_b \sin \omega t$$
$$i_{1q} = -i_a \sin \omega t + i_b \cos \omega t$$

Rotor:

$$i_{2d} = i_A \cos \theta_s + i_B \sin \theta_s$$
$$i_{2q} = -i_A \sin \theta_s + i_B \cos \theta_s$$

Also, write the reverse equations for phase variables in terms of dq variables.

   c. Show that the dq linkage relations are still given by Eqs. 6-45 through 6-48. Identify L_{11}, L_{22}, and L_{12} in terms of L_{aa}, L_{AA}, and L_{aA}.

   d. Show that the component voltage relations of Eqs. 6-50 through 6-53 are correct in this case.

   e. Show that the instantaneous power input to the 2-phase stator is

$$p_1 = v_{1d}i_{1d} + v_{1q}i_{1q}$$

   f. Show that the motor torque is given by

$$T = \frac{\text{poles}}{2} (\lambda_{2q}i_{2d} - \lambda_{2d}i_{2q})$$

   6-5. Equations 6-45 through 6-48 and 6-50 through 6-53 constitute the basic electrical relations in dq variables for an induction machine with no zero-sequence currents. On the basis of these equations, set up a block diagram to represent the electrical performance of the machine. The voltages v_{1d} and v_{1q} are signals to be received from the stator supply system. The slip angular velocity $p\theta_s = s\omega$ is either constant or a signal to be received from a representation of the mechanics of the machine and the equipment coupled to its shaft. Constraints are placed on the rotor component voltages and currents, not only by the machine, but also by the circuitry or equipment connected to the rotor terminals.

   6-6. Modify the block diagram of Prob. 6-5 so that it represents the common case with a short-circuited rotor winding.

   6-7. A 100-hp 3-phase Y-connected 440-volt 60-cps 8-pole squirrel-cage induction motor has the following equivalent-circuit constants in ohms per phase referred to the stator:

$$r_1 = 0.085 \qquad r_2 = 0.067$$
$$x_1 = 0.196 \qquad x_2 = 0.161 \qquad x_\varphi = 6.65$$

No-load rotational loss = 2.7 kw.   Stray load loss = 0.5 kw.   The rotational and stray load losses may be considered constant.

   a. Compute the horsepower output, stator current, power factor, and efficiency at rated voltage and frequency for a slip of 3.00 per cent.

   b. Compute the starting current and the internal starting torque in pound-feet at rated voltage and frequency.

   6-8. A 10-hp 3-phase 60-cps 6-pole induction motor runs at a slip of 3.0 per cent at full load. Rotational and stray load losses at full load are 4.0 per cent of the output power. Compute:

   a. The rotor copper loss at full load

b. The electromagnetic torque at full load, in newton-meters

c. The power delivered by the stator to the air gap at full load

6-9. A 10-hp 230-volt 3-phase Y-connected 60-cps 4-pole squirrel-cage induction motor develops full-load internal torque at a slip of 0.04 when operated at rated voltage and frequency. For the purposes of this problem rotational and core losses can be neglected. Impedance data on the motor are as follows:

Stator resistance $r_1 = 0.36$ ohm per phase

Leakage reactances $x_1 = x_2 = 0.47$ ohm per phase

Magnetizing reactance $x_\varphi = 15.5$ ohms per phase

Determine the maximum internal torque at rated voltage and frequency, the slip at maximum torque, and the internal starting torque at rated voltage and frequency. Express the torques in newton-meters.

6-10. Suppose the induction motor of Prob. 6-9 is supplied from a 240-volt constant-voltage 60-cps source through a feeder whose impedance is $0.50 + j0.30$ ohm per phase. Determine the maximum internal torque that the motor can deliver and the corresponding values of stator current and terminal voltage.

6-11. A 50-hp 6-pole 60-cps high-starting-torque 3-phase induction motor produces rated horsepower at rated voltage and frequency with 10 per cent slip. This motor can develop 300 per cent pull-out torque based on rated full-load torque.

The motor is used to drive a load requiring a torque directly proportional to speed; at 2,000 rpm, the load torque is 350 lb-ft. Consider the torque-speed curve of the motor a straight line between 0 and 15 per cent slip.

a. Sketch the motor and load torque-speed characteristics to approximate scale.

b. At what speed will the motor drive this load? Applied voltage is rated value.

c. While the motor is driving the same load, the voltage applied to the motor is raised 10 per cent. Show whether or not the motor will be loaded beyond its horsepower rating.

d. The rotor is replaced by one having twice the resistance per phase but identical in all other respects with the old one. What will be the motor speed with rated voltage applied to the motor?

6-12. A 3-phase induction motor, at rated voltage and frequency, has a starting torque of 160 per cent and a maximum torque of 200 per cent of full-load torque. Neglect stator resistance and rotational losses, and assume constant rotor resistance. Determine:

a. The slip at full load

b. The slip at maximum torque

c. The rotor current at starting, in per unit of full-load rotor current

6-13. A squirrel-cage induction motor runs at a slip of 5.0 per cent at full load. The rotor current at starting is 5.0 times the rotor current at full load. The rotor resistance is independent of rotor frequency, and rotational losses, stray load losses, and stator resistance may be neglected.

a. Compute the starting torque.

b. Compute the maximum torque and the slip at which maximum torque occurs. Express the torques in per unit of full-load torque.

6-14. The steady-state analysis of Arts. 6-4 and 6-5 assumes the induction-motor voltages and currents to be balanced. When unbalanced voltages are applied, the *method of 3-phase symmetrical components* is ordinarily used. This problem is concerned with the development of that method.

a. Consider that three phasor voltages V_a, V_b, and V_c are applied to the stator with the rotor short-circuited. These voltages do not form a balanced 3-phase system but, for the purposes of this problem, are subject to the restriction that their phasor sum is zero. Show that a transformation to the phasor variables V_a^+ and V_a^- can be made such that

$$V_a = V_a^+ + V_a^-$$
$$V_b = V_a^+ \epsilon^{-j120°} + V_a^- \epsilon^{j120°}$$
$$V_c = V_a^+ \epsilon^{j120°} + V_a^- \epsilon^{-j120°}$$

A similar transformation can be made for currents. Note that we now have on the right two sets of balanced 3-phase voltages. The V_a^+ set has an abc phase sequence, as do the original voltages; these are the *positive-sequence components*. The V_a^- set has an acb phase sequence; they are the *negative-sequence components*.

b. Write the phasor equations for the reverse transformation (i.e., for V_a^+ and V_a^- in terms of V_a, V_b, and V_c).

c. By superposition, the positive- and negative-sequence voltages can be applied separately to the motor and the resulting torques, powers, and currents superimposed to find the resultants. Draw the positive-sequence equivalent circuit of a motor operating at slip s.

d. Show that the slip of the rotor to negative-sequence component fields is $2 - s$. Then draw the negative-sequence equivalent circuit. In which direction is the torque due to negative-sequence components?

e. On the basis of the foregoing, outline the method for computing a torque-slip curve with unbalanced voltages applied.

6-15. In Prob. 6-4 the development of the basic theory of a 2-phase induction machine is outlined as an alternative to the 3-phase machine of the text. Answer the following questions for this 2-phase machine:

a. What modifications, if any, must be made in Arts. 6-4 and 6-5 to be applicable to the 2-phase machine? Specifically, do the equivalent circuits of Figs. 6-3, 6-4, 6-5, and 6-7 still apply?

b. What modifications, if any, must be made in the transient analysis of Art. 6-6? What are the expressions for L' and T_o' which correspond to Eqs. 6-110 and 6-120?

6-16. A 4-pole 440-volt 400-hp 3-phase 60-cps Y-connected wound-rotor induction motor has the following constants in ohms per phase referred to the stator: $x_1 = x_2 = 0.055$, $x_\varphi = 2.23$, $r_1 = 0.0054$, $r_2 = 0.0071$. The motor is supplied at normal terminal voltage through a series reactance of 0.03 ohm per phase representing a step-down transformer bank. It is fully loaded, the slip rings are short-circuited, and the efficiency and power factor are 90.5 and 90.0 per cent, respectively.

A 3-phase short circuit occurs at the high-tension terminals of the transformer bank. Determine the initial symmetrical short-circuit current in the motor, and show how it is decremented.

6-17. A polyphase induction motor has negligible rotor rotational losses and is driving a pure-inertia load. The moment of inertia of the rotor plus load is J mks units.

a. Obtain an expression for the rotor energy loss during starting. Express the result in terms of J and the synchronous angular velocity ω_s.

b. Obtain an expression for the rotor energy loss associated with reversal from full speed forward by reversing the phase sequence of the voltage supply (a process known as *plugging*). Express the result in terms of J and ω_s.

c. State and discuss the degree of dependence of the results in (a) and (b) on the current-limiting scheme which may be used during starting and reversal.

d. A 5-hp 3-phase 4-pole 60-cps squirrel-cage induction motor has a full-load efficiency of 85.0 per cent. The total Wk^2 of rotor plus load is 1.5 lb-ft². The total motor losses for a reversal may be assumed to be 2.25 times the rotor losses. The impairment of ventilation arising from the lower average speed during reversing is to be ignored.

Using the result in (b), compute the number of times per minute that the motor can be reversed without its allowable temperature rise being exceeded.

e. Discuss the optimism or pessimism of the result in (d).

6-18. Following are points on the torque-speed curve of a 3-phase squirrel-cage induction motor with balanced rated voltage impressed:

Torque, per unit	0	1.00	2.00	3.00	3.50	3.25	3.00
Speed, per unit	1.00	0.97	0.93	0.80	0.47	0.20	0

Unit speed is synchronous speed; unit torque is rated torque. The motor is coupled to a machine tool which requires rated torque regardless of speed. The inertia of the motor plus load is such that it requires 1.2 sec to bring them to rated speed with a constant *accelerating* torque equal to rated torque.

With the motor driving the load under normal steady conditions, the voltage at its terminals suddenly drops to 50 per cent of rated value because of a short circuit in the neighborhood. It remains at this reduced value for 0.6 sec and is then restored to its full value by clearing of the short circuit. The undervoltage release on the motor does not operate. Will the motor stop? If not, what is its lowest speed? Neglect any effects of secondary importance.

6-19. A 230-volt 3-phase Y-connected 6-pole 60-cps wound-rotor induction motor has a stator-plus-rotor leakage reactance of 0.50 ohm per phase referred to the stator, a rotor-plus-load moment of inertia of 1.0 kg-m^2, negligible losses (except for rotor copper loss), and negligible exciting current. It is connected to a balanced 230-volt source and drives a pure-inertia load. Across-the-line starting is used, and the rotor-circuit resistance is to be adjusted so that the motor brings its load from rest to one-half synchronous speed in the shortest possible time.

Determine the value of the rotor resistance referred to the stator and the minimum time to reach one-half of synchronous speed.

6-20. A 3-phase induction motor is operating in the steady state at the slip s_1. By suddenly interchanging two stator leads, the motor is to be plugged to a quick stop. Use the notation and assumptions of Example 6-5, and consider the motor to be unloaded.

a. Develop an expression for the braking time of the motor.

b. Suppose that the motor is to be reversed instead of simply brought to a stop. Develop an expression for the reversing time.

6-21. A 4,160-volt 2,500-hp 2-pole 3-phase 60-cps squirrel-cage induction motor is driving a boiler-feed pump in an electric generating plant. The table below lists points on the motor torque-speed curve at rated voltage, speed being in per cent of synchronous speed and torque in per cent of rated torque. Also listed are the torque requirements of the boiler-feed pump expressed in per cent of motor rated torque. The drive is started at rated voltage with the discharge valve open but working against a check valve until the pump head equals the system head. The straight-line portion of the pump characteristic between 0 and 10 per cent speed represents the breakaway-torque requirements. At 92 per cent speed the check valve opens, and there is a discontinuity in the slope of the pump curve. At 98 per cent speed the motor produces its maximum torque.

Per cent speed	0	10	30	50	70	90	92	98	99.5
Per cent motor torque	75	75	75	75	80	125	155	240	100
Per cent pump torque	15	0+	4	12	26	42	44	87	100

The inertia of the drive is such that 5,400 kw-sec of energy is stored in the rotating mass at synchronous speed.

a. Determine the time required for the check valve to open after rated voltage is applied to the motor.

b. Determine the time required to reach the motor maximum-torque point.

6-22. For the boiler-feed-pump drive in Prob. 6-21, consider that the motor must occasionally be started with the motor voltage at 80 per cent of its rated value. The motor torque may be assumed to be proportional to the square of the voltage.

a. Determine the time required for the check valve to open.

b. To what value may the motor starting voltage be reduced without making it impossible to reach a speed at which water is delivered to the system?

6-23. Induction-motor transient and dynamic considerations are important factors in the industrial application of these motors, as in refineries, chemical process plants, auxiliary drives in steam stations, etc. It is common practice to provide two sources of electric power to critical drives, a normal source and an emergency source to which the motor bus is automatically transferred in the event of failure of the normal source. When the normal source has been tripped, flux linkages are "trapped" with the closed rotor circuits of the operating motors. A motor terminal voltage (often called the *residual voltage*) is therefore produced which may require an appreciable time to decay to zero. If the motor is transferred almost immediately to the emergency source, the residual voltage and the emergency-source voltage may be so phase-displaced that the resulting heavy inrush current may damage the motor. One solution is to install a voltage-sensitive relay which delays transfer until the residual voltage has decayed to about 25 per cent of normal motor voltage. In the meantime the motor is slowing down and may have real difficulty in reaccelerating when the emergency source is connected.

To investigate these aspects, consider a 4,160-volt 2,500-hp 2-pole 3-phase 3,580-rpm 60-cps squirrel-cage induction motor driving a boiler-feed pump. The motor has an open-circuit transient time constant of 3.6 sec, short-circuit time constant of 0.12 sec, and transient reactance of 1.3 ohms per phase Y. The motor is operating fully loaded at rated voltage and draws 2,160 kva at 0.90 power factor from the mains. (This problem is based on a single motor. In a practical case, the effects of other parallel motors must be considered.[1])

a. Determine the time required after interruption of the normal supply for the residual voltage to decay to 25 per cent of the normal bus voltage.

b. Determine the speed to which the motor decelerates in this interval. The Wk^2 of the motor rotor and pump impeller is 1,800 lb-ft². Consider that the load torque varies as the square of the speed, and neglect losses.

c. Assume that the emergency source consists of a constant 100 per cent voltage behind a reactive impedance of 0.10 ohm (representing a step-down transformer bank). Assume also that torque-slip and current-slip curves at rated voltage are available for the motor.

Outline a method by which a speed-time curve may be obtained for the reacceleration period. A step-by-step method arranged for either hand computation or digital-computer programming is suggested.

d. Let the torque-slip curve be that given for the motor in Prob. 6-21. Corresponding data for the current-slip curve are given below, the current being in per cent of current under rated conditions.

[1] See D. G. Lewis and W. D. Marsh, Transfer of Steam-electric Generating Station Auxiliary Buses, *Trans. AIEE*, vol. 74, pp. 322–330, 1955.

Per cent speed.....	0	30	50	70	90	92	98	99.5
Per cent current...	620	620	620	620	580	540	390	100

By the method you have outlined in (c), plot motor speed as a function of time during reacceleration.

e. The practical problem may be to determine the maximum allowable impedance and hence the size of the emergency step-down transformer bank which will permit both motor starting and successful reacceleration of all the motor drives after transfer. Describe how you would carry out such an investigation.

6-24. For a 2-phase control motor, determine the transfer functions and the corresponding block-diagram representations as in Example 6-6 but including coulomb friction f_c as well as viscous friction $f_v\omega_o$.

6-25. As indicated in the discussion of Art. 6-8, the 2-phase control motor usually operates with unbalanced applied voltages. Analysis is then often based on the *method of 2-phase symmetrical components*. This problem is concerned with development of that method for steady-state analyses. The motor is assumed to have identical windings in the 2 phases, source impedances are neglected, and currents and voltages considered to be sinusoidal.

a. Consider that two phasor voltages V_a and V_b are applied to the stator with the rotor short-circuited. Show that a transformation to the phasor variables V_a^+ and V_a^- can be made such that

$$V_a = V_a^+ + V_a^-$$
$$V_b = V_a^+\epsilon^{-j90°} + V_a^-\epsilon^{j90°} = -jV_a^+ + jV_a^-$$

A similar transformation can be made for currents. We now have on the right two sets of balanced 2-phase voltages. The V_a^+ set has an ab sequence, as do the original voltages; these are the *positive-sequence components*. The V_a^- set has a ba sequence; they are the *negative-sequence components*.

b. Write the phasor equations for the reverse transformation (i.e., for V_a^+ and V_a^- in terms of V_a and V_b).

c. By superposition, the positive- and negative-sequence voltages can be applied separately to the motor and the resulting torques, powers, and currents superimposed to find the resultants. Draw the positive-sequence equivalent circuit of a motor operating at slip s.

d. Show that the slip of the rotor to negative-sequence component fields is $2 - s$. Then draw the negative-sequence equivalent circuit. In which direction is the torque due to negative-sequence components?

e. On the basis of the foregoing, outline the method of computing a family of torque-slip curves such as those of Fig. 6-17.

f. If Prob. 6-14 has been solved, compare the approaches in the two problems.

PART III

The Realistic Machine

CHAPTER 7

Engineering Considerations
Underlying Machine Application

Our objective in this chapter is to form a transition between Parts II and III of the book by shifting the viewpoint to one emphasizing the problems associated with machine application. Many of these problems are concerned with physical factors limiting the conditions under which a machine may operate successfully. Among them are saturation and the effects of losses on the rating and heating of the machine. These problems, common to all machine types, are discussed in this chapter. The chapter concludes by supplementing the introductory transformer treatment of Art. 1-4 in somewhat the same manner that the later chapters supplement the earlier treatments of rotating machines.

7-1. Physical Factors Influencing Machine Performance. In much of the material of Part II of the book, we have been dealing with mathematical models of machines more than with the machines as physical entities. The viewpoint has been essentially that of the analyst: certain specific and presumably important problems have been stated, and we have sought solutions to them. We have made numerous assumptions in arriving at idealized models and have, in effect, asked acceptance on faith or through laboratory experience that the assumptions lead to adequate answers. In order to provide in a short time a reasonably broad background of analysis emphasizing dynamic and transient aspects, we have based many of our considerations on the self- and mutual-inductance viewpoint.

The engineer in responsible charge of a project involving electric machinery, however, generally needs a much more comprehensive background. He may need to decide, in the first place, whether he can best accomplish the desired result electrically rather than, say, hydraulically, pneumatically, or by use of steam. He needs to specify the system of machines (including types, sizes, voltages, speeds, etc.) and the control and protective equipment to accomplish the result economically. He needs to consider very seriously what happens in case of equipment failure and what to do about it. By virtue of costs, time schedules, space availability, weight, or other unique circumstances of the project, he is usually stressing some aspect of machine performance to its limit. He obviously needs to be familiar with these limits, with the physical factors determining them, and with how they may be raised by new techniques and by improved properties of materials. He needs a strong analytical background, and often the services of an analytical group, to investigate problems which he formulates in assuring that the over-all objectives will be attained.

Of course this type of background depends a greal deal on experience. The interpretation and codification of such experience, however, rest to a considerable extent on a clear physical understanding of internal machine happenings and their relation to the properties of materials. Any electric machine is composed of iron, copper, and insulating material. The total flux which can economically be forced through a specific iron geometry is limited, as are the allowable mechanical stresses in the iron. The current density in the copper is limited by mechanical considerations and, most importantly, by the heat which the insulation can withstand without prohibitively fast deterioration. Sliding contacts at slip rings or commutators introduce limitations of their own. The manner of the changes of flux and current and their interaction under changing operating conditions determine the performance of the machine and hence its suitability for a proposed application.

To bring out these aspects of the energy-conversion process, machine operation is best examined from the viewpoint of interaction of flux and mmf waves. This viewpoint has already been introduced in Chap. 3. The flux wave obviously specifies the magnetic conditions in the iron. The mmf wave is closely related to the armature current and to the machine as a circuit element. As a result, the flux-mmf combination is admirably adapted to promoting a physical understanding of what is going on in the machine.

The flux-mmf approach complements the self- and mutual-inductance attack. The former is very well suited to steady-state examinations. It enables us to establish and evaluate the idealizing assumptions necessary for analysis. The latter is almost invaluable for the investigation of complex transient and dynamic problems. Specific correlation of the two methods is essential to an understanding in depth of electromagnetic energy conversion.

In Part III of this text we shall examine the operation of the basic machine types in terms of interaction of flux and mmf waves. We shall then correlate the results with those already obtained in Part II, particularly in the steady state, and, where appropriate, develop methods of including hitherto neglected but practically important factors in the analysis. We shall give increased attention to physical interpretations and to the range of performance features which can be obtained. Design aspects are touched on only when they have an important bearing on performance limitations.

The next several articles discuss some of the more important common problems which arise in dealing with realistic machines.

7-2. Magnetic Saturation. Both electromagnetic torque and generated voltage in all machines depend on rates of change of flux linkages with the windings of the machines. For specified mmfs in the windings, the fluxes depend on the reluctances of the iron portions of the magnetic circuits as well as of the air gaps. Saturation may therefore appreciably influence the characteristics of the machines. Another aspect of saturation, a more subtle one and one more difficult to evaluate without experimental and theoretical comparisons, concerns its influence on the basic premises from which the analytic approach to machinery is developed. Specifically, all relations for mmf are based on negligible reluctance in the iron. When these relations are applied to practical machines with varying degrees of saturation in the iron, the actual machine is, in effect, replaced for these considerations by an equivalent machine: one whose iron has negligible reluctance but whose air-gap length is increased by an amount sufficient to absorb the magnetic-potential drop in the iron of the actual machine.

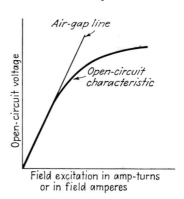

Fig. 7-1. Typical open-circuit characteristic and air-gap line.

Incidentally, the effects of air-gap nonuniformities such as slots and ventilating ducts are also incorporated through the medium of an equivalent smooth gap, a replacement which, in contrast to that above, is made explicitly during magnetic-circuit computations for the machine structure. Thus, serious efforts are made to reproduce the magnetic conditions at the air gap correctly, and the computed performance of machines is based largely on those conditions. Final assurance of the legitimacy of the approach must, of course, be the pragmatic one given by close experimental checks.

Magnetic-circuit data essential to the handling of saturation are given by the *open-circuit characteristic, magnetization curve,* or *saturation curve.* An example is shown in Fig. 7-1. Basically, this characteristic is the magnetization curve for the particular iron and air geometry of the machine under consideration. Frequently the abscissa is plotted in terms of field current or magnetizing current instead of mmf in ampere-turns. Also, the generated voltage with zero armature current is directly proportional to the flux when the speed is constant. For convenience in use, then, open-circuit terminal voltage is plotted on the ordinate scale rather than air-gap flux per pole, and the entire curve is drawn for a stated fixed speed, usually rated speed. The straight line tangent to the lower portion of the curve is the *air-gap line* indicating very closely the mmf required to overcome the reluctance of the air gap. If it were not for the effects of saturation, the air-gap line and open-circuit characteristic would coincide, so that the departure of the curve from the air-gap line is an indication of the degree of saturation present. In a normal machine, the ratio at rated voltage of the total mmf to that required by the air gap alone usually is between 1.1 and 1.25.

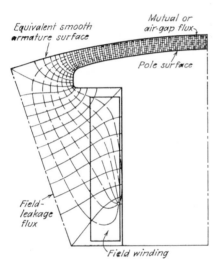

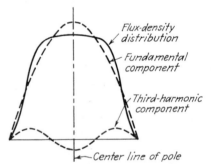

Fig. 7-2. Distribution of flux around a salient pole. The solid lines are flux lines; the dashed lines are loci of equal magnetic potential.

Fig. 7-3. Flux-density wave corresponding to Fig. 7-2, with its fundamental and third-harmonic components.

The open-circuit characteristic may be calculated from design data by magnetic-circuit methods, often guided by flux mapping. A small sample map of the flux distribution around the pole of a salient-pole machine is given in Fig. 7-2. The distribution of air-gap flux found by means of this map, together with the fundamental- and third-harmonic components, are shown in Fig. 7-3. The map is drawn on the basis of infinite permeability in the iron and for a smooth armature surface with the air-gap width increased to compensate for the effect of armature slots on the flux per pole. Slot effects may be studied separately on either an analytical or a graphical basis. The influence of a slot on an otherwise uniform field is indicated graphically in Figs. 7-4 and 7-5. Note that in Fig. 7-4 the scale to which the field is mapped increases at locations where a flux line is drawn only up to a point where it crosses an equi-potential line. When this change is borne in mind, it is seen that the flux density in the slot is far lower than in the tooth. The general nature of the flux-density wave with slot effects superimposed is shown in Fig. 7-6. Slot effects are indicated in a pronounced form here because of

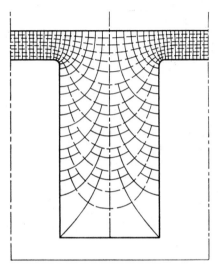

FIG. 7-4. Distribution of flux in a slot. The solid lines are flux lines; the dashed lines are loci of equal magnetic potential.

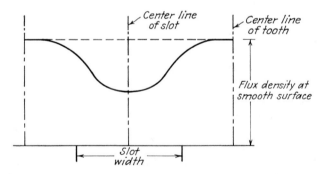

FIG. 7-5. Effect of a slot on the air-gap flux density.

the use of only a few relatively wide slots per pole. Flux maps of the type indicated in Figs. 7-2 and 7-4 yield precise, quantitative results, for they are graphical solutions of Laplace's equation for the assumed boundary conditions.

If the machine is an existing one, the magnetization curve is most commonly determined by operating it as an unloaded generator and

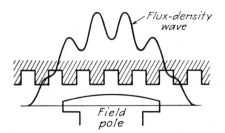

FIG. 7-6. Main-field flux distribution with slot effects superimposed. Slot effects are exaggerated because of showing only a few wide slots per pole.

reading the values of terminal voltage corresponding to a series of values of field current. For an induction motor, the machine is operated at or close to synchronous speed, and values of magnetizing current are obtained for a series of values of impressed stator voltage.

7-3. Excitation Sources. The resultant flux in the magnetic circuit of a machine is established by the combined mmf of all the windings on the machine. For the conventional d-c machine, the bulk of the effective mmf is furnished by the field windings. For the transformer, the net excitation may be furnished by either the primary or the secondary winding, or a portion may be furnished by each. A similar situation exists in a-c machines. The furnishing of excitation to a-c machines has associated with it two different operational aspects which are of economic importance in the application of the machines.

a. Power Factor in A-C Machines. The power factor at which a-c machines operate is an economically important feature because of the cost of reactive kva. Low power factor adversely affects system operation in three principal ways. In the first place, generators, transformers, and transmission equipment are rated in terms of kva rather than kilowatts, because their losses and heating are very nearly determined by voltage and current regardless of power factor. The physical size and cost of a-c apparatus is roughly proportional to its kva rating. The investment in generators, transformers, and transmission equipment for supplying a given useful amount of active power therefore is roughly inversely proportional to the power factor. In the second place, low power factor means more current and greater copper losses in the generating and transmitting equipment. A further disadvantage is poor voltage regulation.

Factors influencing reactive-kva requirements in motors can be visualized readily in terms of the relationship of these requirements to the establishment of magnetic flux. As in any electromagnetic device, the resultant flux necessary for motor operation must be established by a magnetizing component of current. It makes no difference either in the magnetic circuit or in the fundamental energy-conversion process whether this magnetizing current be carried by the rotor or stator winding, just as it makes no basic difference in a transformer which winding carries the exciting current. In some cases, part of it is supplied from each winding. If all or part of the magnetizing current is supplied to an a-c winding, the input to that winding must include lagging reactive kva, because magnetizing current lags voltage drop by 90°. In effect, the lagging reactive kva sets up flux in the motor.

The only possible source of excitation in an induction motor is the stator input. The induction motor therefore must operate at a lagging power factor. This power factor is very low at no load and increases to about 85 or 90 per cent at full load, the improvement being caused by the increased active-power requirements with increasing load.

With a synchronous motor, there are two possible sources of excitation: alternating current in the armature, or direct current in the field winding. If the field current is just sufficient to supply the necessary mmf, no magnetizing-current component or reactive kva is needed in the armature and the motor operates at unity power factor. If the field current is less (i.e., the motor is *underexcited*), the deficit in mmf must be made up by the armature and the motor operates at a lagging power factor. If the field current is greater (i.e., the motor is *overexcited*), the excess mmf must be counterbalanced in the armature and a leading component of current is present; the motor then operates at a leading power factor.

Because magnetizing current must be supplied to inductive loads, such as transformers and induction motors, the ability of overexcited synchronous motors to supply lagging current is a highly desirable feature which may have considerable economic importance. In effect, overexcited synchronous motors act as generators of lagging reactive kva and thereby relieve the power source of the necessity for supplying this component. They thus may perform the same function as a local capacitor installation. Sometimes unloaded synchronous machines are installed in power systems solely for power-factor correction or for control of reactive-kva flow. Such machines, called *synchronous condensers*, may be more economical in the larger sizes than static capacitors.

Both synchronous and induction machines may become self-excited when a sufficiently heavy capacitive load is present in their stator circuits. The capacitive current then furnishes the excitation and may cause serious overvoltage or excessive transient torques. Because of the inherent capacitance of transmission lines, the problem may arise when synchronous generators are energizing long unloaded or lightly loaded lines. The use of shunt reactors at the sending end of the line to compensate the capacitive current is sometimes necessary. For induction motors, it is normal practice to avoid self-excitation by limiting the size of any parallel capacitor when the motor and capacitor are switched as a unit.

b. Brushless Excitation Systems. As the available ratings of turbine-generators have increased, the problems of supplying the d-c field excitation (amounting to 4,000 amp or more in the larger units) have grown progressively more difficult. The conventional excitation source, of course, is a d-c generator whose output is supplied to the alternator field through brushes and slip rings. Cooling and maintenance problems are inevitably associated with slip rings, commutators, and brushes. The development of brushless excitation, first for aircraft alternators and then for turbine-generators, has eliminated these problems by eliminating all sliding contacts and brushes.[1]

A schematic diagram of a typical system is given in Fig. 7-7. At the heart of the system are the silicon diode rectifiers, which are mounted on the same shaft as the generator field and which furnish d-c excitation directly to the field. An a-c exciter with a rotating armature feeds power along the shaft to the revolving rectifiers. The stationary field of the a-c exciter is fed through a magnetic amplifier which controls and regulates the output voltage of the main generator. To make the system self-contained and free of sliding contacts, the excitation power for the

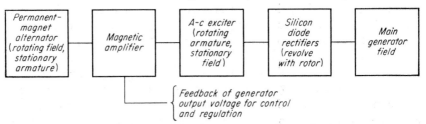

FIG. 7-7. Diagrammatic representation of brushless excitation system.

magnetic amplifier is obtained from the stationary armature of a small permanent-magnet alternator also driven from the main shaft.

The voltage and frequency of the a-c exciter are chosen so as to optimize the performance and design of the over-all system. Time delays in the response to a controlling signal are all short compared with the time constant of the main generator field. The system may have the additional advantage of doing away with need for spare exciters, generator-field circuit breakers, and field rheostats.

7-4. Losses. Consideration of machine losses is important for three reasons: losses determine the efficiency of the machine and appreciably influence its operating cost; losses determine the heating of the machine and hence the rating or power output that may be obtained without undue deterioration of the insulation; and the voltage drops or current components associated with supplying the losses must be properly accounted for in machine representation. Machine efficiency, like that of any

[1] See, for example, R. W. Ferguson, R. Herbst, and R. W. Miller, Analytical Studies of the Brushless Excitation System, *Trans. AIEE*, paper 59-1108, 1959; and E. C. Whitney, D. B. Hoover, and P. O. Bobo, An Electric Utility Brushless Excitation System, *Trans. AIEE*, paper 59-1113, 1959.

energy-transforming device, is given by

$$\text{Efficiency} = \frac{\text{output}}{\text{input}} \qquad (7\text{-}1)$$

which can also be expressed as

$$\text{Efficiency} = \frac{\text{input} - \text{losses}}{\text{input}} = 1 - \frac{\text{losses}}{\text{input}} \qquad (7\text{-}2)$$

$$\text{Efficiency} = \frac{\text{output}}{\text{output} + \text{losses}} \qquad (7\text{-}3)$$

Rotating machines in general operate efficiently except at light loads. The full-load efficiency of average motors, for example, is in the neighborhood of 74 per cent for 1-hp size, 89 per cent for 50-hp, 93 per cent for 500-hp, and 97 per cent for 5,000 hp. The efficiency of slow-speed motors is usually lower than that of high-speed motors, the total spread being 3 or 4 per cent.

The forms given by Eqs. 7-2 and 7-3 are often used for electric machines, for their efficiency is most commonly determined by measurement of losses instead of by directly measuring the input and output under load. Loss measurements have the advantage of convenience and economy and of yielding more accurate and precise values of efficiency because a given percentage error in measuring losses causes only about one-tenth of that percentage error in the efficiency. Efficiencies determined from loss measurements can be used in comparing competing machines provided that exactly the same methods of measurement and computation are used in each case. For this reason, the various losses and the conditions for their measurement are precisely defined by the American Standards Association (ASA). The following discussion of individual losses incorporates many of these provisions as given in American Standard C50, although no attempt is made to present all the details.

1. *Copper losses*, or I^2R losses, are, of course, found in all the windings of the machine. By convention, these losses are computed on the basis of the d-c resistances of the winding at 75°C. Actually the I^2R loss depends on the effective resistance of the winding under the operating frequency and flux conditions. The increment in loss represented by the difference between d-c and effective resistances is included with stray load losses, discussed below. In the field circuits of synchronous and d-c machines, only the losses in the field winding are charged against the machine; the I^2R loss in the rheostat controlling the field current and all losses in external sources supplying the excitation are charged against the plant of which the machine is a part. Closely associated with I^2R loss is the *brush-contact loss* at slip rings and commutators. By convention, this loss is normally neglected for induction and synchronous machines, and for industrial-type d-c machines the voltage drop at the brushes is

regarded as constant at 2 volts total when carbon and graphite brushes with shunts (pigtails) are used.

2. *Mechanical losses* consist of brush and bearing friction, windage, and the power required to circulate the air through the machine and ventilating system, if one is provided, whether by self-contained or external fans (except for the power required to force air through long or restricted ducts external to the machine). Friction and windage losses may be measured by determining the input to the machine running at the proper speed but unloaded and unexcited. Frequently they are lumped with core loss and determined at the same time.

3. *Open-circuit*, or *no-load*, *core loss* consists of the hysteresis and eddy-current losses arising from changing flux densities in the iron of the machine with only the main exciting winding energized. In d-c and synchronous machines, these losses are confined largely to the armature iron, although the flux pulsations arising from slot openings will cause losses in the field iron as well, particularly in the pole shoes or surfaces of the field iron. In induction machines, the losses are confined largely to the stator iron. Open-circuit core loss may be found by measuring the input to the machine when it is operating unloaded at rated speed or frequency and under the appropriate flux or voltage conditions, and deducting the friction and windage loss and, if the machine is self-driven during the test, the no-load armature copper loss (no-load stator copper loss for an induction motor). Usually data are taken for a curve of core loss as a function of armature voltage in the neighborhood of rated voltage. The core loss under load is then considered to be the value at a voltage equal to rated voltage corrected for armature ohmic-resistance drop under load (a phasor correction for an a-c machine). For induction motors, however, this correction is dispensed with, and the core loss at rated voltage is used. For efficiency determination alone, there is no need to segregate open-circuit core loss and friction and windage loss; the sum of these two losses is termed the *no-load rotational loss*.

Eddy-current loss is dependent on the squares of the flux density, frequency, and thickness of laminations. Under normal machine conditions, it may be expressed to a sufficiently close approximation as

$$P_e = K_e(B_{max}f\tau)^2 \tag{7-4}$$

where τ is the lamination thickness, B_{max} the maximum flux density, f the frequency, and K_e a proportionality constant whose value depends on the units used, the volume of iron, and the resistivity of the iron. Variation of hysteresis loss can be expressed in equation form only on an empirical basis. The most commonly used relation is

$$P_h = K_h f B_{max}^n \tag{7-5}$$

where K_h is a proportionality constant dependent on the characteristics and volume of iron and the units used and the exponent n ranges from 1.5 to 2.5 with a value of 2.0 often used for estimating purposes in machines. In both Eqs. 7-4 and 7-5, frequency may be replaced by speed and flux density by the appropriate voltage when the proportionality constants are changed accordingly. Such replacements are implied when the core-loss tests are made at rated speed and the appropriate voltage.

When the machine is loaded, the space distribution of flux density is significantly changed by the mmf of the load currents. The actual core losses increase noticeably. For example, mmf harmonics cause appreciable losses in the iron near the air-gap surfaces. The total increment in core loss is classified as part of the stray load loss.

4. *Stray load loss* consists of the losses arising from nonuniform current distribution in the copper and the additional core losses produced in the iron by distortion of the magnetic flux by the load current. It is a difficult loss to determine accurately. By convention it is taken as 1.0 per cent of the output for d-c machines. For synchronous machines it may be found from a short-circuit test as described in Chap. 9. For induction motors use may be made of a d-c excitation test which will not be described in this text.[1]

Study of the foregoing classification of the losses in a machine shows it to have a few features which, from a fundamental viewpoint, are somewhat artificial. Illustrations are offered by the division of iron losses into no-load core loss and an increment which appears under load, the division of copper losses into ohmic I^2R losses and an increment created by nonuniform current distribution, and the lumping of these two increments in the scavenger-like stray-load-loss category. These features are dictated by ease of testing. They are justified by the fact that the principal motivation is the determination of the total losses and efficiency suitable for economic comparison of machines and at the same time as nearly equal to the actual values as possible. Because of this seeming dominance of efficiency aspects, it may be appropriate to emphasize once more that losses play more than a bookkeeping type of part in machine operation.

In a generator, for example, components of mechanical input torque to the shaft are obviously required to supply copper and iron losses as well as friction and windage losses and the generator output. These losses may therefore be appreciable factors in the damping of electrical

---

[1] For complete descriptions of all accepted methods of measuring machine losses, the latest editions of the following AIEE Standards should be consulted:
Test Code for Polyphase Induction Machines, No. 500
Test Code for Direct-current Machines, No. 501
Test Code for Polyphase Synchronous Machines, No. 503

and mechanical transients in the machine. Components of the stray load loss, although they may be individually only a fraction of a per cent of the output, may be of first importance in the design of the machine. Thus rotor heating is usually a limiting factor in the design of large high-speed alternators, and the components of stray loss on the surface of the rotor structure are of great importance because they directly affect the dimensions of an alternator of given output. Of more direct concern in theoretical aspects is the influence of hysteresis and eddy currents in causing flux to lag behind mmf. There is a small angle of lag between the rotating mmf waves in a machine and the corresponding component flux-density waves. Associated with this influence is a torque on magnetic material in a rotating field, a torque proportional to the hysteresis and eddy-current losses in the material. Although the torque accompanying these losses is relatively small in normal machines, direct use of it is made in one type of small motor, the hysteresis motor.

7-5. Rating and Heating. One of the most common and important questions in the application of machines, transformers, and other electrical equipment is: What maximum output may be obtained? The answer, of course, depends on various factors, for the machine, while providing this output, must in general meet definite performance standards. A universal requirement is that the life of the machine shall not be unduly shortened by overheating. The temperature rise resulting from the losses considered in the previous article is therefore a major factor in the rating of a machine.

The operating temperature of a machine is closely associated with its life expectancy because deterioration of the insulation is a function of both time and temperature. Such deterioration is a chemical phenomenon involving slow oxidation and brittle hardening and leading to loss of mechanical durability and dielectric strength. In many cases the deterioration rate is such that the life of the insulation is an exponential[1]

$$\text{Life} = A\epsilon^{B/T} \tag{7-6}$$

where A and B are constants and T is the absolute temperature. Thus, according to Eq. 7-6, when life is plotted to a logarithmic scale against the reciprocal of absolute temperature on a uniform scale, a straight line should result. Such plots form valuable guides in the thermal evaluation of insulating materials and systems. A very rough idea of the life-temperature relation can be obtained from the old and more or less obsolete rule of thumb that the time to failure of organic insulation is halved for each 8 to 10°C rise.

---

[1] See Thomas W. Dakin, Electrical Insulation Deterioration Treated as a Chemical Rate Phenomenon, *Trans. AIEE*, vol. 67, pp. 113–122, 1948.

The evaluation of insulating materials and complete systems of insulation (which may include widely different materials and techniques in combination) is to a large extent a functional one based on accelerated life tests. Both normal life expectancy and service conditions will vary widely for different classes of electrical equipment. Life expectancy, for example, may be a matter of minutes in some military and missile applications, may be 500 to 1,000 hr in certain aircraft and electronic equipment, and ranges from 10 to 30 years or more in large industrial equipment. The test procedures will accordingly vary with the type of equipment.[1] Accelerated life tests on models, called *motorettes*, are commonly used in insulation evaluation. Such tests, however, cannot be easily applied to all equipment, especially the insulation systems of large machines.

Life tests generally attempt to simulate service conditions. They usually include the following elements:[2]

1. Thermal shock resulting from heating to the test temperature
2. Sustained heating at that temperature
3. Thermal shock resulting from cooling to room temperature or below
4. Vibration and mechanical stress such as may be encountered in actual service
5. Exposure to moisture
6. Dielectric testing to determine the condition of the insulation

A sufficiently large number of samples must be tested so that statistical methods may be applied in analyzing the results. The life-temperature relations obtained from these tests lead to the classification of the insulation or insulating system in the appropriate temperature class.

The three classes of insulation of chief interest for industrial machines, together with the corresponding values of recommended hottest-spot temperature, are the following:[3]

Class A.............. 105°C
Class B.............. 130°C
Class H.............. 180°C

[1] Typical procedures for rotating machines and transformers may be examined in such publications as Test Procedure for Evaluation of Systems of Insulating Materials for Random-wound Electric Machinery, *AIEE Standard* 510, November, 1956; Test Procedure for Evaluation of Systems of Insulating Materials for Electric Machinery Employing Form-wound Pre-insulated Coils, *AIEE Publ.* 511, October, 1956; Test Procedure for Thermal Evaluation of Ventilated Dry-type Power and Distribution Transformers, *AIEE Publ.* 65, November, 1956. This is a rapidly developing field, and care should be used to refer to the latest standard publications of the AIEE.

[2] See L. J. Berberich and T. W. Dakin, Guiding Principles in the Thermal Evaluation of Electrical Insulation, *Trans. AIEE*, vol. 75, pt. III, pp. 752–61, August, 1956.

[3] From General Principles upon Which Temperature Limits are Based in the Rating of Electric Equipment, *AIEE Standard* 1, June, 1957.

Since the limiting ambient temperature is normally taken as 40°C, these values correspond to temperature rises of 65, 90, and 140°C at the hottest point in the machine. Insulating materials commonly found in Class A include cotton, silk, and paper when impregnated or immersed in a dielectric liquid such as oil. Class B insulation often is made up of mica, glass fiber, asbestos, and similar materials with suitable bonding substances. Class H insulation may consist of materials such as silicone elastomer and combinations including mica, glass fiber, asbestos, etc., with bonding substances such as appropriate silicone resins. Experience and tests showing the material or system to be capable of operation at the recommended temperature form the important classifying criteria.

When the temperature class of the insulation is established, the permissible observable temperature rises for the various parts of industrial-type machines may be found by consulting the appropriate Standards.[1] Reasonably detailed distinctions are made with respect to type of machine, method of temperature measurement, machine part involved, whether the machine is enclosed or not, and the type of cooling (air-cooled, fan-cooled, hydrogen-cooled, etc.). Distinctions are also made between general-purpose machines and definite- or special-purpose machines. The term *general-purpose motor* refers to one of standard rating "up to 200 hp with standard operating characteristics and mechanical construction for use under usual service conditions without restriction to a particular application or type of application." In contrast, a *special-purpose motor* is "designed with either operating characteristics or mechanical construction, or both, for a particular application." For the same class of insulation, the permissible rise of temperature is lower for a general-purpose motor than for a special-purpose motor, largely to allow a greater factor of safety where service conditions are unknown. Partially compensating the lower rise, however, is the fact that general-purpose motors are allowed a service factor of 1.15 when operated at rated voltage; *service factor* is a multiplier which, applied to the rated output, indicates a permissible loading which may be carried continuously under the conditions specified for that service factor.

General-purpose motors are of open-type construction, usually with Class A insulation, and have an allowable temperature rise by thermometer of 40°C for insulated windings or parts adjacent to or in contact with the insulation. The comparable rise for special-purpose motors

---

[1] See, for example, the latest editions of the following American Standards: C50.1, Synchronous Generators, Synchronous Motors, and Synchronous Machines in General; C50.2, Alternating-current Induction Motors, Induction Machines in General, and Universal Motors; C50.4, Direct-current Generators, Direct-current Motors, and Direct-current Commutating Machines in General. All are published by the American Standards Association, New York.

with Class A insulation is commonly 50 or 55°C. An additional rise of 20°C by thermometer is permitted with Class B insulation. The addition for Class H over Class A is 60°C by thermometer in most cases. The principal applications of Class H insulation are in apparatus where size and weight are at a premium and can be reduced through increased operating temperature without undue sacrifice in performance features, where operation at high ambient temperatures must be tolerated, as in certain powerhouse auxiliary drive motors, and in other special-purpose machines.

The most common machine rating is the *continuous rating* defining the output (in kilowatts for d-c generators, kilovolt-amperes at a specified power factor for a-c generators, and horsepower for motors) which can be carried indefinitely without exceeding established limitations. For intermittent, periodic, or varying duty a machine may be given a *short-time rating* defining the load which can be carried for a specified time. Standard periods for short-time ratings are 5, 15, 30, and 60 min. Speeds, voltages, and frequencies are also specified in machine ratings, and provision is made for possible variations in voltage and frequency. Motors, for example, must operate successfully at voltages 10 per cent above and below rated voltage and, for a-c motors, at frequencies 5 per cent above and below rated frequency; the combined variation of voltage and frequency may not exceed 10 per cent. Other performance conditions are so established that reasonable short-time overloads may be carried. Thus, the user of a motor may expect to be able to apply for a short time an overload of, say, 25 per cent at 90 per cent of normal voltage with an ample margin of safety.

The converse problem to the rating of machinery, that of choosing the size of machine for a particular application, is a relatively simple one when the load requirements remain substantially constant. For many motor applications, however, the load requirements vary more or less cyclically and over a wide range. The duty cycle of a typical crane or hoist motor may readily be visualized as an example. From the thermal viewpoint, the average heating of the motor must be found by detailed study of the motor losses during the various parts of the cycle. Account must be taken of changes in ventilation with motor speed for open and semienclosed motors. Judicious selection is based on a large number of experimental data and considerable experience with the motors involved. For estimating the required size of motors operating at substantially constant speeds, it is sometimes assumed that the heating of the insulation varies as the square of the horsepower load, an assumption which obviously overemphasizes the role of armature I^2R loss at the expense of the core loss. The rms ordinate of the horsepower-time curve representing the duty cycle is obtained by the same technique used to find the rms value of periodically varying currents, and a motor rating is chosen on the basis of the result; i.e.,

$$\text{rms hp} = \sqrt{\frac{\Sigma\ (\text{hp})^2 \times (\text{time})}{\text{running time} + (\text{standstill time}/k)}} \qquad (7\text{-}7)$$

where the constant k accounts for the poorer ventilation at standstill and equals approximately 4 for an open motor. The time for a complete cycle must be short compared with the time for the motor to reach a steady temperature.

Although crude, the rms-horsepower method is used fairly often. The necessity for rounding off the result to a commercially available motor size obviates the need for precise computations; if the rms horsepower were 87, for example, a 100-hp motor would be chosen. Special consideration must be given to motors that are frequently started or reversed, for such operations are thermally equivalent to heavy overloads. Consideration must also be given to duty cycles having such high torque peaks that motors with continuous ratings chosen on purely thermal bases would be unable to furnish the torques required. It is to such duty cycles that special-purpose motors with short-time ratings are often applied. Short-time-rated motors in general have better torque-producing ability than motors rated to produce the same power output continuously, although, of course, they have a lower thermal capacity. Both these properties follow from the fact that a short-time-rated motor is designed for high flux densities in the iron and high current densities in the copper. In general, the ratio of torque capacity to thermal capacity increases as the period of the short-time rating decreases. Higher temperature rises are allowed than for general-purpose motors. A motor with a 150-hp 1-hr 50°C rating, for example, may have the torque ability of a 200-hp continuously rated motor; it will be able to carry only about 0.8 of its rated output, or 120 hp, continuously, however. In many cases it will be the economical solution for a drive requiring a continuous thermal capacity of 120 hp but having torque peaks which require the ability of a 200-hp continuously rated motor.

7-6. Cooling Means for Electric Machines. The cooling problem in electric apparatus in general increases in difficulty with increasing size. The surface area from which the heat must be carried away increases roughly as the square of the dimensions, whereas the heat developed by the losses is roughly proportional to the volume and therefore increases approximately as the cube of the dimensions. This problem is a particularly serious one in large turbine-generators, where economy, mechanical requirements, shipping, and erection all demand compactness, especially for the rotor forging. It is also important in large power transformers. Even in moderate sizes of machines (e.g., above a few thousand kva for generators), a closed ventilating system is commonly used. Rather elaborate systems of cooling ducts must be provided to ensure that the cooling medium effectively removes the heat arising from the losses.

For turbine-generators, hydrogen is commonly used as the cooling medium in the totally enclosed ventilating system. Hydrogen has the following properties which make it well suited to the purpose:

1. Its density is only about 0.07 that of air at the same temperature and pressure, and therefore windage and ventilating losses are much less.

2. Its specific heat on an equal-weight basis is about 14.5 times that of air. This means that, for the same temperature and pressure, hydrogen and air are about equally effective in their heat-storing capacity per unit volume. But the heat transfer by forced convection between the hot parts of the machine and the cooling gas is considerably greater with hydrogen than with air.

3. The life of the insulation is increased, and maintenance expenses are decreased, because of the absence of dirt, moisture, and oxygen.

4. The fire hazard is minimized. A hydrogen-air mixture will not explode if the hydrogen content is above about 70 per cent.

The result of the first two properties is that for the same operating conditions the heat which must be dissipated is reduced and at the same time the ease with which it can be carried off is improved.

The machine and its water-cooled heat exchanger for cooling the hydrogen must be sealed in a gastight envelope. The crux of the problem is in sealing the bearings. The system is maintained at a slight pressure (at least 0.5 psi) above atmospheric so that gas leakage is outward and an explosive mixture cannot accumulate within the machine. At this pressure, the rating of the machine can be increased by about 30 per cent above its air-cooled rating and the full-load efficiency increased by about 0.5 per cent. The trend is toward the use of higher pressures (15 to 30 psi). Increasing the hydrogen pressure from 0.5 to 15 psi increases the output for the same temperature rise by about 15 per cent; a further increase to 30 psi provides about an additional 10 per cent.

An important step which has made it possible almost to double the output of a hydrogen-cooled turbine-generator of given physical size is the development of *conductor cooling*, also called *inner cooling*. Here the coolant (liquid or gas) is forced through hollows or ducts inside the conductor or conductor strands. Thus, the thermal barrier presented by the electrical insulation is largely circumvented, and the conductor losses may be absorbed directly by the coolant. Hydrogen is the cooling medium for the rotor conductors. Either gas or liquid cooling may be used for the stator conductors. Hydrogen is the coolant in the former case, and transil oil or water is commonly used in the latter. A sectional view of a conductor-cooled turbine-generator is given in Fig. 7-8.

Oil and air have long been the principal cooling agents for transformers. The windings and core of the majority of the larger transformers are oil-immersed for cooling and insulation. The entire unit may be cooled by any of the following means or by a combination of them depending on the rating or loading of the transformer: *self-cooling*, with or without radiators attached to the tank; *forced-air cooling* by means of fans on the radiators; *forced-oil cooling* with an oil-circulating pump and oil-to-air

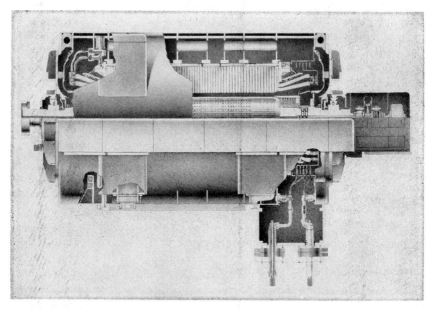

FIG. 7-8. Sectional view of a 3,600-rpm conductor-cooled synchronous generator with a liquid-cooled stator and gas-cooled rotor. (*Courtesy of General Electric Company.*)

heat exchanger; *water cooling*, involving an oil-to-water heat exchanger. A view of a 3-phase power transformer cooled by means of forced oil and air is presented in Fig. 7-9.

Among the newer developments in power transformers are *gas-insulated* transformers and *vapor-cooled* units. These developments are generally similar in nature and objectives. Sulfur hexafluoride is used in place of oil in the gas-insulated transformer, and a mixture of fluorocarbon vapor and sulfur hexafluoride gas is used in the vapor-cooled units. The gas and the vapor-gas mixture are nonflammable and nontoxic. The primary advantage of both types is safety, and most of the installations are expected to be in congested areas and in indoor or underground substations.

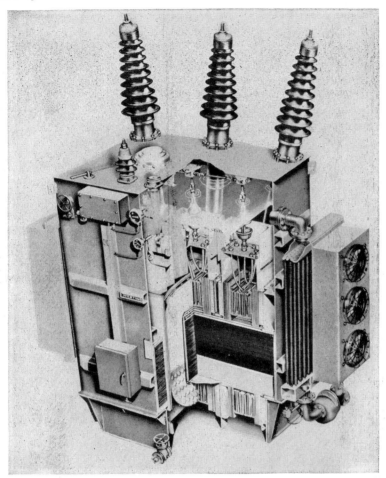

FIG. 7-9. Cutaway view of 3-phase power transformer showing radiators and fans for cooling. (*Courtesy of Westinghouse Electric Corporation.*)

7-7. Ideal and Realistic Transformers. The introductory transformer discussion of Art. 1-4 views the analysis of iron-core transformers as an example of the treatment of closely coupled circuits. As we have seen, the theory of these closely coupled circuits is a basic part of machinery theory. Amplification of this theory and its application to engineering analysis of realistic transformers may therefore be expected to illustrate some of the corresponding thought processes for rotating machines. Such amplification and application are undertaken in the remaining articles of this chapter.

a. Exciting and Magnetizing Currents. Comparison of ideal and realistic transformers reduces essentially to an examination of the idealizing assumptions listed at the beginning of Art. 1-4a. The effects of finite core permeability, as well as of saturation, hysteresis, and eddy currents, will be considered here. The influence of these factors and of winding resistance and leakage flux on the equivalent circuit will be taken up in the second part of the article.

Consider the transformer of Fig. 7-10 with its secondary open and a sinusoidal voltage v_1 applied to the primary. The no-load resistance drop is very small, and the induced emf e_1 very nearly equals the applied

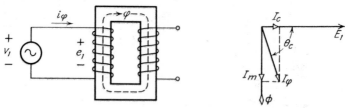

FIG. 7-10. Transformer with open secondary.

voltage v_1. Furthermore the waveforms of voltage and flux are very nearly sinusoidal. If the instantaneous flux is

$$\varphi = \phi_{\max} \sin \omega t \tag{7-8}$$

the induced voltage is

$$e_1 = N_1 \frac{d\varphi}{dt} = \omega N_1 \phi_{\max} \cos \omega t \tag{7-9}$$

where $\phi_{\max}$ is the maximum value of the flux and $\omega = 2\pi f$, the frequency being f cps. For the positive directions shown in Fig. 7-10, the induced emf leads the flux by 90°. The rms value of the induced emf is

$$E_1 = \frac{2\pi}{\sqrt{2}} f N_1 \phi_{\max} = 4.44 f N_1 \phi_{\max} \tag{7-10}$$

With negligible resistance drop, the counter emf equals the applied voltage. Under these conditions, if a sinusoidal voltage is applied to a winding, a sinusoidally varying core flux must be established whose maximum value $\phi_{\max}$ satisfies the requirement that E_1 in Eq. 7-10 equals the rms value V_1 of the applied voltage; thus

$$\phi_{\max} = \frac{V_1}{4.44 f N_1} \tag{7-11}$$

The flux is determined solely by the applied voltage, its frequency, and the number of turns in the winding. The magnetic properties of the core determine the exciting current. It must adjust itself so as to produce the mmf required to create the flux demanded by Eq. 7-11.

Because of the nonlinear magnetic properties of iron, the waveform of the exciting current differs from the waveform of the flux. A curve

of the exciting current as a function of time can be found graphically
from the magnetic characteristics of the core material in the manner
illustrated in Fig. 7-11.   Sine waves of voltage e_1 and flux φ in accordance
with Eqs. 7-8 to 7-11 are shown in Fig. 7-11a.   The corresponding
flux-mmf loop for the core is shown in Fig. 7-11b.   Values of the mmf
corresponding to various values of the flux can be found from this hysteresis loop.   For example, at time t' the instantaneous flux is φ' and
the flux is increasing; the corresponding value of the mmf is $\mathfrak{F}'$ read from
the increasing flux portion of the hysteresis loop.   The corresponding
value i_φ' of the exciting current is plotted at time t' in Fig. 7-11a.   At
time t'' the flux also has the instantaneous value φ', but it is decreasing,
and the corresponding values of mmf and current are $\mathfrak{F}''$ and i_φ''.   In

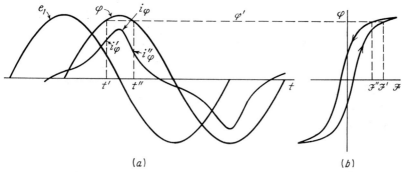

(a)   (b)

FIG. 7-11. Excitation phenomena.   (a) Voltage, flux, and exciting-current waveforms and (b) corresponding flux-mmf loop.

this manner the complete curve of exciting current i_φ can be plotted, as
shown in Fig. 7-11a.

The exciting current contains a fundamental and a family of odd
harmonics.   The fundamental can be resolved into two components,
one in phase with the counter emf and the other lagging the counter emf
by 90°.   The fundamental inphase component accounts for the power
absorbed by hysteresis and eddy-current losses in the core.   It is called
the *core-loss component* of the exciting current.   When the core-loss
component is subtracted from the total exciting current, the remainder
is called the *magnetizing current*.   It comprises a fundamental component lagging the counter emf by 90°, together with all the harmonics.
The principal harmonic is the third.   For typical power transformers,
the third harmonic usually is about 40 per cent of the exciting current.

Except in problems concerned directly with the effects of harmonics,
the peculiarities of the exciting-current waveform usually need not be
taken into account, because the exciting current itself is small.   For
example, the exciting current of a typical power transformer is about

5 per cent of full-load current. Consequently the effects of the harmonics usually are swamped out by the sinusoidal-current requirements of other linear elements in the circuit. The exciting current may then be represented by its *equivalent sine wave*, which has the same effective value and frequency and produces the same average power as the actual wave. Such representation is essential to the construction of a phasor diagram.

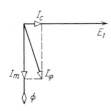

In Fig. 7-12, the phasors E_1 and ϕ, respectively, represent the induced emf and the flux. The phasor I_φ represents the equivalent sinusoidal exciting current. The component I_c in phase with E_1 represents the core-loss current. The component I_m in phase with the flux represents an equivalent sine wave having the same rms value as the magnetizing current.

FIG. 7-12. No-load phasor diagram.

Note that the magnetizing current contributes nothing to the active power because its fundamental component is in quadrature with the induced voltage.

b. Equivalent Circuit. When the transformer is loaded, it may be necessary to include not only the effects of exciting current and core loss but also the winding resistances and leakage fluxes. These elements are included by assigning resistances r_1 and r_2 and leakage reactances x_{l1} and x_{l2} to the windings. In the steady state, the impressed voltage V_1 is

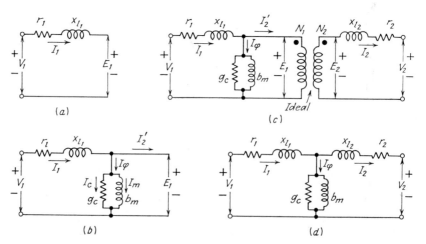

FIG. 7-13. Steps in development of the transformer equivalent circuit.

then opposed by three phasor voltages: the I_1r_1 drop in the primary resistance, the I_1x_{l1} drop arising from primary leakage flux, and the counter emf E_1 induced in the primary by the resultant mutual flux. All these voltages are appropriately included in the equivalent circuit of Fig. 7-13a.

The resultant mutual flux links both the primary and secondary windings and is created by their combined mmfs. It is convenient to treat these mmfs by considering that the primary current must meet two requirements of the magnetic circuit: it must not only (1) counteract the demagnetizing effect of the secondary current but also (2) produce sufficient mmf to create the resultant mutual flux. According to this physical picture, it is convenient to resolve the primary current into two components, a load component and an exciting component. The *load component* I_2' is defined as the component current in the primary which would exactly counteract the mmf of the secondary current I_2. Thus for opposing currents,

$$I_2' = \frac{N_2}{N_1} I_2 \tag{7-12}$$

It equals the secondary current referred to the primary as in an ideal transformer. The *exciting component* i_φ is defined as the additional primary current required to produce the resultant mutual flux.

The exciting current can be treated as an equivalent sinusoidal current I_φ and can be resolved into a core-loss component I_c in phase with the counter emf E_1 and a magnetizing component I_m lagging E_1 by 90°. In the equivalent circuit (Fig. 7-13b) the equivalent sinusoidal exciting current is accounted for by means of a shunt branch connected across E_1, comprising a noninductive resistance whose conductance is g_c in parallel with a lossless inductance whose susceptance is b_m. Alternatively a series combination of resistance and reactance can be connected across E_1. In the parallel combination (Fig. 7-13b) the power $E_1^2 g_c$ accounts for the core loss due to the resultant mutual flux. When g_c is assumed constant, the core loss is thereby assumed to vary as E_1^2 or (for sine waves) as $\phi_{max}^2 f^2$, where ϕ_{max} is the maximum value of the resultant mutual flux. The magnetizing susceptance b_m varies with the saturation of the iron. Both g_c and b_m are usually determined at rated voltage and frequency; they are then assumed to remain constant for the small departures from rated values associated with normal operation.

The resultant mutual flux φ induces an emf E_2 in the secondary, and since this flux links both windings, the induced-voltage ratio is

$$\frac{E_1}{E_2} = \frac{N_1}{N_2} \tag{7-13}$$

just as in an ideal transformer. This voltage transformation and the current transformation of Eq. 7-12 can be accounted for by introducing an ideal transformer in the equivalent circuit, as in Fig. 7-13c. The emf E_2 is not the secondary terminal voltage, however, because of the secondary resistance and because the secondary current I_2 creates *second-*

ary leakage flux. The secondary terminal voltage V_2 differs from the induced voltage E_2 by the voltage drops due to secondary resistance r_2 and *secondary leakage reactance* x_{l2}, as in the portion of the equivalent circuit (Fig. 7-13c) to the right of E_2.

The actual transformer therefore is equivalent to an ideal transformer plus external impedances. By referring all quantities to the primary or secondary, the ideal transformer in Fig. 7-13c may be moved out to the right or left, respectively, of the equivalent circuit. This is almost invariably done, and the equivalent circuit is usually drawn as in Fig. 7-13d with the ideal transformer not shown and all voltages, currents, and impedances referred to the same side. In order to avoid a complicated notation, the same symbols have been used for the *referred* values in Fig. 7-13d as were used for the *actual* values in Fig. 7-13c. In what follows we shall almost always deal with the referred values. One simply keeps in mind the side of the transformer to which all quantities have been referred. The circuit of Fig. 7-13d is often called the T *circuit* for a transformer. It may be compared with the circuits of Figs. 1-13 and 1-14 in Art. 1-4.

Example 7-1. A 50-kva 2,400:240-volt 60-cps distribution transformer has a leakage impedance of $0.72 + j0.92$ ohm in the high-voltage winding and $0.0070 + j0.0090$ ohm in the low-voltage winding. At rated voltage and frequency the admittance Y_φ of the shunt branch accounting for the exciting current is $(0.324 - j2.24) \times 10^{-2}$ mho when viewed from the low-voltage side.

Draw the equivalent circuit (*a*) referred to the high-voltage side and (*b*) referred to the low-voltage side, and label the impedances numerically.

Solution. The circuits are given in Fig. 7-14a and b, respectively, with the high-voltage side numbered 1 and the low-voltage side numbered 2. The voltages given

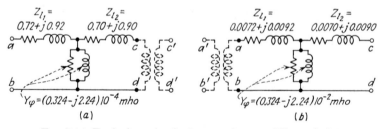

FIG. 7-14. Equivalent circuits for transformer of Example 7-1.

on the nameplate of a power-system transformer are based on the turns ratio and neglect the small leakage-impedance voltage drops under load. Since this is a 10 to 1 transformer, impedances are referred by multiplying or dividing by 100. The value of an impedance referred to the high-voltage side is greater than its value referred to the low-voltage side. Since admittance is the reciprocal of impedance, an admittance is referred from one side to the other by use of the reciprocal of the referring factor for impedance. The value of an admittance referred to the high-voltage side is smaller than its value referred to the low-voltage side.

The ideal transformer may be explicitly drawn, as shown dashed in Fig. 7-14, or it may be omitted in the diagram and remembered mentally, making the unprimed letters the terminals.

7-8. Engineering Aspects of Transformer Analysis. In engineering analyses involving the transformer as a circuit element, it is customary to adopt one of several approximate forms of the equivalent circuit of Fig. 7-13 rather than the full circuit. The approximations chosen in a particular case depend largely on physical reasoning based on orders of magnitude of the neglected quantities. The more common approximations are presented in this article. In addition, test methods are given for determining the transformer constants.

a. Approximate Equivalent Circuits—Power Transformers. The approximate equivalent circuits commonly used for constant-frequency

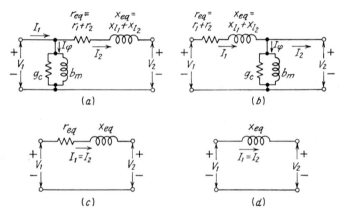

FIG. 7-15. Approximate equivalent circuits.

power-transformer analyses are summarized for comparison in Fig. 7-15. All quantities in these circuits are referred to either the primary or the secondary, and the ideal transformer is not shown.

The computational labor involved often can be appreciably reduced by moving the shunt branch representing the exciting current out from the middle of the T circuit to either the primary or the secondary terminals, as in Fig. 7-15a and b. These are *cantilever circuits*. The series branch is the combined resistance and leakage reactance referred to the same side. This impedance is sometimes called the *equivalent impedance* and its components the *equivalent resistance* r_{eq} and *equivalent reactance* x_{eq}, as shown in Fig. 7-15a and b. Error is introduced by neglect of the voltage drop in the primary or secondary leakage impedance caused by the exciting current, but this error is insignificant in most problems involving power-system transformers.

Further simplification results from neglecting the exciting current entirely, as in Fig. 7-15c, in which the transformer is represented as an equivalent series impedance. If the transformer is large (several hundred kva or over), the equivalent resistance r_{eq} is small compared with the equivalent reactance x_{eq} and may frequently be neglected, giving Fig. 7-15d. The circuits of Fig. 7-15c and d are sufficiently accurate for most ordinary power-system problems. Finally, in situations where the currents and voltages are determined almost wholly by the circuits external to the transformer or when a high degree of accuracy is not required, the entire transformer impedance may be neglected and the transformer may be considered to be ideal as in Art. 1-4a.

The circuits of Fig. 7-15 have the additional advantage that the total equivalent resistance r_{eq} and equivalent reactance x_{eq} can be found from a very simple test, whereas measurement of the values of the component leakage reactances x_{l1} and x_{l2} is a difficult experimental task.

Example 7-2. The 50-kva 2,400:240-volt transformer whose constants are given in Example 7-1 is used to step down the voltage at the load end of a feeder whose impedance is $0.30 + j1.60$ ohms. The voltage V_s at the sending end of the feeder is 2,400 volts.

Find the voltage at the secondary terminals of the transformer when the load connected to its secondary draws rated current from the transformer and the power factor of the load is 0.80 lagging. Neglect the voltage drops in the transformer and feeder caused by the exciting current.

Solution. The circuit with all quantities referred to the high-voltage (primary) side of the transformer is shown in Fig. 7-16a, wherein the transformer is represented

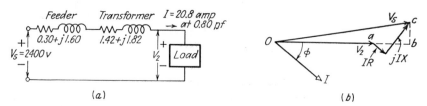

(a)   (b)

FIG. 7-16. Equivalent circuit and phasor diagram, Example 7-2.

by its equivalent impedance, as in Fig. 7-15c. From Fig. 7-14a, the value of the equivalent impedance is $Z_{eq} = 1.42 + j1.82$ ohms, and the combined impedance of the feeder and transformer in series is $Z = 1.72 + j3.42$ ohms. From the transformer rating, the load current referred to the high-voltage side is $I = 50,000/2,400 = 20.8$ amp.

The phasor diagram referred to the high-voltage side is shown in Fig. 7-16b, from which

$$Ob = \sqrt{V_s^2 - (bc)^2}$$

and

$$V_2 = Ob - ab$$

Note that

$$bc = IX \cos \phi - IR \sin \phi$$
$$ab = IR \cos \phi + IX \sin \phi$$

where R and X are the combined resistance and reactance, respectively. Thus

$$bc = (20.8)(3.42)(0.80) - (20.8)(1.72)(0.60) = 35.5 \text{ volts}$$
$$ab = (20.8)(1.72)(0.80) + (20.8)(3.42)(0.60) = 71.4 \text{ volts}$$

Substitution of numerical values shows that Ob very nearly equals V_s, or 2,400 volts. Then $V_2 = 2,329$ volts referred to the high-voltage side. The actual voltage at the secondary terminals is 2,329/10, or

$$V_2 = 233 \text{ volts}$$

b. Approximate Equivalent Circuits—Variable-frequency Transformers. Small iron-core transformers operating in the audio-frequency range (hence called *audio-frequency transformers*) are often used as coupling devices in electronic circuits for communications, measurements, and control. Their principal functions are either to step up voltage, thereby contributing to the over-all voltage gain in amplifiers, or to act as imped-ance-transforming devices bringing about the optimum relation between the apparent impedance of a load and the impedance of a source. They may also serve other auxiliary functions, such as providing a path for direct current through the primary while keeping it out of the secondary circuit.

Application of transformers for impedance matching makes direct use of the impedance-transforming property shown in Eq. 1-37. Oscillators and amplifiers, for example, give optimum performance when working into a definite order of magnitude of load impedance, and transformer coupling may be used to change the apparent impedance of the actual load to this optimum. A transformer so used is called an *output transformer*.

When the frequency varies over a wide range, it is important that the output voltage be as closely as possible instantaneously proportional to the input voltage. Ideally this means that voltages should be ampli-fied equally and phase shift should be zero for all frequencies. The *amplitude-frequency characteristic* (often abbreviated to *frequency char-acteristic*) is a curve of the ratio of the load voltage on the secondary side to the internal source voltage on the primary side plotted as a function of frequency, a flat characteristic being the most desirable. The *phase characteristic* is a curve of the phase angle of the load voltage relative to the source voltage plotted as a function of frequency, a small phase angle being desirable. These characteristics are dependent not only on the transformer but also on the constants of the entire primary and secondary circuits.

As an example of these characteristics, consider an amplifier coupled to its load through an output transformer. The amplifier is considered as equivalent to a source of voltage E_G in series with an internal resist-ance r_G, and the load is considered as a resistance r_L, as shown in Fig. 7-17a, wherein the transformer is represented by the equivalent circuit of Fig. 7-13c, with core loss neglected.   Sometimes the stray capacitances of the windings must be taken into account at high audio frequencies, especially when the source impedance is higher than a few thousand ohms.

The analysis of a properly designed circuit breaks down into three frequency ranges:

1. At intermediate frequencies (around 500 cps) none of the inductances is important, and the equivalent circuit reduces to a network of resistances, as shown in Fig. 7-17b, wherein all quantities have been referred to the primary, as indicated by the prime superscripts.   Analysis

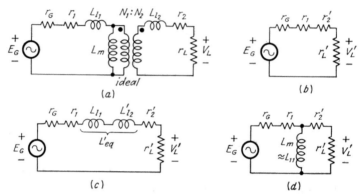

Fig. 7-17. Equivalent circuits of an output transformer.   (a) Complete equivalent circuit.   (b) Approximate equivalent in the middle range of audio frequencies.   (c) High-frequency equivalent.   (d) Low-frequency equivalent.

of this circuit shows that the ratio of load voltage V_L to source voltage E_G is

$$\frac{V_L}{E_G} = \frac{N_2}{N_1} \frac{r'_L}{R'_{se}} \tag{7-14}$$

where

$$R'_{se} = r_G + r_1 + r'_2 + r'_L \tag{7-15}$$

In this middle range (which usually extends over several octaves) the voltage ratio is very nearly constant; i.e., the amplitude characteristic is flat, and the phase shift is zero.

2. As the frequency is increased, however, the leakage reactances of the transformer become increasingly important.   The equivalent circuit in the high audio range is shown in Fig. 7-17c.   Analysis of this circuit shows that at high frequencies

$$\frac{V_L}{E_G} = \frac{N_2}{N_1} \frac{r'_L}{R'_{se}} \frac{1}{\sqrt{1 + (\omega L'_{eq}/R'_{se})^2}} \tag{7-16}$$

where L'_{eq} is the equivalent leakage inductance.   The voltage ratio relative to its midrange value is

$$\text{Relative voltage ratio} = \frac{1}{\sqrt{1 + (\omega L'_{eq}/R'_{se})^2}} \qquad (7\text{-}17)$$

The phase angle by which the load voltage lags the source voltage is

$$\phi = \tan^{-1} \frac{\omega L'_{eq}}{R'_{se}} \qquad (7\text{-}18)$$

Curves of the relative voltage ratio and phase angle as functions of the reactance-to-resistance ratio $\omega L'_{eq}/R'_{se}$ are shown in the right-hand half of Fig. 7-18.

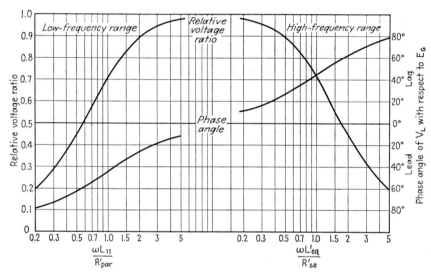

FIG. 7-18. Normalized frequency characteristics of output transformers.

3. At low frequencies, the leakage reactances are negligible, but the shunting effect of the magnetizing branch becomes increasingly important as its reactance decreases. The inductance of the magnetizing branch very nearly equals the self-inductance L_{11} of the primary. The equivalent circuit at low frequencies is shown in Fig. 7-17d, from which

$$\frac{V_L}{E_G} = \frac{N_2}{N_1} \frac{r'_L}{R'_{se}} \frac{1}{\sqrt{1 + (R'_{par}/\omega L_{11})^2}} \qquad (7\text{-}19)$$

where

$$R'_{par} = \frac{(r_G + r_1)(r'_2 + r'_L)}{r_G + r_1 + r'_2 + r'_L} \qquad (7\text{-}20)$$

The voltage ratio relative to its midrange value is

$$\text{Relative voltage ratio} = \frac{1}{\sqrt{1 + (R'_{par}/\omega L_{11})^2}} \qquad (7\text{-}21)$$

and the phase angle by which the load voltage leads the source voltage is

$$\phi = \tan^{-1} \frac{R'_{par}}{\omega L_{11}} \tag{7-22}$$

Curves of the relative voltage ratio and phase angle as functions of the reactance-to-resistance ratio $\omega L_{11}/R'_{par}$ are shown in the left-hand half of Fig. 7-18.

The points at which the relative voltage ratio is 0.707 are called the *half-power points*. From Eq. 7-17, the upper half-power point occurs at a frequency f_h for which the equivalent leakage reactance $\omega_h L'_{eq}$ equals the series resistance R'_{se}, or

$$f_h = \frac{R'_{se}}{2\pi L'_{eq}} \tag{7-23}$$

and from Eq. 7-21 the lower half-power point occurs at a frequency f_l for which the self-reactance ωL_{11} equals the parallel resistance R'_{par}, or

$$f_l = \frac{R'_{par}}{2\pi L_{11}} \tag{7-24}$$

The bandwidth is describable in terms of the ratio

$$\frac{f_h}{f_l} = \frac{R'_{se}}{R'_{par}} \frac{L_{11}}{L'_{eq}} \tag{7-25}$$

A broad bandwidth requires a high ratio of self-inductance to leakage inductance, or a coefficient of coupling as close as possible to unity.

c. Short-circuit and Open-circuit Tests. Two very simple tests serve to determine the constants of the equivalent circuits of Fig. 7-15 and the power losses in a transformer. These consist in measuring the input voltage, current, and power to the primary, first with the secondary short-circuited, and then with the secondary open-circuited.

With the secondary short-circuited, a primary voltage of only 2 to 12 per cent of the rated value need be impressed to obtain full-load current. For convenience, the high-voltage side is usually taken as the primary in this test. If V_{sc}, I_{sc}, and P_{sc} are the impressed voltage, primary current, and power input, the short-circuit impedance Z_{sc} and its resistance and reactance components R_{sc} and X_{sc} referred to the primary are

$$Z_{sc} = \frac{V_{sc}}{I_{sc}} \tag{7-26}$$

$$R_{sc} = \frac{P_{sc}}{I_{sc}^2} \tag{7-27}$$

$$X_{sc} = \sqrt{Z_{sc}^2 - R_{sc}^2} \tag{7-28}$$

The equivalent circuit with the secondary terminals short-circuited is shown in Fig. 7-19. The voltage induced in the secondary by the resultant core flux equals the secondary leakage-impedance voltage drop, and at rated current this voltage is only about 1 to 6 per cent of rated voltage. At the correspondingly low value of core flux, the exciting current and core losses are entirely negligible. The exciting admittance, shown dashed in Fig. 7-19, then can be omitted, and the primary and secondary currents are very nearly equal when referred to the same side. The power input very nearly equals the total copper loss in the primary and secondary windings, and the impressed voltage equals the drop in the combined primary and secondary leakage impedance Z_{eq}. The equivalent resistance and reactance referred to the primary very nearly equal the short-circuit resistance and reactance of Eqs. 7-27 and 7-28, respectively. The equivalent impedance can, of course, be referred from one side to the other in the usual manner.

On the rare occasions when the equivalent T circuit of Fig. 7-13d must be resorted to, approximate values of the individual primary and secondary resistances and leakage reactances can be obtained by assuming that $r_1 = r_2 = 0.5r_{eq}$ and $x_{l1} = x_{l2} = 0.5x_{eq}$ when all impedances are referred to the same side.

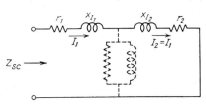

Fig. 7-19. Equivalent circuit with short-circuited secondary.

With the secondary open-circuited and rated voltage impressed on the primary, an exciting current of only 2 to 6 per cent of full-load current is obtained. If the transformer is to be used at other than its rated voltage, the test should be taken at that voltage. For convenience, the low-voltage side is usually taken as the primary in this test. The voltage drop in the primary leakage impedance caused by the small exciting current is entirely negligible, and the primary impressed voltage V_1 very nearly equals the emf E_1 induced by the resultant core flux. Also the primary copper loss caused by the exciting current is entirely negligible so that the power input P_1 very nearly equals the core loss P_c. Thus the exciting admittance $Y_\varphi = g_c - jb_m$ in Fig. 7-13d very nearly equals the open-circuit admittance $Y_{oc} = g_{oc} - jb_{oc}$ determined from the impressed voltage V_1, exciting current I_φ, and power input P_1 measured in the primary with the secondary open-circuited; thus the exciting admittance and its conductance and susceptance components are very nearly

$$Y_\varphi = Y_{oc} = \frac{I_\varphi}{V_1} \qquad (7\text{-}29)$$

$$g_c = g_{oc} = \frac{P_1}{V_1^2} \qquad (7\text{-}30)$$

$$b_m = b_{oc} = \sqrt{Y_{oc}^2 - g_{oc}^2} \qquad (7\text{-}31)$$

The values so obtained are, of course, referred to the side which was used as the primary in this test. When the approximate equivalent circuits of

Fig. 7-15c and d are used, the open-circuit test is used only to obtain core loss for efficiency computations and to check the magnitude of the exciting current. Sometimes the voltage at the terminals of the open-circuited secondary is measured as a check on the turns ratio.

Example 7-3. With the instruments located in the high-voltage side and the low-voltage side short-circuited, the short-circuit test readings for the 50-kva 2,400:240-volt transformer of Example 7-1 are 48 volts, 20.8 amp, and 617 watts. An open-circuit test with the low-voltage side energized gives instrument readings on that side of 240 volts, 5.41 amp, and 186 watts.

Determine the efficiency and the voltage regulation at full load, 0.80 power factor lagging.

Solution. From the short-circuit test, the equivalent impedance, resistance, and reactance of the transformer (referred to the high-voltage side as denoted by the subscript H) are

$$Z_{eqH} = \frac{48}{20.8} = 2.31 \text{ ohms}$$

$$r_{eqH} = \frac{617}{(20.8)^2} = 1.42 \text{ ohms}$$

$$x_{eqH} = \sqrt{(2.31)^2 - (1.42)^2} = 1.82 \text{ ohms}$$

Full-load high-tension current is

$$I_H = \frac{50,000}{2,400} = 20.8 \text{ amp}$$

Copper loss $= I_H^2 r_{eqH} = (20.8)^2(1.42) =$ 617 watts
Core loss $=$ 186

Total losses at full load $=$ 803
Output $= (50,000)(0.80)$ $= 40,000$
Input $= 40,803$ watts

$$\frac{\text{Losses}}{\text{Input}} = \frac{803}{40,803} = 0.0197$$

By Eq. 7-2

$$\text{Efficiency} = 1 - 0.0197 = 0.980$$

The *voltage regulation* of a transformer is the change in secondary terminal voltage from no load to full load and is usually expressed as a percentage of the full-load value. The equivalent circuit of Fig. 7-15c will be used with everything still referred to the high-voltage side. The primary voltage is assumed to be adjusted so that the secondary terminal voltage has its rated value at full load, or $V_{2H} = 2,400$ volts referred to the high-voltage side. The required value of the

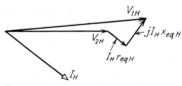

FIG. 7-20. Phasor diagram, Example 7-3.

primary voltage V_{1H} can be computed from the phasor diagram shown in Fig. 7-20.

$$V_{1H} = V_{2H} + I_H(r_{eqH} + jx_{eqH})$$
$$= 2,400 + (20.8)(0.80 - j0.60)(1.42 + j1.82)$$
$$= 2,446 + j13$$

The magnitude of V_{1H} is 2,446 volts. If this voltage were held constant and the load removed, the secondary voltage on open circuit would rise to 2,446 volts referred to the high-voltage side. Then,

$$\text{Regulation} = \frac{2,446 - 2,400}{2,400} (100) = 1.92\%$$

7-9. Transformers in Three-phase Circuits. Three single-phase transformers may be connected to form a 3-phase bank in any of the four ways shown in Fig. 7-21. In all four parts of this figure, the windings at the left are the primaries, those at the right are the secondaries, and any primary winding is mated in one transformer with the secondary winding drawn parallel to it. Also shown are the voltages and currents resulting from balanced impressed primary line-to-line voltages V and line currents

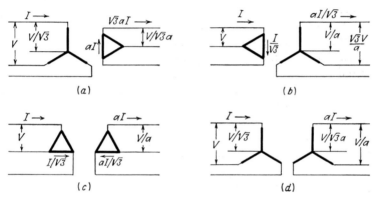

FIG. 7-21. Common 3-phase transformer connections. The transformer windings are indicated by the heavy lines.

I when the ratio of primary to secondary turns N_1/N_2 is a and ideal transformers are assumed. It will be noted that, for fixed line-to-line voltages and total kva, the kva rating of each transformer is one-third of the kva rating of the bank, regardless of the connections used, but that the voltage and current ratings of the individual transformers depend on the connections.

The Y-Δ connection is commonly used in stepping down from a high voltage to a medium or low voltage. One of the reasons is that a neutral is thereby provided for grounding on the high-voltage side, a procedure which may be shown to be desirable in most cases. Conversely, the Δ-Y connection is commonly used for stepping up to a high voltage. The Δ-Δ connection has the advantage that one transformer may be removed for repair or maintenance while the remaining two continue to function as a 3-phase bank with, however, the rating reduced to 58 per cent of that of the original bank; this is known as the *open-delta*, or V, *connection*.

The Y-Y connection is seldom used, because of difficulties with exciting-current phenomena.

Instead of three single-phase transformers, a 3-phase bank may consist of one 3-phase transformer having all 6 windings on a common core and contained within a common tank. Advantages of 3-phase transformers are that they cost less, weigh less, require less floor space, and have somewhat higher efficiency.

Circuit computations involving 3-phase transformer banks under balanced conditions can be made by dealing with only one of the transformers or phases and recognizing that conditions are the same in the other two transformers except for the phase displacements associated with a 3-phase system. It is usually convenient to carry out the computations on a per-phase-Y line-to-neutral basis, since transformer impedances can then be added directly in series with transmission-line impedances. The impedances of transmission lines can be referred from one side of the transformer bank to the other by use of the square of the ideal line-to-line voltage ratio of the bank. In dealing with Y-Δ or Δ-Y banks, all quantities can be referred to the Y-connected side. In dealing with Δ-Δ banks in series with transmission lines, it is convenient to replace the Δ-connected impedances of the transformers by equivalent Y-connected impedances. It is well known that a balanced Δ-connected circuit of Z_Δ ohms per phase is equivalent to a balanced Y-connected circuit of Z_Y ohms per phase if

$$Z_Y = \frac{1}{3}Z_\Delta \tag{7-32}$$

Example 7-4. Three single-phase 50-kva 2,400:240-volt transformers identical with that of Example 7-3 are connected Y-Δ in a 3-phase 150-kva bank to step down the voltage at the load end of a feeder whose impedance is $0.15 + j1.00$ ohm per phase. The voltage at the sending end of the feeder is 4,160 volts, line to line. On their secondary sides the transformers supply a balanced 3-phase load through a feeder whose impedance is $0.0005 + j0.0020$ ohm per phase.

Find the line-to-line voltage at the load when the load draws rated current from the transformers at a power factor of 0.80 lagging.

Solution. The computations can be made on a per-phase-Y basis by referring everything to the high-voltage Y-connected side of the transformer bank. The voltage at the sending end of the feeder is equivalent to a source voltage V_s of

$$V_s = \frac{4,160}{\sqrt{3}} = 2,400 \text{ volts to neutral}$$

From the transformer rating, the rated current on the high-voltage side is 20.8 amp per phase Y. The low-voltage feeder impedance referred to the high-voltage side by means of the square of the ideal line-to-line voltage ratio of the bank is

$$\left(\frac{4,160}{240}\right)^2 (0.0005 + j0.0020) = 0.15 + j0.60 \text{ ohm}$$

and the combined series impedance of the high-voltage and low-voltage feeders referred to the high-voltage side is

$$Z_{\text{feeder}} = 0.30 + j1.60 \text{ ohms per phase Y}$$

From Example 7-3, the equivalent impedance of the transformer bank referred to its high-voltage Y-connected side is

$$Z_{eqH} = 1.42 + j1.82 \text{ ohms per phase Y}$$

The equivalent circuit for 1 phase referred to the Y-connected primary side then is exactly the same as Fig. 7-16a, and the solution on a per-phase basis is exactly the same as the solution of Example 7-2, whence the load voltage referred to the high-voltage side is 2,329 volts to neutral. The actual load voltage is

$$V_{\text{load}} = 233 \text{ volts, line to line}$$

This is the line-to-line voltage because the secondaries are Δ-connected.

7-10. Autotransformers. Multicircuit Transformers.

The principles discussed in the foregoing three articles have been developed with specific reference to 2-winding transformers. They are also generally applicable to transformers with other than 2 separate windings. Aspects relating to autotransformers and multiwinding transformers are considered in this article.

a. Autotransformers. Viewed from the terminals, substantially the same transformation effect on voltages, currents, and impedances can be obtained with the connections of Fig. 7-22a as in the normal transformer with 2 separate windings shown in Fig. 7-22b. In Fig. 7-22a, the winding

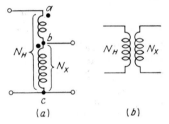

FIG. 7-22. (a) Autotransformer compared with (b) 2-winding transformer.

bc is common to both the primary and secondary circuits. This type of transformer is called an *autotransformer*. It is really nothing but a normal transformer connected in a special way. The only difference structurally is that winding ab must be provided with extra insulation. The performance of an autotransformer is governed by the same fundamental considerations already discussed for transformers having 2 separate windings. Autotransformers have lower leakage reactances, lower losses, and smaller exciting current and cost less than 2-winding transformers when the voltage ratio does not differ too greatly from 1 to 1. A disadvantage is the direct copper connection between the high- and low-voltage sides.

Example 7-5. The 2,400:240-volt 50-kva transformer of Examples 7-3 and 7-4 is connected as an autotransformer as shown in Fig. 7-23, in which ab is the 240-volt winding and bc is the 2,400-volt winding. (It is assumed that the 240-volt winding has sufficient insulation so that it can withstand a voltage of 2,640 volts to ground.)

a. Compute the voltage ratings V_H and V_X of the high-tension and low-tension sides, respectively, when the transformer is connected as an autotransformer.

b. Compute the kva rating as an autotransformer.

c. Data with respect to the losses are given in Example 7-3. Compute the full-load efficiency as an autotransformer at 0.80 power factor.

Solution. *a.* Since the 2,400-volt winding *bc* is connected to the low-tension circuit, $V_X = 2,400$ volts.

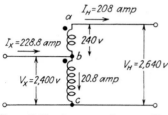

When $V_{bc} = 2,400$ volts, a voltage $V_{ab} = 240$ volts in phase with V_{bc} will be induced in winding *ab* (leakage-impedance voltage drops being neglected). The voltage of the high-tension side therefore is

$$V_H = V_{ab} + V_{bc} = 2,640 \text{ volts}$$

Fig. 7-23. Autotransformer, Example 7-5.

b. From the rating of 50 kva as a normal 2-winding transformer, the rated current of the 240-volt winding is 50,000/240, or 208 amp. Since the 240-volt winding is in series with the high-tension circuit, the rated current of this winding is the rated current I_H on the high-tension side as an autotransformer. The kva rating as an autotransformer therefore is

$$\frac{V_H I_H}{1,000} = \frac{(2,640)(208)}{1,000} = 550 \text{ kva}$$

The rating can also be computed on the low-tension side in a manner which highlights the current-transforming properties. Thus, if the current in the 240-volt winding has its rated value of 208 amp, the current in the 2,400-volt winding must produce an equal and opposite mmf (exciting current being neglected) and therefore must be 20.8 amp in the arrow direction (Fig. 7-23). The current I_X on the low-tension side as an autotransformer therefore is

$$I_X = 208 + 20.8 = 228.8 \text{ amp}$$

and the kva rating is

$$\frac{V_X I_X}{1,000} = \frac{(2,400)(228.8)}{1,000} = 550 \text{ kva}$$

Note that this transformer, whose rating as a normal 2-winding transformer is 50 kva, is capable of handling 550 kva as an autotransformer. The higher rating as an autotransformer is a consequence of the fact that all of the 550 kva does not have to be transformed by electromagnetic induction. In fact, all that the transformer has to do is to boost a current of 208 amp through a potential rise of 240 volts, corresponding to a rating of 50 kva.

c. When connected as an autotransformer with the currents and voltages shown in Fig. 7-23, the losses are the same as in Example 7-3, namely, 803 watts. But the output as an autotransformer at 0.80 power factor is $(0.80)(550,000) = 440,000$ watts. The efficiency therefore is

$$1 - \frac{803}{440,803} = 0.9982$$

The efficiency is so high because the losses are those incident to transforming only 50 kva.

b. Multicircuit Transformers. Transformers having 3 or more windings, known as *multicircuit*, or *multiwinding, transformers*, are often used to interconnect three or more circuits which may have different voltages. For these purposes a multicircuit transformer costs less and is more efficient than an equivalent number of two-circuit transformers. A transformer having a primary and two secondaries is generally used to supply power to electronic units. One secondary supplies power at a few volts to heat the cathodes of the electron tubes, and the other supplies power at a few hundred volts to the plate circuits. The distribution transformers used to supply power for domestic purposes usually have two 120-volt secondaries connected in series. Lighting circuits are connected across each of the 120-volt windings, while electric ranges, domestic hot-water heaters, and other similar loads are supplied with 240-volt power from the series-connected secondaries. A large distribution system may be supplied through a 3-phase bank of multicircuit transformers from two or more transmission systems having different voltages. The 3-phase transformer banks used to interconnect two transmission systems of different voltages often have a third, or *tertiary*, set of windings to provide voltage for auxiliary power purposes in the substation or to supply a local distribution system. Static capacitors, or synchronous condensers, may be connected to the tertiary windings for purposes of power-factor correction or voltage regulation. Sometimes Δ-connected tertiary windings are put on 3-phase banks to provide a circuit for the third harmonics of the exciting current.

Some of the problems arising in the use of multicircuit transformers concern the effects of leakage impedances on voltage regulation, short-circuit currents, and division of load among circuits. These problems can be solved by an equivalent-circuit technique similar to that used in dealing with two-circuit transformers. The details and assumptions concerning the self-, mutual, and leakage inductances and reactances of such a multiply excited, closely coupled magnetic system have already been presented in Art. 1-4. We shall be concerned here only with the development of an equivalent circuit representing the transformer as viewed from its terminals.

The equivalent circuits of multiwinding transformers are more complicated than in the 2-winding case because they must take into account the leakage impedances associated with each pair of windings. For example, the leakage-impedance voltage drops in a three-circuit transformer can be represented by three impedances, but a four-circuit transformer requires six. In these equivalent circuits all quantities are referred to a common base, either by use of the appropriate turns ratios as referring factors or by expressing all quantities in per unit. The exciting current usually is neglected.

The following discussion will be confined to three-circuit transformers. A three-circuit transformer is shown schematically in Fig. 7-24a, in which

1-1' is the primary winding. Secondary and tertiary quantities are referred to the primary, and windings 2-2' and 3-3' indicate the equivalent secondary and tertiary on the basis of a 1-to-1-to-1 turns ratio. Terminals 1', 2', and 3' are of like polarity. These terminals can be considered to be connected together to a common terminal 0, as shown by the dashed lines. The three external circuits can then be considered to be connected between terminals 1, 2, and 3, respectively, and the common terminal 0. If the exciting current is neglected, the phasor sum of the currents I_1, I_2, and I_3 is zero. The current in the connection between terminal 0 and the junction of terminals 1', 2', 3' therefore is zero, and this connection can be omitted without disturbing the currents. The transformer then is equivalent to the arrangement shown in Fig. 7-24b, in which the box is a network with three terminals and contains

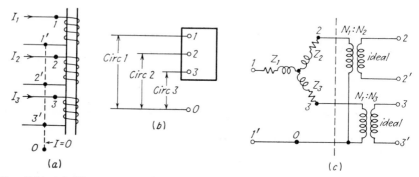

FIG. 7-24. (a) Elementary 3-winding transformer. (b and c) Steps in the development of its equivalent circuit.

impedances accounting for the leakage-impedance voltage drops. In so far as its effects on the external circuits are concerned, such a three-terminal network is equivalent to three impedances connected either in Δ or in Y. The Y arrangement usually is more convenient. The transformer therefore is equivalent to the circuit shown to the left of the dashed line in Fig. 7-24c, in which the impedances Z_1, Z_2, and Z_3 account for the effects of the leakage impedances among the three pairs of windings. If desired the factors referring all quantities to, say, the primary can be shown explicitly by means of ideal transformers as shown to the right of the dashed line in Fig. 7-24c. The terminals 2-2' and 3-3' to the right of these ideal transformers then are equivalent to the actual secondary and tertiary terminals. When the ideal transformers are included, the equivalent circuit does not require a conductive connection among the three circuits. Usually the ideal transformers can be omitted, however, and the external circuits can be considered to be connected between the common point 0 and terminals 1, 2, and 3, respectively, to the left of the dashed line. One then simply remembers that all quantities are referred to a common base.

This equivalent circuit represents the impedance phenomena associated with 3 windings on a common magnetic core. It applies equally well to the external behavior of autotransformers and of transformers having separate windings, although the internal phenomena differ.

The impedances of Fig. 7-24c can readily be determined from the results of three simple short-circuit tests. Thus if Z_{12} is the short-circuit impedance of circuits 1 and 2 with circuit 3 open, inspection of the equivalent circuit (Fig. 7-24c) shows that

$$Z_{12} = Z_1 + Z_2 \tag{7-33}$$

Similarly

$$Z_{13} = Z_1 + Z_3 \tag{7-34}$$

$$Z_{23} = Z_2 + Z_3 \tag{7-35}$$

where Z_{13} is the short-circuit impedance of circuits 1 and 3 with circuit 2 open and Z_{23} is the short-circuit impedance of circuits 2 and 3 with circuit 1 open. These short-circuit impedances are the values referred to a common base. Solution of Eqs. 7-33, 7-34, and 7-35 then gives

$$Z_1 = \tfrac{1}{2}(Z_{12} + Z_{13} - Z_{23}) \tag{7-36}$$

$$Z_2 = \tfrac{1}{2}(Z_{23} + Z_{12} - Z_{13}) \tag{7-37}$$

$$Z_3 = \tfrac{1}{2}(Z_{13} + Z_{23} - Z_{12}) \tag{7-38}$$

Example 7-6. The results of three short-circuit tests on a 7,960:2,400:600-volt 60-cps single-phase transformer are as follows:

Test	Winding excited	Winding short-circuited	Applied voltage, volts	Current in excited winding, amp
1	1	2	252	62.7
2	1	3	770	62.7
3	2	3	217	208

Resistances may be neglected. The rating of the 7,960-volt primary winding is 1,000 kva, of the 2,400-volt secondary is 500 kva, and of the 600-volt tertiary is 500 kva.

a. Compute the per-unit values of the equivalent-circuit impedances of this transformer on a 1,000-kva rated-voltage base.

b. Three of these transformers are used in a 3,000-kva Y-Δ-Δ 3-phase bank to supply 2,400-volt and 600-volt auxiliary power circuits in a generating station. The Y-connected primaries are connected to the 13,800-volt main bus. Compute the per-unit values of the steady-state short-circuit currents and of the voltage at the terminals of the secondary windings if a 3-phase short circuit occurs at the terminals of the tertiary windings with 13,800 volts maintained at the primary line terminals. Use a 3,000-kva 3-phase rated-voltage base.

Solution.   *a.* First convert the short-circuit data to per unit on 1,000 kva per phase.

For primary: $\qquad\qquad\qquad\qquad V_{\text{base}} = 7{,}960$ volts

$$I_{\text{base}} = \frac{1{,}000}{7.96} = 125.4 \text{ amp}$$

For secondary: $\qquad\qquad\qquad V_{\text{base}} = 2{,}400$ volts

$$I_{\text{base}} = \frac{1{,}000}{2.4} = 416 \text{ amp}$$

Conversion of the test data to per unit then gives

Test	Windings	V	I
1	1 and 2	0.0316	0.500
2	1 and 3	0.0967	0.500
3	2 and 3	0.0905	0.500

From test 1, the short-circuit impedance Z_{12} is

$$Z_{12} = \frac{0.0316}{0.500} = 0.0632 \text{ per unit}$$

Similarly, from tests 2 and 3,

$$Z_{13} = \frac{0.0967}{0.500} = 0.1934 \text{ per unit}$$

$$Z_{23} = \frac{0.0905}{0.500} = 0.1910 \text{ per unit}$$

From Eqs. 7-36, 7-37, and 7-38, the equivalent-circuit constants are

$$Z_1 = jX_1 = j0.0378 \text{ per unit}$$
$$Z_2 = jX_2 = j0.0254 \text{ per unit}$$
$$Z_3 = jX_3 = j0.1556 \text{ per unit}$$

b. Base line-to-line voltage for the Y-connected primaries is $\sqrt{3}\,(7{,}960) = 13{,}800$ volts, or the bus voltage is 1.00 per unit. From the equivalent circuit with a short circuit on the tertiaries,

$$I_{sc} = \frac{V_1}{Z_1 + Z_3} = \frac{V_1}{Z_{13}} = \frac{1.00}{0.1934} = 5.18 \text{ per unit}$$

(Note, however, that this current is 10.36 per unit on the rating of the tertiaries.) If the voltage drops caused by the secondary load current are neglected in comparison with those due to the short-circuit current, the secondary terminal voltage equals the voltage at the junction of the three impedances Z_1, Z_2, and Z_3 in Fig. 7-24c, whence

$$V_2 = I_{sc}Z_3 = (5.18)(0.1556) = 0.805 \text{ per unit}$$

7-11. Résumé.   The principal object of this chapter is to form a transition between Part II of the book, where the emphasis is primarily on mathematical analysis of idealized machines, and Part III, where engineering aspects of the realistic machine are introduced.   In making this transition it is recognized that the performance limitations of a machine are basically determined by the properties of the materials of which it is composed. Thus, much of the great progress in electric machinery over the years has stemmed from improvements in the quality and characteristics of steel and insulating material and in the cooling of the machines.

Magnetic saturation is one of the important considerations in reconciling the ideal and the realistic machine. It is handled on a magnetic-circuit basis rather than in terms of field theory. The field-theory approach, however, is frequently used on detailed aspects (flux mapping is an example) and to provide valuable guides and checking points in the development of the magnetic-circuit attack.[1]

Another group of interrelated problems common to all machine types is created by the losses in the machine and the necessity of dissipating the associated heat. The rating of the machine is closely connected with its ability to operate at temperatures compatible with reasonable life of the insulation and of the machine as a whole. Matters of rating, allowable temperature rise, and determination of losses are all subjects of standardization by professional organizations such as the AIEE, NEMA (National Electrical Manufacturers Association), and ASA. Such matters are obviously of great importance in the economics and engineering of a project involving machinery.

In the last half of the chapter, the introductory transformer discussion of Chap. 1 is supplemented by treatment of certain aspects arising in the application of transformers. The combination of the two discussions gives an over-all picture of transformer operation not unlike that to be sought for rotating machines in the remaining chapters. Although no electromechanical energy conversion is involved in a static transformer, its performance has many points of similarity with the electrical behavior of a-c rotating machines. The following discussion of these points will therefore constitute a brief preview of the approach in the last three chapters.

In both transformers and rotating machines, a magnetic field is created by the combined action of the currents in the windings. In an iron-core transformer most of this flux is confined to the core and links all the windings. This resultant mutual flux induces voltages in the windings proportional to their numbers of turns and provides the voltage-changing property. In rotating machines most of the flux crosses the air gap and, like the core flux in a transformer, links all the windings on both

---

[1] See, for instance, B. Hague, "Electromagnetic Problems in Electrical Engineering," Oxford University Press, New York, 1929, which is devoted almost entirely to the application of electromagnetic-field theory to rotating machines. Note that most of the analyses are based on infinitely permeable iron and uniform air gaps.

stator and rotor. The voltages induced in the windings by this resultant mutual air-gap flux are similar to those induced by the resultant core flux in a transformer. The difference is that mechanical motion together with electromechanical energy conversion is involved in rotating machines. The torque associated with this energy-conversion process is created by the interaction of the air-gap flux with the magnetic field of the rotor currents.

In addition to the useful mutual fluxes, in both transformers and rotating machines there are leakage fluxes which link one winding without linking the other. Although the detailed picture of the leakage fluxes in rotating machines is more complicated than in transformers, their effects are essentially the same. In both, the leakage fluxes induce voltages in a-c windings which are accounted for as leakage-reactance voltage drops. In both, the leakage-flux paths are mostly in air, and the leakage fluxes are nearly linearly proportional to the currents producing them. The leakage reactances therefore are often assumed to be constant, independent of the degree of saturation of the main magnetic circuit.

From the viewpoint of the winding, the induced-voltage phenomena in transformers and rotating machines are essentially the same, although the internal phenomena causing the time variations in flux linkages are different. In a rotating machine the time variation in flux linkages is caused by relative motion of the field and the winding, and the induced voltage is sometimes referred to as a speed voltage. Speed voltages accompanied by mechanical motion are a necessary counterpart of electromechanical energy conversion. In a static transformer, however, the time variation of flux linkages is caused by the growth and decay of a stationary magnetic field, no mechanical motion is involved, and no electromechanical energy conversion takes place.

The resultant core flux in a transformer induces a counter emf in the primary which, together with the primary resistance and leakage-reactance voltage drops, must balance the applied voltage. Since the resistance and leakage-reactance voltage drops usually are small, the counter emf must approximately equal the applied voltage and the core flux must adjust itself accordingly. Exactly similar phenomena must take place in the armature windings of an a-c motor—the resultant air-gap flux wave must adjust itself to generate a counter emf approximately equal to the applied voltage. In both transformers and rotating machines, the net mmf of all the currents must accordingly adjust itself to create the resultant flux required by this voltage balance. In any a-c electromagnetic device in which the resistance and leakage-reactance voltage drops are small, the resultant flux is very nearly determined by the applied voltage and frequency, and the currents must adjust themselves accordingly so as to produce the mmf required to create this flux.

In a transformer, the secondary current is determined by the voltage induced in the secondary, the secondary leakage impedance, and the electrical load. In an induction motor, the secondary (rotor) current is determined by the voltage induced in the secondary, the secondary leakage impedance, and the mechanical load on its shaft. Essentially the same phenomena take place in the primary winding of the transformer and in the armature (stator) windings of induction and synchronous motors. In all three, the primary, or armature, current must adjust itself so that the combined mmf of all the currents creates the flux required by the applied voltage.

Further examples of these basic similarities can be cited. Except for friction and windage, the losses in transformers and rotating machines are essentially the same. Tests for determining the losses and equivalent-circuit constants are essentially the same: an open-circuit, or no-load, test gives information regarding the excitation requirements and core losses (and friction and windage in rotating machines), while a short-circuit test together with d-c resistance measurements gives information regarding leakage reactances and copper losses. The handling of the effects of magnetic saturation is another example: in both transformers and a-c rotating machines, the leakage reactances are usually assumed to be unaffected by saturation, and the saturation of the main magnetic circuit is assumed to be determined by the resultant mutual or air-gap flux.

PROBLEMS

7-1. General-purpose 3-phase 60-cps induction motors are available in 2-, 4-, 6-, and 8-pole designs and in the following horsepower ratings: 2, 3, 5, 7.5, 10, 15, 20, etc. These motors develop rated output at a slip of about 5 per cent and develop a maximum torque of 200 per cent of rated torque at a slip of about 15 per cent.

Select the appropriate motor for an application requiring a torque of 50 lb-ft at a speed of about 1,500 rpm for a period of 30 sec, followed by 4 min running at no load, followed by repetitions of the same load cycle. Specify the horsepower and synchronous-speed ratings.

7-2. A d-c compound motor is to be selected for the operation of a lift. The motor is to drive continuously a steel cable which runs over pulleys at the bottom and the top of the lift. When the load is descending, the motor becomes a generator and pumps power back into the line, the resulting torque supplying a braking action.

The operating cycle is as follows and is repeated continuously throughout the day:

Load going up (1 min) = 75 hp
Loading period at top (2 min) = 5 hp
Load going down (1 min) = −60 hp
Loading period at bottom (3 min) = 5 hp

On the basis of heating, select the smallest motor suitable for this application. Motors are available in the following sizes: 25, 30, 40, 50, 60, 75, and 100 hp.

What other factors, besides heating, should be considered?

7-3. In the design of a grab-bucket hoist for unloading coal from a barge into a bunker, a study is made of the mechanical requirements to determine the motor duty cycle. The results are given in the following table for an average cycle:

Part of cycle	Elapsed time, sec	Required output, hp
Close bucket.............	6	40
Hoist...................	10	80
Open bucket.............	3	30
Lower bucket...........	10	45
Rest...................	16	0

Because of the conditions of service, a dustproof enclosed motor without forced ventilation is to be used, and the constant k associated with the standstill time may be taken as unity.

a. Using the rms method, specify the continuous horsepower rating of the motor. Choose a commercially available motor size.

b. Proposals to furnish this motor are submitted by two manufacturers. These proposals contain the following efficiency guarantees and prices:

Motor	Efficiencies, per cent					
	1/4 load	1/2 load	3/4 load	1.0 load	1 1/4 load	1 1/2 load
A	83.4	90.5	90.3	88.0	86.8	85.0
B	81.3	88.6	90.3	90.6	90.3	89.6

Motor A, net price \$2,500; motor B, net price \$3,000. (Both prices f.o.b. factory, freight allowed.)

The average net cost of energy at this plant is 1.5 cents per kilowatthour. Total fixed charges on invested capital are 25 per cent. The hoist will be in operation an average of 2,000 hr/year.

Which of these two motors would you recommend?

7-4. A 500-kva 60-cps transformer with an 11,000-volt primary winding takes 3.35 amp and 2,960 watts at no load, rated voltage and frequency. Another transformer has a core with all its linear dimensions $\sqrt{2}$ times as large as the corresponding dimensions of the first transformer. Core material and lamination thickness are the same in both transformers.

If the primary windings of both transformers have the same number of turns, what no-load current and power will the second transformer take with 22,000 volts at 60 cps impressed on its primary?

7-5. The flux density and core loss of a transformer operating on a voltage of 6,600 volts at 60 cps are, respectively, 70 kilolines/in.^{2} and 2,500 watts. Suppose that all the linear dimensions of the transformer core are doubled, the numbers of turns in the primary and secondary windings are halved, and the new transformer is operated on a voltage of 13,200 volts at 60 cps. The same grade of iron and the same thickness of laminations are used for both transformers.

What are the values of flux density and core loss for the new transformer?

7-6. The resistances and leakage reactances of a 10-kva 60-cps 2,400:240-volt distribution transformer are as follows:

$$r_1 = 4.20 \text{ ohms} \qquad r_2 = 0.0420 \text{ ohm}$$
$$x_{l1} = 5.50 \qquad x_{l2} = 0.0550$$

where subscript 1 denotes the 2,400-volt winding, and subscript 2 the 240-volt winding. Each quantity is referred to its own side of the transformer.

a. Find the equivalent impedance referred to the high-voltage side and referred to the low-voltage side.

b. Consider the transformer to deliver its rated kva at 0.80 power factor lagging to a load on the low-tension side with 240 volts across the load. Find the high-tension terminal voltage.

7-7. A single-phase load is supplied through a 33,000-volt feeder whose impedance is $105 + j360$ ohms and a 33,000:2,400-volt transformer whose equivalent impedance is $0.26 + j1.08$ ohms referred to its low-voltage side. The load is 180 kw at 0.85 leading power factor and 2,250 volts.

a. Compute the voltage at the sending end of the feeder.

b. Compute the voltage at the primary terminals of the transformer.

c. Compute the power and reactive-power input at the sending end of the feeder.

7-8. When a 50-kva 2,300:230-volt 60-cps transformer is operated at no load on rated voltage, the input is 200 watts at 0.15 power factor. When it is operating at rated load, the voltage drops in the total resistance and leakage reactance are, respectively, 1.2 and 1.8 per cent of rated voltage.

Determine the input power and power factor when the transformer delivers 30 kw at 0.80 power factor lagging and 230 volts to a load on the low-voltage side.

7-9. A source which may be represented by a constant voltage of 5 volts rms in series with an internal resistance of 2,000 ohms is connected to a 50-ohm load resistance through an ideal transformer. Plot the power in milliwatts supplied to the load as a function of the transformer ratio, covering ratios ranging from 0.1 to 10.0.

7-10. An audio-frequency output transformer has a primary-to-secondary turns ratio of 31.6. Its primary inductance measured with the secondary open is 19.6 henrys and measured with the secondary short-circuited is 0.207 henry. The winding resistances are negligible.

This transformer is used to connect an 8-ohm resistance load to a source which may be represented by a variable-frequency internal emf in series with an internal impedance of 5,000 ohms resistance. Compute the following that relate to the frequency characteristics of the circuit:

a. The upper half-power frequency
b. The lower half-power frequency
c. The geometric mean of these frequencies
d. The ratio of load voltage to source voltage at the frequency of (*c*)

7-11. An audio-frequency output transformer, having a turns ratio of 17.32, is to be used to match a source, having an internal resistance of 3,000 ohms, to a resistance load of 10 ohms. The upper and lower half-power frequencies are to be 50 and 10,000 cps. Neglect core loss and winding resistances. Specify:

a. The primary self-inductance
b. The equivalent leakage inductance referred to the primary

7-12. The following data were obtained for a 20-kva 60-cps 2,400:240-volt distribution transformer tested at 60 cps:

	Voltage, volts	Current, amp	Power, watts
With high-voltage winding open-circuited..........	240	1.066	126.6
With low-voltage terminals short-circuited........	57.5	8.34	284

a. Compute the efficiency at full-load current and rated terminal voltage at 0.8 power factor.

b. Assume that the load power factor is varied while the load current and secondary terminal voltage are held constant. By means of a phasor diagram, determine the load power factor for which the regulation is greatest. What is this regulation?

7-13. *a.* Show that the maximum efficiency of a transformer operating at a constant output voltage and power factor occurs at that kva load for which the copper losses equal the core losses. In doing so, recall that the core losses remain constant, while the copper losses vary as the square of the kva load.

b. For the transformer of Prob. 7-12, determine the kva output at maximum efficiency.

7-14. The high-voltage terminals of a 3-phase bank of three single-phase transformers are connected to a 3-wire 3-phase 13,800-volt (line to line) system. The low-voltage terminals are connected to a 3-wire 3-phase substation load rated at 1,500 kva and 2,300 volts line to line.

Specify the voltage, current, and kva ratings of each transformer (both high- and low-voltage windings) for the following connections:

a. High-voltage windings Y, low-voltage windings Δ
b. High-voltage windings Δ, low-voltage windings Y
c. High-voltage windings Y, low-voltage windings Y
d. High-voltage windings Δ, low-voltage windings Δ

7-15. Figure 7-25 shows a Δ-Δ bank of 2,400:240-volt transformers. The secondaries *ab*, *bc*, *ca* have center taps *p*, *q*, *r*. Neglect leakage-impedance voltage drops,

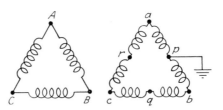

FIG. 7-25. Transformer bank, Prob. 7-15.

and assume rated primary impressed voltage. With secondary voltage V_{ab} as reference phasor, draw a phasor diagram showing voltages *ab*, *bc*, *ca*, *pq*, *qr*, *rp*, *ap*, *bp*, *cp*. Find the magnitudes of these voltages.

7-16. A Δ-Y-connected bank of three identical 100-kva 2,400:120-volt 60-cps transformers is supplied with power through a feeder whose impedance is $0.80 + j0.30$ ohm per phase. The voltage at the sending end of the feeder is held constant at 2,400 volts line to line. The results of a single-phase short-circuit test on one of the transformers with its low-voltage terminals short-circuited are

$$V_H = 52.0 \text{ volts} \qquad f = 60 \text{ cps}$$
$$I_H = 41.6 \text{ amp} \qquad P = 950 \text{ watts}$$

a. Determine the secondary line-to-line voltage when the bank delivers rated current to a balanced 3-phase 1.00-power-factor load.

b. Compute the currents in the transformer primary and secondary windings and in the feeder wires if a solid 3-phase short circuit occurs at the secondary line terminals.

7-17. A 480:120-volt 5-kva 2-winding transformer is to be used as an autotransformer to supply a 480-volt circuit from a 600-volt source. When tested as a 2-winding transformer at rated load, 0.80 power factor lagging, its efficiency is 0.965.

  a. Show a diagram of connections as an autotransformer.

  b. Determine its kva rating as an autotransformer.

  c. Find its efficiency as an autotransformer at full load, 0.80 power factor lagging.

7-18. Figure 7-26 shows a 3-winding autotransformer supplying two loads L_1 and L_2. Voltage drops and exciting current may be neglected. Find the currents in the 3 windings for the following load conditions:

  a. $L_1 = 360$ kva, $L_2 = 0$

  b. $L_1 = 0$, $L_2 = 120$ kva

  c. $L_1 = 360$ kva, $L_2 = 120$ kva at same power factor

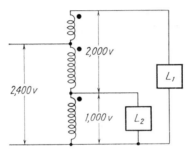

FIG. 7-26. Three-winding autotransformer, Prob. 7-18.

7-19. A 3-phase bank consisting of three single-phase 3-winding transformers is used to step down the voltage of a 3-phase 110-kv transmission line. The following data apply to one of the transformers:

Ratings:
  Primary 1: 10,000 kva, 63,500 volts
  Secondary 2: 5,000 kva, 11,000 volts
  Tertiary 3: 5,000 kva, 7,580 volts
Short-circuit reactances on 5,000-kva base:
  $X_{12} = 0.071$ per unit
  $X_{23} = 0.054$ per unit
  $X_{13} = 0.092$ per unit
Resistances are negligible.

The transformers are connected Y-Δ-Y. The Δ-connected secondaries supply their rated current to a balanced load at 0.80 power factor. The tertiaries supply their rated current to a balanced load at 1.00 power factor.

  a. Compute the primary line-to-line voltage to maintain rated voltage at the secondary terminals.

  b. For the conditions of part a, compute the line-to-line voltage at the tertiary terminals.

  c. If the primary voltage is held constant as in part a, to what value will the tertiary voltage rise if the secondary load is removed? Consider that the tertiary load behaves as a constant resistance.

CHAPTER 8

D-C Machines

In order to place the d-c machine on a fully realistic basis, we first reexamine the flux and mmf conditions in the machine. This reexamination, together with consideration of the switching action at the commutator, brings out conditions limiting the capability of the machine as well as means for combating the conditions. It also leads to methods for including saturation and armature-mmf effects in the analysis of the machine. The results of the analysis illustrate the versatility of the d-c machine by itself and in combination with other d-c machines.

8-1. Flux and MMF Waves in D-C Machines. Armature mmf has definite effects on both the space distribution of the air-gap flux and the magnitude of the net flux per pole. The effect on flux distribution is important because the limits of successful commutation are directly influenced; the effect on flux magnitude is important because both the generated voltage and torque per unit of armature current are influenced thereby. These effects and the problems arising from them are described in this article.

  a. Effect of Armature MMF. It is shown in Art. 3-2 and by Fig. 3-20 that the armature-mmf wave may be closely approximated by a triangle, corresponding to the wave produced by a finely distributed armature winding or current sheet. For a machine with brushes in the neutral position, the idealized mmf wave is again shown by the dotted triangle in Fig. 8-1, in which a positive mmf ordinate denotes flux lines leaving the armature surface. Current directions in all windings other than the main field are indicated by black and crosshatched bands. Because of the salient-pole field structure found in almost all d-c machines, the associated space distribution of flux will not be triangular. The distribution of air-gap flux density with only the armature excited is given by the solid curve of Fig. 8-1. As may readily be seen, it is appreciably decreased by the long air path in the interpolar space.

  The axis of the armature mmf is fixed at 90 electrical degrees from the main-field axis by the brush position. The corresponding flux follows the paths shown in Fig. 8-2.   The effect of the armature mmf is seen to be that of creating flux sweeping across the pole faces; thus its path in the pole shoes crosses the path of the main-field flux.   For this reason, armature reaction of this type is called *cross-magnetizing armature reaction.* It evidently causes a decrease in the resultant air-gap flux density under one half of the pole and an increase under the other half.

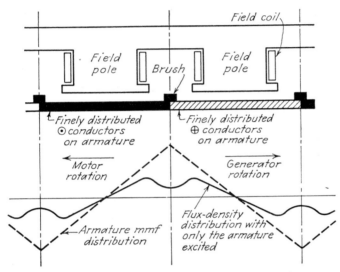

Fig. 8-1. Armature-mmf and flux-density distribution with brushes on neutral and only the armature excited.

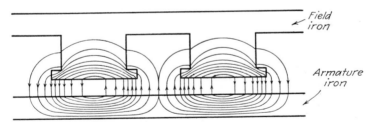

Fig. 8-2. Sketch showing flux with only the armature excited and brushes on neutral.

When the armature and field windings are both excited, the resultant air-gap flux-density distribution is of the form given by the solid curve of Fig. 8-3.   Superimposed on this figure are the flux distributions with only the armature excited (dashed curve) and only the field excited (dotted curve).   The effect of cross-magnetizing armature reaction in decreasing the flux under one pole tip and increasing it under the other may be seen by comparing the solid and dotted curves.   In general, the solid curve is not the algebraic sum of the dotted and dashed curves because of the nonlinearity of the iron magnetic circuit. Because of saturation of the iron, the flux density is decreased by a greater amount under one pole tip than it is increased under the other. Accordingly, the resultant flux per pole is lower than would be produced by the field winding alone, a consequence known as the *demagnetizing effect of cross-magnetizing armature reaction.* Since it is caused by saturation, its magnitude is a nonlinear function of both the field current and the armature current. For normal machine operation at the flux densities used commercially, the effect is

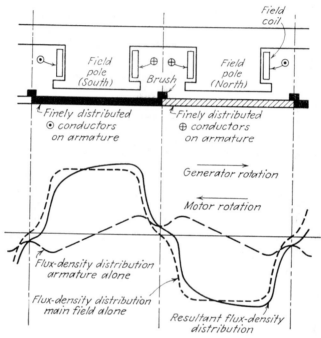

Fig. 8-3. Armature, main-field, and resultant flux-density distributions with brushes on neutral.

usually significant, especially at heavy loads, and must often be taken into account in analyses of performance.

The distortion of the flux distribution caused by cross-magnetizing armature reaction may be a detrimental influence on ability to commutate the current, especially if the distortion becomes excessive. In fact, this distortion is usually an important factor limiting the short-time overload of a d-c machine. Tendency toward distortion of flux distribution is most pronounced in a machine, such as a shunt motor, where the field excitation remains substantially constant while the armature mmf may reach very significant proportions at heavy loads. The tendency is least pronounced in a series-excited machine, such as the series motor, for both the field and armature mmfs increase with load.

The effect of cross-magnetizing armature reaction may be limited in the design and construction of the machine. The mmf of the main field should exert predominating control on the air-gap flux, so that the condition of weak-field mmf and strong armature mmf may be avoided. The reluctance of the cross-flux path—essentially, the armature teeth, pole shoes, and the air gap, especially at the pole tips—may be increased by increasing the degree of saturation in the teeth and pole faces, by avoiding too small an air gap, and by using a chamfered or eccentric pole face, which increases the air gap at the pole tips. These expedients affect the path of the main flux as well, but the influence on the cross flux is much greater. The best but also the most expensive curative measure is to compensate the armature mmf by means of a winding embedded in the pole faces, a measure which is discussed in part *c* of this article.

b. Commutation and Interpoles. One of the most important limiting factors on satisfactory operation of a d-c machine is the ability to transfer the necessary armature current through the brush contact at the commutator without sparking and without excessive local losses and heating of the brushes and commutator. Sparking causes destructive blackening, pitting, and wear of both commutator and brushes, conditions which rapidly become worse and lead to burning away of the copper and carbon. It may be caused by faulty mechanical conditions, such as chattering of the brushes or a rough, unevenly worn commutator, or, as in any switching problem, by electrical conditions. The latter conditions are seriously influenced by the armature mmf and the resultant flux wave.

As indicated in Art. 3-7, a coil undergoing commutation is in transition between two groups of armature coils: at the end of the commutation period, the coil current must be equal but opposite to that at the beginning. Figure 3-32b shows the armature in an intermediate position during which the coils formed by inductors are being commutated. The commutated coils are short-circuited by the brushes. During this period, the brushes must continue to conduct the armature current I_a from the armature winding to the external circuit. The short-circuited coil constitutes an inductive circuit with time-varying resistances at the brush contact, with, in general, rotational voltages induced in the coil, and with both conductive and inductive coupling to the rest of the armature winding.

The attainment of good commutation is more an empirical art than a quantitative science. The principal obstacle to quantitative analysis lies in the electrical behavior of the carbon-copper contact film. Its resistance is nonlinear and is a function of current density, current direction, temperature, brush material, moisture, and atmospheric pressure.

Its behavior in some respects is like that of an ionized gas. The most significant fact is that an unduly high current density in a portion of the brush surface (and hence an unduly high energy density in that part of the contact film) results in sparking and a breakdown of the film at that point. The boundary film also plays an important part in the mechanical behavior of the rubbing surfaces. At high altitudes, definite steps must be taken to preserve it, or extremely rapid brush wear takes place.

The empirical basis of securing sparkless commutation, then, is to avoid excessive current densities at any point in the copper-carbon contact. This basis, combined with the principle of utilizing all material to the fullest extent, indicates that optimum conditions are obtained when the current density is uniform over the brush surface during the entire commutation period. A linear change of current with time in the commutated coil, corresponding to linear commutation as shown in Fig. 3-33, brings about this condition and is accordingly the optimum.

The principal factors tending to produce linear commutation are changes in brush-contact resistance resulting from the linear decrease in area at the trailing brush edge and linear increase in area at the leading edge. Several electrical factors militate against linearity. Resistance in the commutated coil is one example. Usually, however, the voltage drop at the brush contacts is sufficiently large (of the order of 1.0 volt) in comparison with the resistance drop in a single armature coil so that the latter may be ignored. Coil inductance is a much more serious factor. Both the voltage of self-induction in the commutated coil and the voltage of mutual induction from other coils (particularly those in the same slot) undergoing commutation at the same time oppose changes in current in the commutated coil. The sum of these two voltages is often referred to as the *reactance voltage*. Its result is that current values in the short-circuited coil lag in time the values dictated by linear commutation. This condition is known as *undercommutation,* or *delayed commutation.*

Armature inductance thus tends to produce high losses and sparking at the trailing brush tip. For best commutation, inductance must be held to a minimum by using the fewest possible number of turns per armature coil and by using a multipolar design with a short armature. The effect of a given reactance voltage in delaying commutation is minimized when the resistive brush-contact voltage drop is significant compared with it. This fact is one of the main reasons for the use of carbon brushes with their appreciable contact drop. When good commutation is secured by virtue of resistance drops, the process is referred to as *resistance commutation.* It is used today as the exclusive means only in fractional-horsepower machines.

Another important factor in the commutation process is the rotational voltage induced in the short-circuited coil. Depending on its sign, this voltage may hinder or aid commutation. In Fig. 8-3, for example, cross-magnetizing armature reaction creates a definite flux in the interpolar region. The direction of the corresponding rotational voltage in the commutated coil is the same as the current under the immediately preceding pole face. This voltage then encourages the continuance of current in the old direction and, like the reactance voltage, opposes its reversal. To aid commutation, the rotational voltage must oppose the reactance voltage. The general principle of producing in the coil undergoing commutation a rotational voltage which approximately compensates for the reactance voltage, a principle called *voltage commutation*, is used in almost all modern commutating machines. The appropriate flux density is introduced in the commutating zone by means of small, narrow poles located between the main poles. These auxiliary poles are called *interpoles*, or *commutating poles*.

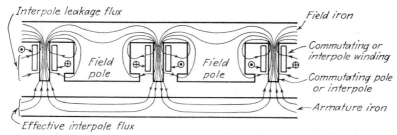

Fig. 8-4. Interpoles and their associated component flux.

The general appearance of interpoles and an approximate map of the flux produced when they alone are excited may be seen in Fig. 8-4. (The interpoles are the smaller poles between the larger main poles in Fig. 8-6.) The polarity of a commutating pole must be that of the main pole just ahead of it (i.e., in the direction of rotation) for a generator and just behind it for a motor. The interpole mmf must be sufficient to neutralize the cross-magnetizing armature mmf in the interpolar region and enough more to furnish the flux density required for the rotational voltage in the short-circuited armature coil to cancel the reactance voltage. Since both the armature mmf and the reactance voltage are proportional to the armature current, the commutating winding must be connected in series with the armature. To preserve the desired linearity, the commutating pole should operate at low saturations. By the use of commutating fields, then, sparkless commutation is secured over a wide range in modern machines. In accordance with the performance standards of the NEMA, general-purpose d-c machines must be capable of carrying with successful commutation for 1 min loads of 150 per cent of the current corresponding to the continuous rating with the field rheostat set for rated-load excitation.

c. Compensating Windings. For machines subjected to heavy overloads, rapidly changing loads, or operation with a weak main field, there is the possibility of trouble other than simply sparking at the brushes. At the instant when an armature coil is located at the peak of a badly distorted flux wave, the coil voltage may be high enough to break down the air between the adjacent segments to which the coil is connected and result in *flashover*, or arcing, between segments. The breakdown voltage here is not high, because the air near the commutator is in a condition favorable to breakdown. The maximum allowable voltage between segments is of the order of 30 to 40 volts, a fact which limits the average voltage between segments to lower values and thus determines the minimum number of segments which may be used in a proposed design. Under transient conditions, high voltages between segments may result from the induced voltages associated with growth and decay of armature

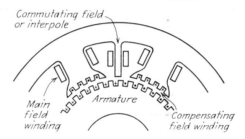

FIG. 8-5. Section of a d-c machine showing compensating field.

flux. Inspection of Fig. 8-2, for instance, may enable one to visualize very appreciable voltages of this nature being induced in a coil under the pole centers by the growth or decay of the armature flux shown in the sketch. Consideration of the sign of this induced voltage will show that it adds to the normal rotational emf when load is dropped from a generator or added to a motor. Flashing between segments may quickly spread around the entire commutator and, in addition to its possibly destructive effects on the commutator, constitutes a direct short circuit on the line. Even with interpoles present, therefore, armature reaction under the poles definitely limits the conditions under which a machine may operate.

These limitations may be considerably extended by compensating or neutralizing the armature mmf under the pole faces. Such compensation can be achieved by means of a *compensating*, or *pole-face*, *winding* (Fig. 8-5) embedded in slots in the pole face and having a polarity opposite to that of the adjoining armature winding. The physical appearance of such a winding may be seen in the stator of Fig. 8-6. Since the axis of the compensating winding is the same as that of the armature, it will

FIG. 8-6. Section of d-c motor stator or field showing shunt and series coils, interpoles, and pole-face, or compensating, winding. (*Courtesy of Westinghouse Electric Corporation.*)

almost completely neutralize the armature reaction of the armature inductors under the pole faces when it is given the proper number of turns. It must be connected in series with the armature in order that it may carry a proportional current. The net effect of the main field, armature, commutating winding, and compensating winding on the air-gap flux is that, except for the commutation zone, the resultant flux-density distribution is substantially the same as that produced by the main field alone (Fig. 8-3). Furthermore, the addition of a compensating winding improves the speed of response, because it reduces the armature-circuit time constant.

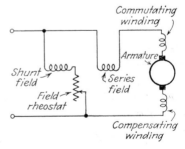

FIG. 8-7. Schematic connection diagram of d-c machine.

The main disadvantage of pole-face windings is their expense. They are used in machines designed for heavy overloads or rapidly changing loads—steel-mill motors are a good example of machines subjected to severe duty cycles—or in motors intended to operate over wide speed ranges by shunt-field control. By way of a schematic summary, Fig. 8-7 shows the circuit diagram of a compound machine with a compensating winding. The relative position of the coils in this diagram indicates that the commutating and compensating fields act along the armature axis and the shunt and series fields act along the axis of the main poles. Rather complete control of air-gap flux around the entire armature periphery is thus achieved.

8-2. Analytical Fundamentals: Electric-circuit Aspects. From Eqs. 3-68 and 3-72, the electromagnetic torque and generated voltage of a d-c machine are, respectively,

$$T = K_a \Phi_d I_a \tag{8-1}$$
$$E_a = K_a \Phi_d \omega_m \tag{8-2}$$

where
$$K_a = \frac{PZ_a}{2\pi a} \tag{8-3}$$

Here the capital-letter symbols E_a for generated voltage and I_a for armature current are used to emphasize that we are primarily concerned with

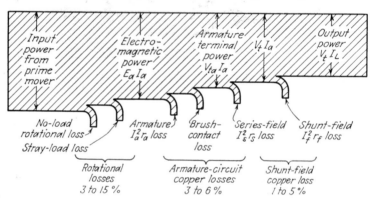

FIG. 8-8. Power division in a d-c generator.

steady-state considerations in this chapter. The remaining symbols are as defined in Art. 3-8. These are basic equations for analysis of the machine. The quantity $E_a I_a$ is frequently referred to as the *electromagnetic power;* from Eqs. 8-1 and 8-2, it is related to electromagnetic torque by the relation

$$T = \frac{E_a I_a}{\omega_m} \tag{8-4}$$

Figures 8-8 and 8-9 present in graphical form power balances for d-c generators and motors, respectively, with both shunt and series fields. The connection diagram is given in Fig. 8-10. When either the shunt or the series field is not present in the machine, the associated entry is omitted from Figs. 8-8 to 8-10. In these diagrams, V_t is the machine terminal voltage, V_{ta} the armature terminal voltage, I_L the line current, I_s the series-field current (equal to I_a for the connections shown in Fig. 8-10), I_f the shunt-field current, r_a the armature resistance, r_f the shunt-field resistance, and r_s the series-field resistance. Included in r_a is the resistance of any commutating and compensating winding. The armature-circuit copper losses, field-circuit copper losses, and rotational losses are those originally considered in Art. 7-4; typical full-load orders of

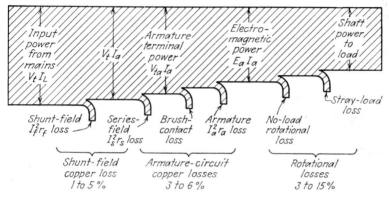

Fig. 8-9. Power division in a d-c motor.

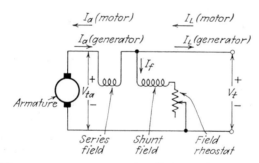

Fig. 8-10. Motor or generator connection diagram with current directions.

magnitude of these losses, expressed in per cent of the machine input, are quoted in Figs. 8-8 and 8-9 for general-purpose generators and motors in the 1- to 100-kw or 1- to 100-hp range, with the smaller percentages applying to the larger ratings.

The electromagnetic power differs from the mechanical power at the machine shaft by the rotational losses and differs from the electrical power at the machine terminals by the copper losses. The electromagnetic power is that measured at the points across which E_a exists; numerical addition of the rotational losses for generators and subtraction for motors yield the mechanical power at the shaft.

The interrelations between voltage and current are immediately evident from the connection diagram. Thus,

$$V_{ta} = E_a \pm I_a r_a \tag{8-5}$$
$$V_t = E_a \pm I_a(r_a + r_s) \tag{8-6}$$
and
$$I_L = I_a \pm I_f \tag{8-7}$$

where the plus sign is used for a motor and the minus sign for a generator. Some of the terms in Eqs. 8-5 to 8-7 may be omitted when the machine connections are simpler than those shown in Fig. 8-10. The resistance r_a is to be interpreted as that of the armature plus brushes unless specifically stated otherwise. Sometimes, r_a is taken as the resistance of the armature winding alone, and the brush-contact drop is accounted for as a separate item, usually assumed to be 2 volts.

For compound machines, another variation may occur. Figure 8-10 shows a so-called *long-shunt connection* in that the shunt field is connected

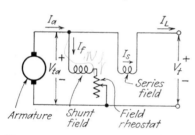

Armature   Shunt   Field
            field   rheostat

Fig. 8-11. Short-shunt compound generator.

directly across the line terminals with the series field between it and the armature. An alternative possibility is the *short-shunt connection*, illustrated in Fig. 8-11 for a compound generator, with the shunt field directly across the armature and the series field between it and the line terminals. The series-field current is then I_L instead of I_a, and the voltage equations are modified accordingly. There is so little practical difference between these two connections that the distinction may usually be ignored; unless otherwise stated, compound machines will be treated as though they were long-shunt-connected.

Although the difference between terminal voltage V_t and armature generated voltage E_a is comparatively small for normal operation, it has a definite bearing on performance characteristics. In effect, this difference, acting in conjunction with the circuit resistances and energy-conversion requirements, affects the value of armature current I_a and hence the rotor-field strength. Complete determination of machine behavior requires a similar investigation of factors influencing the stator-field strength or, more particularly, the net flux per pole Φ_d.

8-3. Analytical Fundamentals: Magnetic-circuit Aspects. The flux per pole is that resulting from the combined armature and field mmfs. The interdependence of armature generated voltage E_a and magnetic-circuit conditions in the machine is accordingly a function of the sum of all the mmfs on the polar- or direct-axis flux path. We shall first consider the mmf purposely placed on the stator main poles to create the working flux—i.e., the *main-field mmf*—and then include armature-mmf effects.

　a. No-load Magnetization Curve. With no load on the machine or with armature-reaction effects ignored, the resultant mmf is the algebraic sum of the mmfs on the main or direct-axis poles. For the usual compound generator or motor having N_f shunt-field turns per pole and N_s series-field turns per pole,

$$\text{Main-field mmf} = N_f I_f \pm N_s I_s \qquad (8\text{-}8)$$

Additional terms will appear in this equation when there are additional field windings on the main poles (and, unlike the compensating windings of Art. 8-1c, wound concentric with the normal field windings) to permit specialized control. In Eq. 8-8, the plus sign is used when the two mmfs are aiding, or when the two fields are cumulatively connected; the minus sign is used when the series field opposes the shunt field, or for a differential connection. When either the series or the shunt field is absent, the corresponding term in Eq. 8-8 naturally is omitted.

　Equation 8-8 thus sums up in ampere-turns per pole the gross mmf acting on the main magnetic circuit. The magnetization curve for a d-c machine is generally given in terms of current in only the principal field winding, which is almost invariably the shunt-field winding when one is present. The mmf units of such a magnetization curve and of Eq. 8-8 may be made the same by one of two rather obvious steps. The field current on the magnetization curve may be multiplied by the turns per pole in that winding, giving a curve in terms of ampere-turns per pole; or both sides of Eq. 8-8 may be divided by N_f, converting the units to the equivalent current in the N_f coil alone which produces the same mmf. Thus

$$\text{Main-field mmf} = I_f \pm \frac{N_s}{N_f} I_s \qquad \text{equivalent shunt-field amp} \qquad (8\text{-}9)$$

The latter procedure is often the more convenient and the one more commonly adopted.

　An example of a no-load magnetization characteristic is given by the curve for $I_a = 0$ in Fig. 8-12. The numerical scales on the left-hand and lower axes give representative values for a 100-kw 250-volt 1,200-rpm generator; the mmf scale is given in both shunt-field current and ampere-turns per pole, the latter being derived from the former on the basis of a 1,000-turn-per-pole shunt field. The characteristic may also be presented in *normalized*, or *per-unit, form*, as shown by the upper mmf and right-hand voltage scale. On these scales, 1.0-*per-unit field current* or mmf is that required to produce rated voltage at rated speed when the machine is unloaded; similarly, 1.0-*per-unit voltage* equals rated voltage.

　Use of the magnetization curve with generated voltage rather than flux plotted on the vertical axis may be somewhat complicated by the fact that the speed of a d-c machine need not remain constant, and speed enters into the relation between flux and generated voltage. Hence generated-voltage ordinates correspond to a unique machine speed. The

Change in curves for different I_a caused by armature reaction. If neglected No longer changed is true of ideal machine [handwritten margin notes]

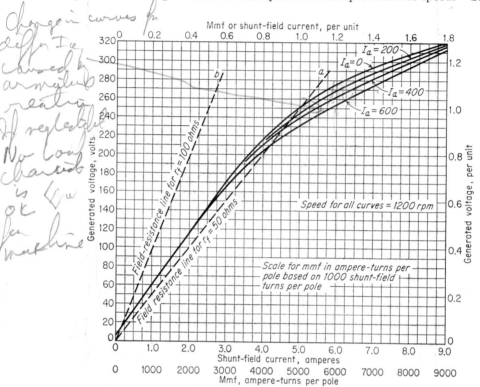

FIG. 8-12. Magnetization curves for a 250-volt 1,200-rpm d-c machine.

generated voltage E_a at any speed ω_m is, in accordance with Eq. 8-2, given by

$$E_a = E_{a0} \frac{\omega_m}{\omega_{m0}} \qquad (8\text{-}10)$$

where ω_{m0} is the magnetization-curve speed and E_{a0} the corresponding armature emf.

Example 8-1. A 100-kw 250-volt 400-amp long-shunt compound generator has armature resistance (including brushes) of 0.025 ohm, a series-field resistance of 0.005 ohm, and the magnetization curve of Fig. 8-12. There are 1,000 shunt-field turns per pole and 3 series-field turns per pole.

Compute the terminal voltage at rated current output when the shunt-field current is 4.7 amp and the speed is 1,150 rpm. Neglect armature reaction.

Solution. $I_s = I_a = I_L + I_f = 400 + 4.7 = 405$ amp. From Eq. 8-9, the main-field mmf is

$$4.7 + \frac{3}{1,000} \times 405 = 5.9 \text{ equivalent shunt-field amp}$$

By entering the $I_a = 0$ curve of Fig. 8-12 with this current, one reads 274 volts. Accordingly, the actual emf is

$$E_a = 274 \times \frac{1,150}{1,200} = 262 \text{ volts}$$

Then
$$V_t = E_a - I_a(r_a + r_s)$$
$$= 262 - 405(0.025 + 0.005) = 250 \text{ volts}$$

b. Effect of Armature MMF. As described in Art. 8-1a, excitation of the armature winding gives rise to a demagnetizing effect caused by cross-magnetizing armature reaction. Analytic inclusion of this effect is not a straightforward task, because of the nonlinearities involved. One common approach is to base the work on experimentally determined data for the machine involved or for one of similar design and frame size. Data are taken with both the field and armature excited, and the tests are conducted so that the effects on generated emf of varying both main-field excitation and the armature mmf may be noted.

One form of summarizing and correlating the results is illustrated in Fig. 8-12. Curves are plotted not only for the no-load characteristic ($I_a = 0$) but for a family of values of I_a. In the analysis of machine performance, then, the inclusion of armature reaction becomes simply a matter of using the magnetization curve corresponding to the armature current involved. Note that the ordinates of all these curves give values of armature generated voltage E_a, not terminal voltage under load. Note also that all the curves tend to merge with the air-gap line as saturation of the iron decreases.

The amount of armature reaction present in Fig. 8-12 is chosen so that some of its disadvantageous effects will appear in a pronounced form in subsequent numerical examples and problems illustrating generator and motor performance features. It is definitely more than one would expect to find in a normal, well-designed machine operating at normal currents.

8-4. Analysis of Steady-state Performance. Although identically the same principles apply to analysis of a d-c machine acting as a generator as to one acting as a motor, the general nature of the problems ordinarily encountered is somewhat different for the two methods of operation. For a generator, the speed is usually fixed by the prime mover, and problems often met are to determine the terminal voltage corresponding to a specified load and excitation or to find the excitation required for a specified load and terminal voltage. For a motor, on the other hand, problems frequently encountered are to determine the speed corresponding to a specified load and excitation or to find the excitation required for specified load and speed conditions; terminal voltage is often fixed at the value of the available supply mains. The routine techniques of applying the common basic principles therefore differ to the extent that the problems differ.

a. Generator Analysis. Since the main-field current is independent of the generator voltage, separately excited generators are the simplest to analyze. For a given load, the main-field excitation is given by Eq. 8-9, and the associated armature generated voltage E_a is determined by the appropriate magnetization curve. This voltage, together with Eq. 8-5 or 8-6, fixes the terminal voltage.

In self-excited generators, the shunt-field excitation depends on the terminal voltage and the series-field excitation on the armature current. Dependence of shunt-field current on terminal voltage may be incorporated graphically in an analysis by drawing the *field-resistance line*, the line Oa in Fig. 8-12, on the magnetization curve. The field-resistance line Oa is simply a graphical representation of Ohm's law for the shunt field. It is the locus of the terminal-voltage vs. shunt-field-current operating point. Thus, the line Oa is drawn for $r_f = 50$ ohms and hence passes through the origin and the point (1.0 amp, 50 volts).

One instance of the interdependence of magnetic- and electric-circuit conditions may be seen by examining the *build-up of voltage* for an unloaded shunt generator. When the field circuit is closed, the small voltage from residual magnetism (the 6-volt intercept of the magnetization curve, Fig. 8-12) causes a small field current. If the flux produced by the resulting ampere-turns adds to the residual flux, progressively greater voltages and field currents are obtained. If the field ampere-turns oppose the residual magnetism, the shunt-field terminals must be reversed to obtain build-up. Build-up continues until the volt-ampere relations represented by the magnetization curve and the field-resistance line are simultaneously satisfied (i.e., at their intersection, 250 volts for line Oa in Fig. 8-12). This statement ignores the extremely small voltage drop caused by the shunt-field current in the armature-circuit resistance. Notice that if the field resistance is too high, as shown by line Ob for $r_f = 100$ ohms, the intersection is at very low voltage and build-up is not obtained. Notice also that if the field-resistance line is essentially tangent to the lower part of the magnetization curve, corresponding to 57 ohms in Fig. 8-12, the intersection may be anywhere from about 60 to 170 volts, resulting in very unstable conditions. The corresponding resistance is the *critical field resistance*, beyond which build-up will not be obtained. The same build-up process and the same conclusions apply to compound generators; in a long-shunt compound generator, the series-field mmf created by the shunt-field current is entirely negligible.

This build-up of voltage is evidently a transient process in which, at any particular point, the vertical difference between the field-resistance line and the magnetization curve is the voltage serving to increase the current through the shunt-field inductance. The transient process is discussed in Art. 4-8.

For a shunt generator, the magnetization curve for the appropriate value of I_a is the locus of E_a versus I_f. The field-resistance line is the locus of V_t versus I_f. With steady-state operation and at any value of I_f, therefore, the vertical distance between the line and the curve must be the $I_a r_a$ drop at the load corresponding to that condition. Determination of the terminal voltage for a specified armature current is then simply a matter of finding where the line and curve are separated vertically by the proper amount; the ordinate of the field-resistance line at that field current is then the terminal voltage. For a compound generator, however, the series-field mmf causes corresponding points on the line and curve to be displaced horizontally as well as vertically. The horizontal displacement equals the series-field mmf measured in equivalent shunt-field amperes, and the vertical displacement is still the $I_a r_a$ drop.

Great precision is evidently not obtained from the foregoing computational process. The uncertainties caused by magnetic hysteresis in d-c machines make high precision unattainable in any event. In general, the magnetization curve on which the machine operates on any given occasion may range from the rising to the falling part of the rather fat hysteresis loop for the magnetic circuit of the machine, depending essentially on the magnetic history of the iron just prior to that occasion. The curve used for analysis is usually the mean magnetization curve, and thus the results obtained are substantially correct on the average. Significant departures from the average may be encountered in the performance of any d-c machine at a particular time, however.

Example 8-2. A 100-kw 250-volt 400-amp 1,200-rpm d-c shunt generator has the magnetization curves (including armature-reaction effects) of Fig. 8-12. The armature-circuit resistance, including brushes, is 0.025 ohm. The generator is driven at a constant speed of 1,200 rpm, and the excitation is adjusted to give rated voltage at no load.

a. Determine the terminal voltage at an armature current of 400 amp.

b. A series field of 4 turns per pole having a resistance of 0.005 ohm is to be added. There are 1,000 turns per pole in the shunt field. The generator is to be flat-compounded so that the full-load voltage is 250 volts when the shunt-field rheostat is adjusted to give a no-load voltage of 250 volts. Show how a resistance across the series field (a so-called *series-field diverter*) may be adjusted to produce the desired performance.

Solution. *a.* The field-resistance line *Oa* (Fig. 8-12) passes through the 250-volt 5.0-amp point of the no-load magnetization curve. At $I_a = 400$ amp,

$$I_a r_a = 400 \times 0.025 = 10 \text{ volts}$$

A vertical distance of 10 volts exists between the magnetization curve for $I_a = 400$ amp and the field-resistance line at a field current of 4.1 amp, corresponding to $V_t = 205$ volts. The associated line current is

$$I_L = I_a - I_f = 400 - 4 = 396 \text{ amp}$$

Note that a vertical distance of 10 volts also exists at a field current of 1.2 amp, corresponding to $V_t = 60$ volts. The voltage-load curve is accordingly double-valued in this region. The point for which $V_t = 205$ is the normal operating point.

b. For the no-load voltage to be 250 volts, the shunt-field resistance must be 50 ohms, and the field-resistance line is *Oa* (Fig. 8-12).

At full load, $I_f = 5.0$ amp because $V_t = 250$ volts. Then,

$$I_a = 400 + 5.0 = 405 \text{ amp}$$
and
$$E_a = 250 + 405(0.025 + 0.005) = 262 \text{ volts}$$

In the last equation, the effect of the diverter in reducing the series-field circuit resistance is ignored, a neglect which is permissible in view of the degree of precision warranted. From the 400-amp magnetization curve, an E_a of 262 volts requires a main-field excitation of 5.95 equivalent shunt-field amperes. (Strictly speaking, of course, a curve for $I_a = 405$ amp should be used, but such a small distinction is obviously meaningless.) From Eq. 8-9,

$$5.95 = 5.0 + \frac{4}{1,000} I_s$$
$$I_s = 238 \text{ amp}$$

Hence only 238 of the total 405 amp of armature current must pass through the series field, a process requiring that the series field be shunted by a resistor of

$$\frac{238 \times 0.005}{405 - 238} = 0.0071 \text{ ohm}$$

b. Motor Analysis. Since the terminal voltage of motors is usually substantially constant at a specified value, there is no dependence of shunt-field excitation on a varying voltage as in shunt and compound generators. Hence, motor analysis most nearly resembles that for separately excited generators, although speed is now an important variable and often the one whose value is to be found. Analytical essentials include Eqs. 8-5 and 8-6 relating terminal voltage and generated or counter emf, Eq. 8-9 for main-field excitation, the magnetization curve for the appropriate armature current as the graphical relation between counter emf and excitation, Eq. 8-1 showing the dependence of electromagnetic torque on flux and armature current, and Eq. 8-2 relating counter emf with flux and speed. The last two relations are particularly significant in motor analysis. The former is pertinent because the interdependence of torque and the stator and rotor field strengths must often be examined. The latter is the usual medium for determining motor speed from other specified operating conditions.

Motor speed corresponding to a given armature current I_a may be found by first computing the actual generated voltage E_a from Eq. 8-5 or 8-6. Next obtain the main-field excitation from Eq. 8-9. Since the magnetization curve will be plotted for a constant speed ω_{m0} which in general will be different from the actual motor speed ω_m, the generated voltage read from the magnetization curve at the foregoing main-field excitation will correspond to the correct flux conditions but to the speed ω_{m0}. Substitution in Eq. 8-10 then yields the actual motor speed.

It will be noted that knowledge of the armature current is postulated at the start of this process. When, as is frequently the case, the speed at a stated shaft power or torque output is to be found, successive trials based on assumed values of I_a usually form the simplest procedure. Plotting of the successive trials permits speedy determination of the correct armature current and speed at the desired output.

Example 8-3. A 100-hp 250-volt d-c shunt motor has the magnetization curves (including armature-reaction effects) of Fig. 8-12. The armature circuit resistance, including brushes, is 0.025 ohm. No-load rotational losses are 2,000 watts, and stray load losses equal 1.0 per cent of the output. The field rheostat is adjusted for a no-load speed of 1,100 rpm.

a. As an example of computing points on the speed-load characteristic, determine the speed in rpm and output in horsepower corresponding to an armature current of 400 amp.

b. Because the speed-load characteristic referred to in (a) is considered undesirable, a *stabilizing winding* consisting of $1\frac{1}{2}$ cumulative series turns per pole is to be added. The resistance of this winding is negligible. There are 1,000 turns per pole in the shunt field. Compute the speed corresponding to an armature current of 400 amp.

Solution. *a.* At no load, $E_a = 250$ volts. The corresponding point on the 1,200-rpm no-load saturation curve is

$$E_{a0} = 250 \times \frac{1,200}{1,100} = 273 \text{ volts}$$

for which $I_f = 5.90$ amp. The field current remains constant at this value.

At $I_a = 400$ amp, the actual counter emf is

$$E_a = 250 - 400 \times 0.025 = 240 \text{ volts}$$

From Fig. 8-12 with $I_a = 400$ and $I_f = 5.90$, the value of E_a would be 261 volts if the speed were 1,200 rpm. The actual speed is then

$$n = {}^{240}\!/_{261} \times 1,200 = 1,100 \text{ rpm}$$

The electromagnetic power is

$$E_a I_a = 240 \times 400 = 96,000 \text{ watts}$$

Deduction of the rotational losses leaves 94,000 watts. With stray load losses accounted for, the power output P_o is given by

$$94,000 - 0.01P_o = P_o$$

or
$$P_o = 93.1 \text{ kw} = 124.7 \text{ hp}$$

Note that the speed at this load is the same as at no load, indicating that armature-reaction effects have caused an essentially flat speed-load curve.

b. With $I_f = 5.90$ amp and $I_s = I_a = 400$ amp, the main-field mmf in equivalent shunt-field amperes is

$$5.90 + \frac{1.5}{1,000} \times 400 = 6.50$$

From Fig. 8-12, the corresponding value of E_a at 1,200 rpm would be 273 volts. Accordingly, the speed is now

$$n = {}^{240}\!/_{273} \times 1,200 = 1,055 \text{ rpm}$$

The power output is the same as in (a). The speed-load curve is now drooping.

Example 8-4. To limit the starting current to the value which the motor can commutate successfully, all except very small d-c motors are started with external resistance in series with their armatures. This resistance is cut out either manually or automatically as the motor comes up to speed. In Fig. 8-13, for example, the contactors 1A, 2A, and 3A cut out successive steps R_1, R_2, and R_3 of the starting resistor.

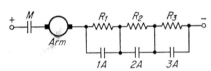

FIG. 8-13. Starting resistors and accelerating contactors for a d-c motor.

Consider that a motor is to be started with normal field flux. Armature reaction and armature inductance are to be ignored. During starting, the armature current and hence the electromagnetic torque are not to exceed twice the rated values, and a step of the starting resistor is to be cut out whenever the armature current drops to its rated value. Except in part f, computations are to be made in the per-unit system with magnitudes expressed as fractions of base values. (Base voltage equals rated line voltage, base armature current equals full-load armature current, and base resistance equals the ratio of base voltage to base current.)

a. What is the minimum per-unit value of armature resistance which will permit these conditions to be met by a three-step starting resistor?

b. Above what per-unit value of armature resistance will a two-step resistor suffice?

c. For the armature resistance of (a), what are the per-unit resistance values R_1, R_2, and R_3 of the starting resistor?

d. For a motor with the armature resistance of (a), the contactors are to be closed by voltage-sensitive relays connected across the armature (called the *counter-emf method*). At what fractions of rated line voltage should the contactors close?

e. For a motor with the armature resistance of (a), sketch approximate curves of armature current, electromagnetic torque, and speed during the starting process, and label the ordinates with the appropriate per-unit values at significant instants of time.

f. For a 10-hp 230-volt 500-rpm d-c shunt motor having a full-load armature current of 37 amp and fulfilling the conditions of (a), list numerical values in their usual units for armature resistance, the results of (c) and (d), and the ordinate labelings of (e).

Solution. a. In order that the armature current not exceed 2.00 per unit at the instant main contactor M closes,

$$R_1 + R_2 + R_3 + r_a = \frac{V_t}{I_a} = \frac{1.00}{2.00} = 0.50$$

When the current has dropped to 1.00 per unit,

$$E_{a1} = V_t - I_a(R_1 + R_2 + R_3 + r_a) = 1.00 - 1.00 \times 0.50 = 0.50$$

At the instant that accelerating contactor $1A$ closes, short-circuiting R_1, the counter emf has attained this numerical value.   Then, in order that the allowable armature current shall not be exceeded,

$$R_2 + R_3 + r_a = \frac{V_t - E_{a1}}{I_a} = \frac{1.00 - 0.50}{2.00} = 0.25$$

When the current has again dropped to 1.00 per unit,

$$E_{a2} = V_t - I_a(R_3 + R_3 + r_a) = 1.00 - 1.00 \times 0.25 = 0.75$$

Repetition of this procedure for the closing of accelerating contactors $2A$ and $3A$ yields the following results:

$$R_3 + r_a = 0.125$$
$$E_{a3} = 0.875$$
$$r_a = 0.0625$$

and   Final E_a at full load $= 0.938$

The desired minimum per-unit value of r_a is therefore 0.0625, for a lower value will allow the armature current to exceed twice the rated value when contactor $3A$ is closed.

b. If a two-step resistor is to suffice, R_3 must be zero.   Since, from (a),

$$R_3 + r_a = 0.125$$

it follows that a three-step resistor is not required when r_a is equal to or greater than 0.125.

Under the specified starting conditions, a three-step resistor is appropriate for motors whose armature-circuit resistances are between 0.0625 and 0.125 per unit. For general-purpose continuously rated shunt motors, these values correspond to the lower integral-horsepower sizes.   On the average, motor sizes up to about 10 hp will conform to these requirements, although the size limit will be lower for high-speed motors and higher for slow-speed motors.   For larger motors, either additional steps must be provided, or the limit on current and torque peaks must be relaxed. The results of this analysis are conservative because the armature resistance under transient conditions is higher than the static value.

c. From the relations in part a, the per-unit starting resistances are

$$R_3 = 0.125 - 0.0625 = 0.0625$$
$$R_2 = 0.25 - 0.0625 - 0.0625 = 0.125$$

and $$R_1 = 0.50 - 0.0625 - 0.0625 - 0.125 = 0.25$$

d. Just before contactor $1A$ closes,

$$V_{ta1} = E_{a1} + I_a r_a = 0.50 + 1.00 \times 0.0625 = 0.563$$

In like manner,

$$V_{ta2} = 0.75 + 1.00 \times 0.0625 = 0.813$$
and $$V_{ta3} = 0.875 + 1.00 \times 0.0625 = 0.938$$

Accelerating contactors $1A$, $2A$, and $3A$, respectively, should pick up at these fractions of rated line voltage.

e. Consider that main contactor M closes at $t = 0$ and that accelerating contactors $1A$, $2A$, and $3A$ close, respectively, at times t_1, t_2, and t_3.   These values of time are not known (when armature and load inertias and torque-speed curve of the load are given, values of time can be computed by the methods of Chap. 4), so that only the general shapes of the current, electromagnetic torque, and speed curves can be given. They are indicated in Fig. 8-14.

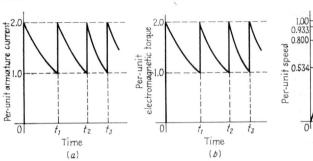

FIG. 8-14. (a) Armature current, (b) electromagnetic torque, and (c) speed during starting of a d-c motor.

The labeling of the speed curve follows from the fact that a counter emf $E_a = 0.938$ corresponds to rated speed at rated load and hence to unity speed. Other speeds are in proportion to E_a; thus, at t_1, t_2, and t_3, respectively,

$$n_1 = \frac{0.50}{0.938} \times 1.00 = 0.534$$

$$n_2 = \frac{0.75}{0.938} \times 1.00 = 0.800$$

and

$$n_3 = \frac{0.875}{0.938} \times 1.00 = 0.933$$

f. Base quantities for this motor are as follows:

Base voltage = 230 volts
Base armature current = 37 amp
Base armature circuit resistance = $^{230}\!/_{37}$ = 6.22 ohms
Base speed = 500 rpm

$$\text{Base electromagnetic torque} = \frac{60}{2\pi n} E_a I_a$$

$$= \frac{60}{2\pi \times 500} (230 - 37 \times 0.0625 \times 6.22) \times 37$$

$$= 152 \text{ newton-m}$$

Note that rated electromagnetic torque will be greater than rated shaft torque because of rotational and stray load losses.

The motor armature resistance is

$$r_a = 0.0625 \times 6.22 = 0.389 \text{ ohm}$$

Values for the other quantities desired are listed in Table 8-1.

Table 8-1
Absolute Values for Example 8-4f

Part c	Part d	Part e, scales of Fig. 8-14
$R_1 = 1.56$ ohms	Relay 1A: 129 volts	1.0 armature current = 37 amp
$R_2 = 0.778$ ohm	Relay 2A: 187 volts	1.0 electromagnetic torque = 152 newton-m
$R_3 = 0.389$ ohm	Relay 3A: 216 volts	1.0 speed = 500 rpm

8-5. Motor Speed Control.   Direct-current machines are in general much more adaptable to adjustable-speed service than are the a-c machines associated with a constant-speed rotating field.   Indeed, the ready susceptibility of d-c motors to adjustment of their operating speed over wide ranges and by a variety of methods is one of the important reasons for the strong competitive position of d-c machinery in modern industrial applications.

The three most common speed-control methods are adjustment of the flux, usually by means of a shunt-field rheostat, adjustment of the resistance associated with the armature circuit, and adjustment of the armature terminal voltage.   These methods are also described in Art. 4-4, and the last of the three is discussed from the dynamic viewpoint.   The present discussion will supplement the earlier one by concentrating on factors limiting the speed ranges as well as on the general applicability of the methods.

Shunt-field-rheostat control is the most commonly used of the three methods and forms one of the outstanding advantages of shunt motors. The method is, of course, also applicable to compound motors.   Adjustment of field current and hence of flux and speed by adjustment of the shunt-field circuit resistance is accomplished simply, inexpensively, and without much change in motor losses.

The lowest speed obtainable is that corresponding to full field or zero resistance in the field rheostat; the highest speed is limited electrically by the effects of armature reaction under weak-field conditions in causing motor instability or poor commutation.   Addition of a stabilizing winding increases the speed range appreciably, and the alternative addition of a compensating winding still further increases the range.   With a compensating winding, the over-all range may be as high as 8 to 1 for a small integral-horsepower motor.   Economic factors limit the feasible range for very large motors to about 2 to 1, however, with 4 to 1 often regarded as the limit for the average-sized motor.

To examine approximately the limitations on the allowable continuous motor output as the speed is changed, neglect the influence of changing ventilation and changing rotational losses on the allowable output.   The maximum armature current I_a is then fixed at the nameplate value in order that the motor shall not overheat, and the counter emf E_a remains constant because the effect of a speed change is compensated by the change of flux causing it.   The $E_a I_a$ product and hence the allowable motor output then remain substantially constant over the speed range. The d-c motor with shunt-field-rheostat speed control is accordingly referred to as a *constant-horsepower drive.*   Torque, on the other hand, varies directly with flux and therefore has its highest allowable value at the lowest speed.   Field-rheostat control is thus best suited to drives requiring increased torque at low speeds. When a motor so controlled is used with a load requiring constant torque over the speed range, the rating and size of the machine are determined by the product of the torque and the highest speed. Such a drive is inherently oversize at the lower speeds, which is the principal economic factor limiting the practical speed range of large motors.

Armature-circuit-resistance control consists in obtaining reduced speeds by the insertion of external series resistance in the armature circuit. It may be used with series, shunt, and compound motors; for the last two types, the series resistor must be connected between the shunt field and the armature, not between the line and the motor. It is the common method of speed control for series motors and is generally analogous in action to wound-rotor induction-motor control by series rotor resistance.

For a fixed value of series armature resistance, the speed will vary widely with load, since the speed depends on the voltage drop in this resistance and hence on the armature current demanded by the load. For example, a 1,200-rpm shunt motor whose speed under load is reduced to 750 rpm by series armature resistance will return to almost 1,200-rpm operation when the load is thrown off, because the effect of the no-load current in the series resistance is insignificant. The disadvantage of poor speed regulation may not be important in a series motor, which is used only where varying speed service is required or satisfactory anyway.

Also, the power loss in the external resistor is large, especially when the speed is greatly reduced. In fact, for a constant-torque load, the power input to the motor plus resistor remains constant, while the power output to the load decreases in proportion to the speed. Operating costs are therefore comparatively high for long-time running at reduced speeds. Because of its low initial cost, however, the series-resistance method (or the variation of it discussed in the next paragraph) will often be attractive economically for short-time or intermittent slowdowns. Unlike shunt-field control, armature-resistance control offers a *constant-torque drive* because both flux and, to a first approximation, allowable armature current remain constant as speed changes.

A variation of this control scheme is given by the *shunted-armature method*, which may be applied to a series motor as in Fig. 8-15a or a shunt motor as in Fig. 8-15b. In effect, resistors R_1 and R_2 act as a voltage divider applying a reduced voltage to the armature. Greater flexibility is possible because two resistors may now be adjusted to provide the desired performance. For series motors, the no-load speed may be adjusted to a finite, reasonable value, and the scheme is therefore applicable to the production of slow speeds at light loads. For shunt motors, the speed regulation in the low-speed range is appreciably improved because the no-load speed is definitely lower than the value with no controlling resistors.

Armature-terminal-voltage control, also called the *Ward Leonard system,* utilizes the fact that a change in the armature terminal voltage of a shunt motor is accompanied in the steady state by a substantially equal change

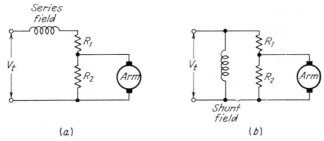

(a)   (b)

FIG. 8-15. Shunted-armature method of speed control applied to (a) series motor and (b) shunt motor.

in the counter emf and, with constant motor flux, a consequent proportional change in motor speed. The conventional scheme, shown schematically in Fig. 8-16, requires an individual motor-generator set to supply power to the armature of the motor whose speed is to be controlled. Control of the armature voltage of the main motor M is obtained by field-rheostat adjustment in the separately excited generator G, permitting close control of speed over a wide range. An obvious disadvantage is the initial investment in three full-size machines in contrast to

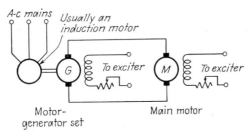

FIG. 8-16. Adjustable-armature-voltage, or Ward Leonard, method of speed control.

that in a single motor. The speed-control equipment is located in low-power field circuits, however, rather than in the main power circuits. The smoothness and versatility of control are such that the method or one of its variants is often applied.

Frequently the control of generator voltage is combined with motor-field control, as indicated by the rheostat in the field of motor M in Fig. 8-16, in order to achieve the widest possible speed range. With such dual control, *base speed* may be defined as the normal-armature-voltage full-field speed of the motor. Speeds above base speed are obtained by motor-field control; speeds below base speed are obtained by armature-voltage control. As discussed in connection with shunt-field-rheostat control, the range above base speed is that of a constant-horsepower drive. The range below base speed is that of a constant-torque drive because, as in armature-resistance control, the flux and the allowable armature current remain approximately constant. The over-all output limitations are therefore as shown in Fig. 8-17a for approximate allowable torque and Fig. 8-17b for approximate allowable horsepower. The constant-torque characteristic is well suited to many applications in the machine-tool industry, where many loads consist largely in overcoming the friction of moving parts and hence have essentially constant-torque requirements.

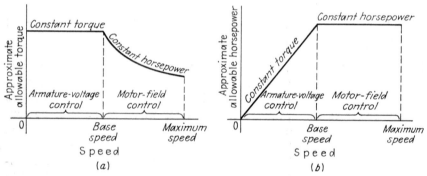

FIG. 8-17. (a) Torque and (b) power limitations of combined armature-voltage and field-rheostat methods of speed control.

The speed regulation and the limitations on the speed range above base speed are those already presented with reference to shunt-field-rheostat control; the maximum speed thus does not ordinarily exceed four times base speed, and preferably not twice base speed. In the region of armature-voltage control, the principal limitation in the basic system is residual magnetism in the generator, although considerations of speed regulation may also be determining. For conventional machines, the lower limit for reliable and stable operation is about 0.1 of base speed, corresponding to a total maximum-to-minimum range not exceeding 40 to 1. With armature reaction ignored, the decrease in speed from no-load to full-load torque is caused entirely by the full-load armature-resistance drop in the d-c generator and motor. This full-load armature-resistance drop is constant over the voltage-control range, since full-load torque and hence full-load current are usually regarded as constant in that range. When measured in rpm, therefore, the speed decrease from no-load to full-load torque is a constant, independent of the no-load speed. The torque-speed curves accordingly are closely approximated by a series of parallel straight lines for the various generator-field adjustments. Now a speed decrease of, say, 40 rpm from a no-load speed of 1,200 rpm is often of little importance; a decrease of 40 rpm from a no-load speed of 120 rpm, however, may at times be of critical importance and require corrective steps in the layout of the system.

Many detailed variations of the basic Ward Leonard system have been devised to overcome these limitations when precise speed control over a wide range is required and also to utilize fully the versatility of d-c machines in providing a variety of inherent performance characteristics. Flat compounding of the d-c generator, for example, is one simple method of improving the natural speed regulation. Control-type generators such as the Amplidyne and Rototrol, discussed in Chap. 4, may be used either as the main generator G (Fig. 8-16) in low-power systems or to supply and control the excitation for this generator in heavy-power systems. Greater flexibility is thereby provided, the residual-magnetism limitation may be alleviated, and excellent speed regulation over a range as high as 120 to 1 may be obtained. As illustrated in Chap. 4, the basic method is frequently used in closed-cycle control systems.

When a motor armature is supplied from its own individual d-c generator, the shape of the speed-torque curve of the system may also be controlled by incorporating special features in the generator. An example is the use of a *three-field generator* to supply the armature of a shunt motor. This special-purpose generator has a separately excited winding, a shunt-connected winding, and a differentially connected series winding, a combination which permits the placing of an adjustable limit on the torque output of the system and in particular on the torque and current when the motor is stalled. In other systems, the torque and current while accelerating may be limited by the appropriate controls. In effect, the degrees of freedom are such that, within rather wide limits, a tailor-made drive may be devised.

8-6. Résumé. D-C Machine Applications. Discussion of d-c machine applications involves recapitulation of the highlights of the machine's performance features, together with economic and technical evaluation of the machine's position with respect to competing energy-conversion devices. For d-c machines in general, the outstanding advantage lies in their flexibility and versatility. The principal disadvantage is likely to be the initial investment concerned. Yet the advantages of d-c motors are such that they retain a strong competitive position for industrial applications.

Direct-current generators are the obvious answer to the problem of converting mechanical energy to electrical energy in d-c form. When the consumer of electrical energy is geographically removed from the site of energy conversion by any appreciable distance, however, the advantages of a-c generation, voltage transformation, and transmission are such that energy conversion and transmission in a-c form are almost always adopted with a-c to d-c transformation taking place at or near the consumer. For a-c to d-c transformation, the d-c generator as part of an a-c to d-c motor-generator set must compete with mercury-arc rectifiers, ignitrons, and semiconductor rectifiers. When large-power rectification from a-c to constant-voltage d-c form is involved, the electronic methods usually possess determining economic advantages. The principal applications of d-c generators, therefore, are to cases where ability freely to control the output voltage in a prescribed manner is necessary or where the primary energy conversion occurs very near the point of consumption.

Among d-c generators themselves, separately excited and cumulatively compounded self-excited machines are the most common. Separately excited generators have the advantage of permitting a wide range of output voltages, whereas self-excited machines may produce unstable voltages in the lower ranges where the field-resistance line becomes essentially tangent to the magnetization curve. Cumulatively compounded generators may produce a substantially flat voltage characteristic or one which rises with load, whereas shunt or separately excited generators (assuming no series field in the latter, which, of course, is not at all a practical restriction) produce a drooping voltage characteristic unless external regulating means are added. So far as the control potentialities of d-c generators are concerned, the control-type generators (Amplidynes, Rototrols, and similar machines) discussed in Chap. 4 represent the results of a fuller exploration of the inherent possibilities.

Among d-c motors, the outstanding characteristics of each type are as follows: The series motor operates with a decidedly drooping speed as load is added, the no-load speed usually being prohibitively high; the torque is proportional to almost the square of the current at low saturations and to some power between 1 and 2 as saturation increases. The shunt motor at constant field current operates at a slightly drooping but almost constant speed as load is added, the torque being almost proportional to armature current; equally important, however, is the fact that its speed may be controlled over wide ranges by shunt-field control or armature-voltage control or a combination of both. Depending on the relative strengths of shunt and series field, the cumulatively compounded motor is intermediate between the other two and may be given essentially the advantages of one or the other.

By virtue of its ability to handle heavy torque overloads while cushioning the associated power overload with a speed drop, and by virtue of its ability to withstand severe starting duties, the series motor is best adapted to hoist, crane, and traction-type loads. Its ability is almost unrivaled in this respect. Speed changes are usually achieved by arma-ture-resistance control. In some instances, the wound-rotor induction motor with rotor-resistance control competes with the series motor, but the principal argument concerns the availability and economics of a d-c power supply rather than inherent motor characteristics.

Compound motors with a heavy series field have performance features approaching those of series motors except that the shunt field limits the no-load speed to safe values; the general remarks for series motors there-fore apply. Compound motors with lighter series windings not infre-quently find competition from squirrel-cage induction motors with high-resistance rotors—so-called *high-slip* motors (referred to in Chap. 10 as Class D induction motors). Both motors provide a definitely drooping speed-load characteristic such as is desirable, for example, when flywheels are used as load equalizers to smooth out intermittent load peaks. Com-plete economic comparison of the two competing types must reflect both the usually higher initial cost of a compound-motor installation and the usually higher cost of losses in the high-slip induction motor.

Because of the comparative simplicity, cheapness, and ruggedness of the squirrel-cage induction motor, the shunt motor is not in a favorable competitive position for constant-speed service except at low speeds, where it becomes difficult and expensive to build high-performance induction motors with the requisite number of poles. The comparison at these low speeds is often likely to be between synchronous and d-c motors. The outstanding feature of the shunt motor is its adaptability to adjustable-speed service by means of armature-resistance control for speeds below the full-field speed, field-rheostat control for speeds above the full-field speed, and armature-voltage, or Ward Leonard, control for speeds below (and, at times, somewhat above) the normal-voltage full-field speed. The combination of armature-voltage control and shunt-field control, together with the possibility of additional field windings in either the motor or the associated generator to provide desirable inherent characteristics, gives the d-c drives an enviable degree of flexibility. The control-type d-c generators of Chap. 4 definitely reinforce the com-petitive position of d-c machines where complete control of operation is important.

It should be emphasized that the choice of equipment for a significant engineering application to adjustable-speed drives is rarely a cut-and-dried matter or one to be decided from a mere verbal list of advantages and disadvantages. In general, specific, quantitative, economic, and technical comparison of all possibilities should be undertaken. Con-sideration must be given to the transient- and dynamic-response details of Chap. 4. Local conditions and the characteristics of the driven equip-ment (e.g., constant-horsepower, constant-torque, and variable-horsepower variable-torque requirements) invariably play an important role. One should also remember that comparative studies of motor cost and characteristics are based on the combination of motor and control equipment, for the latter plays an important part in determining motor performance under specific conditions and represents a by no means negligible portion of the total initial cost. Control equipment coupled with susceptibility to control makes d-c machines the versatile energy-conversion devices that they are.

PROBLEMS

8-1. A cumulatively compounded generator with interpoles and with its brushes on neutral is to be used as a compound motor.

If no changes are made in the internal connections, will the motor be cumulatively or differentially compounded? Will the polarity of the interpoles be correct? Will the direction of rotation be the same as or opposite to the direction in which it was driven as a generator?

8-2. A self-excited d-c machine with interpoles is adjusted for proper operation as an overcompounded generator. The machine is shut down, the connections to the shunt field are reversed, and the machine is then started with the direction of rotation reversed. The machine builds up normal terminal voltage. Answer the following questions, and give a brief explanation:

Is the terminal-voltage polarity the same as before? Is the machine still cumulatively compounded? Do the interpoles have the proper polarity for good commutation?

8-3. A 10-kw 230-volt 1,150-rpm shunt generator is driven by a prime mover whose speed is 1,195 rpm when the generator delivers no load. The speed falls to 1,150 rpm when the generator delivers 10 kw and may be assumed to decrease in proportion to the generator output. The generator is to be changed into a short-shunt compound generator by equipping it with a series field which will cause its voltage to rise from 230 volts at no load to 250 volts for a load of 43.5 amp. It is estimated that the series field will have a resistance of 0.09 ohm. The armature resistance (including brushes) is 0.26 ohm. The shunt-field winding has 1,800 turns per pole.

In order to determine the necessary series-field turns, the machine is run as a separately excited generator and the following load data obtained: armature terminal voltage, 254 volts; armature current, 44.7 amp; field current, 1.95 amp; speed, 1,145 rpm.

The magnetization curve at 1,195 rpm is as follows:

E_a, volts	230	240	250	260	270
I_f, amp	1.05	1.13	1.26	1.46	1.67

a. Determine the necessary number of series-field turns per pole.

b. Determine the armature reaction in equivalent demagnetizing ampere-turns per pole for $I_a = 44.7$ amp.

8-4. A small, lightweight d-c shunt generator for use in aircraft has a rating of 9 kw, 30 volts, 300 amp. It is driven by one of the main engines of the airplane through an auxiliary power shaft. The generator speed is proportional to the main-engine speed and may have any value from 4,500 rpm to 8,000 rpm. The terminal voltage of the generator is held constant at 30 volts for all speeds and loads by means of a voltage regulator which automatically adjusts a carbon-pile field rheostat whose minimum resistance is 0.75 ohm. The resistances of the shunt-field, commutating, and armature (including brushes) windings are, respectively, 2.50, 0.0040, and 0.0120 ohms.

Data for the magnetization curve at 4,550 rpm are:

I_m amp.........	0	2.0	4.0	5.0	6.0	8.0	11.7
E_a, volts........	1.0	18.0	30.5	33.6	35.5	38.0	40.5

In a load test at 4,550 rpm, the field current required to maintain rated terminal voltage at rated load is 7.00 amp.

Determine the following characteristics of this generator:

a. Maximum resistance required in the field rheostat
b. Maximum power dissipated in the field rheostat
c. Demagnetizing effect of armature reaction at rated load and 4,550 rpm, expressed in terms of equivalent shunt-field current

8-5. Assume that the demagnetizing effect of armature reaction in the aircraft generator of Prob. 8-4 is equivalent to a demagnetizing mmf proportional to the armature current.

a. Plot the curve of terminal voltage as a function of line current for minimum field-rheostat resistance and 4,550 rpm.

b. When the airplane is on the ground and the engines are idling, the generator speed may be below 4,500 rpm. Plot a curve of terminal voltage as a function of speed with minimum field-rheostat resistance and a constant line current of 300 amp covering the subnormal speed range from 4,550 to 3,500 rpm. Estimate the minimum speed at which the generator is capable of delivering 300 amp.

8-6. A d-c series motor operates at 750 rpm with a line current of 80 amp from the 230-volt mains. Its armature circuit resistance is 0.14 ohm, and its field resistance is 0.11 ohm.

Assuming that the flux corresponding to a current of 20 amp is 40 per cent of that corresponding to a current of 80 amp, find the motor speed at a line current of 20 amp at 230 volts.

8-7. A certain series motor is so designed that flux densities in the iron part of the magnetic circuit are low enough to result in a linear relationship between field flux and field current throughout the normal range of operation. The rating of this motor is 50 hp, 190 amp, 220 volts, 600 rpm. Losses at full load in percentage of motor input are:

Armature copper loss (including brush loss) = 3.7 per cent
Field copper loss = 3.2 per cent
Rotational loss = 2.8 per cent

Rotational loss may be assumed constant; armature reaction and stray load loss may be neglected.

When this motor is operating from a 220-volt supply with a current of half the rated value, what will be:

a. The speed in rpm?
b. The shaft power output in horsepower?

8-8. A 150-hp 600-volt 600-rpm d-c series-wound railway motor has a combined field and armature resistance (including brushes) of 0.155 ohm. The full-load current at rated voltage and speed is 206 amp. The magnetization curve at 400 rpm is as follows:

Induced volts..........	375	400	425	450	475
Field amp.............	188	216	250	290	333

Determine the internal starting torque when the starting current is limited to 350 amp. Assume armature reaction to be equivalent to a demagnetizing mmf which varies as the square of the current.

8-9. Following are the nameplate data of a certain d-c motor: 230 volts, 75.7 amp, 20 hp, 900 rpm full-load, 50°C 1-hr rating, series-wound. The field winding has 33 turns per pole and a hot resistance of 0.06 ohm; the hot armature-circuit resistance is 0.09 ohm (including brushes). Points on the magnetization curve at 900 rpm are as follows:

Amp-turns per pole.......	500	1,000	1,500	2,000	2,500	3,000
Generated voltage........	95	150	188	212	229	243

To determine the fitness of this motor for driving a skip hoist, points on the motor speed-load curve are to be computed.

a. For currents equal to ⅓, ⅔, 1, and 4⁄3 of the nameplate value, compute the speed of the motor. Neglect armature reaction.

b. For the same currents, compute the shaft-horsepower outputs. For this purpose, consider rotational losses to remain constant at the value determined by nameplate conditions.

c. Compute the pulley torques in pound-feet corresponding to the values in (*b*). Arrange the results of parts *a*, *b*, and *c* in tabular form for convenience in checking.

d. The maximum safe speed for the motor is 250 per cent of full-load speed. What is the motor power input at this point?

e. What value of resistance connected in series with the motor will enable the production of full-load electromagnetic torque at a speed of 500 rpm?

8-10. A 10-hp 230-volt shunt motor has an armature-circuit resistance of 0.30 ohm and a field resistance of 170 ohms. At no load and rated voltage, the speed is 1,200 rpm, and the armature current is 2.7 amp. At full load and rated voltage, the line current is 38.4 amp, and, because of armature reaction, the flux is 4 per cent less than its no-load value.

What is the full-load speed?

8-11. A 36-in. axial-flow disk pressure fan is rated to deliver 27,120 ft³ of air per minute against a static pressure of ½ in. of water when rotating at a speed of 1,165 rpm. This fan has the following speed-load characteristics:

Speed, rpm....	700	800	900	1,000	1,100	1,200
Input, hp.....	2.9	3.9	5.2	6.7	8.6	11.1

It is proposed to drive the fan by a 10-hp 230-volt 37.5 amp 4-pole d-c shunt motor. The motor has an armature winding with two parallel paths and $Z = 666$ active inductors. Armature-circuit resistance is 0.267 ohm. The armature flux per pole is $\Phi = 10^6$ lines; armature reaction is negligible. No-load rotational losses (considered constant) are estimated at 600 watts, a typical value for such a motor.

Determine the shaft-horsepower output and the operating speed of the motor when it is connected to the fan load.

8-12. A 100-hp 250-volt d-c shunt motor has the magnetization curve of Fig. 8-12 and an armature resistance (including brushes) of 0.025 ohm. There are 1,000 turns per pole on the shunt field.

When the shunt-field rheostat is set for a motor speed of 1,200 rpm at no load, the armature current is 8.0 amp. How many series-field turns per pole must be added if the speed is to be 950 rpm for a load requiring an armature current of 350 amp? Neglect the added resistance of the series field.

8-13. A shunt motor operating from a 230-volt line draws a full-load armature current of 38.5 amp and runs at a speed of 1,200 rpm at both no load and full load. The following data are available on this motor:

Armature-circuit resistance (including brushes) = 0.21 ohm
Shunt-field turns per pole = 2,000 turns
Magnetization curve taken as a generator at no load and 1,200 rpm

E_a, volts.........	180	200	220	240	250
I_f, amp..........	0.74	0.86	1.10	1.45	1.70

a. Determine the shunt-field current of this motor at no load and 1,200 rpm when connected to a 230-volt line. Assume negligible armature-circuit resistance drop and armature reaction at no load.

b. Determine the effective armature reaction at full load in ampere-turns per pole.

c. How many series-field turns should be added to make this machine into a long-shunt cumulatively compounded motor whose speed will be 1,090 rpm when the armature current is 38.5 amp and the applied voltage is 230 volts? The series field will have a resistance of 0.052 ohm.

d. If a series-field winding having 25 turns per pole and a resistance of 0.052 ohm is installed, determine the speed when the armature current is 38.5 amp and the applied voltage is 230 volts.

8-14. A 10-hp 230-volt shunt motor has 2,000 shunt-field turns per pole, an armature resistance (including brushes) of 0.20 ohm, and a commutating-field resistance of 0.041 ohm. The shunt-field resistance (exclusive of rheostat) is 235 ohms. When the motor is operated at no load with rated terminal voltage and varying field resistance, the following data are taken:

Speed, rpm.....	1,110	1,130	1,160	1,200	1,240
I_f, amp.........	0.932	0.880	0.830	0.770	0.725

The no-load armature current is negligible. When the motor is operated at full load and rated terminal voltage, the armature current is 37.5 amp, the field current is 0.770 amp, and the speed is 1,180 rpm.

a. Calculate the full-load armature reaction in equivalent demagnetizing ampere-turns per pole.

b. Calculate the full-load electromagnetic torque.

c. What starting torque will the motor exert with maximum field current if the starting armature current is limited to 75 amp? The armature reaction under these conditions is 160 amp-turns per pole.

d. Design a series field to give a full-load speed of 1,100 rpm when the no-load speed is 1,200 rpm.

8-15. When operated at rated voltage, a 230-volt shunt motor runs at 1,600 rpm at full load and also at no load. The full-load armature current is 50.0 amp. The shunt-field winding has 1,000 turns per pole. The resistance of the armature circuit (including brushes and interpoles) is 0.20 ohm. The magnetization curve at 1,600 rpm is:

E_a, volts....	200	210	220	230	240	250
I_f, amp.....	0.80	0.88	0.97	1.10	1.22	1.43

a. Compute the demagnetizing effect of armature reaction at full load, in ampere-turns per pole.

b. A long-shunt cumulative series-field winding having 5 turns per pole and a resistance of 0.05 ohm is added to the machine. Compute the speed at full-load current and rated voltage, with the same shunt-field circuit resistance as in (*a*).

c. With the series-field winding of (*b*) installed, compute the internal starting torque in newton-meters if the starting armature current is limited to 100 amp and the shunt-field current has its normal value. Assume that the corresponding demagnetizing effect of armature reaction is 260 amp-turns per pole.

8-16. A weak shunt-field winding is to be added to a 50-hp 230-volt 600-rpm series hoist motor for the purpose of preventing excessive speeds at very light loads. Its resistance will be 230 ohms. The combined resistance of the interpole and armature winding (including brushes) is 0.055 ohm. The series-field winding has 24 turns per pole with a total resistance of 0.021 ohm.

In order to determine its design, the following test data were obtained before the shunt field was installed:

Load test as a series motor (output not measured):

$$V_t = 230 \text{ volts} \qquad I_a = 184 \text{ amp} \qquad n = 600 \text{ rpm}$$

No-load test with series field separately excited:

Voltage applied to armature, volts	Speed, rpm	Armature current, amp	Series-field current, amp
230	1,500	10.0	60
230	1,200	9.2	74
230	900	8.0	103
215	700	7.7	135
215	600	7.5	175
215	550	7.2	201
215	525	7.1	225
215	500	7.0	264

a. Determine the number of shunt-field turns per pole if the no-load speed at rated voltage is to be 1,500 rpm. The armature, series-field, and interpole winding resistance drops are negligible at no load.

b. Determine the speed after installation of the shunt field when the motor is operated at rated voltage with a load which results in a line current of 185 amp. Assume that the demagnetizing mmf of armature reaction is unchanged by addition of the shunt field.

8-17. *a.* A 230-volt d-c shunt-wound motor is used as an adjustable-speed drive over the range from 0 to 1,000 rpm. Speeds from 0 to 500 rpm are obtained by adjusting the armature terminal voltage from 0 to 230 volts with the field current kept constant. Speeds from 500 to 1,000 rpm are obtained by decreasing the field current with the armature terminal voltage maintained at 230 volts. Over the entire speed range, the torque required by the load remains constant.

Show the general form of the curve of armature current vs. speed over the entire range. Ignore machine losses and armature-reaction effects.

b. Suppose that, instead of keeping the load torque constant, the armature current is not to exceed a specified value. Show the general form of the curve of allowable load torque vs. speed. Conditions otherwise are as in (*a*).

8-18. *a.* Two adjustable-speed d-c shunt motors have maximum speeds of 1,650 rpm and minimum speeds of 450 rpm. Speed adjustment is obtained by field-rheostat control. Motor *A* drives a load requiring constant horsepower over the speed range; motor *B* drives one requiring constant torque. All losses and armature reaction may be neglected.

1. If the horsepower outputs are equal at 1,650 rpm and the armature currents are each 100 amp, what will be the armature currents at 450 rpm?

2. If the horsepower outputs are equal at 450 rpm and the armature currents are each 100 amp, what will be the armature currents at 1,650 rpm?

b. Answer part *a* for speed adjustment by armature-voltage control with conditions otherwise the same.

8-19. A 230-volt d-c shunt motor has an armature-circuit resistance of 0.1 ohm. This motor operates on the 230-volt mains and takes an armature current of 100 amp. An external resistance of 1.0 ohm is now inserted in series with the armature, and the electromagnetic torque and field-rheostat setting are unchanged.

a. Give the percentage change in the total current taken by the motor from the mains.

b. Give the percentage change in the speed of the motor, and state whether this will be an increase or a decrease.

8-20. A punch press is found to operate satisfactorily when driven by a 10-hp 230-volt compound motor having a no-load speed of 1,800 rpm and a full-load speed of 1,200 rpm when the torque is 43.8 lb-ft. The motor is temporarily out of service, and the only available replacement is a compound motor with the following characteristics:

> Rating = 230 volts, 12.5 hp
> No-load current = 4 amp
> No-load speed = 1,820 rpm
> Full-load speed = 1,600 rpm
> Full-load current = 57.0 amp
> Full-load torque = 43.8 lb-ft
> Armature-circuit resistance = 0.2 ohm
> Shunt-field current = 1.6 amp

It is desired to use this motor as an emergency drive for the press without making any change in its field windings.

a. How can it be made to have the desired speed regulation?

b. Draw the pertinent circuit diagram, and give complete specifications of the necessary apparatus.

8-21. Consider a d-c shunt motor connected to constant-voltage mains and driving a load requiring constant electromagnetic torque. Show that, if $E_a > 0.5V_t$ (the normal situation), increasing the resultant air-gap flux decreases the speed, whereas, if $E_a < 0.5V_t$ (as might be brought about by inserting a relatively high resistance in series with the armature), increasing the resultant air-gap flux increases the speed.

8-22. Two identical 5-hp 230-volt 17-amp d-c shunt machines are to be used as the generator and motor, respectively, in a Ward Leonard system. The generator is driven by a synchronous motor whose speed is constant at 1,200 rpm. The armature-circuit resistance of each machine is 0.47 ohm (including brushes). Armature reaction is negligible. Data for the magnetization curve of each machine at 1,200 rpm are as follows:

I_f, amp	0.2	0.4	0.6	0.8	1.0	1.2
E_a, volts	108	183	230	254	267	276

a. Compute the maximum and minimum values of generator-field current needed to give the motor a speed range from 300 to 1,500 rpm at full-load armature current (17.0 amp), with the motor-field current held constant at 0.50 amp.

b. Compute the speed regulation of the motor for the conditions of maximum speed and minimum speed found in part *a.*

c. Compute the maximum motor speed obtainable at full-load armature current if the motor-field current is reduced to 0.20 amp and the generator-field current is not allowed to exceed 1.10 amp.

8-23. One of the commonest industrial applications of d-c series motors is for crane and hoist drives. This problem relates to the computation of selected motor performance characteristics for such a drive. The specific motor concerned is a series-wound 230-volt totally enclosed motor having a ½-hr crane rating of 65 hp with a 75°C temperature rise. The performance characteristics of the motor alone on 230 volts as taken from the manufacturer's catalogue are listed in Table 8-2.

Table 8-2

Line current, amp	Shaft torque, lb-ft	Speed, rpm
50	80	940
100	210	630
150	380	530
200	545	475
250	730	438
300	910	407
350	1,105	385
400	1,365	370

The resistance of the armature (including brushes) plus commutating field is 0.090 ohm, and that of the series-field winding is 0.040 ohm. Armature reaction should be ignored. The handling of rotational and stray load losses is to be discussed in part *i* of the problem.

The motor is to be connected as in Fig. 8-18*a* for hoisting and Fig. 8-18*b* for lowering. The former connection is simply one for series-resistance control. The latter connection is one for lowering by dynamic braking with the field reconnected in shunt and having an adjustable resistance in series with it.

A few samples of the torque-speed curves determining the suitability of the motor and control for its particular application are to be plotted. Plot all these curves on the same sheet, torque horizontally and speed vertically, covering about the torque-magnitude range embraced in Table 8-2. Provide for both positive and negative values of speed, corresponding, respectively, to hoisting and lowering;

provide also for both positive and negative values of torque, corresponding, respectively, to torque in the direction of raising the load and torque in the direction of lowering the load; thus, use all four quadrants of the conventional rectangular coordinate system.

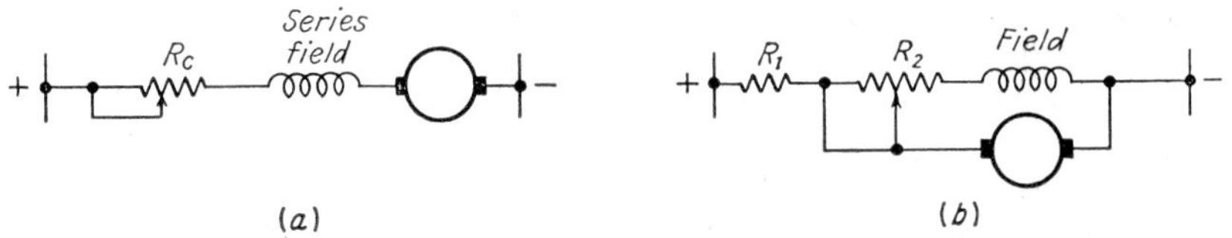

FIG. 8-18. Series crane motor, Prob. 8-23. (*a*) Hoisting connection. (*b*) Lowering connection.

a. For the hoisting connection, plot torque-speed curves for the control resistor R_c set at 0, 0.65 ohm, and 1.30 ohms. If any of these curves extend into the fourth quadrant within the range of torques covered, plot them in that region, and interpret physically what operation there means.

b. Discuss the suitability of these characteristics for the hoisting operation.

c. For the lowering connection, plot a torque-speed curve for $R_1 = 0.65$ ohm and R_2 set at 0.65 ohm. The most important portion of this curve is in the fourth quadrant, but if it extends into the third quadrant, that region should also be plotted and interpreted physically.

d. In (*c*) what is the lowering speed corresponding to rated torque?

e. How is the speed in (*d*) affected by decreasing R_2? Why?

f. How is the speed in (*d*) affected by decreasing R_1? Why?

g. How would the speed of (*d*) be affected by adding resistance in series with the motor armature? Why?

h. Discuss the suitability of these characteristics for the lowering operation.

i. What assumptions, if any, concerning rotational and stray load losses have you found it necessary to make because of having limited data on the motor? Discuss this point.

8-24. An automatic starter is to be designed for a 15-hp 230-volt shunt motor. The resistance of the armature circuit is 0.162 ohm. When operated at rated voltage and loaded until its armature current is 32 amp, the motor runs at a speed of 1,100 rpm with a field-circuit resistance of 115 ohms. When the motor is delivering rated output, the armature current is 56 amp.

The motor is to be started with a load which requires a torque proportional to speed and which under running conditions requires 15 hp. The field winding is connected across the 230-volt mains, and the resistance in series with the armature is to be adjusted automatically so that during the starting period the armature current does not exceed 200 per cent of rated value or fall below rated value. That is, the machine is to start with 200 per cent of rated armature current, and as soon as the current falls to rated value, sufficient series resistance is to be cut out to restore current to 200 per cent. This process is repeated until all the series resistance has been cut out.

a. What should be the total resistance of the starter?

b. How much resistance should be cut out at each step in the starting operation?

8-25. Figure 8-19 shows schematically the connections of the three-field Ward Leonard system mentioned at the end of Art. 8-5. The separately excited motor *M* drives the forward motion of the scoop on a very large power shovel used for open-pit strip mining of coal. The motor has a commutating winding *C* and a separately

excited field winding F_m. Its armature is connected to the armature of a generator G
having a commutating winding C and 3 field windings: a separately excited control
field F_1, a self-excited shunt field F_2, and a differential series field S. The purpose of
field S is to limit the armature current if the motor should be stalled. The exciter E
supplies a constant voltage of 250 volts to the motor field F_m and to the generator

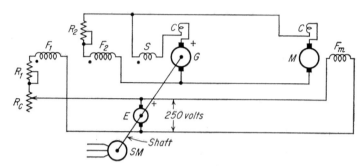

Fig. 8-19. Ward Leonard system with three-field generator, Prob. 8-25.

control field F_1. The generator G and exciter E are driven by a 2,300-volt 3-phase
synchronous motor SM.

Main generator G (rating 500 kw, 500 volts):
    S_1: 1 turn per pole, total resistance = 0.001 ohm
    F_1: 200 turns per pole, resistance = 25 ohms
    F_2: 100 turns per pole, resistance = 12 ohms
    R_1 and R_2 are fixed resistors
    R_c is the controller
    Resistance of armature plus commutating winding = 0.009 ohm
    Armature reaction negligible
  Data for the generator magnetization curve are as follows:

Field excitation, amp-turns per pole.....	500	1,000	1,500	2,000	2,500	3,000
Generated volts........................	250	450	540	585	615	640

Motor M (rating 500 volts, 1,000 amp):
    F_m: Excited at 250 volts
    With 500 volts applied to motor armature, no-load speed = 600 rpm
    Resistance of armature plus commutating winding plus cables = 0.015 ohm
    Armature reaction negligible
  The following results are required:
    a. Find the resistance of R_2 which makes the excitation line of F_2 coincide with the
magnetization-curve air-gap line.
    b. Find the resistance of R_1 which limits the stalled torque of the motor to 1.5 per
unit with $R_c = 0$.
    c. With the above settings of R_1 and R_2, plot the generator volt-ampere character-
istic and the motor speed-torque characteristic with $R_c = 0$. Use per-unit values of
the variables, with 600 rpm, 500 volts, 1,000 amp, and motor torque at 1,000 amp
as base values.

CHAPTER 9

Synchronous Machines

The elementary physical picture of how a synchronous machine works, given in Art. 3-5, emphasizes energy conversion in terms of the interactions of magnetic fields. In this chapter we shall build on these interactions to develop both a more complete picture and a quantitative theory. Through the medium of the equivalent circuit, we shall correlate this theory with the results of the self- and mutual-inductance approach in Chap. 5. Finally, with this background available, we shall treat saturation and its effects.

This chapter supplements Chap. 5 in two respects. First, a more comprehensive physical picture of internal happenings is given. Second, methods of handling saturation are developed. The latter development largely removes the most serious restriction on the idealized theory of Chap. 5.

9-1. Flux and MMF Waves in Synchronous Machines. To examine in detail the interaction of flux and mmf waves under various operating conditions, let us continue to ignore saturation for the moment. Consider the machine to be in the steady state and connected to a balanced 3-phase system capable of either absorbing or supplying electric power.

a. Cylindrical-rotor Machines. Developed sketches of the armature and field windings of a cylindrical-rotor generator are given in Figs. 9-1 and 9-2. As far as the armature winding is concerned, these are the same type of sketch used in discussing rotating magnetic fields in Art. 3-4. The results as well as the underlying assumptions of that article apply to the two cases.[1]

In both figures, the space-fundamental mmf produced by the field winding is shown by the sinusoid F. As indicated by the alternative designation B_f, this wave may also represent the corresponding component flux-density wave. Both Figs. 9-1a and 9-2a show the F wave at the specific instant when the excitation emf of phase a has its maximum

---

[1] Those who wish to examine windings and waveforms in greater detail are referred to Appendix C.

value.   The axis of the field is then 90° ahead of the axis of phase a in
order that the time rate of change of flux linkages with phase a shall be a
maximum.   The excitation emf is represented by the rotating time
phasor E_f in Figs. 9-1b and 9-2b.   The projection of this phasor on the

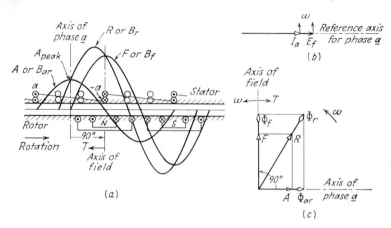

Fig. 9-1. (a) Spatial mmf and flux-density waves in a cylindrical-rotor synchronous
generator.   Armature current in phase with excitation voltage.   (b) Time phasor
diagram.   (c) Space phasor diagram.

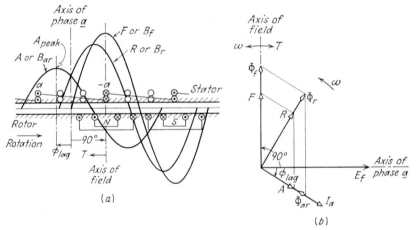

Fig. 9-2. (a) Magnetic fields in a synchronous generator.   Armature current lags
excitation voltage.   (b) Combined space and time phasor diagram.

reference axis for phase a is proportional to the instantaneous emf in the
arrow direction defined by the dots and crosses (representing the heads
and tails of arrows) in the phase a conductors.

The mmf wave created by the armature current, commonly called the
armature-reaction mmf, can now be superimposed through use of the

principles in Art. 3-4.   Recall that balanced polyphase currents in a symmetrical polyphase winding create an mmf wave whose space-fundamental component rotates at synchronous speed.   Recall also that the mmf wave is directly opposite phase a at the instant when the phase a current has its maximum value.   Figure 9-1a is drawn with I_a and E_f in phase; hence the armature reaction wave A is drawn opposite phase a because at this instant both I_a and E_f have their maximum values.   Figure 9-2a is drawn with I_a lagging E_f by the time-phase angle ϕ_{lag}; hence A is drawn behind its position in Fig. 9-1a by the space angle ϕ_{lag} because I_a has not yet reached its maximum value.   In both figures the armature-reaction wave bears the alternative designation B_{ar} to indicate that, in the absence of saturation, the armature-reaction flux-density wave is proportional to the A wave.

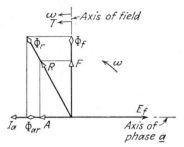

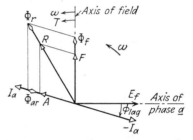

FIG. 9-3. Phasor diagram of a synchronous motor. Unity power factor with respect to excitation voltage.

FIG. 9-4. Phasor diagram of a synchronous motor. Lagging power factor with respect to excitation voltage.

The resultant magnetic field in the machine is the sum of the two components produced by the field current and armature reaction.   The resultant mmf waves R (also labeled B_r to denote that the resultant flux-density wave can be similarly represented) in Figs. 9-1a and 9-2a are obtained by graphically adding the F and A waves.   Because sinusoids can conveniently be added by phasor methods, the same addition can be performed by means of the phasor diagrams of Figs. 9-1c and 9-2b.   In these diagrams phasors are also drawn to represent the fundamental flux per pole Φ_f, Φ_{ar}, and Φ_r produced, respectively, by the mmfs F, A, and R and proportional to these mmfs with a uniform air gap and no saturation.

The air-gap flux and mmf conditions in a synchronous machine can therefore be represented by phasor diagrams like those of Figs. 9-1c and 9-2b without troubling to draw the wave diagrams.   For example, the corresponding phasor diagrams for motor action are given in Fig. 9-3 for unity power factor with respect to excitation voltage and in Fig. 9-4 for lagging power factor with respect to that voltage.   To maintain the same conventions as in Figs. 9-1 and 9-2, it is recognized that the phasor $-I_a$ rather than I_a should be in phase with or lag E_f in Figs. 9-3 and 9-4.

These phasor diagrams show how the space-phase position of the armature mmf wave with respect to the field poles depends on the time-phase angle between armature current and excitation voltage.   They are also helpful in correlating the simple, physical picture of torque production with the way in which the armature current adjusts itself to the operating conditions.

The electromagnetic torque on the rotor acts in a direction to urge the field poles into alignment with the resultant air-gap flux and armature-reaction flux waves, as shown by the arrows labeled T attached to the field axes in Figs. 9-1 to 9-4.   If the field poles lead the resultant air-gap flux wave, as in Figs. 9-1 and 9-2, the electromagnetic torque on the rotor acts in opposition to the rotation—in other words, the machine must be acting as a generator.   On the other hand, if the field poles lag the resultant air-gap flux wave, as in Figs. 9-3 and 9-4, the electromagnetic torque acts in the direction of rotation—i.e., the machine must be acting as a motor.   An alternative statement is that for generator action the field poles must be driven ahead of the resultant air-gap flux wave by the forward torque of a prime mover, while for motor action the field poles must be dragged behind the resultant air-gap flux by the retarding torque of a shaft load.

The magnitude of the torque can be expressed in terms of the resultant fundamental air-gap flux per pole Φ_r and the peak value F of the space-fundamental field-mmf wave.   From Eq. 3-37,

$$T = \frac{\pi}{2} \left(\frac{\text{poles}}{2} \right)^2 \Phi_r F \sin \delta_{RF} \qquad (9\text{-}1)$$

where δ_{RF} is the space-phase angle in electrical degrees between the resultant-flux and field-mmf waves.   When F and Φ_r are constant, the machine adjusts itself to changing torque requirements by adjusting the torque angle δ_{RF}.

Example 9-1.   Consider a synchronous machine with negligible armature resistance and leakage reactance and negligible losses to be connected to an *infinite bus* (i.e., to a system so large that its voltage and frequency remain constant regardless of the power delivered or absorbed).   The field current is kept constant at the value which causes the armature current to be zero at no load.

With the aid of phasor diagrams, describe how the machine readjusts itself to varying torque requirements.   Include both motor and generator action.

Solution.   The resultant air-gap flux Φ_r generates the voltage E_r in each armature phase.   It is usually called the air-gap voltage.   In the absence of resistance and leakage reactance, E_r must remain constant at the value of the infinite-bus voltage. At no load, the torque and δ_{RF} are zero.   With I_a also zero, A is zero, and the phasor diagram is that of Fig. 9-5a.

When shaft load is now added, causing the machine to become a motor, the rotor momentarily slows down slightly under the influence of the retarding torque and the field poles slide back in space phase with respect to the resultant air-gap flux wave;

that is, δ_{RF} increases, and the machine develops motor torque. After a transient period, steady-state operation at synchronous speed is resumed when δ_{RF} has assumed the value required to supply the load torque, as shown by point m in the torque-angle characteristic of Fig. 9-6. The phasor diagram is now as shown in Fig. 9-5b. The field mmf is no longer in phase with the resultant-flux wave, and the discrepancy in mmf must be made up by the armature reaction, thus giving rise to the armature

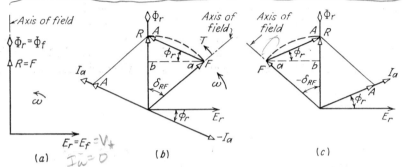

FIG. 9-5. Phasor diagrams showing the effects of shaft torque. (a) No load. (b) Motor action. (c) Generator action.

current needed to supply the electrical power input corresponding to the mechanical power output. Note that

$$F \sin \delta_{RF} = A \cos \phi_r$$

as indicated by the dashed line ab, where ϕ_r is the power-factor angle of the armature current with respect to the air-gap voltage E_r. But $A \cos \phi_r$ is proportional to the active-power component $I_a \cos \phi_r$ of the armature current, and, from Eq. 9-1, $F \sin \delta_{RF}$ is proportional to the torque. That is, the electrical active-power input is proportional to the mechanical torque output as, of course, it must be.

If, instead of being loaded as a motor, the shaft is driven forward by the torque of a prime mover, the field poles advance in phase ahead of the resultant-flux wave to an angle $-\delta_{RF}$ where the counter torque $-T$ developed by the machine equals the driving torque of the prime mover, as shown by point g in Fig. 9-6. The effects on the armature reaction and armature current are shown in the phasor diagram of Fig. 9-5c. The machine has now become a generator.

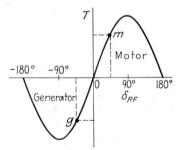

FIG. 9-6. Torque-angle characteristic.

In Fig. 9-5b and c, note that, for the components of F and A in phase with R,

$$F \cos \delta_{RF} + A \sin \phi_r = R$$

That is, not only must the active-power component $I_a \cos \phi_r$ of the armature current adjust itself to supply the torque, but also the reactive component $I_a \sin \phi_r$ must adjust itself so that the corresponding component $A \sin \phi_r$ of the armature-reaction mmf combines with the component $F \cos \delta_{RF}$ of the field mmf to produce the required resultant mmf R. The reactive kva can therefore be controlled by adjusting the field excitation.

b. Salient-pole Machines. The flux produced by an mmf wave in the uniform-air-gap machine is independent of the spatial alignment of the wave with respect to the field poles. The salient-pole machine, on the other hand, has a preferred direction of magnetization determined by the protruding field poles. The permeance along the polar, or direct, axis is appreciably greater than that along the interpolar, or quadrature, axis.

We have seen that the armature-reaction flux wave lags the field flux wave by a space angle of $90° + \phi_{\text{lag}}$, where ϕ_{lag} is the time-phase angle by which the armature current in the direction of the excitation emf lags the excitation emf. If the armature current I_a lags the excitation emf E_f by

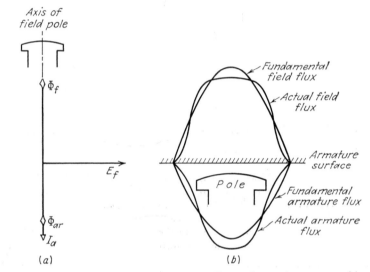

Fig. 9-7. Direct-axis air-gap fluxes in a salient-pole synchronous machine.

$90°$, the armature-reaction flux wave Φ_{ar} is directly opposite the field poles and in the opposite direction to the field flux Φ_f, as shown in the phasor diagram of Fig. 9-7a. The corresponding component flux-density waves at the armature surface produced by the field current and by the synchronously rotating space-fundamental component of armature-reaction mmf are shown in Fig. 9-7b, in which the effects of slots are neglected. The waves consist of a space fundamental and a family of odd-harmonic components. The harmonic effects usually are small (see Appendix C). Accordingly only the space-fundamental components will be considered. It is the fundamental components which are represented by the flux per pole phasors Φ_f and Φ_{ar} in Fig. 9-7a.

Conditions are quite different when the armature current is in phase with the excitation emf, as shown in the phasor diagram of Fig. 9-8a. The axis of the armature-reaction wave then is opposite an interpolar

space, as shown in Fig. 9-8b.   The armature-reaction flux wave is badly
distorted, comprising principally a fundamental and a prominent third
space harmonic.   The third-harmonic flux wave generates third-harmonic
emfs in the armature phases, but these voltages do not appear between the
line terminals (see Appendix C).

Because of the high reluctance of the air gap between poles, the space-
fundamental armature-reaction flux when the armature reaction is in
quadrature with the field poles (Fig. 9-8b) is less than the space-fundamental armature-reaction flux which would be created by the same armature current if the armature flux wave were directly opposite the field
poles (Fig. 9-7b).   Hence the magnetizing reactance is less when the

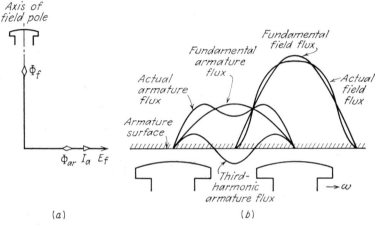

Fig. 9-8. Quadrature-axis air-gap fluxes in a salient-pole synchronous machine.

armature current is in time phase with the excitation emf (Fig. 9-8a) than
when it is in time quadrature with respect to the excitation emf (Fig.
9-7a).

The effects of salient poles can be taken into account by resolving the
armature current I_a into two components, one in time quadrature with
and the other in time phase with the excitation voltage E_f, as shown in
the phasor diagram of Fig. 9-9.   This diagram is drawn for an unsaturated salient-pole generator operating at a lagging power factor.   The
component I_d of the armature current, in time quadrature with the
excitation voltage, produces a component fundamental armature-reaction
flux Φ_{ad} along the axes of the field poles, as in Fig. 9-7.   The component
I_q, in phase with the excitation voltage, produces a component fundamental armature-reaction flux Φ_{aq} in space quadrature with the field
poles, as in Fig. 9-8.   The subscripts d and q refer to the space phase of
the armature-reaction fluxes, and not to the time phase of the component

currents producing them. Thus a *direct-axis* quantity is one whose magnetic effect is centered on the axes of the field poles. Direct-axis mmfs act on the main magnetic circuit. A *quadrature-axis* quantity is one whose magnetic effect is centered on the interpolar space. For an unsaturated machine, the armature-reaction flux Φ_{ar} is the sum of the components Φ_{ad} and Φ_{aq}. As in Fig. 9-5, the resultant flux Φ_r is the sum of Φ_{ar} and the main-field flux Φ_f.

This situation, of course, is the one already discussed in Art. 5-2 and handled by means of the dq transformation. Thus, in Fig. 5-3 the phase a mmf wave is split into two sinusoidal space components, one along the d axis and one along the q axis. In like manner, the combined armature-mmf wave for all three phases can be resolved into components

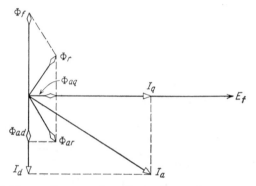

FIG. 9-9. Phasor diagram of a salient-pole synchronous generator.

along the two axes. The mmf components, acting through their individual permeances, give rise to component armature fluxes centered on these axes.

9-2. Synchronous-machine Equivalent Circuits. The foregoing flux-mmf viewpoint can readily be correlated with the steady-state equivalent circuit of Art. 5-5 if the effect of the armature-reaction flux is represented by an inductive reactance. Such replacement is made for the unsaturated machine in this article. We shall then be in a position to use the flux-mmf concepts in later articles to show how saturation effects may be incorporated in many of the theoretical considerations of Chap. 5.

a. Cylindrical-rotor Machines. The resultant air-gap flux in the machine can be considered as the phasor sum of the component fluxes created by the field and armature-reaction mmfs, respectively, as shown by phasors Φ_f, Φ_{ar}, and Φ_r in Fig. 9-10. From the viewpoint of the armature windings, these fluxes manifest themselves as generated emfs. The resultant air-gap voltage E_r can then be considered as the phasor sum of the excitation voltage E_f generated by the field flux and the voltage E_{ar}

generated by the armature-reaction flux. The component emfs E_f and E_{ar} are proportional to the field and armature currents, respectively, and each lags the flux which generates it by 90°. The armature-reaction flux Φ_{ar} is in phase with the armature current I_a, and consequently the armature-reaction emf E_{ar} lags the armature current by 90°. Thus,

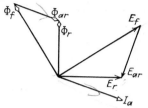

$$E_f - jI_a x_\varphi = E_r \qquad (9\text{-}2)$$

FIG. 9-10. Phasor diagram of component fluxes and corresponding voltages.

where x_φ is the constant of proportionality relating the rms values of E_{ar} and I_a. Equation 9-2 also applies to that portion of the circuit of Fig. 9-11a to the left of E_r. The effect of armature reaction therefore is simply that of an inductive reactance x_φ accounting for the component voltage generated by the space-fundamental flux created by armature reaction. This reactance is commonly called the *magnetizing reactance*, or *reactance of armature reaction*.

The air-gap voltage E_r differs from the terminal voltage by the armature-resistance and leakage-reactance voltage drops, as shown to the right of E_r in Fig. 9-11a, wherein r_a is the armature resistance, x_l is the armature leakage reactance, and V_t is the terminal voltage. All quantities are per phase (line to neutral in a Y-connected machine). The armature leakage reactance accounts for the voltages induced by the component

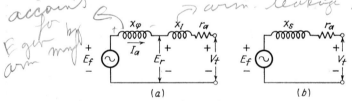

FIG. 9-11. Equivalent circuits.

fluxes which are not included in the air-gap voltage E_r. These fluxes include not only leakage across the armature slots and around the coil ends but also those associated with the space-harmonic fields created by the departure from a sinusoid necessarily present in the actual armature-mmf wave.

Finally, the equivalent circuit reduces to the form shown in Fig. 9-11b. The machine is represented on a per-phase basis by its excitation voltage E_f in series with the *synchronous impedance* $r_a + jx_s$. The synchronous reactance x_s is

$$x_s = x_\varphi + x_l \qquad (9\text{-}3)$$

This reactance, of course, is the same as that arrived at in Art. 5-5c by the coupled-circuit route. From either viewpoint, x_s takes into account all the flux produced by balanced polyphase armature currents, while the excitation voltage takes into account the flux produced by the field current. The usefulness of this equivalent circuit has already been illustrated in Arts. 5-5 and 5-6.

b. Salient-pole Machines. A very similar step applies to the salient-pole machine. Thus, the inductive effects of the *d*- and *q*-axis armature-reaction fluxes Φ_{ad} and Φ_{aq} (Fig. 9-9) can be accounted for by *d*- and *q*-axis magnetizing reactances $x_{\varphi d}$ and $x_{\varphi q}$, respectively. The *d*- and *q*-axis synchronous reactances then are

$$x_d = x_{\varphi d} + x_l \tag{9-4}$$
$$x_q = x_{\varphi q} + x_l \tag{9-5}$$

where the armature leakage reactance x_l is assumed to be the same for *d*- and *q*-axis currents. The quantities $x_{\varphi d}$ and $x_{\varphi q}$ are the reactances corresponding to the inductances $\frac{3}{2}(L_{g0} + L_{g2})$ and $\frac{3}{2}(L_{g0} - L_{g2})$, respectively, in Eqs. 5-47 and 5-48; the reactances x_d, x_q, and x_l correspond to the inductances L_d, L_q, and L_{al} in the same two equations. The associated two-reaction phasor diagrams are illustrated in Figs. 5-8 to 5-11, and applications are treated in Arts. 5-5 and 5-6.

9-3. Open-circuit and Short-circuit Characteristics. Three basic sets of characteristic curves for a synchronous machine are involved in the inclusion of saturation effects and in the determination of the appropriate machine constants. Two of these sets are discussed here; the third is considered in the next article. Except for a few remarks on the degree of validity of certain assumptions, the discussions apply to both cylindrical-rotor and salient-pole machines.

a. Open-circuit Characteristic and No-load Rotational Losses. Like the magnetization curve for a d-c machine, the open-circuit characteristic of a synchronous machine is a curve of the armature terminal voltage on open circuit as a function of the field excitation when the machine is running at synchronous speed, as shown by the curve *occ* in Fig. 9-12a. The curve often is plotted in per-unit terms as in Fig. 9-12b, where unity voltage is the rated voltage and unity field current is the excitation corresponding to rated voltage on the air-gap line. Essentially, the open-circuit characteristic represents the relation between the space-fundamental component of the air-gap flux and the mmf on the magnetic circuit when the field winding constitutes the only mmf source. When the machine is an existing one, the open-circuit characteristic is usually determined experimentally by driving it mechanically at synchronous speed with its armature terminals on open circuit and reading the terminal voltage corresponding to a series of values of field current. If the mechanical power required to drive the synchronous machine during the open-circuit test is measured, the no-load rotational losses can be obtained. These losses comprise friction, windage, and core loss corresponding to the flux in the machine at no load. The friction and windage losses at synchronous speed are constant, while the open-circuit

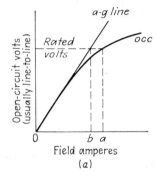 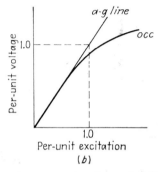

FIG. 9-12. Open-circuit characteristic. (a) In terms of volts and field amperes. (b) In per unit.

core loss is a function of the flux, which in turn is proportional to the open-circuit voltage.

The mechanical power required to drive the machine at synchronous speed and unexcited is its friction and windage loss. When the field is excited, the mechanical power equals the sum of the friction, windage, and open-circuit core loss. The open-circuit core loss therefore can be found from the difference between these two values of mechanical power. A curve of open-circuit core loss as a function of open-circuit voltage is shown in Fig. 9-13.

b. *Short-circuit Characteristic and Short-circuit Load Loss.* If the armature terminals of a synchronous machine which is being driven as a generator at synchronous speed are short-circuited through suitable ammeters, as shown in Fig. 9-14a, and the field current is gradually increased until the armature current has reached a maximum safe value

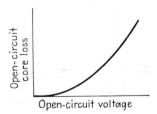

FIG. 9-13. Open-circuit core-loss curve.

(perhaps twice rated current), data can be obtained from which the short-circuit armature current can be plotted against the field current. This relation is known as the *short-circuit characteristic*. An open-circuit characteristic *occ* and a short-circuit characteristic *scc* are shown in Fig. 9-14b.

The phasor relation between the excitation voltage E_f and the steady-state armature current I_a under polyphase short-circuit conditions is

$$E_f = I_a(r_a + jx_s) \tag{9-6}$$

The phasor diagram is shown in Fig. 9-15. Because the resistance is much smaller than the synchronous reactance, the armature current lags

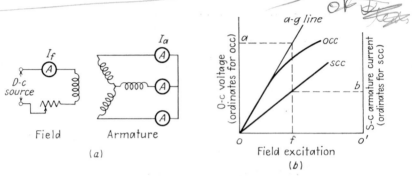

FIG. 9-14. (a) Connections for short-circuit test. (b) Open-circuit and short-circuit characteristics.

the excitation voltage by very nearly 90°. Consequently the armature-reaction–mmf wave is very nearly in line with the axis of the field poles and in opposition to the field mmf, as shown by the phasors A and F representing the space waves of armature-reaction and field mmf, respectively.

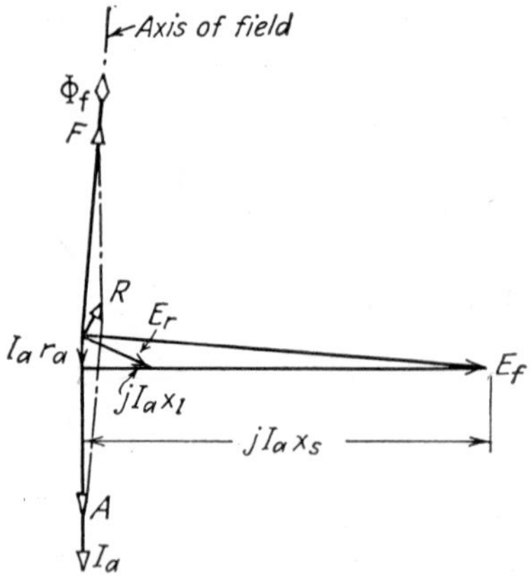

The resultant mmf creates the resultant air-gap flux wave which generates the air-gap voltage E_r equal to the voltage consumed in armature resistance r_a and leakage reactance x_l; as an equation,

$$E_r = I_a(r_a + jx_l) \tag{9-7}$$

FIG. 9-15. Phasor diagram for short-circuit conditions.

In most synchronous machines the armature resistance is negligible, and the leakage reactance is between 0.10 and 0.20 per unit—a representative value is about 0.15 per unit. That is, at rated armature current the leakage-reactance voltage drop is about 0.15 per unit. From Eq. 9-7, therefore, the air-gap voltage at rated armature current on short circuit is about 0.15 per unit; that is to say, the resultant air-gap flux is only about 0.15 of its normal-voltage value. Consequently the machine is operating

in an unsaturated condition. The short-circuit armature current therefore is directly proportional to the field current over the range from zero
to well above rated armature current.

The unsaturated synchronous reactance can be found from the open-
circuit and short-circuit data. At any convenient field excitation, such
as Of in Fig. 9-14b, the armature current on short circuit is $O'b$, and the
excitation voltage for the same field current corresponds to Oa read from
the air-gap line. Note that the voltage on the air-gap line should be
used, because the machine is operating on short circuit in an unsaturated
condition. If the voltage per phase corresponding to Oa is $E_{f(ag)}$ and
the armature current per phase corresponding to $O'b$ is $I_{a(sc)}$, then from
Eq. 9-6, with armature resistance neglected, the unsaturated value $x_{s(ag)}$
of the synchronous reactance is

$$x_{s(ag)} = \frac{E_{f(ag)}}{I_{a(sc)}} \qquad (9\text{-}8)$$

where the subscripts (ag) indicate air-
gap-line conditions. If $E_{f(ag)}$ and $I_{a(sc)}$
are expressed in per unit, the synchronous reactance will be in per unit. If
$E_{f(ag)}$ and $I_{a(sc)}$ are expressed in volts
per phase and amperes per phase,
respectively, the synchronous reactance will be in ohms per phase.

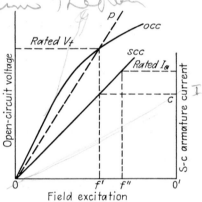

FIG. 9-16. Open-circuit and short-circuit characteristics.

For operation at or near rated terminal voltage, it is sometimes assumed
that the machine is equivalent to an
unsaturated one whose magnetization
curve is a straight line through the origin and the rated-voltage point
on the open-circuit characteristic, as shown by the dashed line Op in
Fig. 9-16. According to this approximation, the saturated value of the
synchronous reactance at rated voltage V_t is

$$x_s = \frac{V_t}{I'_{a(sc)}} \qquad (9\text{-}9)$$

where $I'_{a(sc)}$ is the armature current $O'c$ read from the short-circuit characteristic at the field current Of' corresponding to V_t on the open-circuit
characteristic, as shown in Fig. 9-16. This method of handling the effects
of saturation usually gives satisfactory results when great accuracy is not
required. A more accurate method is described in Art. 9-5.

The *short-circuit ratio* is defined as the ratio of the field current required
for rated voltage on open circuit to the field current required for rated
armature current on short circuit. That is, in Fig. 9-16 the short-circuit

ratio SCR is

$$SCR = \frac{Of'}{Of''} \tag{9-10}$$

It can be shown that the short-circuit ratio is the reciprocal of the per-unit value of the saturated synchronous reactance given by Eq. 9-9.

Example 9-2. The following data are taken from the open-circuit and short-circuit characteristics of a 45-kva 3-phase Y-connected 220-volt (line to line) 6-pole 60-cps synchronous machine:

From open-circuit characteristic:

$$\text{Line-to-line voltage} = 220 \text{ volts}$$
$$\text{Field current} = 2.84 \text{ amp}$$

From short-circuit characteristic:

Armature current, amp.........	118	152
Field current, amp.............	2.20	2.84

From air-gap line:

$$\text{Field current} = 2.20 \text{ amp}$$
$$\text{Line-to-line voltage} = 202 \text{ volts}$$

Compute the unsaturated value of the synchronous reactance, its saturated value at rated voltage in accordance with Eq. 9-9, and the short-circuit ratio. Express the synchronous reactance in ohms per phase and also in per unit on the machine rating as a base.

Solution. At a field current of 2.20 amp, the voltage to neutral on the air-gap line is

$$E_{f(ag)} = \frac{202}{\sqrt{3}} = 116.7 \text{ volts}$$

and, for the same field current, the armature current on short circuit is

$$I_{a(sc)} = 118 \text{ amp}$$

From Eq. 9-8,

$$x_{s(ag)} = \frac{116.7}{118} = 0.987 \text{ ohm per phase}$$

Note that rated armature current is $45,000/\sqrt{3}\,(220) = 118$ amp. Therefore $I_{a(sc)} = 1.00$ per unit. The corresponding air-gap-line voltage is

$$E_{f(ag)} = {}^{202}\!\!/_{220} = 0.92 \text{ per unit}$$

From Eq. 9-8 in per unit,

$$x_{s(ag)} = \frac{0.92}{1.00} = 0.92 \text{ per unit}$$

From the open-circuit and short-circuit characteristics and Eq. 9-9,

$$x_s = \frac{220}{\sqrt{3}\,(152)} = 0.836 \text{ ohm per phase}$$

In per unit, $I'_{a(sc)} = {}^{152}\!/_{118} = 1.29$, and from Eq. 9-9

$$x_s = \frac{1.00}{1.29} = 0.775 \text{ per unit}$$

From the open-circuit and short-circuit characteristics and Eq. 9-10,

$$\text{SCR} = \frac{2.84}{2.20} = 1.29$$

If the mechanical power required to drive the machine is measured while the short-circuit test is being made, information can be obtained regarding the losses caused by the armature current. The mechanical power required to drive the synchronous machine during the short-circuit test equals the sum of friction and windage plus losses caused by the armature current. The losses caused by the armature current can then be found by subtracting friction and windage from the driving power. The losses caused by the short-circuit armature current are known collectively as the *short-circuit load loss*. A curve of short-circuit load loss plotted against armature current is shown in Fig. 9-17. It is approximately parabolic.

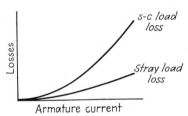

FIG. 9-17. Short-circuit load-loss and stray-load-loss curves.

The short-circuit load loss comprises copper loss in the armature winding, local core losses caused by the armature leakage flux, and a very small core loss caused by the resultant flux. The d-c resistance loss can be computed if the d-c resistance is measured and corrected, when necessary, for the temperature of the windings during the short-circuit test. For copper conductors

$$\frac{r_T}{r_t} = \frac{234.5 + T}{234.5 + t} \tag{9-11}$$

where r_T and r_t are the resistances at centigrade temperatures T and t, respectively. If this d-c resistance loss is subtracted from the short-circuit load loss, the difference will be the loss due to skin effect and eddy currents in the armature conductors plus the local core losses caused by the armature leakage flux. (The core loss caused by the resultant flux on short circuit is customarily neglected.) This difference between the short-circuit load loss and the d-c resistance loss is the additional loss caused by the alternating current in the armature. It is the stray load loss described in Art. 7-4 and is commonly considered to have the same value under normal load conditions as on short circuit. It is a function of the armature current, as shown by the curve in Fig. 9-17.

As with any a-c device, the effective resistance of the armature is the power loss attributable to the armature current divided by the square of the current. On the assumption that the stray load loss is a function of only the armature current, the effective resistance $r_{a(\text{eff})}$ of the armature can be determined from the short-circuit load loss; thus

$$r_{a(\text{eff})} = \frac{\text{short-circuit load loss}}{(\text{short-circuit armature current})^2} \qquad (9\text{-}12)$$

If the short-circuit load loss and armature current are in per unit, the effective resistance will be in per unit. If they are in watts per phase and amperes per phase, respectively, the effective resistance will be in ohms per phase. Usually it is sufficiently accurate to find the value of $r_{a(\text{eff})}$ at rated current and then to assume it to be constant.

Example 9-3. For the 45-kva 3-phase Y-connected synchronous machine of Example 9-2, at rated armature current (118 amp) the short-circuit load loss (total for 3 phases) is 1.80 kw at a temperature of 25°C. The d-c resistance of the armature at this temperature is 0.0335 ohm per phase.

Compute the armature effective resistance, in per unit and in ohms per phase at 25°C.

Solution. In per unit, the short-circuit load loss is

$$\frac{1.80}{45} = 0.040$$

at $I_a = 1.00$ per unit. Therefore

$$r_{a(\text{eff})} = \frac{0.040}{(1.00)^2} = 0.040 \text{ per unit}$$

On a per-phase basis the short-circuit load loss is

$$\frac{1,800}{3} \text{ watts per phase}$$

and consequently the effective resistance is

$$r_{a(\text{eff})} = \frac{1,800}{(3)(118)^2} = 0.043 \text{ ohm per phase}$$

The ratio of a-c to d-c resistance is

$$\frac{r_{a(\text{eff})}}{r_{a(dc)}} = \frac{0.043}{0.0335} = 1.28$$

Because this is a small machine, its per-unit resistance is relatively high. The armature resistance of machines with ratings above a few hundred kva usually is less than 0.01 per unit.

c. Saturation under Load. When a synchronous machine is loaded, magnetic conditions are determined by the combined influence of field and armature mmfs. The treatment of saturation under these circumstances is inherently a difficult problem requiring the use of judiciously chosen simplifying assumptions for its solution. The thought process has much in common with that regarding saturation effects in d-c machines and transformers.

Two assumptions usually are made, assumptions which concern principally the leakage fluxes:

1. The armature leakage reactance is assumed to be constant and independent of saturation. The leakage fluxes are in air for a considerable portion of their path lengths, so that they are relatively little affected by saturation. Tests seem to confirm the validity of this assumption. The thought process here is essentially the same as that which leads to the conclusion that the leakage reactances of a transformer should be unaffected by saturation.

2. The saturation is assumed to be determined by the resultant air-gap flux, and it is assumed that the resultant mmf corresponding to a specified value of air-gap flux is the same under load as on open circuit. The open-circuit characteristic can then be interpreted as the relation between the air-gap voltage E_r and the resultant mmf R of field excitation and armature reaction. This assumption neglects the effects of armature leakage flux on the saturation of the armature iron and of changes in field-leakage flux on the saturation of the field iron. Omission of these effects usually is not serious, because the leakage fluxes usually are small and their paths coincide with the main flux for only a small part of the main flux path. Here also the thought process is like that for transformers. Also neglected are the effect of the armature mmf on the waveform of the synchronously rotating air-gap flux wave and the effect on the flux in the body of the rotor caused by the shifting of the resultant flux wave from its no-load position with respect to the field poles. None of these effects is important in cylindrical-rotor machines, though some of them may be appreciable in salient-pole machines.

9-4. Zero-power-factor Characteristic and Potier Triangle. A special case of considerable theoretical importance is that of a synchronous machine operating at zero (or near-zero) power factor overexcited. Information needed for the handling of saturation effects at normal loads and power factors can be obtained from relatively simple tests at near-zero power factor.

Figure 9-18*a* shows a synchronous generator G supplying power to an unloaded synchronous motor M of about the same kva rating. The generator G is driven at synchronous speed. The equivalent circuit is shown in Fig. 9-18*b*, in which I_a is the armature current in the arrow direction, V_t is the terminal voltage, E_{fg} and E_{fm} are the excitation voltages, and Z_{sg} and Z_{sm} are the synchronous impedances. As a phasor,

$$I_a = \frac{E_{fg} - E_{fm}}{Z_{sg} + Z_{sm}} \tag{9-13}$$

If the difference between the two excitation voltages is made sufficiently great, the armature current can be adjusted to equal its rated full-load value. But the power required by the synchronous motor is only the small amount consumed by its losses. The power factor therefore is very nearly zero. The phasor diagram when the generator is overexcited is shown in Fig. 9-18c.

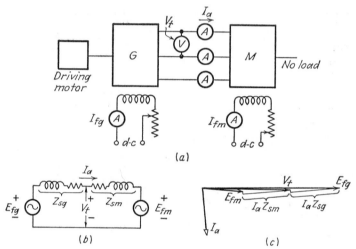

FIG. 9-18. Zero-power-factor test. (a) Connections. (b) Equivalent circuit. (c) Phasor diagram.

By varying the two field currents, data can be obtained for a curve of terminal voltage as a function of generator field current when the armature current is constant at its rated full-load value and the power factor is near zero. This curve is known as the *zero-power-factor characteristic* of the generator at rated armature current. If the generator is overexcited while the motor is underexcited, the power factor is lagging, as in Fig. 9-18c. A typical overexcited zero-power-factor characteristic is shown in Fig. 9-19. Alternatively, the motor can be overexcited while the generator is underexcited, and data can be obtained for the overexcited zero-power-factor characteristic of the synchronous motor. Because the losses have very little effect, the characteristic obtained by testing a machine as an overexcited generator at near-zero power factor is very nearly the same as that obtained by testing it as an overexcited motor at no load.

Figure 9-19 shows that the zero-power-factor curve looks like the open-circuit characteristic shifted downward and to the right.   This shape can be explained in terms of the phasor diagram and open-circuit characteristic shown in Fig. 9-20.

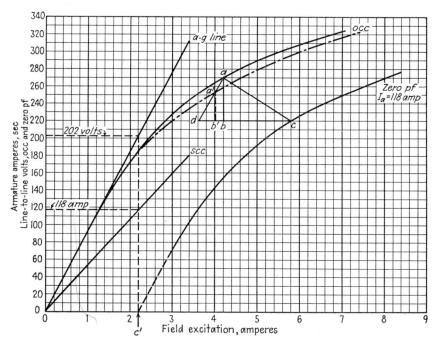

FIG. 9-19. Measured open-circuit, short-circuit, and zero-power-factor characteristics of a 3-phase Y-connected 45-kva 220-volt 118-amp 1,200-rpm 60-cps salient-pole synchronous machine.

The phasor diagram is shown in Fig. 9-20a, from which it can be seen that the terminal voltage V_t and the air-gap voltage E_r are very nearly in phase and related by the simple algebraic equation

$$V_t = E_r - I_a x_l \tag{9-14}$$

where x_l is the armature leakage reactance.   Also, the resultant mmf R and the field mmf F are very nearly in phase and related by the simple algebraic equation

$$F = R + A \tag{9-15}$$

where A is the magnitude of the armature-reaction mmf.

In accordance with Art. 9-3c, assume that the open-circuit characteristic occ in Fig. 9-20b is also the relation between the air-gap voltage E_r and the resultant mmf R under load.   Corresponding to a point a on the open-circuit characteristic is an operating point c at zero power factor for which the terminal voltage V_t is given by Eq. 9-14 and the field excitation F is given by Eq. 9-15, as shown graphically by the triangle abc in Fig. 9-20b, in which ab equals the leakage-reactance voltage drop $I_a x_l$ and bc equals the armature-reaction mmf A. If the field excitation is increased to F' and the armature current is held constant, the triangle abc remains constant in size, shifting parallel to itself to the position $a'b'c'$ with its corner a remaining on the open-circuit characteristic and its corner c tracing out the zero-power-factor characteristic. Thus, if the open-circuit characteristic were an exact relation between the air-gap voltage and the resultant mmf under load, if the leakage reactance were

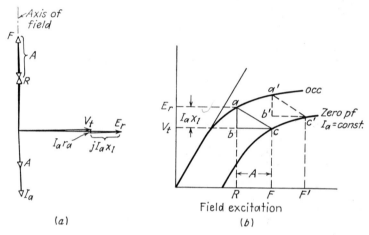

FIG. 9-20. Overexcited synchronous machine at near-zero power factor. (a) Phasor diagram. (b) Open-circuit and zero-power-factor characteristics.

constant, and if the armature resistance were zero, the zero-power-factor characteristic would be a curve of exactly the same shape as the open-circuit characteristic shifted vertically downward by an amount equal to the leakage-reactance voltage drop and horizontally to the right by an amount equal to the armature-reaction mmf.

The shape of the zero-power-factor characteristic suggests that, if the open-circuit characteristic truly represented the relation between the air-gap voltage E_r and the resultant mmf R, then the leakage reactance and armature-reaction mmf could be determined experimentally by finding a triangle, like abc of Fig. 9-20b, which would fit everywhere between the open-circuit and zero-power-factor characteristics. These test curves, together with the test short-circuit characteristic scc, are shown in Fig. 9-19. The point c', which is the extension of the zero-power-factor characteristic to zero terminal voltage, can be determined by reading from the short-circuit characteristic the field current corresponding to the armature current at which the zero-power-factor test was taken.

The geometrical construction for finding the triangle abc is as follows: Select a point c on the zero-power-factor characteristic above the knee of the curve—say, at rated voltage (Fig. 9-19). Draw the horizontal line cd equal in length to the field excitation $c'O$ on short circuit. Through point d draw the straight line da parallel to the air-gap line, intersecting the open-circuit characteristic at a. Draw the vertical line ab. The triangle abc is commonly called the *Potier triangle* after its inventor. The voltage represented by the length ab is known as the *Potier-reactance voltage drop*. The *Potier reactance* x_p is given by

$$x_p = \frac{\text{voltage drop } ab \text{ per phase}}{\text{zero-power-factor armature current } I_a \text{ per phase}} \qquad (9\text{-}16)$$

Example 9-4. Find the value of the Potier reactance of the synchronous machine of Fig. 9-19 at rated voltage. Express the result in ohms per phase and also in per unit on the rating of the machine as a base.

Solution. From the Potier triangle abc (Fig. 9-19) the Potier-reactance voltage drop ab is 50 volts, line to line, at 118 amp per phase. Therefore

$$x_p = \frac{50}{\sqrt{3}\,(118)} = 0.245 \text{ ohm per phase}$$

The per-unit value of the Potier-reactance voltage drop is $50\!\!/\!220 = 0.227$ at $I_a = 1.00$ per unit. Hence

$$x_p = \frac{0.227}{1.00} = 0.227 \text{ per unit}$$

Comparison of the Potier triangle with the triangle abc of Fig. 9-20b shows that if the relation between the air-gap voltage E_r and the resultant mmf R were exactly the same as the open-circuit characteristic, and if the leakage reactance were constant, then the Potier reactance x_p would equal the leakage reactance x_l. Also, the horizontal side bc of the Potier triangle would equal the armature-reaction mmf A corresponding to the armature current at which the zero-power factor test was taken. The same Potier triangle abc moved parallel to itself would fit between the open-circuit and zero-power-factor characteristics at any part of the curves.

The saturation curve relating the air-gap voltage E_r and the resultant mmf R under load is not, however, exactly the same as the open-circuit characteristic. The most important factor causing the discrepancy is the difference between the field-leakage flux under load and at no load. In cylindrical-rotor machines this discrepancy usually is small, and the Potier reactance usually nearly equals the armature leakage reactance.

The effects of field-leakage flux usually are more important in salient-pole machines, particularly those having long, slim poles and hence rather large field leakage. At zero power factor overexcited, the field current is larger for a given air-gap voltage than for the same voltage on open circuit. Consequently the field-leakage flux is larger, and the magnetic circuit is more saturated to an extent determined by the magnetization curve for the portion of the flux path common to the main air-gap flux and the field-leakage flux. This path includes the field poles and rotor core. The saturation curve relating the air-gap voltage and the resultant mmf at zero power factor then lies somewhat to the right of the open-circuit characteristic, as shown by the dash-dot curve in Fig. 9-19. This load saturation curve intersects the line da at a'. The armature leakage-reactance voltage drop equals the vertical distance $a'b'$, whereas the Potier-reactance voltage drop is ab. Thus, if the effects of field leakage are appreciable, the Potier reactance is somewhat larger than the armature leakage reactance. The load saturation curve and the open-circuit characteristic usually become vertically nearer together as saturation is increased to high values. The value of the armature leakage reactance can usually be measured with fair accuracy by measuring the Potier triangle at very high values of saturation.

Occasionally the effects on saturation of changes in field leakage under load are included by use of a family of load saturation curves computed with the appropriate values of field-leakage flux. This refinement will not be adopted here, however. Instead, it will be assumed that the open-circuit characteristic is also the saturation curve under load. The use of the Potier reactance at normal voltage as if it were the armature leakage reactance then makes an empirical allowance for the errors introduced by using the open-circuit characteristic as if it were the saturation curve under load.

9-5. Saturated Synchronous Machines. We now have available both the necessary physical background and the essential machine characteristics to develop methods for including saturation in synchronous-machine theory. In the first three parts of this article, we are primarily concerned with saturation under balanced steady loadings—i.e., in the effect on x_s for cylindrical-rotor machines or the very similar effect on x_d for the salient-pole case. The fourth part is devoted to the effects on other machine reactances.

a. Saturated Synchronous Reactance. The effects of saturation under load can be taken into account with good accuracy by use of a saturation factor determined from the open-circuit characteristic.[1] Although this method of handling saturation is based on simple cylindrical-rotor theory,

[1] Charles Kingsley, Jr., Saturated Synchronous Reactance, *Trans. AIEE*, vol. 54, no. 3, pp. 300–305, March, 1935.

it is also commonly applied as an approximation to salient-pole machines, with satisfactory results over the normal operating range.

According to the assumptions of Art. 9-3c, conditions in the magnetic circuit are determined by the air-gap voltage E_r and the resultant mmf R read from the saturation curve, as shown by point a in Fig. 9-21. If it were not for the effects of saturation, however, the resultant mmf corresponding to E_r would be the value R_{ag} read from the air-gap line. The degree of saturation can be described in terms of a *saturation factor* k defined as

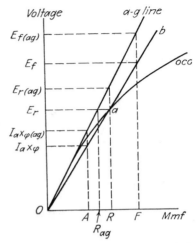

$$k = \frac{R}{R_{ag}} \qquad (9\text{-}17)$$

It can be shown by simple proportion that k is also given by

$$k = \frac{E_{r(ag)}}{E_r} \qquad (9\text{-}18)$$

FIG. 9-21. Open-circuit characteristic, showing the effects of saturation on the component mmfs and voltages.

where $E_{r(ag)}$ is the voltage corresponding to the resultant mmf R as read from the air-gap line. The saturation factor k is a function of the air-gap voltage E_r, as shown by the curve k in Fig. 9-22.

If it were not for the effects of saturation, the excitation voltage would equal the voltage $E_{f(ag)}$ read from the air-gap line corresponding to the

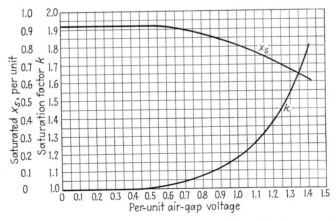

FIG. 9-22. Curves of saturation factor k and saturated synchronous reactance x_s as functions of air-gap voltage for machine of Fig. 9-19.

field mmf F, as shown in Fig. 9-21, and the voltage generated by the armature-reaction flux would be $I_a x_{\varphi(ag)}$ on the air-gap line corresponding to the armature-reaction mmf A, where $x_{\varphi(ag)}$ is the *unsaturated value* of the magnetizing reactance. In terms of the unsaturated value $x_{s(ag)}$ of the synchronous reactance

$$x_{\varphi(ag)} = x_{s(ag)} - x_l \tag{9-19}$$

where x_l is the leakage reactance.

Because of the effects of saturation, however, the reluctance of the magnetic circuit is k times its unsaturated value, and the component fluxes are reduced to $1/k$ times their unsaturated values. Under *saturated* conditions the excitation voltage E_f therefore is

$$E_f = \frac{E_{f(ag)}}{k} \tag{9-20}$$

and the *saturated value* x_φ of the magnetizing reactance is

$$x_\varphi = \frac{x_{\varphi(ag)}}{k} = \frac{x_{s(ag)} - x_l}{k} \tag{9-21}$$

The *saturated synchronous reactance* x_s then is

$$x_s = x_l + \frac{x_{s(ag)} - x_l}{k} \tag{9-22}$$

In accordance with the assumptions of Art. 9-4, the Potier reactance x_p may be used in place of the leakage reactance x_l when the open-circuit characteristic is used as the saturation curve under load. The saturated synchronous reactance is a function of the air-gap voltage, as shown by the curve x_s in Fig. 9-22.

Comparison of Eqs. 9-20 and 9-21 with Fig. 9-21 shows that the saturated values of the component voltages generated by the component fluxes produced by field excitation and armature reaction are given by readings taken from the straight line Oab drawn through the point a on the saturation curve at the air-gap voltage E_r. In other words, the machine has been linearized at the magnetic state corresponding to the resultant flux. If the reluctance of the magnetic circuit stayed constant, the component mmfs F and A would then create component fluxes and voltages along the straight line Oab, as shown by the voltage readings E_f and $I_a x_\varphi$ in Fig. 9-21.

Example 9-5. Compute the field current required for a power factor of 0.80, leading current, when the 45-kva synchronous machine of Fig. 9-19 is running as a synchronous motor at a terminal voltage of 230 volts and with a power input to its armature of 45 kw.

Solution. The phasor diagram is shown in Fig. 9-23, in which I_a represents motor input current. The per-unit system of units will be used. From Example 9-2,

$x_{s(ag)}$ = 0.92 per unit, and from Example 9-4, x_p = 0.227 per unit.   Since this is a small machine, armature-resistance voltage drop is appreciable, but refinements such as the effects of temperature on resistance may be neglected.   From Example 9-3,

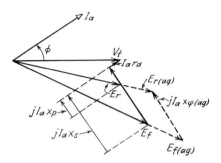

Fig. 9-23. Phasor diagram of a saturated synchronous motor, Example 9-5.

$r_{a(eff)}$ = 0.040 per unit.   (The d-c resistance may be used without introducing appreciable error.)   The voltage V_t in per unit is $^{230}\!/_{220}$ = 1.045, and the kva input is 1.00/0.80 = 1.25 per unit.   With V_t as the reference phasor,

$$I_a = \frac{1.25}{1.045}\,(0.80 + j0.60) = 0.956 + j0.718 \text{ per unit}$$

The next step is to compute the air-gap voltage E_r, so that the saturation can be determined.   From Fig. 9-23,

$$E_r = V_t - I_a(r_a + jx_p)$$
$$= 1.045 - (0.956 + j0.718)(0.040 + j0.227) = 1.170 - j0.246$$

The magnitude of E_r = 1.20 per unit.   We can then proceed in either of the two ways shown below:

1. From the curves of Fig. 9-22 at E_r = 1.20, k = 1.375, and x_s = 0.730.   The saturated value E_f of the excitation voltage is given by

$$E_f = V_t - I_a(r_a + jx_s)$$
$$= 1.045 - (0.956 + j0.718)(0.040 + j0.730) = 1.531 - j0.727$$

The magnitude of E_f = 1.70.   This can be translated to field current by computing the corresponding air-gap-line value; thus, from Eq. 9-20

$$E_{f(ag)} = kE_f = (1.375)(1.70) = 2.33$$

This is the per-unit value of the field excitation, when unit excitation is defined as the value corresponding to unit voltage on the air-gap line, as in Fig. 9-12b.   For the machine of this problem, from Fig. 9-19, 1.00 per-unit excitation is 2.40 field amperes. Therefore the field current for the specified load is

$$I_f = (2.33)(2.40) = 5.60 \text{ amp}$$

2. If the curves of Fig. 9-22 have not been plotted, the saturation factor k can be determined directly from Fig. 9-21.   Then, from Eq. 9-18, the unsaturated value of the air-gap voltage is

$$E_{r(ag)} = kE_r$$

as shown by the dotted phasor $E_{r(ag)}$ in Fig. 9-23. The unsaturated value of the excitation voltage is

$$E_{f(ag)} = E_{r(ag)} - jI_a x_{\varphi(ag)}$$

as shown by the dotted phasor in Fig. 9-23, where $x_{\varphi(ag)}$ is found from Eq. 9-19 with x_p used in place of x_l; the magnitude of $E_{f(ag)}$ is, of course, identical with the value found by the first method. As before, the corresponding field current is 5.60 amp. The value obtained by an actual load test is

$$I_{f(\text{test})} = 5.50 \text{ amp}$$

Results calculated by these methods usually check tests with errors of only a few per cent for normally saturated machines of either cylindrical-rotor or salient-pole construction.

b. Approximations. The methods of handling saturation illustrated in Example 9-5 are well suited to problems in which the air-gap voltage is known or can readily be computed. It may be necessary to resort to a cut-and-try process when the data are given in such a way that the air-gap voltage cannot be computed directly. The difficulties encountered and two approximate methods of handling saturation are illustrated in the following example.

Example 9-6. A turboalternator supplies power to a large system through a transmission line, as shown in Fig. 9-24a. The receiving system may be considered

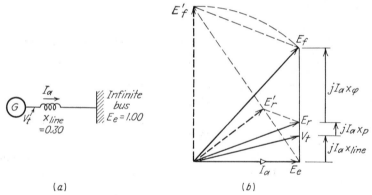

Fig. 9-24. Synchronous generator and transmission line, Example 9-6. (a) Single-line diagram. (b) Phasor diagram.

an infinite bus whose voltage $E_e = 1.00$ per unit. The line has a reactance of 0.30 per unit on the generator rating as a base. The unsaturated value of the synchronous reactance of the generator is $x_{s(ag)} = 0.970$ per unit, and its Potier reactance at rated voltage is $x_p = 0.105$ per unit. Resistances can be neglected. The saturation factor of the generator is given in Fig. 9-25.

Let the generator excitation be adjusted so that the power factor is 1.00 at the receiving end of the line when the generator delivers rated current. The excitation is then held constant.

Compute the steady-state power limit of the system on the assumption that the

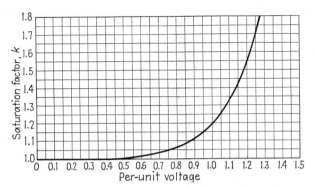

Fig. 9-25. Saturation factor k for machine of Example 9-6.

saturation of the machine stays constant at the value corresponding to the stated initial operating conditions. Discuss the effects of this assumption.

Solution. The phasor diagram for the stated initial conditions is shown by the solid lines in Fig. 9-24b, with the voltage E_e as the reference phasor. The air-gap voltage E_r is

$$E_r = E_e + jI_a(x_{\text{line}} + x_p)$$
$$= 1.00 + j(1.00)(0.405) = 1.00 + j0.405$$

The magnitude of E_r is 1.08, and, from Fig. 9-25, $k = 1.30$. From Eq. 9-22, the saturated synchronous reactance is

$$x_s = 0.105 + \frac{0.970 - 0.105}{1.30} = 0.770$$

and the saturated value of the complete system reactance is

$$x_{\text{total}} = x_{\text{line}} + x_s = 1.07$$

The saturated value of the excitation voltage is

$$E_f = E_e + jI_a x_{\text{total}} = 1.00 + j1.07$$

and the magnitude of E_f is 1.46 per unit. The initial values have now been computed.

If it is assumed that the saturation stays constant when the driving torque of the prime mover is increased, the power limit would occur when the angle by which the excitation voltage leads the receiver-bus voltage becomes 90°, as shown by the dashed phasor E_f' in Fig. 9-24b. The corresponding power limit for constant excitation is

$$P_{\text{max}} = \frac{E_f E_e}{x_{\text{total}}} = \frac{(1.46)(1.00)}{1.07} = 1.37 \text{ per unit}$$

However, the saturation actually does not stay constant. When the excitation voltage has swung to the position E_f', the air-gap voltage has decreased as shown by the phasor E_r' in Fig. 9-24b. The saturation therefore has decreased. The saturated values of E_f and x_φ are not constant, and, strictly speaking, the power limit does not occur at exactly 90°. In general, the saturation decreases as the power limit is approached. The field current therefore is able to produce a larger component flux, and the maximum power actually is somewhat larger than the value computed here.

A much longer calculation based on the method described by Kingsley[1] gives $P_{max} =$ 1.45.

Sometimes it is assumed that the saturation is determined by the *terminal voltage* (rather than by the air-gap voltage) and that the leakage reactance and magnetizing reactance both are reduced by the effects of saturation. With these assumptions, the saturated value of the synchronous reactance is

$$x_s = \frac{x_{s(ag)}}{k_t}$$

where k_t is the saturation factor at the terminal voltage. Note that this method of handling saturation is the same as the approximate method of Eq. 9-9 and Fig. 9-16. Although this method probably does not reflect the true state of affairs in the magnetic circuit as accurately as does Eq. 9-22, it has the advantage of simplicity. Recomputation of the power limit on this basis gives a value of 1.36 per unit.

c. ASA Method. The method of handling saturation recommended by the ASA is primarily concerned with the calculation of field current for specified conditions of terminal voltage, armature current, and power factor. Essentially it consists in treating the machine as an unsaturated one and then adding an additional component of excitation to account for saturation. This additional component is found from the saturation corresponding to the air-gap voltage. The same data are required as for the saturated-synchronous-reactance method of Example 9-5, the computations are similar, and the results are almost identical. The essentials of the method are described in the following example. We shall, however, depart slightly from the ASA method in the working out of details.

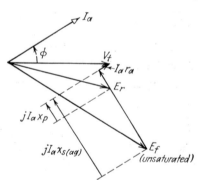

FIG. 9-26. Phasor diagram of synchronous motor with saturation neglected, Example 9-7.

Example 9-7. Solve Example 9-5 by the ASA method.

Solution. First the field current will be computed, neglecting saturation. The constants of the machine are given in Example 9-5. The phasor diagram is shown in Fig. 9-26, wherein I_a represents motor input current. The per-unit values of V_t and I_a are the same as in Example 9-5. If the machine were unsaturated, the excitation

[1] *Ibid.*

voltage E_f (unsaturated) would be

$$E_f \text{ (unsaturated)} = V_t - I_a(r_a + jx_{s(ag)})$$
$$= 1.045 - (0.956 + j0.718)(0.040 + j0.92) = 1.667 - j0.909$$

The magnitude of E_f (unsaturated) is 1.90 per unit. The corresponding field current on the air-gap line is

$$I_{f(ag)} = (1.90)(2.40) = 4.55 \text{ amp}$$

where 2.40 amp is the field current corresponding to 1.00 per-unit voltage (220 volts) on the air-gap line in Fig. 9-19.

The increment in field current caused by saturation is now found from the air-gap voltage and the open-circuit characteristic. The air-gap voltage E_r is 1.20 per unit, or 264 volts line to line. From Fig. 9-19, the corresponding field current on the open-circuit characteristic is 3.95 amp and on the air-gap line is 2.87 amp. The increment ΔI_f caused by saturation is

$$\Delta I_f = 3.95 - 2.87 = 1.08 \text{ amp}$$

In the ASA method this increment is added directly to the field current computed without saturation. Accordingly the field current corrected for saturation is

$$I_f = I_{f(ag)} + \Delta I_f = 4.55 + 1.08 = 5.63 \text{ amp}$$

Compare with the value of 5.60 amp computed in Example 9-5 and the value, 5.50 amp, obtained by an actual load test.

d. Effect of Saturation on Other Machine Reactances. Both the synchronous reactance x_s of a round-rotor machine and the d-axis synchronous reactance x_d of a salient-pole machine may be adjusted for saturation in accordance with Eq. 9-22. Many of the transient and dynamic problems of Chap. 5, however, require knowledge of how saturation affects the reactances x_q, x_d', x_q', x_d'', and x_q''.

The open-circuit characteristic of a machine is essentially a d-axis magnetization curve. It is ordinarily not feasible to obtain a q-axis magnetization curve. Instead of paralleling the adjustment method for x_d, therefore, one of the following two somewhat arbitrary procedures is often used in treating x_q:

1. The reactance x_q is assumed to be unaffected by saturation. This procedure is suitable for most practical purposes, especially where appreciable external impedance is associated with the machine. It is equivalent to saying that, because of the interpolar air space, saturation in the iron portions of the q-axis magnetic circuit plays only a negligible part in determining the permeance.

2. Quadrature-axis saturation is included through the use of two saturation factors, one dependent on total flux and one on direct-axis flux. This procedure is relatively complicated and will not be treated here.[1]

[1] See S. B. Crary, L. A. March, and L. P. Shildneck, Equivalent Reactance of Synchronous Machines, *Trans. AIEE*, vol. 53, no. 1, pp. 124–132, January, 1934.

The d-axis transient and subtransient reactances x_d' and x_d'' are predominantly determined by armature leakage and field or damper-winding leakage, although magnetizing or mutual reactances also enter. They are therefore influenced by saturation to a lesser extent than is x_d. Nevertheless they are influenced, for the heavy armature currents during a disturbance tend to increase the saturation in the leakage-flux paths as well as in the main-flux paths. Usually two values of each reactance are available. One, called the *rated-voltage*, or *saturated*, *value*, is determined from short-circuit tests in which the field current is adjusted to give rated prefault terminal voltage. The other, called the *rated-current*, or *unsaturated*, *value*, is found from short-circuit tests with the field current reduced so that the initial symmetrical transient or subtransient current is equal to rated current.[1]

The rated-voltage value of these reactances is usually 10 to 15 per cent lower than the rated-current value. The choice between them for any specific application is determined by judgment as to suitability to the circumstances and by relative conservatism in the results. For studies involving circuit-interruption duties, protective-relay settings, and short-circuit stresses, the rated-voltage value ordinarily is used. For stability studies, the rated-current value is usually employed because it leads to conservative synchronizing powers and torques.

The q-axis transient and subtransient reactances x_q' and x_q'' also vary with saturation. Since x_q and x_q' are equal for salient-pole machines, they are treated alike in that case. For solid-rotor turboalternators x_q' and x_d' may be treated in the same manner since they are approximately equal. The subtransient reactance x_q'' is handled in the same manner as x_d''.

9-6. Reactance Measurement. The d-axis machine reactances may all be found from short-circuit tests. The synchronous reactance x_d may be obtained from a steady-state short-circuit test as described in Art. 9-3b. The transient and subtransient reactances x_d' and x_d'' are found from tests in which sudden 3-phase short-circuits are applied and oscillograms taken of the short-circuit current. With the d-c component removed, the typical oscillogram and its analysis are illustrated in Figs. 5-32 to 5-34. Use of the current Oa (Fig. 5-33) in conjunction with the peak value of prefault phase voltage gives x_d'; use of Ob leads to x_d''.

Measurement of the q-axis reactances requires special techniques, however, to ensure that only the q-axis magnetic and electric circuits are involved. Two methods of measuring x_q are the slip test and the maximum-lagging-current test.

In the *slip test* the machine is driven mechanically at a speed slightly different from synchronous speed, with its field winding open, and with

---

[1] For a more comprehensive discussion, see L. A. Kilgore, Effects of Saturation on Machine Reactances, *Trans. AIEE*, vol. 54, no. 5, pp. 545–550, May, 1935.

balanced polyphase voltages of the correct phase sequence applied to its armature terminals.   Under these conditions the armature-mmf wave glides slowly past the field poles at slip speed.   Oscillograms are taken of the armature current, voltage applied to the armature terminals, and voltage induced in the open field winding.   Figure 9-27 shows the general appearance of the oscillograms, but for the sake of clarity a much larger value of slip is shown than would be used in practice.   When the armature-mmf wave is in line with the axes of the field poles, the impedance of the machine equals its d-axis value.   One-quarter of a slip cycle later the

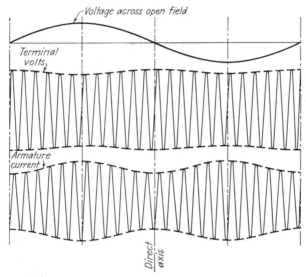

FIG. 9-27. General appearance of oscillograms in slip test.

armature-mmf wave is in line with the q axis, and the impedance equals its q-axis value.   If the armature resistance is negligible, the d-axis synchronous reactance x_d equals the maximum ratio of armature applied voltage per phase to armature current per phase and occurs when the instantaneous voltage induced in the field winding is zero.   The q-axis synchronous reactance x_q is the minimum value of this ratio and occurs when the instantaneous voltage induced in the field winding has its maximum value.   Best results for x_q can be obtained by finding the ratio x_q/x_d from the slip test and using the value of x_d from the open-circuit and short-circuit tests.

The principal shortcoming of the slip test is that large errors may be produced by the effects of current induced in rotor circuits such as damper windings, unless the slip is made to be very small.   It may be difficult to meet this condition because of the tendency of the machine to lock into step and run as a reluctance motor in synchronism with the armature-mmf wave. Usually, therefore, the test must be made at small values of armature voltage. The value obtained for x_q then is its unsaturated value. Since oscillograms usually must be taken, the accuracy of the results is limited by the accuracy with which the oscillograms can be read.

The *maximum-lagging-current* test avoids both these difficulties. For this test the machine is run as an unloaded synchronous motor with normal balanced polyphase voltages applied to its armature terminals. The field current is reduced to zero. The machine is then running as a reluctance motor. The polarity of the field current is then reversed and a small field current applied in the reversed (i.e., negative) direction, causing an increase in armature current. By increasing the negative excitation in small increments the maximum stable armature current is found. Any further increase in negative excitation causes the machine to fall out of step momentarily. Usually it will pull back into synchronism after slipping a pole. It may be shown that the quadrature-axis synchronous reactance is then given approximately by

$$x_q = \frac{V_t}{I_{a(po)}} \qquad (9\text{-}23)$$

where V_t is the armature terminal voltage per phase and $I_{a(po)}$ is the stable armature current per phase when the machine is on the point of, but has not yet begun, slipping a pole.

An advantage of the maximum-lagging-current test over the slip test is that the former can be made at normal voltage and the value of x_q under approximately normal conditions of saturation can be found.

A modification of the slip test is used to determine x_q' for turbine-generators, where x_q and x_q' are not equal. With the rotor magnetized in the q axis (i.e., at the instant of maximum field voltage, positive or negative, Fig. 9-27), the applied armature voltage is suddenly disconnected, and the decay of machine terminal voltage is recorded oscillographically. This terminal voltage is then extrapolated to zero time with the first few cycles of rapid decrement ignored. The extrapolation is carried out in the same manner as illustrated in Figs. 5-32 to 5-34 for short-circuit current. If V_t' is the extrapolated voltage and V_t the terminal voltage just before opening the armature circuit, then

$$x_q' = \frac{V_t - V_t'}{V_t} x_q \qquad (9\text{-}24)$$

The method has the same drawbacks inherent in the slip test for x_q.

To find x_q'', a test may be conducted with the rotor stationary and the field winding short-circuited. A single-phase voltage is applied across

2 armature terminals—i.e., across 2 phases in series for a Y-connected machine. When the rotor position is adjusted so that the induced field current is a minimum, the axis of the pulsating armature mmf is in line with the q axis. Half the ratio of the applied voltage to the armature current then gives x_q'' for 1 phase. The same process with the rotor in the position of maximum induced field current yields x_d''.

9-7. Steady-state Operating Characteristics. The principal steady-state operating characteristics are the interrelations among terminal voltage, field current, armature current, and power factor, and the efficiency. A selection of performance curves which are of importance in practical application of the machines is presented here. All of them can

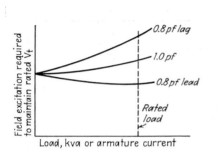

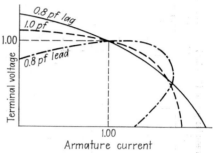

FIG. 9-28. Generator compounding curves.   FIG. 9-29. Generator constant-field-current volt-ampere characteristics.

be computed for application studies by the methods presented in this chapter.

Consider a synchronous generator delivering power at constant frequency to a load whose power factor is constant. The curve showing the field current required to maintain rated terminal voltage as the constant-power-factor load is varied is known as a *compounding curve*. Three compounding curves at various constant power factors are shown in Fig. 9-28.

If the field current is held constant while the load varies, the terminal voltage will vary. Characteristic curves of terminal voltage plotted against armature current for three constant power factors are shown in Fig. 9-29. Each curve is drawn for a different value of constant field current. In each case, the field current equals the value required to give rated terminal voltage at rated armature current and corresponds to the rated-armature-current value read from the compounding curves (Fig. 9-28).

Synchronous generators are usually rated in terms of the maximum kva load at a specific voltage and power factor (often 80, 85, or 90 per cent lagging) which they can carry continuously without overheating.

The active power output of the generator is usually limited to a value within the kva rating by the capability of its prime mover. By virtue of its voltage-regulating system, the machine normally operates at a constant voltage whose value is within ±5 per cent of rated voltage. When the active-power loading and voltage are fixed, the allowable reactive-power loading is limited by either armature or field heating. A typical set of reactive-power capability curves for a large turbine-generator are shown in Fig. 9-30. They give the maximum reactive-power

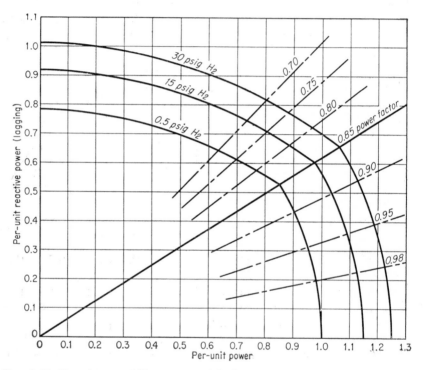

FIG. 9-30. Reactive capability curves of hydrogen-cooled turbine-generator, 0.85 power factor, 0.80 short-circuit ratio. Base kva is rated kva at 0.5 lb hydrogen.

loadings corresponding to various power loadings with operation at rated voltage. Armature heating is the limiting factor in the region from unity to rated power factor (0.85 in Fig. 9-30). For lower power factors, field heating is limiting. Such a set of curves forms a valuable guide in planning and operating the system of which the generator is a part. Also shown in Fig. 9-30 is the effect of increased hydrogen pressure on allowable machine loadings.

The power factor at which a synchronous motor operates, and hence its armature current, can be controlled by adjusting its field excitation.

The curve showing the relation between armature current and field current at a constant terminal voltage and with a constant shaft load is known as a V *curve* because of its characteristic shape. A family of V curves is shown in Fig. 9-31. For constant power output, armature current is, of course, a minimum at unity power factor and increases as power factor decreases. The dashed lines are loci of constant power factor. They are the synchronous-motor compounding curves showing how the field current must be varied as load is changed in order to maintain constant power factor. Points to the right of the unity-power-factor compounding curve correspond to overexcitation and leading current input; points to the left correspond to underexcitation and lagging current input. The synchronous-motor compounding curves are very

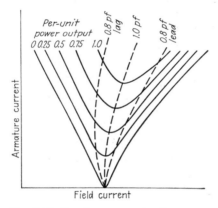

Fig. 9-31. Synchronous-motor V curves.

similar to the generator compounding curves of Fig. 9-28. (Note the interchange of armature-current and field-current axes when comparing Figs. 9-28 and 9-31.) In fact, if it were not for the small effects of armature resistance, the motor and generator compounding curves would be identical except that the lagging- and leading-power-factor curves would be interchanged.

As in all electromagnetic machines, the losses in synchronous machines comprise I^2R losses in the windings, core losses, and mechanical losses. The conventional efficiency is computed in accordance with a set of rules agreed upon by the ASA. The general principles upon which these rules are based are described in Art. 7-4. The purpose of the following example is to show how these rules are applied specifically to synchronous machines.

Example 9-8. Data are given in Fig. 9-32 with respect to the losses of the 45-kva synchronous machine of Examples 9-2 and 9-3. Compute its efficiency when running as a synchronous motor at a terminal voltage of 230 volts and with a power input

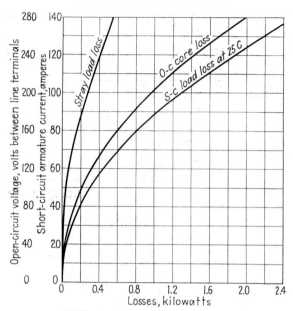

Friction and windage loss = 0.91 kw
Armature d-c resistance at 25C = 0.0335 ohm per phase
Field-winding resistance at 25 C = 29.8 ohms

FIG. 9-32. Losses in 3-phase 45-kva Y-connected 220-volt 60-cps 6-pole synchronous machine, Example 9-8.

to its armature of 45 kw at 0.80 power factor, leading current. The field current measured in a load test taken under these conditions is I_f (test) = 5.50 amp.

Solution. For the specified operating conditions, the armature current is

$$I_a = \frac{45,000}{\sqrt{3}\,(230)(0.80)} = 141 \text{ amp}$$

The copper losses are to be computed on the basis of the d-c resistances of the windings at 75°C. Correcting the winding resistances by means of Eq. 9-11 gives

Field-winding resistance r_f at 75°C = 35.5 ohms
Armature d-c resistance r_a at 75°C = 0.0399 ohm per phase

The field copper loss is

$$I_f^2 r_f = (5.50)^2(35.5) = 1,070 \text{ watts, or } 1.07 \text{ kw}$$

According to the ASA Standards, field-rheostat and exciter losses are not charged against the machine. The armature copper loss is

$$3I_a^2 r_a = (3)(141)^2(0.0399) = 2,380 \text{ watts, or } 2.38 \text{ kw}$$

and from Fig. 9-32, at I_a = 141 amp, stray load loss = 0.56 kw. According to the ASA Standards, no temperature correction is to be applied to the stray load loss.

The core loss is read from the open-circuit core-loss curve at a voltage equal to the internal voltage behind the resistance of the machine. The stray load loss is considered to account for the losses caused by the armature leakage flux. For motor action this internal voltage is, as a phasor,

$$V_t - I_a r_a = \frac{230}{\sqrt{3}} - 141(0.80 + j0.60)(0.0399)$$

$$= 128.4 - j3.4$$

The magnitude is 128.4 volts per phase, or 222 volts between line terminals. From Fig. 9-32, open-circuit core loss = 1.20 kw. Also, friction and windage loss = 0.91 kw. All losses have now been found.

$$\text{Total losses} = 1.07 + 2.38 + 0.56 + 1.20 + 0.91 = 6.12 \text{ kw}$$

The power input is the sum of the a-c input to the armature and the d-c input to the field, or

$$\text{Input} = 46.07 \text{ kw}$$

Therefore $$\text{Efficiency} = 1 - \frac{\text{losses}}{\text{input}} = 1 - \frac{6.12}{46.1} = 0.867$$

9-8. Résumé. The basic theoretical treatment of synchronous machines in Chap. 5 is extended in two important respects in the present chapter. First, the behavior is viewed in terms of interaction of flux and mmf waves in order to correlate theory with physical conditions in the machine. Second, methods for handling the nonlinearities arising from magnetic saturation are developed on the basis of this correlation.

The physical picture of the internal workings in terms of rotating magnetic fields is rather simple. It is that of Art. 3-3: interaction of component fields of rotor and stator when the two are stationary with respect to each other. For both round-rotor and salient-pole machines, the component fields and mmfs, together with the associated voltages and current, can be represented on phasor diagrams like those of Figs. 9-2b and 9-9. The phasor diagrams in turn lead to the concept of the synchronous reactances x_s, x_d, and x_q. These, of course, are the same reactances dealt with in Arts. 5-5 and 5-6, but now they are derived by replacing the effect of the rotating armature-reaction wave by magnetizing reactances x_φ or $x_{\varphi d}$ and $x_{\varphi q}$. Thus, the circuit representations of Chap. 5 are correlated for balanced, steady operation with the flux-mmf viewpoint.

This viewpoint then forms the basis for including saturation effects in our earlier analysis. The required machine characteristics are the open-circuit, short-circuit, and zero-power-factor curves.

The handling of saturation is an excellent example of the engineering approach to problems which are inherently so complex that an exact solution is hopeless. By the use of judiciously chosen simplifying assumptions based on a physical picture of what goes on, a reasonably simple quantitative theory can be formulated and checked against actual load tests. These assumptions are that the leakage reactance is constant and that the open-circuit characteristic can be used as if it were the saturation curve relating air-gap voltage and resultant mmf under load. The thought process has much in common with that applying to d-c machines and transformers. With these assumptions, the degree of saturation can be described quantitatively in terms of a saturation factor k which is a function of the air-gap voltage as in Eq. 9-18. The synchronous reactance is assumed to consist of a constant part and a part which is affected by saturation. The constant part can be found by means of the Potier triangle (Fig. 9-19), which is based on the assumption that the overexcited zero-power-factor characteristic is identical with the open-circuit characteristic shifted vertically downward by a constant voltage drop and horizontally to the right by a constant mmf. The use of the Potier reactance in saturation problems as if it were the leakage reactance makes an empirical allowance for errors resulting from use of the open-circuit characteristic as if it were the saturation curve under load.

The synchronous reactance x_s of a round-rotor machine or x_d for a salient-pole machine may thus be continuously adjusted for saturation as the machine operating conditions change. In general, the remaining reactances x_q, x_d', x_q', x_d'', and x_q'' are affected to an appreciably smaller extent. They may therefore be handled by cruder approximations. Often these approximations take the form of deciding between a saturated and an unsaturated value in accordance with the conditions of the problem and the effects of saturation on the conservatism of the results.

PROBLEMS

9-1. *a.* Draw wave and phasor diagrams like those of Figs. 9-1 and 9-2 but for a synchronous generator whose armature current leads the excitation voltage.

b. Draw a phasor diagram like those of Figs. 9-3 and 9-4 but for a synchronous motor having leading power factor with respect to the excitation voltage.

9-2. A synchronous generator is supplying power to a large system with its field current adjusted so that the armature current lags the terminal voltage. Armature resistance and leakage reactance may be neglected.

The field current is now increased 10 per cent without changing the driving torque of the prime mover. Qualitatively, what changes occur in power output, in magnitude and phase of the armature current, and in magnitude of the torque angle δ_{RF}? Explain by means of phasor diagrams representing the flux and mmf waves.

If, instead of changing the field current, the driving torque of the prime mover is increased 10 per cent, what changes will occur?

9-3. A synchronous motor is operating at half load. An increase in its field excitation causes a decrease in armature current. Before the increase, was the motor delivering or absorbing lagging reactive kva?

9-4. The full-load torque angle δ_{RF} of a synchronous motor at rated voltage and frequency is 30 electrical degrees. Neglect the effects of armature resistance and leakage reactance. If the field current is constant, how would the torque angle be affected by the following changes in operating conditions?

a. Frequency reduced 10 per cent, load torque constant

b. Frequency reduced 10 per cent, load power constant

c. Both frequency and applied voltage reduced 10 per cent, load torque constant

d. Both frequency and applied voltage reduced 10 per cent, load power constant

9-5. Estimating prices for a 200-hp 1,200-rpm synchronous motor and control are as follows, shaft-driven exciter included:

    1.0-power-factor motor, $5,400

    0.8-power-factor motor, $6,200

Estimated full-load losses are 15 kw for the 1.0-power-factor motor and 16 kw for the other. A proposed application calls for operation at full load for 3,000 hr per year, the motor being shut down the remainder of the time. The incremental power cost is 1.0 cent per kilowatthour, and the total investment charges are 17 per cent per year. What is the annual cost per reactive kva of the power-factor correction provided by the 0.8-power-factor motor?

9-6. Two small alternators of equal kva rating have per-unit synchronous reactances of 0.6 and 0.8, respectively, on the alternator rating as a base. They are rigidly coupled to the same prime mover and supply power in parallel to a line at rated voltage and frequency. Ignore saturation.

a. The coupling between the machines is such that their no-load terminal voltages are in phase. What is the greatest power that can be delivered to the line without exceeding the current rating of either machine?

b. The coupling is now readjusted so that the machines can jointly deliver a per-unit power of 2.0 without overload. What is the phase angle between their open-circuit terminal voltages?

c. With constant excitation voltages and a governor having no speed-droop, what per-unit current will circulate between the two alternators after dropping the load in (*b*)? Which machine will act as a motor?

9-7. A synchronous motor has a per-unit synchronous reactance (which may be considered constant) of 0.80. It is operating at rated voltage with an excitation voltage 1.3 times the terminal voltage. The armature power input is 0.50 per unit.

a. Determine the power angle, per-unit current, and power factor of the motor.

b. For the same power input and terminal voltage, what is another value of excitation which yields the same armature current?

c. Of the excitations in (*a*) and (*b*), which gives the higher efficiency at 0.5 per unit power input? Which gives the higher efficiency at 1.0 power input? Which gives the greater margin of stability? Which is more likely to be used in a practical situation? Give reasons for all answers.

9-8. The following readings are taken from the results of an open-circuit and a short-circuit test on a 9,375-kva 3-phase Y-connected 13,800-volt (line to line) 2-pole 60-cps turbine-generator driven at synchronous speed:

Field current	169	192
Armature current, short-circuit test	392	446
Line voltage, open-circuit characteristic	13,000	13,800
Line voltage, air-gap line	15,400	17,500

The armature resistance is 0.064 ohm per phase. The armature leakage reactance is 0.10 per unit on the generator rating as a base.

a. Find the unsaturated value of the synchronous reactance in ohms per phase and also in per unit.

b. Find the short-circuit ratio.

c. Find the value of the synchronous reactance adjusted for saturation at rated voltage. Express in ohms per phase and also in per unit.

d. If a short-circuit test is taken at half speed, find the armature current for a field excitation of 169 amp.

9-9. *a.* Compute the field current required in the generator of Prob. 9-8 at rated voltage, rated kva load, 0.80 power factor lagging. Account for saturation under load by the method described in the paragraph relating to Eq. 9-9.

b. In addition to the data given in Prob. 9-8, more points on the open-circuit characteristic are given below:

Field current............	200	250	300	350
Line voltage..........	14,100	15,200	16,000	16,600

Find the voltage regulation for the load of part *a*. *Voltage regulation* is defined as the rise in voltage when load is removed, the speed and field excitation being held constant. It is usually expressed as a percentage of the voltage under load.

9-10. Loss data for the generator of Prob. 9-8 are as follows:

Open-circuit core loss at 13,800 volts = 68 kw
Short-circuit load loss at 392 amp, 75°C = 50 kw
Friction and windage = 87 kw
Field-winding resistance at 75°C = 0.285 ohm

Compute the efficiency at rated load, 0.80 power factor lagging.

9-11. A 3-phase synchronous generator is rated 12,000 kva, 13,800 volts, 0.80 power factor, 60 cps. What should be its kva and voltage rating at 0.80 power factor and 50 cps if the field and armature copper losses are to be the same as at 60 cps? If its voltage regulation at rated load and 60 cps is 18 per cent, what will be the value of the voltage regulation at its rated load for 50-cps operation? The effect of armature-resistance voltage drop on regulation may be neglected.

9-12. A 150-hp 0.8-power-factor 2,300-volt 38.0-amp 60-cps 3-phase synchronous motor has a direct-connected exciter to supply its field current. For the purposes of this problem, the efficiency of the exciter may be assumed constant at a value of 80 per cent. The synchronous motor is run at no load from a 2,300-volt 60-cps circuit, with its field current supplied by its exciter, and the following readings taken:

Armature voltage between terminals = 2,300 volts
Armature current = 38.0 amp per terminal
Three-phase power input = 13.7 kw
Field current = 20.0 amp
Voltage applied to field from armature terminals of the exciter = 300 volts

When the synchronous motor is loaded so that its input is 38.0 amp at 0.80 power factor and 2,300 volts between terminals, its field current is found to be 17.3 amp. Under these conditions, what is the efficiency of the synchronous motor exclusive of the losses in its exciter? What is the useful mechanical power output in horsepower?

9-13. From the phasor diagram of a synchronous machine with constant synchronous reactance x_s operating at constant terminal voltage V_t and constant excitation voltage E_f, show that the locus of the tip of the armature-current phasor is a circle. On a phasor diagram with terminal voltage chosen as the reference phasor indicate the position of the center of this circle and its radius. Express the coordinates of the center and the radius of the circle in terms of V_t, E_f, and x_s.

9-14. A synchronous motor is supplied from an infinite bus. The open-circuit and short-circuit characteristics are available for the machine. It is possible to remove the shaft load of the motor, but the only source of terminal voltage is the infinite bus. Explain how you would determine the Potier reactance of this machine. Illustrate your explanation with suitable diagrams or sketches.

9-15. Assume that the size of the Potier triangle is proportional to the armature current. Construct a family of zero-power-factor characteristics for the synchronous machine of Fig. 9-19 at several values of armature current, both lagging and leading. From these curves collect data to plot a synchronous-motor no-load V curve for this machine at rated voltage.

9-16. A synchronous generator is operating under conditions corresponding to a saturation factor $k = 1.3$. The resultant mmf R corresponds to a field current of 1.4 per unit.

The leakage reactance is 0.15 per unit, and the unsaturated synchronous reactance is 0.95 per unit. The per-unit armature current is 0.80 and is in phase with the air-gap voltage.

a. Find the saturated value of the air-gap voltage.

b. Find the saturated value of the excitation voltage.

c. If the load is removed and the field current remains unchanged, will the terminal voltage be equal to, higher than, or lower than the excitation voltage of part b?

9-17. The following data relate to a 16,000-kva 3-phase 11,000-volt 60-cps 40-pole hydroelectric generator.

Open-circuit characteristic:

I_f, amp	100	150	205	250	300	350	400	450
V_t (line), kv	6.45	9.0	11.0	12.2	13.4	14.0	14.5	15.0

Short-circuit test:

$$I_f = 186 \text{ amp} \qquad I_a = 840 \text{ amp}$$

Zero-power-factor test:

$$I_f = 550 \text{ amp} \qquad I_a = 840 \text{ amp} \qquad V_t = 11,000 \text{ volts}$$

Plot the test data, and draw the Potier triangle. On the assumption that this triangle stays constant in size, draw the zero-power-factor characteristic. For operation at rated voltage, rated load, 0.80 power factor lagging, compute:

a. The air-gap voltage

b. The saturation factor

c. The saturated synchronous reactance

d. The field current

9-18. Compute the field current of the 45-kva machine of Figs. 9-19 and 9-22 when it is running as a synchronous motor at rated voltage and frequency, with an input of 36 kw at 0.80 power factor leading. Use (a) the saturated-synchronous-reactance method of Example 9-5; (b) the ASA method of Example 9-7. For comparison, the field current measured in an actual load test under these load conditions is 4.80 amp.

9-19. From the phasor diagram of an overexcited synchronous motor, show that

$$x_q = \frac{V_t \sin \delta - I_a r_a \sin (\phi + \delta)}{I_a \cos (\phi + \delta)}$$

From this relation, the saturated value of x_q can be measured under actual load conditions, by measuring V_t, I_a, power, and δ. The torque angle δ can be measured with a stroboscope.

9-20. Show that x_q can be found from the maximum-lagging-current test, as in Eq. 9-23. Neglect armature resistance, and assume that rotational losses are small.

CHAPTER 10

Polyphase Induction Motors

The induction motor is, by a very considerable margin, the most widely used a-c motor. Because of its simplicity and ruggedness, the squirrel-cage motor is often the natural choice when a substantially constant speed of operation will fulfill the requirements. The wound-rotor motor is a competitor of the d-c motor when adjustable speed is required. In extending the theoretical discussion of Chap. 6, therefore, we shall have in mind highlighting primarily those aspects which are of first importance to the motor-applications engineer, especially the considerations entering into starting and speed control.

Once more a reinforced physical picture of internal happenings is desirable. Accordingly, we start with interaction of magnetic fields, just as we did with synchronous machines in the preceding chapter. These views are then tied in with our earlier results through the medium of the equivalent circuit. A by-product is that a helpful background is obtained for the study of single-phase motors in the next chapter.

10-1. Flux and MMF Waves in Induction Machines. When the stator winding of a polyphase induction machine is excited by balanced poly-phase voltages, a rotating magnetic field is produced in the air gap in the manner described in Art. 3-4. The rotating field is traveling at synchronous speed as given by Eq. 3-61. To examine the air-gap flux and mmf waves, let us consider conditions existing when the rotor is turning at a speed n corresponding to a per-unit slip s. The space-fundamental component of the resultant air-gap flux wave then travels past the rotor at slip speed and induces slip-frequency emfs in the rotor circuits. These emfs give rise to slip-frequency currents in the short-circuited rotor phases or bars. With a cage rotor or with a coil-wound rotor wound for the same number of poles as the stator, the slip-frequency rotor currents create an mmf wave whose space fundamental also travels at slip speed with respect to the rotor. The mmf and flux-density waves are thus stationary relative to each other, and a steady torque is produced by their interaction. The torque magnitude is dependent on the space angle between the two waves (see Eq. 3-34).

462

a. Reactions of the Rotor.   For a coil-wound rotor, the flux-mmf situation may be seen with the aid of Fig. 10-1.   This sketch shows a development of a simple 2-pole 3-phase rotor winding in a 2-pole field.   It therefore conforms with the restriction that a wound rotor must have the same number of poles as the stator (although the number of phases need not be the same).   The flux-density wave is moving to the right at slip speed with respect to the winding.   It is shown in Fig. 10-1 in the position of maximum instantaneous voltage in phase *a*.

If rotor leakage reactance is very small compared with rotor resistance (which is very nearly the case at the small slips corresponding to normal

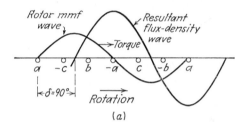

(a)

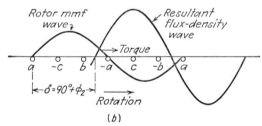

(b)

FIG. 10-1. Developed rotor winding of induction motor with flux-density and mmf waves in their relative positions for (*a*) zero and (*b*) nonzero rotor leakage reactance.

operation), the phase *a* current will also be a maximum.   As shown in Art. 3-4, the rotor-mmf wave will then be centered on phase *a*.   It is so shown in Fig. 10-1*a*.   The displacement angle, or torque angle, δ under these conditions is at its optimum value of 90°.

If the rotor leakage reactance is appreciable, however, the phase *a* current lags the induced voltage by the power-factor angle ϕ_2 of the leakage impedance.   The phase *a* current will not be a maximum until a correspondingly later time.   The rotor-mmf wave will then not be centered on phase *a* until the flux wave has traveled ϕ_2 degrees farther down the gap, as shown in Fig. 10-1*b*.   The angle δ is now 90° + ϕ_2.   In general, therefore, the torque angle of an induction motor is

$$\delta = 90° + \phi_2 \tag{10-1}$$

It departs from the optimum value by the power-factor angle of the rotor leakage impedance at slip frequency.   The electromagnetic rotor torque is directed toward the right in Fig. 10-1, or in the direction of the rotating flux wave.

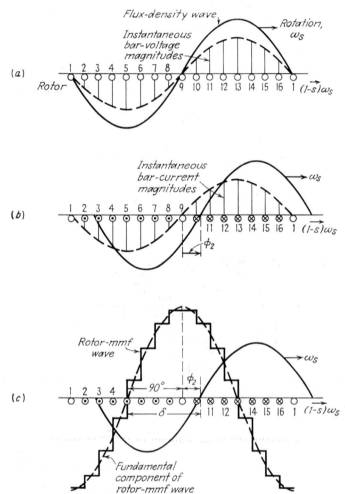

Fig. 10-2. Reactions of a squirrel-cage rotor in a 2-pole field.

The comparable picture for a squirrel-cage rotor is given in Fig. 10-2. A 16-bar rotor, placed in a 2-pole field, is shown in developed form.   For simplicity of drafting, only a relatively small number of rotor bars is chosen, and the number is an integral multiple of the number of poles, a choice normally avoided in order to prevent harmful harmonic effects. In Fig. 10-2a, the sinusoidal flux-density wave induces a voltage in each bar which has an instantaneous value indicated by the solid vertical lines. At a somewhat later instant of time, the bar currents assume the instantaneous values indicated by the solid vertical lines in Fig. 10-2b, the time lag being the rotor power-factor angle ϕ_2. In this time interval, the flux-density wave has traveled in its direction of rotation with respect to the rotor through a space angle ϕ_2 and is then in the position shown in Fig. 10-2b. The corresponding rotor-mmf wave is shown by the step wave of Fig. 10-2c. The fundamental component is shown by the dashed sinusoid and the flux-density wave by the solid sinusoid. Study of these figures confirms the general principle that the number of rotor poles in a squirrel-cage rotor is determined by the inducing flux wave.

b. *Referring Rotor Quantities to the Stator.* Thus we see that, in so far as fundamental components are concerned, both squirrel-cage and wound rotors react by producing an mmf wave having the same number of poles as the inducing flux wave, traveling at the same speed as the flux wave, and with a torque angle 90° greater than the rotor power-factor angle. The reaction of the rotor-mmf wave on the stator calls for a compensating load component of stator current and thereby enables the stator to absorb from the line the power needed to sustain the torque created by the interaction of the flux and mmf waves. The only way in which the stator knows what is happening is through the medium of the air-gap flux and rotor-mmf waves. Consequently, if the rotor were replaced by one having the same mmf and power factor at the same speed, the stator would be unable to detect the change. Such replacement leads to the idea of referring rotor quantities to the stator, an idea which is of great value in translating flux-mmf considerations into an equivalent circuit for the motor.

Consider, for example, a coil-wound rotor, wound for the same number of poles and phases as the stator. The number of effective turns per phase in the stator winding is a times the number in the rotor winding. Compare the magnetic effect of this rotor with that of a magnetically equivalent rotor having the same number of turns as the stator. For the same flux and speed, the relation between the voltage E_{rotor} induced in the actual rotor and the voltage E_{2s} induced in the equivalent rotor is

$$E_{2s} = aE_{\text{rotor}} \tag{10-2}$$

If the rotors are to be magnetically equivalent, their ampere-turns must be equal, and the relation between the actual rotor current I_{rotor} and the current I_{2s} in the equivalent rotor must be

$$I_{2s} = \frac{I_{\text{rotor}}}{a} \tag{10-3}$$

Consequently the relation between the slip-frequency leakage impedance

Z_{2s} of the equivalent rotor and the slip-frequency leakage impedance Z_{rotor} of the actual rotor must be

$$Z_{2s} = \frac{E_{2s}}{I_{2s}} = \frac{a^2 E_{rotor}}{I_{rotor}} = a^2 Z_{rotor} \qquad (10\text{-}4)$$

The voltages, currents, and impedances in the equivalent rotor are defined as their values *referred to the stator*. The thought process is essentially like that involved in referring secondary quantities to the primary in static-transformer theory (see Arts. 1-4 and 7-7). The referring factors are ratios of effective turns and are the same in essence as in transformer theory.

The referring factors must, of course, be known when one is concerned specifically with what is happening in the actual rotor circuits. From the viewpoint of the stator, however, the reflected effects of the rotor show

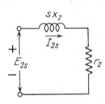

FIG. 10-3. Rotor equivalent circuit for a polyphase induction motor.

up in terms of the referred quantities, and the theory of both coil-wound and cage rotors can be formulated in terms of the referred rotor. We shall assume, therefore, that the referred rotor constants are known.

Since the rotor is short-circuited, the phasor relation between the slip-frequency emf E_{2s} generated in the reference phase of the referred rotor and the current I_{2s} in this phase is

$$\frac{E_{2s}}{I_{2s}} = Z_{2s} = r_2 + jsx_2 \qquad (10\text{-}5)$$

where Z_{2s} is the slip-frequency rotor leakage impedance per phase referred to the stator, r_2 the referred effective resistance, and sx_2 the referred leakage reactance at slip frequency. The reactance is expressed in this way because it is proportional to rotor frequency and therefore to slip. Thus x_2 is defined as the value the referred rotor leakage reactance would have at stator frequency. The slip-frequency equivalent circuit for 1 phase of the referred rotor is shown in Fig. 10-3.

10-2. The Equivalent Circuit. The foregoing considerations of flux and mmf waves can readily be translated into the steady-state equivalent circuit for the machine. Only machines with symmetrical polyphase windings excited by balanced polyphase voltages are considered. As in many other discussions of polyphase devices, it may be helpful to think of 3-phase machines as Y-connected, so that currents are always line values and voltages always line-to-neutral values.

First consider conditions in the stator. The synchronously rotating air-gap flux wave generates balanced polyphase counter emfs in the phases of the stator. The stator terminal voltage differs from the counter emf by the voltage drop in the stator leakage impedance, the phasor relation for the phase under consideration being

$$V_1 = E_1 + I_1(r_1 + jx_1) \tag{10-6}$$

where V_1 is the stator terminal voltage, E_1 is the counter emf generated by the resultant air-gap flux, I_1 is the stator current, r_1 is the stator effective resistance, and x_1 is the stator leakage reactance. The positive directions are shown in the equivalent circuit of Fig. 10-4.

The resultant air-gap flux is created by the combined mmfs of the stator and rotor currents. Just as in the transformer analog, the stator current can be resolved into two components, a load component and an exciting component. The load component I_2 produces an mmf which exactly counteracts the mmf of the rotor current. The exciting component I_φ is the additional stator current required to create the resultant air-gap flux and is a function of the emf E_1. The exciting current can be resolved into a core-loss component I_c in phase with E_1 and a magnetizing component I_m lagging E_1 by 90°. In the equivalent circuit, the exciting current can be accounted for by means of a shunt branch, formed by core-loss conductance g_c and magnetizing susceptance b_m in parallel, connected across E_1, as in Fig. 10-4. Both g_c and b_m are usually determined at rated stator frequency and for a value

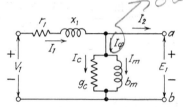

Fig. 10-4. Stator equivalent circuit for a polyphase induction motor.

of E_1 close to the expected operating value; they are then assumed to remain constant for the small departures from that value associated with normal operation of the motor.

So far, the equivalent circuit representing stator phenomena is exactly like that for the primary of a transformer. To complete the circuit, the effects of the rotor must be incorporated. This is done by considering stator and rotor voltages and currents in terms of referred rotor quantities.

The stator sees a flux wave and an mmf wave rotating at synchronous speed. The flux wave induces the slip-frequency rotor voltage E_{2s} and the stator counter emf E_1. If it were not for the effect of speed, the referred rotor voltage would equal the stator voltage, since the referred rotor winding is identical with the stator winding. Because the relative speed of the flux wave with respect to the rotor is s times its speed with respect to the stator, the relation between the effective values of stator and rotor emfs is

$$E_{2s} = sE_1 \tag{10-7}$$

The rotor-mmf wave is opposed by the mmf of the load component I_2 of stator current, and therefore, for effective values,

$$I_{2s} = I_2 \tag{10-8}$$

Division of Eq. 10-7 by Eq. 10-8 then gives

$$\frac{E_{2s}}{I_{2s}} = \frac{sE_1}{I_2} \tag{10-9}$$

Furthermore, the mmf wave created by the stator load current I_2 must be space-displaced from the resultant flux wave by the same space angle as that between the rotor-mmf wave and the resultant flux wave, viz., the torque angle δ.   The time-phase angle between the stator voltage E_1 and the stator load current I_2 therefore must equal the corresponding time angle for the rotor, viz., the rotor power-factor angle ϕ_2.   The fact that the rotor and stator mmfs are in opposition is accounted for, since the rotor current I_{2s} is created by the rotor emf E_{2s}, whereas the stator current I_2 is flowing against the stator counter emf E_1.   Therefore Eq. 10-9 is true, not only for effective values, but also in a phasor sense.   Through substitution of Eq. 10-5 in the phasor equivalent of Eq. 10-9,

$$\frac{sE_1}{I_2} = \frac{E_{2s}}{I_{2s}} = r_2 + jsx_2 \tag{10-10}$$

Division by s then gives

$$\frac{E_1}{I_2} = \frac{r_2}{s} + jx_2 \tag{10-11}$$

That is, the stator sees magnetic conditions in the air gap which result in stator counter emf E_1 and stator load current I_2, and by Eq. 10-11 these conditions are identical with the result of connecting an impedance $(r_2/s) + jx_2$ across E_1.   Consequently the effect of the rotor can be incorporated in the equivalent circuit of Fig. 10-4 by this impedance connected across the terminals ab.   The final result is shown in Fig. 10-5. The combined effect of shaft load and rotor resistance appears as a reflected resistance r_2/s, a function of slip and therefore of the mechanical load.   The current in the reflected rotor impedance equals the load component I_2 of stator current; the voltage across this impedance equals the stator emf E_1.   It should be noted that, when rotor currents and voltages are reflected into the stator, their frequency is also changed to stator frequency.   All rotor electrical phenomena, when viewed from the stator, become stator-frequency phenomena, because the stator winding simply sees mmf and flux waves traveling at synchronous speed.

The equivalent circuit of Fig. 10-5 is the same as that developed in Art. 6-4 using the self- and mutual-inductance approach with the dq transformation of variable.   This statement can be verified by making two simple changes in Fig. 10-5: (1) splitting r_2/s into r_2 and $r_2(1 - s)/s$ in order that the rotor copper loss and the internal mechanical power may be segregated; (2) omitting the conductance g_c and, to compensate, deducting the core loss from the internal mechanical power at the same time that friction, windage, and stray load losses are subtracted. The result is Fig. 10-6, which is identical with Fig. 6-4.

The flux-mmf and the self- and mutual-inductance viewpoints are thus seen to lead to the same result, as, of course, they should. All of Eqs. 6-90 to 6-102, as well as the analysis in Art. 6-5, are accordingly available for extension to motor-application considerations.

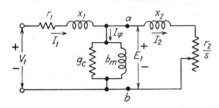

FIG. 10-5. Equivalent circuit for a polyphase induction motor.

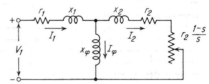

FIG. 10-6. Induction-motor equivalent circuit.

10-3. Normalized Torque-Slip Curves. The expression for the torque-slip curve of an induction motor is given by Eq. 6-99 as

$$T = \frac{1}{\omega_s} \frac{q_1 V_{1a}^2 (r_2/s)}{(R_1 + r_2/s)^2 + (X_1 + x_2)^2} \tag{10-12}$$

where the notation is that of the Thévenin form of the equivalent circuit (Fig. 6-7).

Since the torque-slip curve is one of the key characteristics in motor applications, it is worthwhile to simplify this relation as much as possible for further examination. Specifically, the equation can be normalized by writing it as a relation between the ratios T/T_{max} and $s/s_{max\,T}$. Thus, from Eq. 6-102, the maximum torque is

$$T_{max} = \frac{1}{\omega_s} \frac{0.5 q_1 V_{1a}^2}{R_1 + \sqrt{R_1^2 + (X_1 + x_2)^2}} \tag{10-13}$$

The corresponding slip is, from Eq. 6-101,

$$s_{max\,T} = \frac{r_2}{\sqrt{R_1^2 + (X_1 + x_2)^2}} \tag{10-14}$$

By dividing Eq. 10-12 by 10-13,

$$\frac{T}{T_{max}} = \frac{2[R_1 + \sqrt{R_1^2 + (X_1 + x_2)^2}](r_2/s)}{(R_1 + r_2/s)^2 + (X_1 + x_2)^2} \tag{10-15}$$

Since the final result is to be a function of $s/s_{\text{max } T}$ instead of simply s, r_2 in Eq. 10-15 must now be replaced by its value in terms of $s_{\text{max } T}$ from Eq. 10-14. After algebraic reduction, this process yields

$$\frac{T}{T_{\text{max}}} = \frac{1 + \sqrt{Q^2 + 1}}{1 + \frac{1}{2}\sqrt{Q^2 + 1}\left(\dfrac{s}{s_{\text{max } T}} + \dfrac{s_{\text{max } T}}{s}\right)} \tag{10-16}$$

where

$$Q = \frac{X_1 + x_2}{R_1} \tag{10-17}$$

The symbol Q is used because of the similarity of this ratio to the quality factor Q or reactance-to-resistance ratio in circuit theory.

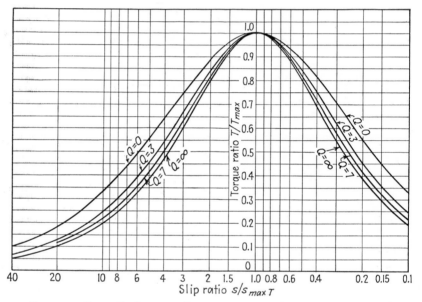

FIG. 10-7. Normalized torque-slip curves for polyphase induction motors.

In a similar manner, the ratio of stator load current I_2 to that at maximum torque $I_{2\text{ max } T}$ can be shown to be

$$\frac{I_2}{I_{2\text{ max } T}} = \sqrt{\frac{(1 + \sqrt{1 + Q^2})^2 + Q^2}{\left(1 + \dfrac{s_{\text{max } T}}{s}\sqrt{1 + Q^2}\right)^2 + Q^2}} \tag{10-18}$$

Curves of T/T_{max} are plotted as functions of the appropriate slip ratio for several values of the Q ratio in Fig. 10-7, and curves of the current ratio $I_2/I_{2\text{ max } T}$ in Fig. 10-8. Most induction motors will fall in the region between $Q = 3$ and $Q = 7$, and the average will lie about midway between the curves for these two values. Notice the rather small influence which variation of Q has on these curves; bear in mind, however, that the curves are plots of ratios, not of absolute magnitudes. As a result of the small influence of Q, a simple approximate expression for the torque-slip relation can be obtained by substituting $Q = \infty$ in Eq. 10-16.

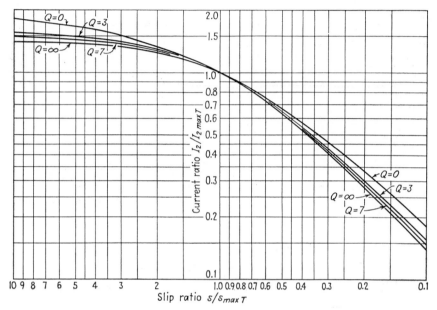

Fig. 10-8. Normalized current-slip curves for polyphase induction motors.

Such substitution is equivalent to saying that the stator resistance R_1 has only a negligible influence. The result is

$$\frac{T}{T_{\max}} = \frac{2}{s/s_{\max T} + s_{\max T}/s} \qquad (10\text{-}19)$$

One characteristic feature of simple induction motors is shown by the very fact that the torque-slip curves can be normalized in the manner of Fig. 10-7: except for the relatively small effect of the Q ratio, if the maximum torque and the slip at which it occurs are specified, the speed-torque characteristic is approximately fixed throughout the entire speed range. This statement is, of course, subject to the limitation that the parameters of the motor are constant and therefore does not apply to motors with variable rotor resistance.

Example 10-1. An induction motor with constant rotor resistance develops a maximum torque of 2.5 times its full-load torque at a slip of 0.20. Estimate its slip at full load and its starting torque at rated voltage.

Solution. At full load, $T/T_{max} = 0.40$. From Fig. 10-7, the corresponding value of $s/s_{max\ T}$ lies between 0.17 and 0.19 for values of Q between 3 and 7, the range for normal motors. Consequently the full-load slip lies between $(0.17)(0.20) = 0.034$ and $(0.19)(0.20) = 0.038$.

At starting, $s/s_{max\ T} = 1/0.20 = 5.0$. From Fig. 10-7 the corresponding value of T/T_{max} lies between 0.42 and 0.45 for values of Q between 7 and 3. The starting torque therefore lies between $(0.42)(2.5) = 1.05$ and $(0.45)(2.5) = 1.13$ times full-load torque.

Example 10-2. When operated at rated voltage and frequency with its rotor windings short-circuited, a 500-hp wound-rotor induction motor develops its rated full-load output at a slip of 1.5 per cent. The maximum torque which this motor can develop is 200 per cent of full-load torque. The Q of its Thévenin equivalent circuit is 7.0. For the purposes of this example, rotational and stray load losses may be neglected. Determine:

a. The rotor I^2R loss at full load, in kilowatts
b. The slip at maximum torque
c. The rotor current at maximum torque
d. The torque at a slip of 20 per cent
e. The rotor current at a slip of 20 per cent

Express the torque and rotor currents in per unit based on their full-load values.

Solution. *a. Rotor I^2R at Full Load.* The power P_{g1} absorbed from the stator divides between mechanical power P and rotor I^2R in the ratio $(1 - s)/s$. Consequently, at full load (neglecting rotational and stray load losses)

$$P_{g1} = \frac{P}{1 - s} = \frac{(500)(0.746)}{0.985} = 379 \text{ kw}$$

$$\text{Rotor } I^2R = sP_{g1} = (0.015)(379) = 5.69 \text{ kw}$$

Parts *b* to *e* can readily be solved by means of the normalized curves (Figs. 10-7 and 10-8).

b. Slip at Maximum Torque. From the data, $T_{fl}/T_{max} = 0.50$, where the subscripts *fl* indicate full load. From Fig. 10-7 at $Q = 7.0$ and $T/T_{max} = 0.50$,

$$\frac{s}{s_{max\ T}} = \frac{s_{fl}}{s_{max\ T}} = 0.25$$

whence

$$s_{max\ T} = \frac{s_{fl}}{0.25} = \frac{0.015}{0.25} = 0.060$$

c. Rotor Current at Maximum Torque. From Fig. 10-8 at $Q = 7.0$ and a slip ratio $s/s_{max\ T} = 0.25$ at full load, the corresponding current ratio is

$$\frac{I_2}{I_{2\,max\ T}} = \frac{I_{2fl}}{I_{2\,max\ T}} = 0.355$$

whence

$$I_{2\,max\ T} = \frac{I_{2fl}}{0.355} = 2.82I_{2fl}$$

d and *e.* *Torque and Rotor Current at $s = 0.20$.* The slip ratio is

$$\frac{s}{s_{max\ T}} = \frac{0.20}{0.060} = 3.33$$

The corresponding torque and current ratios can be read from the curves of Figs.

10-7 and 10-8 at $Q = 7.0$ and $s/s_{\max T} = 3.33$.   From Fig. 10-7

$$\frac{T}{T_{\max}} = 0.60 \qquad \text{or} \qquad T = 0.60T_{\max} = 1.20T_{fl}$$

From Fig. 10-8

$$\frac{I_2}{I_{2\max T}} = 1.40 \qquad \text{or} \qquad I_2 = 1.40I_{2\max T}$$

and from (c)

$$I_2 = (1.40)(2.82I_{2fl}) = 3.95I_{2fl}$$

10-4. Effects of Rotor Resistance.   Double-squirrel-cage Rotors.   A basic limitation of induction motors with constant rotor resistance is that the rotor design has to be a compromise.   High efficiency under normal running conditions requires a low rotor resistance; but a low rotor resistance results in a low starting torque and high starting current at a low starting power factor.

a. Wound-rotor Motors.   The use of a wound rotor is one effective way of avoiding the necessity for compromise.   The terminals of the rotor winding are connected to slip rings in contact with brushes.   For starting, resistors may be connected in series with the rotor windings, the result being increased starting torque and reduced starting current at an improved power factor.   The general nature of the effects on the torque-speed characteristics caused by varying rotor resistance is shown in Fig. 6-10.   By use of the appropriate value of rotor resistance, the maximum torque can be made to occur at standstill if high starting torque is needed.   As the rotor speeds up, the external resistances can be decreased, making maximum torque available throughout the accelerating range.   Since most of the rotor I^2R loss is dissipated in the external resistors, the rotor temperature rise during starting is lower than it would be if the resistance were incorporated in the rotor winding.   For normal running, the rotor winding can be short-circuited directly at the brushes.   The rotor winding is designed to have low resistance so that running efficiency is high and full-load slip is low.   Besides their use when starting requirements are severe, wound-rotor induction motors may be used for adjustable-speed drives.   Their chief disadvantage is greater cost as compared with squirrel-cage motors.

The principal effects of varying rotor resistance on the starting and running characteristics of induction motors can be shown quantitatively by means of the following example.

Example 10-3.   The rotor winding of the motor of Example 10-2 is 3-phase, Y-connected, and has a resistance of r_{rotor}.

If the rotor-circuit resistance is increased to $5r_{\text{rotor}}$ by connecting noninductive resistances in series with each rotor slip ring, determine:

a. The slip at which the motor will develop the same full-load torque as in Example 10-2

b. The total rotor-circuit I^2R loss at full-load torque

c. The horsepower output at full-load torque

d. The slip at maximum torque

e. The rotor current at maximum torque

f. The starting torque

g. The rotor current at starting

Express the torques and rotor currents in per unit based on the full-load-torque values.

Solution. The solution involves recognition of the fact that the only way in which the stator is cognizant of the happenings in the rotor is through the effect of the resistance r_2/s. Examination of the equivalent circuit shows that for specified applied voltage and frequency everything concerning the stator performance is fixed by the value of r_2/s, the other impedance elements being constant. For example, if r_2 is doubled and s is simultaneously doubled, the stator is unaware that any change has been made. The stator current and power factor, the power delivered to the air gap, and the torque are constant so long as the ratio r_2/s is the same.

Added physical significance can be given to the argument by examining the effects of simultaneously doubling r_2 and s from the viewpoint of the rotor. An observer on the rotor then sees the resultant air-gap flux wave traveling past him at twice the original slip speed, generating twice the original rotor voltage at twice the original slip frequency. The rotor reactance therefore is doubled, and since the original premise is that the rotor resistance also is doubled, the rotor impedance is doubled but the rotor power factor is unchanged. Since rotor voltage and impedance are both doubled, the effective value of the rotor current remains the same; only its frequency is changed. The air gap still has the same synchronously rotating flux and mmf waves with the same torque angle. The observer on the rotor therefore agrees with his counterpart on the stator that the torque is unchanged when both rotor resistance and slip are changed proportionally.

The observer on the rotor, however, is aware of two changes not apparent in the stator: (1) the rotor I^2R loss has doubled, and (2) the rotor is turning more slowly and therefore developing less mechanical power with the same torque. In other words, more of the power absorbed from the stator goes into I^2R heat in the rotor, and less is available for mechanical power.

The preceding thought processes now can readily be applied to the solution of Example 10-3.

a. *Slip at Full-load Torque.* If the rotor resistance is increased 5 times, the slip must increase 5 times for the same value of r_2/s and therefore for the same torque. But the original slip at full load, as given in Example 10-2, is 0.015. The new slip at full-load torque therefore is $(5)(0.015) = 0.075$.

b. *Rotor I^2R at Full-load Torque.* The effective value of the rotor current is the same as its full-load value in Example 10-2, and therefore the rotor I^2R loss is 5 times the full-load value of 5.69 kw found in part *a* of Example 10-2; or

$$\text{Rotor } I^2R = (5)(5.69) = 28.45 \text{ kw}$$

c. *Power Output at Full-load Torque.* The increased slip has caused the per-unit speed at full-load torque to drop from $1 - s = 0.985$ in Example 10-2 down to $1 - s = 0.925$ with added rotor resistance. The torque is the same. The power output therefore has dropped proportionally, or

$$P = \frac{0.925}{0.985}(500) = 469.5 \text{ hp}$$

The decrease in output equals the increase in rotor I^2R loss.

d. Slip at Maximum Torque. If rotor resistance is increased 5 times, the slip at maximum torque simply increases 5 times. But the original slip at maximum torque is 0.060, as found in part *b* of Example 10-2. The new slip at maximum torque with the added rotor resistance therefore is

$$s_{\max T} = (5)(0.060) = 0.30$$

e. Rotor Current at Maximum Torque. The effective value of the rotor current at maximum torque is independent of rotor resistance; only its frequency is changed when rotor resistance is varied. Therefore, from part *c* of Example 10-2,

$$I_{2\max T} = 2.82 I_{2fl}$$

f. Starting Torque. With the rotor resistance increased 5 times, the starting torque will be the same as the original running torque at a slip of 0.20 and therefore equals the running torque in part *d* of Example 10-2, viz.,

$$T_{\text{start}} = 1.20 T_{fl}$$

g. Rotor Current at Starting. The rotor current at starting with the added rotor resistances will be the same as the rotor current when running at a slip of 0.20 with the slip rings short-circuited as in part *e* of Example 10-2, viz.,

$$I_{2\text{start}} = 3.95 I_{2fl}$$

b. Deep-bar and Double-squirrel-cage Rotors. An ingenious and simple way for obtaining a rotor resistance which will automatically vary with speed makes use of the fact that, at standstill, the rotor frequency equals the stator frequency; as the motor accelerates, the rotor frequency decreases to a very low value—perhaps 2 or 3 cps at full load in a 60-cps motor. By use of suitable shapes and arrangements of rotor bars, squirrel-cage rotors can be designed so that their effective resistance at 60 cps is several times their resistance at 2 or 3 cps. The various schemes all make use of the inductive effect of the slot-leakage flux on the current distribution in the rotor bars. The phenomena are basically the same as the skin and proximity effect in any system of conductors with alternating current in them.

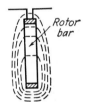

Fig. 10-9. Deep rotor bar and slot-leakage flux.

Consider first a squirrel-cage rotor having deep, narrow bars like that shown in cross section in Fig. 10-9. The general character of the slot-leakage field produced by the current in the bar within this slot is shown in the figure. If the rotor iron had infinite permeability, all the leakage-flux lines would close in paths below the slot, as shown. Now imagine the bar to consist of an infinite number of layers of differential depth; one at the bottom and one at the top are indicated crosshatched in Fig. 10-9. The leakage inductance of the bottom layer is greater than that of the top layer, because the bottom layer is linked by more leakage flux. But all the layers are electrically in parallel. Consequently, with alternating current, the current in the low-reactance upper layers will be greater than that in the high-reactance lower layers; the current will be forced toward the top of the slot, and the current in the upper layers will lead the current in the lower ones. The nonuniform current distribution results in an increase in the effective resistance and a smaller decrease in the effective leakage inductance of the bar. Since the distortion in current distribution depends on an inductive effect, the effective resistance is a function of the frequency. It is also a function of the depth of the bar and of the permeability and resistivity of the bar material.[1] Figure 10-10 shows a curve of the ratio of a-c effective resistance to d-c resistance as a function of frequency computed for a copper bar 1.00 in. deep. A squirrel-cage rotor with deep bars can readily be designed to have an effective resistance at stator frequency (standstill) several times greater than its d-c resistance. As the motor accelerates, the rotor frequency decreases and therefore the rotor effective resistance decreases, approaching its d-c value at small slips.

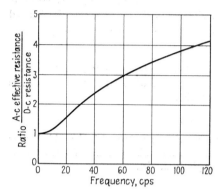

FIG. 10-10. Skin effect in a copper rotor bar 1.00 in. deep.

An alternative way of attaining similar results is the double-cage arrangement shown in Fig. 10-11. The squirrel-cage winding consists of two layers of bars short-circuited by end rings. The upper bars are of smaller cross-sectional area than the lower bars and consequently have higher resistance. The general nature of the slot-leakage field is shown in Fig. 10-11, from which it can be seen that the inductance of the lower bars is greater than that of the upper ones, because of the flux crossing the slot between the two layers. The difference in inductance can be made quite large by properly proportioning the constriction in the slot between the two bars. At standstill, when rotor frequency equals stator frequency, there is relatively little current in the lower bars because of their high reactance; the effective resistance of the rotor at standstill then approximates that of the high-resistance upper layer. At the low rotor frequencies corresponding to small slips, however, reactance becomes unimportant, and the rotor resistance then approaches that of the two layers in parallel.

FIG. 10-11. Double-squirrel-cage rotor bars and slot-leakage flux.

[1] For a detailed analysis, see W. V. Lyon, Heat Losses in the Conductors of Alternating-current Machines, *Trans. AIEE*, vol. 40, pp. 1361–1395, 1921.

Note that, since the effective resistance and leakage inductance of double-cage and deep-bar rotors vary with frequency, the parameters r_2 and x_2 representing the referred effects of rotor resistance and leakage inductance as viewed from the stator are not constant. The normalizing processes of Art. 10-3 are therefore no longer strictly applicable, and their use in such cases is more or less of an approximation. A more complicated form of equivalent circuit is required if the reactions of the rotor are to be represented by the effects of slip together with constant resistance and reactance elements.[1]

The simple equivalent circuit derived in Art. 10-2 still correctly represents the motor, however, but now r_2 and x_2 are functions of slip. All the basic relations still apply to the motor if the values of r_2 and x_2 are properly adjusted with changes in slip. For example, in computing the starting performance, r_2 and x_2 should be taken as their effective values at stator frequency; in computing the running performance at small slips, however, r_2 should be taken as its effective value at a low frequency, and x_2 should be taken as the stator-frequency value of the reactance corresponding to a low-frequency effective value of the rotor leakage inductance. Over the normal running range of slips, the rotor resistance and leakage inductance usually can be considered constant at substantially their d-c values.

c. Motor-application Considerations. By use of double-cage and deep-bar rotors, squirrel-cage motors can be designed to have the good starting characteristics resulting from high rotor resistance and at the same time the good running characteristics resulting from low rotor resistance. The design is necessarily somewhat of a compromise, however, and the motor lacks the flexibility of the wound-rotor machine with external rotor resistance. The wound-rotor motor should be used when starting requirements are very severe.

To meet the usual needs of industry, integral-horsepower 3-phase squirrel-cage motors are available from manufacturers' stock in a range of standard ratings up to 200 hp at various standard frequencies, voltages, and speeds. (Larger motors are generally regarded as special-purpose rather than general-purpose motors.) According to the terminology established by the NEMA, several standard designs are available to meet various starting and running requirements. Representative torque-speed characteristics of the four commonest designs are shown in Fig. 10-12. These curves are fairly typical of 1,800-rpm (synchronous-speed) motors in ratings from 7.5 to 200 hp, although it should be understood that individual motors may differ appreciably from these average curves. Briefly, the characteristic features of these designs are as follows.

[1] For example, see S. S. L. Chang, General Theory of Multiple-cage Induction Motors, *Trans. AIEE*, vol. 68, pt. 2, pp. 1139–1143, 1949.

DESIGN CLASS A. *Normal starting torque, normal starting current, low slip.* This design usually has a low-resistance single-cage rotor. It emphasizes good running performance at the expense of starting. The full-load slip is low and the full-load efficiency high. The maximum torque usually is well over 200 per cent of full-load torque and occurs at a small slip (less than 20 per cent). The starting torque at full voltage varies from about 200 per cent of full-load torque in small motors to about 100 per cent in large motors. The high starting current (500 to 800 per cent of full-load current when started at rated voltage) is the principal disadvantage of this design. In sizes below about 7.5 hp, these

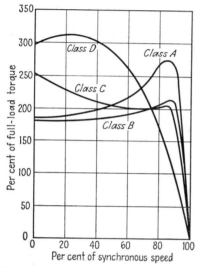

FIG. 10-12. Typical torque-speed curves for 1,800-rpm general-purpose induction motors.

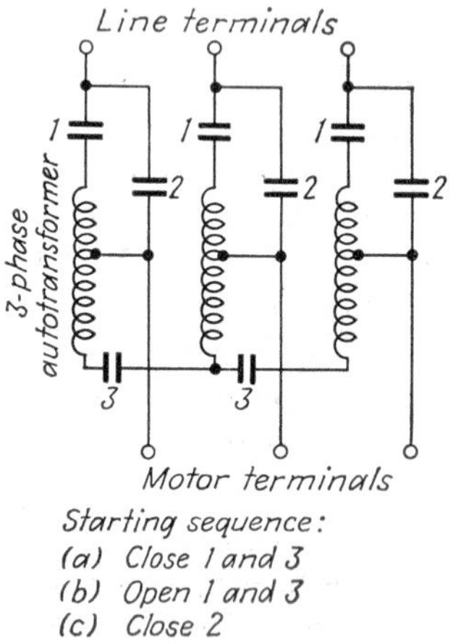

FIG. 10-13. Connections of a one-step starting autotransformer.

starting currents usually are within the limits on inrush current which the distribution system supplying the motor can withstand, and across-the-line starting at full voltage then can be used; otherwise, reduced-voltage starting must be used. Reduced-voltage starting results in a decrease in starting torque, because the starting torque is proportional to the volt-ampere input to the motor, which in turn is proportional to the square of the voltage applied to the motor terminals. The reduced voltage for starting is usually obtained from an autotransformer, called a *starting compensator*, which may be manually operated or automatically operated by relays which cause full voltage to be applied after the motor is up to speed. A circuit diagram of one type of compensator is shown in Fig. 10-13. If a smoother start is necessary, series resistance or reactance in the stator may be used.

The Class A motor is the basic standard design in sizes below about 7.5 and above about 200 hp. It is also used in intermediate ratings wherein design considerations may make it difficult to meet the starting-current limitations of the Class B design. Its field of application is about the same as that of the Class B design described below.

DESIGN CLASS B. *Normal starting torque, low starting current, low slip.* This design has approximately the same starting torque as the Class A design with but 75 per cent of the starting current. Full-voltage starting therefore may be used with larger sizes than with Class A. The starting current is reduced by designing for relatively high leakage reactance, and the starting torque is maintained by use of a double-cage or deep-bar rotor. The full-load slip and efficiency are good—about the same as for the Class A design. However, the use of high reactance slightly decreases the power factor and decidedly lowers the maximum torque (usually only slightly over 200 per cent of full-load torque being obtainable).

This design is the commonest in the 7.5- to 200-hp range of sizes. It is used for substantially constant-speed drives where starting-torque requirements are not severe, such as in driving fans, blowers, pumps, and machine tools.

DESIGN CLASS C. *High starting torque, low starting current.* This design uses a double-cage rotor with higher rotor resistance than the Class B design. The result is higher starting torque with low starting current but somewhat lower running efficiency and higher slip than the Class A and Class B designs. Typical applications are in driving compressors and conveyers.

DESIGN CLASS D. *High starting torque, high slip.* This design usually has a single-cage high-resistance rotor (frequently brass bars). It produces very high starting torque at low starting current, high maximum torque at 50 to 100 per cent slip, but runs at a high slip at full load (7 to 11 per cent) and consequently has low running efficiency. Its principal uses are for driving intermittent loads involving high accelerating duty and for driving high-impact loads such as punch presses and shears. When driving high-impact loads, the motor is generally aided by a flywheel which helps supply the impact and reduces the pulsations in power drawn from the supply system. A motor whose speed falls appreciably with increase in torque is required in order that the flywheel may slow down and deliver some of its kinetic energy to the impact.

10-5. Performance Calculations from No-load and Blocked-rotor Tests. The data needed for computing the performance of a polyphase induction motor under load can be obtained from the results of a no-load test, a blocked-rotor test, and measurements of the d-c resistances of the stator windings. The stray load losses, which must be taken into account when accurate values of efficiency are to be calculated, can also be measured by tests which do not require loading the motor. The stray-load-loss tests will not be described here, however.[1]

Like the open-circuit test on a transformer, the no-load test on an induction motor gives information with respect to exciting current and no-load losses. The test is ordinarily taken at rated frequency and with balanced polyphase voltages applied to the stator terminals. Readings are taken at rated voltage, after the motor has been running long enough so that the bearings are properly lubricated. The total rotational loss at rated voltage and frequency under load usually is considered to be constant and equal to its no-load value.

At no load, the rotor current is only the very small value needed to produce sufficient torque to overcome friction and windage. The no-load rotor copper loss therefore is negligibly small. Unlike a transformer, whose no-load primary copper loss is negligible, the no-load stator copper loss of an induction motor may be appreciable, because of its larger exciting current. The rotational loss P_R for normal running conditions is

$$P_R = P_{nl} - q_1 I_{nl}^2 r_1 \tag{10-20}$$

where P_{nl} and I_{nl} are, respectively, the total polyphase power input and the current per phase, q_1 is the number of stator phases, and r_1 is the stator resistance per phase.

Because the slip at no load is very small, the reflected rotor resistance r_2/s_{nl} is very large. The parallel combination of rotor and magnetizing branches then becomes jx_φ shunted by a very high resistance, and the reactance of this parallel combination therefore very nearly equals x_φ. Consequently the apparent reactance X_{nl} measured at the stator terminals at no load very nearly equals $x_1 + x_\varphi$, which is the self-reactance x_{11} of the stator; i.e.,

$$x_{11} = x_1 + x_\varphi = X_{nl} \tag{10-21}$$

The self-reactance of the stator therefore can be determined from the instrument readings at no load. For a 3-phase machine, considered to be Y-connected, the magnitude of the no-load impedance Z_{nl} per phase is

$$Z_{nl} = \frac{V_{nl}}{\sqrt{3}\, I_{nl}} \tag{10-22}$$

where V_{nl} is the line-to-line terminal voltage in the no-load test. The no-load resistance R_{nl} is

$$R_{nl} = \frac{P_{nl}}{3 I_{nl}^2} \tag{10-23}$$

---

[1] For information concerning test methods, see AIEE Test Code for Polyphase Induction Machines, No. 500, American Institute of Electrical Engineers, New York.

where P_{nl} is the total 3-phase power input at no load; the no-load reactance X_{nl} then is

$$X_{nl} = \sqrt{Z_{nl}^2 - R_{nl}^2} \qquad (10\text{-}24)$$

Usually the no-load power factor is about 0.1, so that the no-load reactance very nearly equals the no-load impedance.

Like the short-circuit test on a transformer, the blocked-rotor test on an induction motor gives information with respect to the leakage impedances. The rotor is blocked so that it cannot rotate, and balanced polyphase voltages are applied to the stator terminals. Sometimes the blocked-rotor torque also is measured.

The equivalent circuit for blocked-rotor conditions is identical to that of a short-circuited transformer. An induction motor is more complicated than a transformer, however, because its leakage impedance may be affected by magnetic saturation of the leakage-flux paths and by rotor frequency. The blocked impedance may also be affected by rotor position, although this effect generally is small with cage rotors. The guiding principle is that the blocked-rotor test should be taken under conditions of current and rotor frequency approximately the same as those existing in the operating condition for which the performance is later to be calculated. For example, if one is interested in the characteristics at slips near unity, as in starting, the blocked-rotor test should be taken at normal frequency and with currents near the values encountered in starting. If, however, one is interested in the normal running characteristics, the blocked-rotor test should be taken at a reduced voltage which results in about rated current; the frequency also should be reduced, since the values of rotor effective resistance and leakage inductance at the low rotor frequencies corresponding to small slips may differ appreciably from their values at normal frequency, particularly with double-cage or deep-bar rotors. The AIEE Test Code[1] suggests a frequency of 15 cps for 60-cps motors, although a frequency of 25 cps may be used provided the results obtained at 25 cps do not differ materially from those obtained at 60 cps. The value of the blocked reactance at normal frequency can be computed from the test value at reduced frequency by considering the reactance to be proportional to frequency. The effects of frequency often are negligible for normal motors of less than 25-hp rating, and the blocked impedance may then be measured directly at normal frequency.

If exciting current is neglected, the blocked-rotor reactance X_{bl}, corrected to normal frequency, equals the sum of the normal-frequency stator and rotor leakage reactances, x_1 and x_2. The performance of the motor is relatively little affected by the way in which the total leakage

[1] Ibid.

Table 10-1

Empirical Distribution of Leakage Reactances in Induction Motors

Class of motor	Fraction of $x_1 + x_2$	
	x_1	x_2
Class A (normal starting torque, normal starting current).........	0.5	0.5
Class B (normal starting torque, low starting current)............	0.4	0.6
Class C (high starting torque, low starting current)...............	0.3	0.7
Class D (high starting torque, high slip).......................	0.5	0.5
Wound rotor..	0.5	0.5

reactance $x_1 + x_2$ is distributed between stator and rotor. The AIEE Test Code recommends the empirical distribution shown in Table 10-1.

The magnetizing reactance x_φ now can be determined from the no-load test and the value of x_1; thus

$$x_\varphi = X_{nl} - x_1 \qquad (10\text{-}25)$$

The stator resistance r_1 can be considered as its d-c value. The rotor resistance then can be determined as follows: From the blocked-rotor test, the blocked resistance R_{bl} can be computed by means of a relation similar to Eq. 10-23. The difference between the blocked resistance and the stator resistance then can be determined from the test data. Denoting this resistance by R, then

$$R = R_{bl} - r_1 \qquad (10\text{-}26)$$

From the equivalent circuit, with $s = 1$, the resistance R is the resistance of the combination of $r_2 + jx_2$ in parallel with jx_φ. For this parallel combination,

$$R = r_2 \frac{x_\varphi^2}{r_2^2 + x_{22}^2} \approx r_2 \left(\frac{x_\varphi}{x_{22}}\right)^2 \qquad (10\text{-}27)$$

where $x_{22} = x_2 + x_\varphi$ is the self-reactance of the rotor. If x_{22} is greater than $10r_2$, as is usually the case, less than 1 per cent error results from use of the approximate form of Eq. 10-27. Substitution of this approximate form in Eq. 10-26 and solution for r_2 then gives

$$r_2 = R \left(\frac{x_{22}}{x_\varphi}\right)^2 = (R_{bl} - r_1)\left(\frac{x_{22}}{x_\varphi}\right)^2 \qquad (10\text{-}28)$$

All the equivalent-circuit constants have now been determined, and the motor performance under load can be computed.

Example 10-4.   The following test data apply to a 7.5-hp 3-phase 220-volt 19-amp 60-cps 4-pole induction motor with a double-squirrel-cage rotor of the high-starting-torque low-starting-current type (design class C):

Test 1.   *No-load test at 60 cps:*
  Applied voltage $V = 219$ volts, line to line
  Average line current $I_{nl} = 5.70$ amp
  Power (two wattmeters): $W_1 = 680$, $W_2 = -300$ watts

Test 2.   *Blocked-rotor test at 15 cps:*
  $V = 26.5$ volts $I = 18.57$ amp
  $W_1 = 215$ watts $W_2 = 460$ watts

Test 3.   *Average d-c resistance per stator phase* (measured immediately after test 2):
  $r_1 = 0.262$ ohm per phase (Y connection assumed)

Test 4.   *Blocked-rotor test at 60 cps:*
  $V = 212$ volts $I = 83.3$ amp
  $W_1 = 3,300$ watts $W_2 = 16,800$ watts
  Measured starting torque $T_{\text{start}} = 54.6$ lb-ft

  a. Compute the no-load rotational loss and the equivalent-circuit constants applying to the normal running conditions.   Assume the same temperature as in test 3.

  b. Compute the internal starting torque from the input measurements of test 4. Assume the same temperature as in test 3.

  Solution.   *a.* From test 1, $P_{nl} = 380$ watts, and, by Eq. 10-20,

$$P_R = 380 - (3)(5.70)^2(0.262) = 354 \text{ watts}$$

From test 1 and Eqs. 10-22, 10-23, and 10-24,

$$Z_{nl} = \frac{219}{\sqrt{3}\,(5.70)} = 22.2 \text{ ohms per phase Y}$$

$$R_{nl} = \frac{380}{(3)(5.70)^2} = 3.9 \text{ ohms} \qquad X_{nl} = 21.8 \text{ ohms}$$

The blocked-rotor test at reduced frequency and rated current reproduces approximately normal running conditions in the rotor.   From test 2,

$$Z'_{bl} = \frac{26.5}{\sqrt{3}\,(18.57)} = 0.825 \text{ ohm per phase at 15 cps}$$

$$R_{bl} = \frac{675}{(3)(18.57)^2} = 0.654 \text{ ohm} \qquad X'_{bl} = 0.503 \text{ ohm at 15 cps}$$

where the primes indicate 15-cps values.   The blocked reactance referred to normal frequency then is

$$X_{bl} = {}^{60}\!/_{15} \times (0.503) = 2.01 \text{ ohms per phase at 60 cps}$$

According to Table 10-1,

$$x_1 = (0.3)(2.01) = 0.603 \qquad x_2 = (0.7)(2.01) = 1.407 \text{ ohms per phase}$$

and by Eq. 10-25

$$x_\varphi = 21.8 - 0.6 = 21.2 \text{ ohms per phase}$$

From test 3 and Eqs. 10-26 and 10-28,

$$R = 0.654 - 0.262 = 0.392 \qquad r_2 = 0.392\left(\frac{22.6}{21.2}\right)^2 = 0.445 \text{ ohm per phase}$$

The constants of the equivalent circuit for small values of slip have now been calculated.

b. The internal starting torque can be computed from the input measurements in test 4. From the power input and stator copper losses, the air-gap power P_{g1} is

$$P_{g1} = 20{,}100 - (3)(83.3)^2(0.262) = 14{,}650 \text{ watts}$$

Synchronous speed $\omega_s = 188.5$ rad/sec, and

$$T_{\text{start}} = \frac{14{,}650}{188.5} = 77.6 \text{ newton-m, or } 57.3 \text{ lb-ft}$$

The test value, $T_{\text{start}} = 54.6$ lb-ft, is a few per cent less than the calculated value, because the calculations do not account for the power absorbed in stator core loss and in stray load losses.

10-6. Speed Control of Induction Motors.
The simple induction motor fulfills admirably the requirements of substantially constant-speed drives. Many motor applications, however, require several speeds, or even a continuously adjustable range of speeds. From the earliest days of a-c power systems engineers have been interested in the development of adjustable-speed a-c motors. The purpose of this article is to investigate the general principles upon which speed-control methods for induction motors are based. To maintain perspective, the competitive position of d-c motors combined with a-c to d-c conversion equipment should be borne in mind throughout this discussion.

The synchronous speed of an induction motor can be changed by (*a*) changing the number of poles or (*b*) varying the line frequency. The slip can be changed by (*c*) varying the line voltage, (*d*) varying the rotor resistance, or (*e*) inserting voltages of the appropriate frequency in the rotor circuits. The salient features of speed-control methods based on these five possibilities are discussed in the following five sections of this article.

a. Pole-changing Motors. The stator winding can be designed so that by simple changes in coil connections the number of poles can be changed in the ratio 2 to 1. Either of two synchronous speeds can be selected. The rotor is almost always of the squirrel-cage type. A cage winding always reacts by producing a rotor field having the same number of poles as the inducing stator field. If a wound rotor is used, additional complications are introduced because the rotor winding also must be arranged for pole changing. With two independent sets of stator windings, each arranged for pole changing, as many as four synchronous speeds can be obtained in a squirrel-cage motor—for example, 600, 900, 1,200, and 1,800 rpm.

The basic principles of the pole-changing winding are shown in Fig. 10-14, in which *aa* and *a'a'* are 2 coils comprising part of the phase *a* stator winding. An actual winding would, of course, consist of several coils in each group.   The windings for the other stator phases (not shown in the figure) would be similarly arranged.   In Fig. 10-14a the coils are connected to produce a 4-pole field; in Fig. 10-14b the current in the $a'a'$ coil has been reversed by means of a controller, the result being a 2-pole field.   At the same time that the controller reverses the $a'a'$ coils, the connections of the two groups of coils may be changed from series to parallel and the connections among the phases from Y to Δ, or vice versa. By these means the air-gap flux density can be adjusted to produce the desired torque-speed characteristics on the two connections.   Figure 10-15 shows three possibilities and their corresponding torque-speed characteristics for three motors having identical characteristics on the high-speed connection.   Figure 10-15a results in approximately the same maximum torque on both speeds and is applicable to drives requiring approximately the same torque on both speeds (loads in which friction

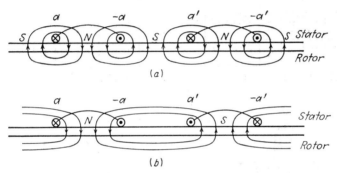

FIG. 10-14. Principles of pole-changing winding.

predominates, for example).   Figure 10-15b results in approximately twice the maximum torque on the low speed and is applicable to drives requiring approximately constant power (such as machine tools and winches).   Figure 10-15c results in considerably less maximum torque on the low speed and is applicable to drives requiring less torque on the low speed (fans and centrifugal pumps, for example).   The constant-horsepower type is the most expensive because it is physically the largest.

b. *Line-frequency Control.*   The synchronous speed of an induction motor can be controlled by varying the line frequency.   In order to maintain approximately constant flux density, the line voltage should also be varied directly with the frequency.   The maximum torque then remains very nearly constant.   An induction motor used in this way has characteristics similar to those of a separately excited d-c motor with constant flux and variable armature voltage, as in the Ward Leonard system.

The major difficulty is how to get the variable frequency.   One way is by means of a wound-rotor induction machine as a frequency changer. This arrangement requires a variable-speed drive for the frequency changer. In spite of the fact that this scheme is complicated, there are occasions when the compactness and simplicity of the squirrel-cage

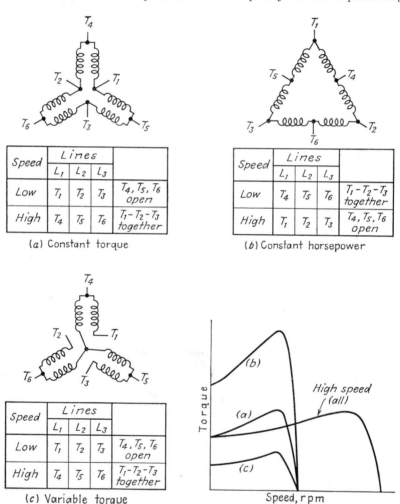

FIG. 10-15. Connections and torque-speed curves for three types of pole-changing induction motors.

induction motor make the variable-frequency system highly desirable. A good example is the testing of scale-model airplanes in a wind tunnel. The motors driving the propellers on powered models must be extremely compact and capable of high speeds. The requirements can be met with a water-cooled squirrel-cage motor supplied with the appropriate frequency.

c. Line-voltage Control. The internal torque developed by an induction motor is proportional to the square of the voltage applied to its primary terminals, as shown by the two torque-speed characteristics in Fig. 10-16. If the load has the torque-speed characteristic shown by the dashed line, the speed will be reduced from n_1 to n_2. This method of

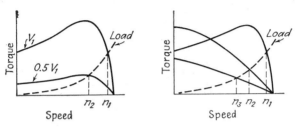

FIG. 10-16. Speed control by means of line voltage.

speed control is commonly used with small squirrel-cage motors driving fans.

d. Rotor-resistance Control. The possibility of speed control of a wound-rotor motor by changing its rotor-circuit resistance has already been pointed out in Art. 10-4a. The torque-speed characteristics for three different values of rotor resistance are shown in Fig. 10-17. If the load has the torque-speed characteristic shown by the dashed line, the speeds corresponding to each of the values of rotor resistance are n_1, n_2, and n_3. This method of speed control has characteristics similar to those of d-c shunt-motor speed control by means of resistance in series with the armature.

The principal disadvantages of both line-voltage and rotor-resistance control are low efficiency at reduced speeds and poor speed regulation with respect to change in load.

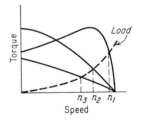

FIG. 10-17. Speed control by means of rotor resistance.

e. Control of Slip by Auxiliary Machines. In considering schemes for speed control by varying the slip, the fundamental laws relating the flow of power in induction machines should be borne in mind. The fraction s of the power absorbed from the stator is transformed by electromagnetic induction to electric power in the rotor circuits. If the rotor circuits are short-circuited, this power is wasted as rotor copper loss and operation at reduced speeds is inherently inefficient.

Numerous schemes have been invented for recovering this slip-frequency electric power. Although some of them are rather complicated in their details, they all comprise a means for introducing adjustable voltages of slip frequency into the rotor circuits of a wound-rotor induction motor. Broadly, they can be classified in two types, as shown in Fig. 10-18, where *IM* represents a 3-phase wound-rotor induction motor whose speed is to be regulated. In Fig. 10-18*a* the rotor circuits of *IM* are connected to auxiliary frequency-changing apparatus, represented by the box *FC*, in which the slip-frequency electric power generated in the

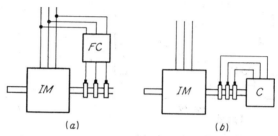

(a)   (b)

Fig. 10-18. Two basic schemes for induction-motor speed control by auxiliary machines.

rotor of the main motor is converted to electric power at line frequency and returned to the line. In Fig. 10-18*b* the rotor circuits of *IM* are connected to auxiliary apparatus, represented by the box *C*, in which the slip-frequency electric power is converted to mechanical power and added to the shaft power developed by the main motor. The boxes *FC* and *C* contain commutator-type machines of some kind. In both these schemes the speed and power factor of the main motor can be adjusted by con-

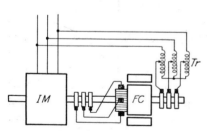

Fig. 10-19. Leblanc system of speed control.

trolling the magnitude and phase of the slip-frequency emfs of the auxiliary machines. The auxiliary apparatus may be a fairly complicated system of rotating machines and adjustable-ratio transformers. However, it can usually be relatively small compared with the main motor, because it has to handle only the fraction *s* of the stator power in the main motor. Three specific examples—the Leblanc system, the Schrage-type motor, and the modified Kramer system—are described briefly below.

One of the simplest arrangements is the *Leblanc system* shown in Fig. 10-19. The frequency changer *FC* comprises an armature winding like that of a d-c machine having the same number of poles as the main induction motor *IM*. This winding is connected to a commutator and also to three slip rings. Three sets of brushes spaced 120 electrical degrees apart bear on the commutator. The rotor is mechanically driven by the main induction motor and therefore runs at a per-unit speed of $1 - s$. The stator has no windings at all—it merely provides a low-reluctance path for the magnetic flux. Line-frequency voltages are applied to the slip rings and create a magnetic field rotating at synchronous speed with respect to the rotor and in the opposite direction. As viewed from the stator, therefore, this field rotates at slip speed, and 3-phase voltages of slip frequency are generated between pairs of brushes on the commutator. These voltages are connected in series with the rotor circuits of the main motor. The speed and power factor of the main motor can be controlled by adjusting the magnitude and phase of these voltages by means of the

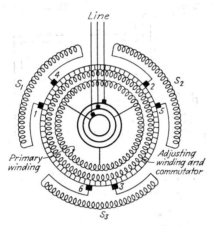

FIG. 10-20. Schematic diagram of adjustable-speed brush-shifting motor.

adjustable-ratio autotransformer Tr and by shifting the brushes. The slip-frequency electric power output of the main motor is converted to line-frequency power in the frequency changer and returned to the line.

The *Schrage-type brush-shifting motor* combines the frequency changer and the main motor in one frame. It is basically an inside-out induction motor with its secondary winding on the stator and its primary winding on the rotor connected to the supply line through slip rings, as shown in Fig. 10-20. Embedded in the same rotor slots is an adjusting winding connected to a commutator. Line-frequency voltages are induced in the adjusting winding by transformer action from the primary, and slip-frequency voltages appear between brushes on the commutator, just as in the frequency changer of the Leblanc system.

Six sets of brushes are arranged on the commutator, and each phase S_1, S_2, S_3 of the secondary winding is connected to a pair of them, as shown in Fig. 10-20. Brushes 1, 2, and 3 are mounted 120 electrical degrees apart on a yoke and can be shifted as a group. Brushes 4, 5, and 6 are similarly mounted on another movable yoke. The two sets of brushes can be adjusted as to angular position and relative spacing between them by means of a handwheel. The magnitude of the slip-frequency voltages inserted in series with the secondary windings depends on the spacing between the two sets of brushes, and the phase depends on their angular position. Thus both the speed and power factor can be controlled by means of the handwheel.

Machines of this type are mainly used in sizes up to about 50 hp and for speed ranges of 6 to 1 or below.

The *modified Kramer system* is a type of adjustable-speed drive which can be built in very large sizes. It has been applied to large wind-tunnel drives in sizes up to 40,000 hp. As shown in Fig. 10-21, it comprises

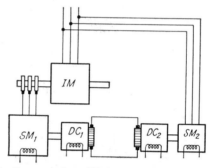

FIG. 10-21. Schematic diagram of modified Kramer system for speed control of large induction motors.

a wound-rotor induction motor IM whose slip-frequency rotor power is delivered to a synchronous motor SM_1 which drives a d-c generator DC_1 at a speed proportional to the slip of the main motor IM. The electrical output of DC_1 is delivered to a constant-speed d-c motor DC_2 which drives a synchronous generator SM_2 whose electrical output is returned to the line, as in Fig. 10-18a. The field circuits of the four auxiliary machines are supplied from a d-c bus, and the speed of the main motor IM is adjusted by controlling the speed of the auxiliary set SM_1DC_1 through field control of the two d-c machines, as in the Ward Leonard system. The variable-speed synchronous machine SM_1 must have about the same rating as the main induction motor, but the two d-c machines and the constant-speed synchronous machine SM_2 are smaller. For example, in a wind-tunnel drive the rating of SM_2 need be only about 20 per cent of the rating of IM.

An advantage of this system is that it uses conventional synchronous and d-c machines, which can be built in large sizes and for less cost than some of the more elaborate regulating machines required by other systems. A further advantage is that a very large induction motor can be started with no more disturbance to the supply line than that incident to starting the relatively small synchronous machine SM_2.

10-7. Résumé. Examination of the flux-mmf interactions in a polyphase induction motor shows that, electrically, the machine is a generalized transformer. The synchronously rotating air-gap flux wave in the induction machine is the counterpart of the mutual core flux in the transformer. The rotating field induces emfs of stator frequency in the stator windings and of slip frequency in the rotor windings for all rotor speeds other than synchronous speed. Thus the induction machine transforms voltages and at the same time changes frequency. When viewed from the stator, all rotor electric and magnetic phenomena are transformed to stator frequency. The rotor mmf reacts on the stator windings in the same manner that the mmf of the secondary current in a transformer reacts on the primary.

Pursuit of this line of reasoning leads to the same equivalent circuit as obtained in Chap. 6, but significant physical insight is added. The effects of saturation on the equivalent circuit are less serious than in the corresponding steady-state circuit for synchronous machines. This is largely because, as in the transformer, the performance is determined to a considerably greater extent by the leakage impedances than by the magnetizing impedance. Care must be used in both testing and analysis, however, to reflect the effects of saturation on leakage reactances as well as of nonuniformity of current distribution on rotor resistance.

One of the salient facts affecting induction-motor applications is that the slip at which maximum torque occurs can be controlled by varying the rotor resistance. A high rotor resistance gives optimum starting conditions but poor running performance. A low rotor resistance, on the other hand, may result in unsatisfactory starting conditions. The design of a squirrel-cage motor is therefore quite likely to be a compromise. Marked improvement in the starting performance with relatively little sacrifice in running performance can be built into a squirrel-cage motor by using a deep-bar or double-cage rotor whose effective resistance increases with slip. A wound-rotor motor can be used for very severe starting conditions or when speed control by rotor resistance is required. A wound-rotor motor is more expensive than a squirrel-cage motor.

For applications requiring a substantially constant speed without excessively severe starting conditions, the squirrel-cage motor usually is unrivaled, because of its ruggedness, simplicity, and relatively low cost. Its only disadvantage is its relatively low power factor (about 0.85 to 0.90 at full load for 4-pole 60-cps motors—considerably lower at light loads and for lower-speed motors). The low power factor is a consequence of the fact that all the excitation must be supplied by lagging reactive kva taken from the a-c mains. At speeds below about 500 rpm and ratings above about 50 hp or at medium speeds (500 to 900 rpm) and ratings above about 500 hp, a synchronous motor may cost less than an induction motor.

The induction motor is at a disadvantage for adjustable-speed drives. A machine dependent on a constant-speed rotating magnetic field prefers to be a constant-speed machine. Pole changing is a good solution when only two, or perhaps four, speeds are required. Speed control by varying the slip is inherently inefficient unless one of the more or less elaborate schemes described in Art. 10-6e is used for recovering the slip energy. These schemes all involve an auxiliary commutator machine of some kind. The economic comparison for adjustable-speed drives often is between the cost of a d-c motor plus a-c to d-c conversion equipment and controls, on the one hand, and the relatively elaborate schemes of induction-motor speed control described in Art. 10-6, on the other. The possibilities of a variable-speed mechanical transmission interposed between a constant-speed motor and the driven load must also be considered. In very large sizes, or at high speeds, or when space is at a premium, the simplicity and compactness of the induction motor are a big advantage.

PROBLEMS

10-1. When an induction machine is driven above synchronous speed, it is capable of acting as a generator. Sketch the rotor-mmf wave and the resultant flux-density wave in the manner of Fig. 10-1a and b, but for generator action. Show that the torque angle is $-(90° + \phi_2)$.

10-2. Redraw Fig. 10-2 for the same rotor placed in a sinusoidal 4-pole field.

10-3. A 3-phase 8-pole wound-rotor induction machine driven by an adjustable-speed d-c motor is to be used as an adjustable-frequency source. The stator of the machine is fed from a 60-cps source, and the output is taken from the rotor slip rings. The output-frequency range is to be from 150 to 360 cps. The output power is to be 80 kw at 0.80 lagging power factor and is independent of the output frequency.

For these purposes neglect all machine losses, exciting current, and leakage reactances. Compute:

   a. The required speed range of the d-c motor

   b. The stator kva rating of the induction machine

   c. The maximum torque on the shaft of the d-c motor

10-4. A 3-phase Y-connected 4-pole 60-cps squirrel-cage motor has a stator resistance of 0.5 ohm per phase at operating temperature. When the line current to the motor is 10 amp and the total 3-phase power input is 3,000 watts, what is the internal torque in newton-meters? Neglect stator core loss.

10-5. When operated at rated voltage and frequency, a 3-phase squirrel-cage induction motor (of the design classification known as a high-slip motor) delivers full load at a slip of 8.5 per cent and develops a maximum torque of 250 per cent of full-load torque at a slip of 50 per cent. Neglect core and rotational losses, and assume that the resistances and inductances of the motor are constant.

Determine the torque and rotor current at starting with rated voltage and frequency. Express the torque and rotor current in per unit based on their full-load values.

10-6. For a 25-hp 230-volt 3-phase 60-cps squirrel-cage motor operated at rated voltage and frequency, the rotor copper loss at maximum torque is 9.0 times that at full-load torque, and the slip at full-load torque is 0.030. Stator resistance and rotational losses may be neglected and the reactances and rotor resistance assumed to remain constant. Find:

a. The slip at maximum torque

b. The maximum torque

c. The starting torque

Express the torques in per unit of full-load torque.

10-7. A 220-volt 3-phase 4-pole 60-cps induction motor develops a maximum torque of 225 per cent of the full-load torque at a slip of 0.15 when operated at rated voltage and frequency. The actual rotor resistance (not the referred value) is 0.03 ohm per phase. The stator resistance and rotational losses can be neglected.

a. What external resistance in actual ohms should be inserted in each phase of the rotor winding in order to give maximum torque at starting?

b. What is the slip at full load without the external rotor resistance? Would this slip be larger, the same, or smaller if the stator resistance were considered?

c. What are the slip and torque in per cent when the motor current has its full-load value but resistances of 0.07 ohm are inserted in each phase of the rotor circuit?

d. What would be the maximum torque in per cent of the full-load torque if the motor were connected to a 200-volt 50-cps source?

10-8. The maximum internal power P_{max} of an induction motor occurs at the slip $s_{max\ P}$. Show that the normalized curves of Fig. 10-7 also give the relations between the power ratio P/P_{max} and the slip ratio $s(1 - s_{max\ P})/s_{max\ P}(1 - s)$ with the parameter $Q = (X_1 + x_2)/(R_1 + r_2)$.

10-9. A 50-hp 440-volt 3-phase 4-pole 60-cps wound-rotor induction motor develops a maximum internal torque of 250 per cent at a slip of 16 per cent when operating at rated voltage and frequency with its rotor short-circuited directly at the slip rings. Stator resistance and rotational losses may be neglected, and the rotor resistance may be assumed to be constant, independent of rotor frequency. Determine:

a. The slip at full load, in per cent

b. The rotor copper loss at full load, in watts

c. The starting torque at rated voltage and frequency, in newton-meters

If the rotor resistance is now doubled (by inserting external series resistances), determine:

d. The torque in newton-meters when the stator current has its full-load value

e. The corresponding slip

10-10. A 50-hp 3-phase 440-volt 4-pole wound-rotor induction motor develops its rated full-load output at a speed of 1,746 rpm when operated at rated voltage and frequency with its slip rings short-circuited. The maximum torque it can develop at rated voltage and frequency is 200 per cent of full-load torque. The resistance of the rotor winding is 0.10 ohm per phase Y. Rotational and stray load losses and stator resistance may be neglected.

a. Compute the rotor copper loss at full load.

b. Compute the speed at maximum torque.

c. How much resistance must be inserted in series with the motor to produce maximum starting torque?

The motor is now run from a 50-cps supply with the applied voltage adjusted so that the air-gap flux wave has the same amplitude at the same torque as on 60 cps.

d. Compute the 50-cps applied voltage.

e. Compute the speed at which the motor will develop a torque equal to its 60-cps full-load value with its slip rings short-circuited.

10-11. A 220-volt 3-phase 4-pole 60-cps 50-hp squirrel-cage induction motor takes a blocked-rotor current of 200 per cent and develops an internal starting torque of 16 per cent for an applied voltage of 30 per cent. A starting compensator is to be purchased for this motor. The starting compensator may be regarded as an ideal 3-phase step-down transformer connected between the supply line and the motor. Determine the per cent starting torque if the starting compensator limits the starting current in the supply line to 150 per cent of the motor full-load current. The supply-line voltage is 220 volts.

10-12. A 220-volt 3-phase 4-pole 60-cps wound-rotor induction motor develops an internal torque of 150 per cent with a line current of 155 per cent at a slip of 5.0 per cent when running at rated voltage and frequency with its rotor terminals short-circuited. (Torque and current are expressed as percentages of their full-load values.) The rotor resistance is 0.100 ohm between each pair of rotor terminals and may be assumed to be constant. What should be the resistance of each of three balanced Y-connected resistors inserted in series with each rotor terminal if the starting current at rated voltage and frequency is to be limited to 155 per cent? What internal starting torque will be developed?

10-13. A 220-volt 3-phase 4-pole 60-cps squirrel-cage induction motor develops a maximum internal torque of 250 per cent at a slip of 16 per cent when operating at rated voltage and frequency. If the effect of stator resistance is neglected, determine the maximum internal torque that this motor would develop if it were operated at 200 volts and 50 cps. Under these conditions, at what speed in rpm would maximum torque be developed?

10-14. The following test data apply to a 50-hp 2,300-volt 60-cps 3-phase squirrel-cage induction motor:

No-load test at rated voltage and frequency:
   Line current = 4.1 amp
   3-phase power = 1,550 watts
Blocked-rotor test at 15 cps:
   Line voltage = 268 volts
   Line current = 25.0 amp
   3-phase power = 9,600 watts
   Stator resistance between line terminals = 5.80 ohms
   Stray load loss = 420 watts

Compute the stator current and power factor, horsepower output, and efficiency when this motor is operating at rated voltage and frequency with a slip of 3.00 per cent.

10-15. Two 50-hp 440-volt 59.8 amp 3-phase 6-pole 60-cps squirrel-cage induction motors have identical stators. The d-c resistance measured between any pair of stator line terminals is 0.212 ohm. The blocked-rotor tests at 60 cps are as follows:

Motor 1:
   V = 61.3 volts, line to line
   I = 60.0 amp
   P = 3.16 kw, 3-phase
Motor 2:
   V = 96.0 volts, line to line
   I = 60.0 amp
   P = 8.95 kw, 3-phase

Determine the ratio of the internal starting torque developed by motor 2 to that developed by motor 1, (*a*) for the same current, (*b*) for the same applied voltage.

10-16. The results of a blocked-rotor test on a 25-hp 3-phase 220-volt 60-cps 6-pole squirrel-cage induction motor are given below:

Line-to-line voltage = 110 volts
Line current = 220 amp
3-phase power = 21.0 kw
Torque = 65 lb-ft

Determine the starting torque at a line-to-line voltage of 220 volts and 50 cps.

10-17. What would be the effects on the characteristics of a wound-rotor induction motor caused by rewinding the rotor with twice as many turns of conductors having half the cross-sectional area of copper, the arrangements of the new and old windings being the same, and the space occupied by insulation being assumed to be the same?

10-18. A frequency-changer set is to be designed for supplying variable-frequency power to induction motors driving the propellors on scale-model airplanes for wind-tunnel testing, as described in Art. 10-6b. The frequency changer is a wound-rotor induction machine driven by a d-c motor whose speed can be controlled. The 3-phase stator winding of the induction machine is excited from a 60-cps source, and variable-frequency 3-phase power is taken from its rotor winding. The set must meet the following specifications:

Output frequency range = 120 to 450 cps
Maximum speed not to exceed 3,000 rpm
Maximum power output = 80 kw at 0.80 power factor and 450 cps

The power required by the induction-motor load drops off rapidly with decreasing frequency, so that the maximum-speed condition determines the sizes of the machines.

On the basis of negligible exciting current, losses, and voltage drops in the induction machine, find:

a. The minimum number of poles for the induction machine
b. The corresponding maximum and minimum speeds
c. The kva rating of the stator winding of the induction machine
d. The horsepower rating of the d-c machine

10-19. The resistance measured between each pair of slip rings of a 3-phase 60-cps 300-hp 16-pole induction motor is 0.035 ohm. With the slip rings short-circuited, the full-load slip is 0.025, and it may be assumed that the slip-torque curve is a straight line from no load to full load. This motor drives a fan which requires 300 hp at the full-load speed of the motor. The torque required to drive the fan varies as the square of the speed. What resistances should be connected in series with each slip ring so that the fan will run at 300 rpm?

10-20. An adjustable-speed drive is to be furnished for a large fan in an industrial plant. The fan is to be driven by two wound-rotor induction motors coupled mechanically to the fan shaft and arranged so that lower speeds will be carried on the smaller motor and higher speeds on the larger motor. The speed control is to be arranged in steps so that the control will be uninterrupted from minimum to maximum speed and so that there will not be a sudden change in speed during the transfer from one motor to the other.

The larger motor is to be a 2,300-volt 3-phase 500-hp 60-cps 6-pole motor; the smaller motor is to be a 200-hp 60-cps 8-pole motor. The following motor data are furnished by the manufacturer:

Constants	200-hp motor	500-hp motor
Stator resistance......................	0.57 ohm	0.14 ohm
Rotor resistance......................	0.93	0.24
Stator plus rotor leakage reactance.....	2.6	0.98

These values are per-phase values (Y connection) referred to the stator. Motor rotational losses and exciting requirements may be ignored.

The minimum operating speed of the fan is to be 450 rpm; the maximum speed is to be approximately 1,170 rpm. The fan requires 450 hp at 1,170 rpm, and the power required at other speeds varies nearly as the cube of the speed.

The proposed control scheme is based on the stators of both motors being connected to the line at all times when the drive is in operation. In the lower speed range, the rotor of the 500-hp motor is open-circuited. This lower range is obtained by adjustment of external resistance in the rotor of the 200-hp motor. Above this lower speed range, the rotor of the 200-hp motor is open-circuited; speed adjustment in the upper range is obtained by adjustment of external resistance in the rotor of the 500-hp motor.

The transition between motors from the lower to the upper speed range is to be handled as follows:

1. All external rotor resistance is cut out of the 200-hp motor.

2. By means of a close-before-open type of contactor, the rotor circuit of the 500-hp motor is closed, and then the rotor circuit of the 200-hp motor is opened. The external rotor resistance in the 500-hp motor for this step has such a value that the speed will be the same as in the first step.

3. Higher speeds are obtained by cutting out rotor resistance in the 500-hp motor. This procedure is essentially reversed in going from the higher to the lower speed range.

As plant engineer, you are asked to give consideration to some features of this proposal. In particular, you are asked to:

a. Determine the range of external rotor resistance (referred to the stator) which must be available for insertion in the 200-hp motor.

b. Determine the range of external rotor resistance which must be available for insertion in the 500-hp motor.

c. Discuss any features of the scheme which you may not like, and suggest alternatives.

d. Discuss from both the economic and technical viewpoints the use of two motors here rather than a single 500-hp motor. If you should decide that the question is entirely one of economics, outline how you would justify the expense of the 200-hp motor to a skeptical vice-president.

10-21. A 40,000-hp 60-cps 22-pole wound-rotor induction motor is used to drive a load whose power requirement varies as the cube of its speed and is 40,000 hp at 297 rpm.

The speed must be adjustable over a range from 297 to 37.5 rpm. If rotor-resistance speed control is used, plot curves of the following variables as functions of the speed in rpm:

a. Load power, in kilowatts.

b. Power input to the motor, in kilowatts. Neglect stator copper, rotational, and stray load losses.

c. Total rotor-circuit copper loss, in kilowatts.

CHAPTER 11

Fractional-horsepower A-C Motors

The importance of fractional-horsepower motors in modern civilization is so evident as to require very little comment. Small motors are very widely used in appliances, in business, and in industry. They find interesting applications in automatic control devices of various kinds. Satisfactory solution of problems arising from such uses frequently requires a considerable amount of engineering skill on the part of both application engineers and motor designers.

Although 3-phase induction motors are procurable in stock sizes down to $\frac{1}{6}$ hp, by far the commonest of the fractional-horsepower motors are the single-phase a-c types, for the obvious reason that such is usually the only power available where fractional-horsepower motors are used. The purpose of this chapter is first to give qualitative explanations of the behavior of the common types of small single-phase motors, then to give a quantitative treatment of the induction motor with a single-phase winding in terms of the revolving-field theory, and finally to develop a generalized revolving-field theory of induction motors with 2-phase windings, from which both the starting and running characteristics of a variety of induction-motor types can be determined.[1]

11-1. Single-phase Induction Motors—Qualitative Examination. Structurally, the commonest types of single-phase induction motors resemble polyphase squirrel-cage motors except for the arrangement of the stator windings. An induction motor with a cage rotor and a single-phase stator winding is represented schematically in Fig. 11-1. Instead of being a concentrated coil, the actual stator winding is distributed in slots so as to produce an approximately sinusoidal space distribution of mmf. Such a motor inherently has no starting torque, but if started by auxiliary means, it will continue to run. Before considering auxiliary starting methods, the basic properties of the elementary motor of Fig. 11-1 will be described.

[1] For the theory, design, and performance calculations of a wide variety of fractional-horsepower motors, see C. G. Veinott, "Theory and Design of Small Induction Motors," McGraw-Hill Book Company, Inc., New York, 1959.

Consideration of conditions with the rotor at rest readily shows that no starting torque is produced. From Fig. 11-1, it is evident that the axis of the stator field remains fixed in position along the coil axis. With alternating current in the stator coil, the stator-mmf wave is stationary in space but pulsates in magnitude, the stator-field strength alternating in polarity and varying sinusoidally with time. Currents are induced in the rotor by transformer action, these currents being in such a direction as to produce an mmf opposing the stator mmf. The axis of the rotor-mmf wave coincides with that of the stator field, the torque angle therefore is zero, and no starting torque is produced. The motor is merely a single-phase static transformer with a short-circuited secondary.

Conditions are not so simple, however, when the rotor is made to revolve. Two different viewpoints may then be adopted in explaining the operation of the motor: the first is to derive the conditions from those already established for polyphase motors; the second is to start afresh and show that, under certain circumstances, the necessary conditions for the production of motor torque are satisfied. Both viewpoints, of course, lead to the same results, and both can be presented in quantitative terms. The resulting analytical methods are known as the *revolving-field theory* and the *cross-field theory*, respectively. Both viewpoints have their advantages, but on the whole there is little choice between them for computational purposes.

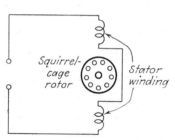

FIG. 11-1. Elementary single-phase induction motor.

According to the cross-field theory, when the rotor is made to revolve, there is, in addition to the transformer voltage, a voltage generated in the rotor by virtue of its rotation in the stationary stator field. In Fig. 11-1, for example, the rotational voltages in the rotor conductors are all in one direction in the upper half of the rotor and all in the other direction in the lower half. The rotational voltage produces a component rotor current and a component rotor-mmf wave whose axis is displaced 90 electrical degrees from the stator axis. The torque angle for this component of the rotor mmf is 90 degrees, and a torque is obtained. Further detailed analysis will show that this torque is in the direction of rotation and that the necessary conditions for the continued production of torque are satisfied.[1]

The argument in the revolving-field theory is that, if a rotating magnetic field is produced, then an induction-motor torque results. Moreover, this torque will be quantitatively similar to that of the polyphase

[1] For discussion and application of the cross-field theory, see *ibid.*, chap. 8.

motor treated in Chaps. 6 and 10, and approximately the same type of performance can be expected. The treatment of single-phase induction motors in the rest of this chapter will be from the revolving-field point of view.

Consider the elementary motor of Fig. 11-1, whose developed stator winding for 1 pole is represented schematically by the concentrated coil sides in Fig. 11-2a. Remember, however, that the stator winding actually is distributed in a number of slots so as to produce approximately a sinusoidal space distribution of mmf centered on the coil axis. If space harmonics are neglected, the space wave of stator mmf F_1 can then be expressed as

$$F_1 = F_{1(\text{peak})} \cos \theta \qquad (11\text{-}1)$$

where θ is the electrical space angle measured from the stator coil axis and $F_{1(\text{peak})}$ is the instantaneous value of the mmf wave at the coil axis and is

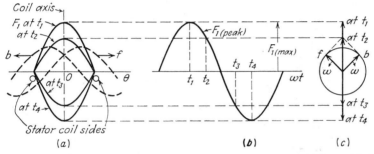

FIG. 11-2. Magnetomotive-force waves in a single-phase induction motor. (a) Space waves. (b) Time variations. (c) Representation by space phasors.

proportional to the instantaneous stator current. If the stator current varies sinusoidally, then $F_{1(\text{peak})}$ varies sinusoidally with time, as shown in Fig. 11-2b. The space distributions of stator mmf F_1 corresponding to several instants of time are shown in Fig. 11-2a. The stator-mmf wave is stationary, and its amplitude varies sinusoidally with time.

For analytical purposes, this pulsating, stationary wave can be resolved into two constant-amplitude traveling waves. Consider that the pulsating stator mmf may be represented by a space phasor of varying length, pointing up half the time, down the other half, and having a magnitude and direction determined by the instantaneous magnitude and direction of the stator current. This space phasor is shown by the vertical arrows in Fig. 11-2c for the same instants of time indicated in Fig. 11-2a and b. But it can be seen from Fig. 11-2c that such a phasor may be considered as the sum of two equal phasors rotating in opposite directions, each component phasor having a constant length equal to half the maximum length of the original pulsating phasor. Consequently the pulsating stator-mmf wave can be divided into two rotating waves of equal magnitudes. These component waves rotate in opposite directions at synchronous speed. The forward- and backward-rotating mmf waves f and b are shown dashed in Fig. 11-2a for the instant of time t_2, and the corresponding rotating vectors representing them are f and b in Fig. 11-2c.

The same conclusions can be reached by analytical methods. The analysis is essentially the same as the rotating-field theory of Art. 3-4 except that we are now concerned with only 1 stator phase, whereas in Art. 3-4 the mmfs of 3 stator phases were involved. Thus, if the stator current is a cosine function of time, the instantaneous value of the spatial peak of the pulsating mmf wave is

$$F_{1(peak)} = F_{1(max)} \cos \omega t \tag{11-2}$$

where $F_{1(max)}$ is the peak value corresponding to maximum instantaneous current. Consequently, by substitution of Eq. 11-2 in Eq. 11-1, the mmf wave as a function of both time and space is

$$F_1 = F_{1(max)} \cos \omega t \cos \theta \tag{11-3}$$

and, from the relation for the product of two cosines,

$$F_1 = \frac{1}{2} F_{1(max)} \cos (\theta - \omega t) + \frac{1}{2} F_{1(max)} \cos (\theta + \omega t) \tag{11-4}$$

Each of the cosine terms in Eq. 11-4 describes a sinusoidal function of the space angle θ. Each has a peak value of half the maximum amplitude of the pulsating wave, and a space-phase angle ωt. Both waves are centered on the axis of the stator winding at the instant when the stator mmf has its maximum value. The angle ωt provides rotation of each wave around the air gap at the constant angular velocity ω electrical radians per second, the waves traveling in opposite directions. The first wave, whose argument is $\theta - \omega t$, travels in the forward direction of θ; the second wave, whose argument is $\theta + \omega t$, travels in the backward direction of θ. With a balanced polyphase winding the backward-rotating components cancel, leaving only the forward components, as in Eq. 3-59 for a 3-phase winding. For a single-phase winding, however, both forward and backward components are present. Thus Eq. 11-4 leads to the same conclusion as that reached by means of the phasor diagram of Fig. 11-2c.

Each of these component-mmf waves produces induction-motor action, but the corresponding torques are in opposite directions. With the rotor at rest, the forward and backward air-gap flux waves created by the combined mmfs of stator and rotor currents are equal, the component torques are equal, and no starting torque is produced. If the forward and backward air-gap flux waves remained equal when the rotor is revolving, each of the component fields would produce a torque-speed characteristic similar to that of a polyphase motor with negligible stator leakage impedance, as illustrated by the dashed curves f and b in Fig. 11-3a. The resultant torque-speed characteristic, which is the algebraic sum of the two component curves, shows that if the motor were started by auxiliary means it would produce torque in whatever direction it was started.

The assumption that the air-gap flux waves remain equal when the rotor is in motion is a rather drastic simplification of the actual state of affairs. In the first place, the effects of stator leakage impedance are ignored. Furthermore the effects of induced rotor currents are not properly accounted for. Both these effects will ultimately be included

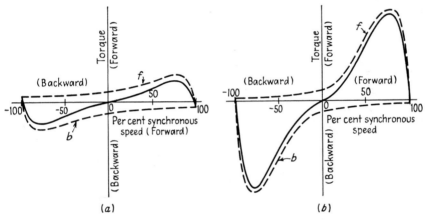

FIG. 11-3. Torque-speed characteristic of a single-phase induction motor. (a) On the basis of constant forward and backward flux waves. (b) Taking into account changes in the flux waves.

in the detailed quantitative theory of Art. 11-6. The following qualitative explanation shows that the performance of a single-phase induction motor is considerably better than would be predicted on the basis of equal forward and backward flux waves.

When the rotor is in motion, the component rotor currents induced by the backward field are greater than at standstill and their power factor is lower. Their mmf, which opposes that of the stator current, results in a reduction of the backward flux wave. Conversely, the magnetic effect of the component currents induced by the forward field is less than at standstill, because the rotor currents are less, and their power factor is higher. As speed increases, therefore, the forward flux wave increases while the backward flux wave decreases, their sum remaining roughly constant since it must induce the stator counter emf, which is approximately constant if the stator leakage-impedance voltage drop is small. Hence, with the rotor in motion, the torque of the forward field is greater and that of the backward field is less than in Fig. 11-3a, the true situation being about as shown in Fig. 11-3b. In the normal running region at a few per cent slip, the forward field is several times greater than the backward field, and the flux wave does not differ greatly from the constant-amplitude revolving field in the air gap of a balanced polyphase motor. In the normal running region, therefore, the torque-speed characteristic of a single-phase motor is not too greatly inferior to that of a polyphase motor having the same rotor and operating with the same maximum air-gap flux density.

In addition to the torques shown in Fig. 11-3, double-stator-frequency torque pulsations are produced by the interactions of the oppositely rotating flux and mmf waves which glide past each other at twice synchronous speed. These interactions produce no average torque, but they tend to make the motor noisier than a polyphase motor. Such torque pulsations are unavoidable in a single-phase motor because of the pulsations in instantaneous power input inherent in a single-phase circuit. The effects of the pulsating torque can be minimized by using an elastic mounting for the motor. The torque referred to on the torque-speed curves is the time average of the instantaneous torque.

11-2. Starting and Running Performance of Single-phase Induction Motors. Single-phase induction motors are classified in accordance with the methods of starting and are usually referred to by names descriptive of these methods. As with integral-horsepower motors, selection of the appropriate type is made from the starting and running characteristics and comparative economies. Starting methods and resulting torque-speed characteristics will be considered qualitatively in this article. A starting method based on the repulsion-motor principle is described in Art. 11-5.

a. Split-phase. Split-phase motors have 2 stator windings, a main winding m and an auxiliary winding a, with their axes displaced 90 electrical degrees in space. They are connected as shown in Fig. 11-4a. The auxiliary winding has a higher resistance-to-reactance ratio than the main winding, so that the two currents are out of phase, as indicated in the phasor diagram of Fig. 11-4b, which is representative of conditions at starting. Since the auxiliary-winding current I_a leads the main-winding current I_m, the stator field first reaches a maximum along the axis of the auxiliary winding and then somewhat later in time reaches a maximum along the axis of the main winding. The winding currents are equivalent to unbalanced 2-phase currents, and the motor is equivalent to an unbalanced 2-phase motor. The result is a rotating stator field which causes the motor to start. After the motor starts, the auxiliary winding is disconnected, usually by means of a centrifugal switch that operates at about 75 per cent of synchronous speed. The simple way to obtain the high resistance-to-reactance ratio for the auxiliary winding is to wind it with smaller wire than the main winding, a permissible procedure because this winding is in circuit only during starting. Its reactance can be

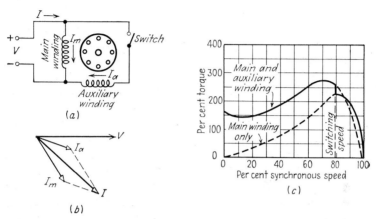

Fig. 11-4. Split-phase motor. (a) Connections. (b) Phasor diagram at starting. (c) Typical torque-speed characteristic.

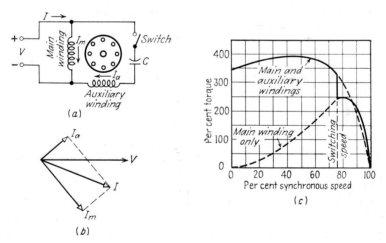

Fig. 11-5. Capacitor-start motor. (a) Connections. (b) Phasor diagram at start-ing. (c) Typical torque-speed characteristic.

reduced somewhat by placing it in the tops of the slots. A typical torque-speed characteristic is shown in Fig. 11-4c.

  b. *Capacitor-start Induction-run.* This is also a split-phase motor, but the time-phase displacement between the two currents is obtained by means of a capacitor in series with the auxiliary winding, as shown in Fig. 11-5a. Again the auxiliary winding is disconnected after the motor has started, and consequently the auxiliary winding and capacitor can be designed cheaply for intermittent service.   Dry-type a-c electrolytic capacitors are commonly used, since they are compact and inexpensive. Such capacitors inherently have intermittent ratings and are sensitive to overvoltage, and care must be taken to apply them properly.   For 110-volt motor-starting duty they are usually guaranteed for 25 per cent overvoltage and for not more than 20 periods of operation per hour, each period not to exceed 3 sec in duration.   By use of a starting capacitor of appropriate value, the auxiliary-winding current I_a at standstill could be made to lead the main-winding current I_m by 90 electrical degrees, as it

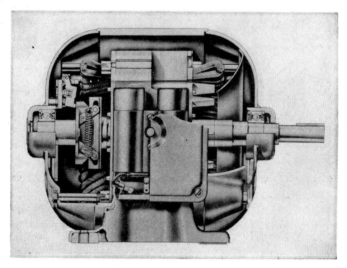

Fig. 11-6. Cutaway view of a capacitor-start induction motor. The centrifugal starting switch is at the left of the rotor.   The starting capacitors are the two cylinders in the box on the side of the motor. (*Courtesy of Westinghouse Electric Corporation.*)

would in a balanced 2-phase motor (see Fig. 11-5b).   Actually, the best compromise among the factors of starting torque, starting current, and costs results with a phase angle somewhat less than 90°.   A typical torque-speed characteristic is shown in Fig. 11-5c, high starting torque being an outstanding feature.   A cutaway view of a capacitor-start motor is shown in Fig. 11-6.

   c. Permanent-split-capacitor.   If the capacitor and auxiliary winding of the preceding motor are not cut out after starting, the construction can be simplified by omission of the switch and the power factor, efficiency, and torque pulsations improved.   For example, the capacitor and aux-iliary winding could be designed for perfect 2-phase operation at any one desired load.   The backward field would then be eliminated, with resulting improvement in efficiency.   The double-stator-frequency torque pulsations also would be eliminated, the capacitor serving as an energy-storage reservoir for smoothing out the pulsations in power input from the single-phase line. The result is a quiet motor. Since electrolytic capacitors are not suitable for continuous service, a more expensive oil-impregnated-paper type of capacitor must be used. Also, starting torque must be sacrificed because the capacitance is necessarily a compromise

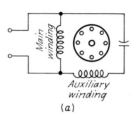
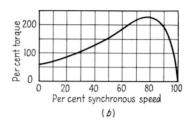

FIG. 11-7. Permanent-split-capacitor motor and typical torque-speed characteristic.

between the best starting and running values. The resulting torque-speed characteristic, together with a schematic diagram, are given in Fig. 11-7.

d. Two-value-capacitor. If two capacitors are used, one for starting and one for running, theoretically optimum starting and running performance can both be obtained. One way of accomplishing this result is shown in Fig. 11-8a. The small value of capacitance required for optimum running conditions is an impregnated-paper capacitor permanently connected in series with the auxiliary winding, and the much larger value

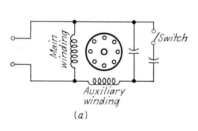
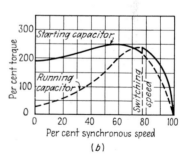

FIG. 11-8. Two-value-capacitor motor and typical torque-speed characteristic.

required for starting is obtained by an a-c electrolytic capacitor connected in parallel with the running capacitor. The starting capacitor is disconnected after the motor starts.

The design is somewhat of a compromise. A top limit on the number of turns in the auxiliary winding is imposed by the necessity for avoiding overvoltage on the electrolytic capacitor during starting. With this limitation on auxiliary-winding design, the running capacitor can seldom be made large enough, for economic reasons, for optimum full-load running conditions.

e. Shaded-pole. As illustrated schematically in Fig. 11-9*a*, the shaded-pole motor usually has salient poles with one portion of each pole surrounded by a short-circuited turn of copper called a *shading coil.* Induced currents in the shading coil cause the flux in the shaded portion of the pole to lag the flux in the other portion. The result is like a rotating field moving in the direction from the unshaded to the shaded portion of the pole, and a low starting torque is produced. A typical torque-speed characteristic is shown in Fig. 11-9*b.* The efficiency is low. This principle is used only in very small motors, such as in small fans, and as a starting method for electric-clock motors. Its chief advantages are simplicity and low cost.

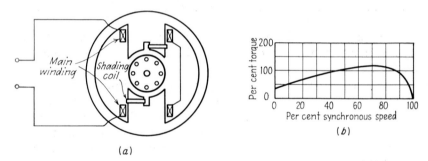

FIG. 11-9. Shaded-pole motor and typical torque-speed characteristic.

11-3. Single-phase Synchronous Motors. Fractional-horsepower synchronous motors are usually of either the *reluctance type* described in Art. 2-2 or the hysteresis type described in part *b* of this article.

a. Self-starting Reluctance Motors. Any one of the induction-motor types described in Art. 11-2 can be made into a self-starting synchronous motor of the reluctance type. Anything which makes the reluctance of the air gap a function of the angular position of the rotor with respect to the stator coil axis will produce reluctance torque when the rotor is revolving at synchronous speed. For example, suppose some of the teeth are removed from a squirrel-cage rotor, leaving the bars and end rings intact as in an ordinary squirrel-cage induction motor. Figure 11-10*a* shows a lamination for such a rotor designed for use with a 4-pole stator. The stator may be polyphase or any one of the single-phase types described in Art. 11-2. The motor will start as an induction motor and at light loads will speed up to a small value of slip. The reluctance torque arises from the tendency of the rotor to try to align itself in the minimum-reluctance position with respect to the synchronously revolving forward air-gap flux wave, in accordance with the principles explained in Chap. 2. At a small slip, this torque alternates slowly in direction; the rotor is accelerated during a positive half cycle of the torque variation and decelerated during the succeeding negative half cycle. If, however, the moment of inertia of the rotor and its mechanical load is sufficiently small, the rotor will be accelerated from slip speed up to synchronous speed during an accelerating half cycle of the reluctance torque. The rotor will then pull into step and continue to run at synchronous speed with characteristics similar to those described in Art. 2-2. A factor omitted in Art. 2-2 is the torque caused by induction-motor action of the backward-revolving field in a single-phase motor. This torque affects

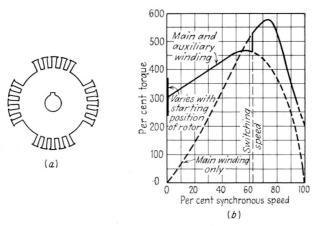

Fig. 11-10. Rotor punching for 4-pole reluctance-type synchronous motor and typical starting characteristics.

the synchronous-motor performance in the same way as an additional shaft load.

A typical torque-speed characteristic for a split-phase-start synchronous motor of the single-phase reluctance type is shown in Fig. 11-10b. Notice the high values of induction-motor torque. The reason for this is that in order to obtain satisfactory synchronous-motor characteristics it has been found necessary to build reluctance-type synchronous motors on frames which would be suitable for induction motors of two or three times the synchronous-motor rating. Also notice that the principal effect of the salient-pole rotor on the induction-motor characteristic is at standstill, where considerable "cogging" is evident; i.e., the torque varies considerably with rotor position.

b. Hysteresis Motors. The phenomenon of hysteresis can be used to produce mechanical torque. In its simplest form, the rotor of a hysteresis motor is a smooth cylinder of magnetically hard steel, without windings or teeth.   It is placed within a slotted stator carrying distributed windings designed to produce as nearly as possible a sinusoidal space distribution of flux, since undulations in the flux wave greatly increase the losses.   In single-phase motors, the stator windings usually are the permanent-split-capacitor type, as in Fig. 11-7.   The capacitor is chosen so as to result in approximately balanced 2-phase conditions within the motor windings.   The stator then produces a rotating field, approximately constant in space waveform and revolving at synchronous speed.

Instantaneous magnetic conditions in the air gap and rotor are indicated in Fig. 11-11a for a 2-pole stator.   The axis SS' of the stator-mmf wave revolves at synchronous speed.   Because of hysteresis, the magnetization of the rotor lags behind the inducing mmf wave, and therefore

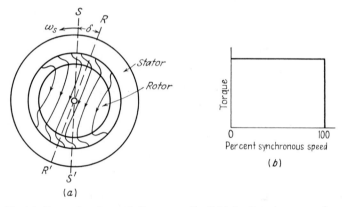

FIG. 11-11. (a) General nature of the magnetic field in the air gap and rotor of a hysteresis motor.   (b) Idealized torque-speed characteristic.

the axis RR' of the rotor flux wave lags behind the axis of the stator-mmf wave by the hysteretic lag angle δ (Fig. 11-11a).   If the rotor is stationary, starting torque is produced proportional to the product of the fundamental components of the stator mmf and rotor flux and the sine of the torque angle δ.   The rotor then accelerates if the counter torque of the load is less than the developed torque of the motor.   So long as the rotor is turning at less than synchronous speed, each particle of the rotor is subjected to a repetitive hysteresis cycle at slip frequency.   While the rotor accelerates, the lag angle δ remains constant if the flux is constant, since the angle δ depends merely on the hysteresis loop of the rotor and is independent of the rate at which the loop is traversed.   The motor therefore develops constant torque right up to synchronous speed, as shown in the idealized torque-speed characteristic of Fig. 11-11b.   This feature is one of the advantages of the hysteresis motor.   In contrast with a reluctance motor, which must "snap" its load into synchronism from an induction-motor torque-speed characteristic, a hysteresis motor can synchronize any load which it can accelerate, no matter how great the inertia. After reaching synchronism, the motor continues to run at synchronous speed and adjusts its torque angle so as to develop the torque required by the load.

The commonest application of hysteresis motors has been in electric clocks and other timing devices with outputs of a few milliwatts, inputs of 2 or 3 watts, and efficiencies of a few tenths of a per cent. They have also been used as record-player motors, where their quietness and ability to synchronize heavy inertia loads are advantageous. There are also designs as large as $\frac{1}{4}$ hp, comparable in size and efficiency with ordinary induction motors.

11-4. A-C Series Motors. Universal Motors. A series motor has the convenient ability to run on either alternating or direct current and with similar characteristics, provided both stator and rotor cores are laminated. Such a single-phase series motor therefore is commonly called a *universal motor*. The torque angle is fixed by the brush position and is normally at its optimum value of 90°. If alternating current is supplied to a series motor, the stator and rotor field strengths will vary in exact time phase. Both will reverse at the same instant, and consequently the torque will always be in the same direction, though

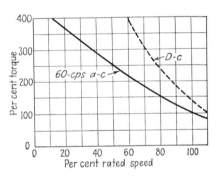

FIG. 11-12. Typical torque-speed characteristics of a universal series motor.

pulsating in magnitude at twice line frequency. Average torque will be produced, and the performance of the motor will be generally similar to that with direct current. Commutation difficulties will be more severe than with direct current, however, limiting heavy-power usage to low frequencies such as 25 cps. In the larger sizes, a-c series motors are used principally for traction purposes. In the fractional-horsepower and small integral-horsepower sizes, the commutation difficulties at 60 cps can be overcome. Small universal motors are used where light weight is important, as in vacuum cleaners and portable tools, and usually operate at high speeds (1,500 to 15,000 rpm). Typical characteristics are shown in Fig. 11-12. They can be made to have constant-speed characteristics by means of mechanical governing devices. In food mixers and similar applications, the speed held by the governor can be adjusted by the user.

The a-c and d-c characteristics differ somewhat for two reasons: (1) with alternating current, reactance-voltage drops in the field and armature absorb part of the applied voltage, and therefore for a specified current and torque the rotational counter emf generated in the armature is less than with direct current and the speed tends to be lower; (2) with alternating current, the magnetic circuit may be appreciably saturated at the peaks of the current wave, and the rms value of the flux may thus be appreciably less with alternating current than with the same rms value of direct current; the torque therefore tends to be less and the speed higher with alternating than with direct current. When it is important to have similar a-c and d-c characteristics, the differences can be minimized by the use of compensating windings.

11-5. Repulsion Motors and Variations. In a-c series motors, the rotor and stator windings are conductively coupled—i.e., the rotor current is obtained by conduction from the stator. Repulsion motors are

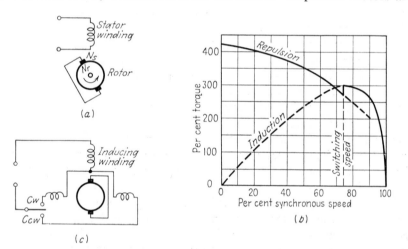

FIG. 11-13. (a) Schematic diagram of a repulsion motor. (b) Typical torque-speed characteristic of a repulsion-start induction motor. (c) Stator windings for reversing a repulsion motor.

similar to series motors except that the rotor and stator windings are inductively coupled—i.e., the rotor current is obtained by transformer action from the stator. The stator usually carries a distributed winding like the main winding of an ordinary single-phase induction motor. The rotor carries a drum winding connected to a commutator. The brushes are short-circuited. Such a motor is shown schematically in Fig. 11-13a. The magnetic axis of the rotor is determined by the brush position. If the rotor axis were in line with the stator-field axis, the current induced in the rotor by transformer action would produce an mmf opposing the stator mmf. No torque would be produced, however, because the torque angle would be zero. If the rotor axis were in quadrature with the stator-field axis, the torque angle would be at its optimum value of 90° but no rotor current would be induced, because the net inductive coupling would be zero.   Actually, the brushes are in an intermediate position, as shown in Fig. 11-13a.   Since the rotor mmf opposes the stator mmf, a rotor pole of the same polarity as the nearest stator pole is produced by the induced rotor current, as indicated by the letters N_s and N_r designating instantaneous stator and rotor polarity, respectively, in Fig. 11-13a. Repulsion between these like poles produces torque on the rotor in the direction in which the brushes are shifted from the maximum-current position.

The pure repulsion motor has the high-starting-torque varying-speed characteristic typical of series motors and permits speed adjustment by brush shifting.   *Repulsion-induction motors* have both a commutated winding and a squirrel-cage rotor winding, the latter being buried in the slots below the commutated winding; hence they combine both repulsion and induction torques.   In *repulsion-start induction-run motors*, a centrifugally operated device short-circuits all the commutator segments and usually also lifts the brushes when the motor reaches about 75 per cent of synchronous speed, after which the rotor winding is like a short-circuited squirrel cage and the motor operates as a single-phase induction motor.   Typical characteristics of a repulsion-start induction-run motor are given in Fig. 11-13b.   Prior to about 1930, these motors were widely used for applications requiring high starting torque.   Since then, however, the simpler capacitor-start motors have generally taken over this field.

The motor of Fig. 11-13a is not electrically reversible.   It must be reversed by shifting its brushes to the opposite side of the stator-field axis.   One way of accomplishing electrical reversibility is to shift the stator axis without moving the brushes.   In Fig. 11-13c the stator winding consists of an inducing winding and 2 field windings of opposite polarity placed on the stator in electrical quadrature with the inducing winding.   Rotation in either direction can be obtained by energizing the inducing winding in series with one or the other of the quadrature field windings, as shown in Fig. 11-13c.

11-6. Revolving-field Theory of Single-phase Induction Motors.   In Art. 11-1, the stator-mmf wave of a single-phase induction motor is shown to be equivalent to two constant-amplitude mmf waves revolving in opposite directions at synchronous speed.   Each of these component stator-mmf waves induces its own component rotor currents and produces induction-motor action just as in a balanced polyphase motor. This double-revolving-field concept not only is useful for qualitative visualization but also can be developed into a quantitative theory applicable to a wide variety of induction-motor types.   A simple and important case is that of the single-phase induction motor running on only its main winding.

First consider conditions with the rotor stationary and only the main stator winding m excited. The motor then is equivalent to a transformer with its secondary short-circuited. The equivalent circuit is shown in Fig. 11-14a, where r_{1m} and x_{1m} are, respectively, the resistance and leakage reactance of the main winding, x_φ is the magnetizing reactance, and r_2 and x_2 are the standstill values of the rotor resistance and leakage reactance referred to the main stator winding by use of the appropriate turns ratio. Core loss, which is omitted here, will be accounted for later

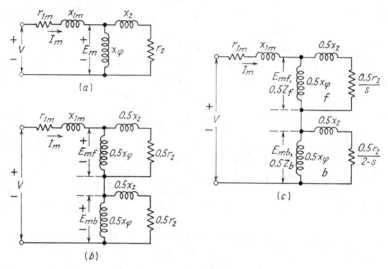

FIG. 11-14. Equivalent circuits for a single-phase induction motor. (a) Rotor blocked. (b) Rotor blocked, showing effects of forward and backward fields. (c) Running conditions.

as if it were a rotational loss. The applied voltage is V, and the main-winding current is I_m. The voltage E_m is the counter emf generated in the main winding by the stationary pulsating air-gap flux wave produced by the combined action of the stator and rotor currents.

In accordance with the double-revolving-field concept of Art. 11-1, the stator mmf can be resolved into half-amplitude forward- and backward-rotating fields. At standstill the amplitudes of the forward and backward resultant air-gap flux waves both equal half the amplitude of the pulsating field. In Fig. 11-14b the portion of the equivalent circuit representing the effects of the air-gap flux is split into two equal portions representing the effects of the forward and backward fields, respectively.

Now consider conditions after the motor has been brought up to speed by some auxiliary means and is running on only its main winding in the direction of the forward field at a per-unit slip s. The rotor currents induced by the forward field are of slip frequency sf, where f is the stator frequency. Just as in any polyphase motor with a symmetrical polyphase or cage rotor, these rotor currents produce an mmf wave traveling forward at slip speed with respect to the rotor and therefore at synchronous speed with respect to the stator. The resultant of the forward waves of stator and rotor mmf creates a resultant forward wave of air-gap flux which generates a counter emf E_{mf} in the main winding m of the stator. The reflected effect of the rotor as viewed from the stator is like that in a poly-phase motor and can be represented by an impedance $0.5r_2/s + j0.5x_2$ in parallel with $j0.5x_\varphi$, as in the portion of the equivalent circuit (Fig. 11-14c) labeled f. The factors of 0.5 come from the resolution of the pulsating stator mmf into forward and backward components.

Now consider conditions with respect to the backward field. The rotor is still turning at a slip s with respect to the forward field, and its per-unit speed n in the direction of the forward field is

$$n = 1 - s \tag{11-5}$$

The relative speed of the rotor with respect to the backward field is $1 + n$, or its slip with respect to the backward field is

$$1 + n = 2 - s \tag{11-6}$$

The backward field then induces rotor currents whose frequency is $(2 - s)f$. For small slips, these rotor currents are of almost twice stator frequency. At a small slip, an oscillogram of rotor current therefore will show a high-frequency component from the backward field superposed on a low-frequency component from the forward field. As viewed from the stator, the rotor-mmf wave of the backward-field rotor currents travels at synchronous speed, but in the backward direction. The equivalent circuit representing these internal reactions from the viewpoint of the stator is like that of a polyphase motor whose slip is $2 - s$ and is shown in the portion of the equivalent circuit (Fig. 11-14c) labeled b. As with the forward field, the factors of 0.5 come from the resolution of the pulsating stator mmf into forward and backward components. The voltage E_{mb} across the parallel combination representing the backward field is the counter emf generated in the main winding m of the stator by the resultant backward field.

By use of the equivalent circuit of Fig. 11-14c, the stator current, power input, and power factor can be computed for any assumed value of slip when the applied voltage and the motor impedances are known. To simplify the notation, let

$$Z_f \equiv R_f + jX_f \equiv \left(\frac{r_2}{s} + jx_2\right) \text{ in parallel with } jx_\varphi \qquad (11\text{-}7)$$

$$Z_b \equiv R_b + jX_b \equiv \left(\frac{r_2}{2-s} + jx_2\right) \text{ in parallel with } jx_\varphi \qquad (11\text{-}8)$$

The impedances representing the reactions of the forward and backward fields from the viewpoint of the single-phase stator winding m are $0.5Z_f$ and $0.5Z_b$, respectively, in Fig. 11-14c. (In much of the technical literature pertaining to single-phase motors, Z_f and Z_b are defined as half the values given by Eqs. 11-7 and 11-8, a notation somewhat simpler for the special case of operation on 1 phase, but not so well adapted to the generalized symmetrical-component theory which will be developed later in this chapter. With the definitions of Z_f and Z_b given in Eqs. 11-7 and 11-8, the factor of 0.5 accounting for the resolution of the stator mmf into half-amplitude forward- and backward-rotating fields must be included as an explicit factor.)

Examination of the equivalent circuit (Fig. 11-14c) confirms the conclusion, reached by qualitative reasoning in Art. 11-1 (Fig. 11-3b) that the forward air-gap flux wave increases and the backward wave decreases when the rotor is set in motion. When the motor is running at a small slip, the reflected effect of the rotor resistance in the forward field, $0.5r_2/s$, is much larger than its standstill value, while the corresponding effect in the backward field, $0.5r_2/(2-s)$, is smaller. The forward-field impedance therefore is larger than its standstill value, while that of the backward field is smaller. The forward-field counter emf E_{mf} therefore is larger than its standstill value, while the backward-field counter emf E_{mb} is smaller; i.e., the forward air-gap flux wave increases, while the backward flux wave decreases.

Moreover, mechanical output conditions can be computed by application of the torque and power relations developed for polyphase motors in Chaps. 6 and 9. The torques produced by the forward and backward fields can each be treated in this manner. The interactions of the oppositely rotating flux and mmf waves cause torque pulsations at twice stator frequency but produce no average torque.

As in Eq. 6-91, the internal torque T_f of the forward field in newton-meters equals $1/\omega_s$ times the power P_{gf} in watts delivered by the stator winding to the forward field, where ω_s is the synchronous angular velocity in mechanical radians per second; thus

$$T_f = \frac{1}{\omega_s} P_{gf} \qquad (11\text{-}9)$$

When the magnetizing impedance is treated as purely inductive, P_{gf} is the power absorbed by the impedance $0.5Z_f$; that is,

$$P_{gf} = I_m^2 0.5 R_f \qquad (11\text{-}10)$$

where R_f is the resistive component of the forward-field impedance defined in Eq. 11-7. Similarly the internal torque T_b of the backward field is

$$T_b = \frac{1}{\omega_s} P_{gb} \qquad (11\text{-}11)$$

where P_{gb} is the power delivered by the stator winding to the backward field, or

$$P_{gb} = I_m^2 0.5 R_b \qquad (11\text{-}12)$$

where R_b is the resistive component of the backward-field impedance Z_b defined in Eq. 11-8. The torque of the backward field is in the opposite direction to that of the forward field, and therefore the net internal torque T is

$$T = T_f - T_b = \frac{1}{\omega_s}(P_{gf} - P_{gb}) \qquad (11\text{-}13)$$

Since the rotor currents produced by the two component air-gap fields are of different frequencies, the total rotor I^2R loss is the numerical sum of the losses caused by each field. In general, as shown by comparison of Eqs. 6-94 and 6-95, the rotor copper loss caused by a rotating field equals the slip of the field times the power absorbed from the stator, whence

$$\text{Forward-field rotor } I^2R = sP_{gf} \qquad (11\text{-}14)$$
$$\text{Backward-field rotor } I^2R = (2 - s)P_{gb} \qquad (11\text{-}15)$$
$$\text{Total rotor } I^2R = sP_{gf} + (2 - s)P_{gb} \qquad (11\text{-}16)$$

Since power is torque times angular velocity and the angular velocity of the rotor is $(1 - s)\omega_s$, the internal power P converted to mechanical form, in watts, is

$$P = (1 - s)\omega_s T = (1 - s)(P_{gf} - P_{gb}) \qquad (11\text{-}17)$$

As in the polyphase motor, the internal torque T and internal power P are not the output values, because rotational losses remain to be accounted for. It is obviously correct to subtract friction and windage effects from T or P, and it is usually assumed that core losses may be treated in the same manner. For the small changes in speed encountered in normal operation, the rotational losses are often assumed to be constant.[1]

---

[1] For a treatment of the experimental determination of motor constants and losses, see *ibid.*, chap. 19.

Example 11-1. A $\frac{1}{4}$-hp 110-volt 60-cps 4-pole capacitor-start motor has the following constants and losses:

$$r_{1m} = 2.02 \text{ ohms} \qquad x_{1m} = 2.79 \text{ ohms}$$
$$r_2 = 4.12 \qquad x_2 = 2.12$$
$$x_\varphi = 66.8$$
$$\text{Core loss} = 24 \text{ watts} \qquad \text{Friction and windage} = 13 \text{ watts}$$

For a slip of 0.05, determine the stator current, power factor, power output, speed, torque, and efficiency when this motor is running as a single-phase motor at rated voltage and frequency with its starting winding open.

Solution. The first step is to determine the values of the forward- and backward-field impedances at the assigned value of slip. The following relations, derived from Eq. 11-7, simplify the computations:

$$R_f = \frac{x_\varphi^2}{x_{22}} \frac{1}{sQ_2 + (1/sQ_2)} \tag{11-18}$$

$$X_f = \frac{x_2 x_\varphi}{x_{22}} + \frac{R_f}{sQ_2} \tag{11-19}$$

where

$$x_{22} = x_2 + x_\varphi \tag{11-20}$$

and

$$Q_2 = \frac{x_{22}}{r_2} \tag{11-21}$$

Substitution of numerical values gives, for $s = 0.05$,

$$R_f + jX_f = 31.9 + j40.3 \text{ ohms}$$

Corresponding relations for the backward-field impedance Z_b are obtained by substituting $2 - s$ for s in Eqs. 11-18 and 11-19. When $(2 - s)Q_2$ is greater than 10, as is usually the case, less than 1 per cent error results from use of the following approximate forms:

$$R_b = \frac{r_2}{2 - s} \left(\frac{x_\varphi}{x_{22}}\right)^2 \tag{11-22}$$

$$X_b = \frac{x_2 x_\varphi}{x_{22}} + \frac{R_b}{(2 - s)Q_2} \tag{11-23}$$

Substitution of numerical values gives, for $s = 0.05$,

$$R_b + jX_b = 1.98 + j2.12 \text{ ohms}$$

Addition of the series elements in the equivalent circuit of Fig. 11-14c gives

$$r_{1m} + jx_{1m} = 2.02 + j2.79$$
$$0.5(R_f + jX_f) = 15.95 + j20.15$$
$$0.5(R_b + jX_b) = 0.99 + j1.06$$
$$\text{Input } Z = \text{sum} = 18.96 + j24.00 = 30.6\underline{/51.7°}$$

$$\text{Stator current } I_m = \frac{110}{30.6} = 3.59 \text{ amp}$$

Power factor $= \cos 51.7° = 0.620$
Power input $= (110)(3.59)(0.620) \doteq 244 \text{ watts}$

Power absorbed by forward field (Eq. 11-10)

$P_{gf} = (3.59)^2(15.95) = 206$ watts

Power absorbed by backward field (Eq. 11-12)

$P_{gb} = (3.59)^2(0.99) = 12.8$ watts

Internal mechanical power (Eq. 11-17)

$P = (0.95)(206 - 13) = 184$

Rotational loss $= 24 + 13 = \underline{37}$

Power output $=$ difference $= 147$ watts, or 0.197 hp

Synchronous speed $= 1,800$ rpm, or 30 rev/sec

$$\omega_s = 2\pi(30) = 188.5 \text{ rad/sec}$$

Rotor speed $= (1 - s) \times$ (synchronous speed)

$$= (0.95)(1,800) = 1,710 \text{ rpm}$$
$$= (0.95)(188.5) = 179 \text{ rad/sec}$$

Torque $=$ power $\div$ angular velocity

$$= {}^{147}\!/_{179} = 0.821 \text{ newton-m, or } 0.605 \text{ lb-ft}$$

Efficiency $= \dfrac{\text{output}}{\text{input}} = \dfrac{147}{244} = 0.602$

As a check on the power bookkeeping, compute the losses:

Stator $I_m^2 r_{1m} = (3.59)^2(2.02)$	$= 26.0$
Forward-field rotor I^2R, Eq. 11-14 $= (0.05)(206)$	$= 10.3$
Backward-field rotor I^2R, Eq. 11-15 $= (1.95)(12.8)$	$= 25.0$
Rotational losses	$= 37.0$
Sum	$= 98.3$
From input $-$ output, total losses	$= 97$

(Checks within accuracy of computations.)

Examination of the order of magnitude of the numerical values in Example 11-1 suggests approximations which usually can be made. These approximations pertain particularly to the backward-field impedance. Note that the impedance $0.5(R_b + jX_b)$ is only about 5 per cent of the total motor impedance for a slip near full load. Consequently an approximation as large as 20 per cent of this impedance would cause only about 1 per cent error in the motor current. Although, strictly speaking, the backward-field impedance is a function of slip, very little error usually results from computing its value at any convenient slip in the normal running region—say, 5 per cent—and then assuming R_b and X_b to be constants. With a slightly greater approximation, the shunting effect of jx_φ on the backward-field impedance can often be neglected, whence

$$Z_b \approx \frac{r_2}{2 - s} + jx_2 \qquad (11\text{-}24)$$

This equation gives values of the backward-field resistance that are a few per cent high, as can be seen by comparison with Eq. 11-22. Neglecting s in Eq. 11-24 would tend to give values of the backward-field resistance that would be too low, and therefore such an approximation would tend to counteract the error in Eq. 11-24. Consequently, for small slips

$$Z_b \approx \frac{r_2}{2} + jx_2 \tag{11-25}$$

In the polyphase motor (Art. 6-5) maximum internal torque and the slip at which it occurs can easily be expressed in terms of the motor constants; the maximum internal torque is independent of rotor resistance. No such simple relations exist for the single-phase motor. The single-phase problem is much more involved because of the presence of the backward field, the effect of which is twofold: first, it absorbs some of the applied voltage, thus reducing the voltage available for the forward field and decreasing the forward torque developed; and second, the backward field then absorbs some of the forward-field torque. Both these effects depend on rotor resistance as well as leakage reactance. Consequently, unlike the polyphase motor, the maximum internal torque of a single-phase motor is influenced by rotor resistance; increasing the rotor resistance decreases the maximum torque and increases the slip at which maximum torque occurs.

Principally because of the effects of the backward field, a single-phase induction motor is somewhat inferior to a polyphase motor using the same rotor and the same stator core. The single-phase motor has a lower maximum torque which occurs at a lower slip. For the same torque, the single-phase motor has a higher slip and greater losses, principally because of the backward-field rotor copper loss. The volt-ampere input to the single-phase motor is greater, principally because of the power and reactive volt-amperes consumed by the backward field. The stator copper loss also is somewhat higher in the single-phase motor, because 1 phase, rather than several, must carry all the current. Because of the greater losses, the efficiency is lower, and the temperature rise for the same torque is higher. A larger frame size must be used for a single-phase motor than for a polyphase motor of the same power and speed rating. Because of the larger frame size, the maximum torque can be made comparable with that of a physically smaller but equally rated polyphase motor. In spite of the larger frame size and the necessity for auxiliary starting arrangements, general-purpose single-phase motors in the standard fractional-horsepower ratings cost less than correspondingly rated polyphase motors, because of the much greater volume of production of the former.

11-7. A-C Tachometers. For automatic-control purposes, it is frequently necessary to obtain a measure of the angular velocity of a shaft, and it is often desirable that this measure be in the form of an alternating voltage of constant frequency. A small 2-phase induction motor may be used for this purpose. The connections are shown in Fig. 11-15. Winding m, often referred to as the *fixed field*, or *reference field*, is energized from a suitable alternating voltage of constant magnitude and frequency. A voltage of the same frequency is then generated in the auxiliary winding, or *control field a*. This voltage is applied to the high-impedance input circuit of an amplifier, and therefore winding a can be considered as open-circuited. The electrical requirements are, ideally, that the magnitude of the signal voltage generated in winding a should be linearly proportional to the speed and that the phase of this voltage should be fixed with respect to the applied voltage V_m.

The operation of the a-c tachometer may be visualized in terms of the double-revolving-field theory of Art. 11-6.[1] As viewed from the reference winding m, the tachometer is equivalent to a small single-phase induction motor, and the equivalent circuit of Fig. 11-14c therefore applies to conditions as viewed from this winding. The voltages across the impedances $0.5Z_f$ and $0.5Z_b$ in Fig. 11-14c are the voltages generated in winding m by the forward and backward flux waves, respectively. These flux waves also generate voltages in the auxiliary winding a. If the ratio of effective turns in winding a to effective turns in winding m is a, then the voltages generated in winding a are a times the corresponding voltages generated in winding m. By effective turns is meant the number of turns corrected for the effects of winding distribution in so far as fundamental space distributions of flux and

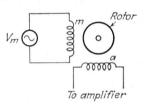

FIG. 11-15. Schematic diagram of a 2-phase tachometer.

mmf are concerned. If the direction of rotation is such that the forward field revolves past winding a a quarter cycle in time before it passes winding m, then the voltage E_{af} generated by the forward field in winding a leads the corresponding voltage E_{mf} generated in winding m by 90°, or, as phasors,

$$E_{af} = jaE_{mf} = jaI_m 0.5Z_f \qquad (11\text{-}26)$$

where I_m is the phasor current in winding m and is determined by the equivalent circuit of Fig. 11-14c. The backward field revolves in the opposite direction, and therefore the voltage E_{ab} generated by it in winding a lags the corresponding voltage E_{mb} generated in winding m by 90°, or

$$E_{ab} = -jaE_{mb} = -jaI_m 0.5Z_b \qquad (11\text{-}27)$$

The total voltage E_a generated in winding a is the sum of the components

[1] For a quantitative analysis, see R. H. Frazier, Analysis of the Drag-cup A-C Tachometer, *Trans. AIEE*, vol. 70, 1951.

generated by each field, or

$$E_a = jaI_m 0.5(Z_f - Z_b) \tag{11-28}$$

At standstill, the forward and backward fields are equal, and no voltage is generated in winding a. When the rotor is revolving, however, the impedance of the forward field increases while that of the backward field decreases, the difference between them being a function of the speed. The voltage generated in winding a is therefore a function of speed. Reversal of the direction of rotation reverses the phase of the auxiliary-winding voltage.

The shapes of the curves of voltage magnitude and phase angle as functions of speed depend on the speed range and tachometer constants—primarily on the rotor self-reactance-to-resistance ratio Q_2. It can be shown that either a low-Q_2 rotor (x_{22}/r_2 less than about 0.1) or a high-Q_2 rotor (x_{22}/r_2 greater than about 10) will provide nearly a constant phase angle and nearly a linear relation between the auxiliary-winding voltage and speed. The sensitivity in volts per rpm is sacrificed if a low-Q_2 rotor is used, but the linear speed range is wide. On the other hand, if a high-Q_2 rotor is used, the speed range around zero speed is limited to a fairly small fraction of synchronous speed when the requirements for linearity of voltage and constancy of phase angle are strict. These restrictions on rotor Q_2 should not be taken too literally, however, since satisfactory performance may be obtained with intermediate values of Q_2 if the requirements for linearity of voltage and constancy of phase angle are not too severe.

In common with other measuring instruments, the a-c tachometer should have as little effect as possible on the system into which it is inserted. In other words, its torque should be small compared with other torques acting in the system, and its inertia should be small when rapid speed variations are encountered, as in automatic control systems. To minimize the inertia, a-c tachometers are often built with a thin, metallic drag-cup rotor like that shown in the simplified sketch of Fig. 6-18. Because of the relatively long air gap, this construction inherently gives a fairly low Q_2, which can be made still lower, if desired, by making the drag cup of high-resistivity material.

Alternating-current tachometers require precise workmanship and care in design and assembly, in order to maintain concentricity and to eliminate direct coupling through the leakage fluxes between the excited winding and the output winding. Such coupling would result in signal voltage at zero speed. Sometimes soft-iron shields are provided to minimize pickup from stray fields. Frequently a-c tachometers are used in 400-cps systems.

11-8. Unbalanced Operation of Symmetrical Two-phase Machines— the Symmetrical-component Concept. In Art. 11-6 we have seen that the internal reactions in a single-phase induction machine with a uniform air gap and a symmetrical polyphase or cage rotor can be expressed in rather simple fashion in terms of the equivalent circuits of Fig. 11-14 when the stator-mmf wave is resolved into forward and backward traveling-wave components. One might expect, therefore, that the double-revolving-field concept should yield useful results when applied to a much wider variety of problems, and indeed this "hunch" proves to be correct. As a matter of fact, the thought process with respect to the double-revolving-field theory of induction machines is what led C. L. Fortescue to invent the method of symmetrical components for analysis of unbalanced polyphase systems.[1] Fortescue showed that an unbalanced polyphase system can be resolved into a number of component symmetrical systems. The internal behavior of rotating machines for each of these component systems can readily be expressed in terms of the simple fields which they produce. Out of this invention has grown an extensive theory with a voluminous literature.[2] It is probably no exaggeration to say, however, that, if it were not for the ease with which many problems involving rotating machines can be treated in terms of constant-amplitude revolving fields, there would have been no impelling incentive for the invention of symmetrical components, since unbalanced static circuits can be treated about as easily by straightforward network theory.

The purpose of this article is to develop the symmetrical-component theory of 2-phase induction motors from the double-revolving-field concept. In Arts. 11-9 and 11-10 it will be shown that this theory can be extended to apply to a variety of problems involving induction motors having 2 stator windings in space quadrature.

First consider in review what happens when balanced 2-phase voltages are applied to the stator terminals of a 2-phase machine having a uniform air gap, a symmetrical polyphase or cage rotor, and 2 identical stator windings a and m in space quadrature. The stator currents are equal in magnitude and in time quadrature. When the current in winding a has its instantaneous maximum, the current in winding m is zero and the stator-mmf wave is centered on the axis of winding a. Similarly, the stator-mmf wave is centered on the axis of winding m at the instant when the current in winding m has its instantaneous maximum. The stator-mmf wave therefore travels 90 electrical degrees in space in an interval of 90° in time, the direction of its travel depending on the phase sequence of

[1] C. L. Fortescue, Method of Symmetrical Co-ordinates Applied to the Solution of Polyphase Networks, *Trans. AIEE*, vol. 37, pt. 2, pp. 1027–1115, 1918.

[2] See, for example, Edith Clarke, "Circuit Analysis of A-C Power Systems," vols. I and II, John Wiley & Sons, Inc., New York, 1943 and 1950.

the currents. A more complete analysis in the manner of Art. 3-4 or Fig. 11-2 proves that the traveling wave has constant amplitude and constant angular velocity. This fact is, of course, the basis of the whole theory of balanced operation of induction machines.

The behavior of the motor for balanced 2-phase applied voltages of either phase sequence can readily be determined. Thus if the rotor is

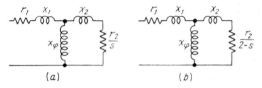

FIG. 11-16. Equivalent circuits for a 2-phase motor under unbalanced conditions. (a) Forward field. (b) Backward field.

turning at a per-unit speed n in the direction from winding a toward winding m, the terminal impedance per phase is given by the equivalent circuit of Fig. 11-16a when the applied voltage v_a leads the applied voltage v_m by 90°. Throughout the rest of this treatment, this phase sequence will be called *positive sequence* and will be designated by subscript f, since positive-sequence currents result in a forward field. With the rotor still forced to run at the same speed and in the same direction, the terminal

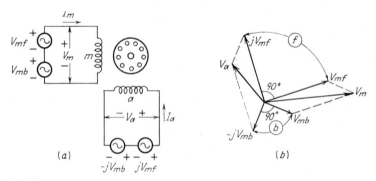

FIG. 11-17. Synthesis of an unbalanced 2-phase system from the sum of two balanced systems of opposite phase sequence.

impedance per phase is given by the equivalent circuit of Fig. 11-16b when v_a lags v_m by 90°. This phase sequence will be called *negative sequence* and will be designated by subscript b, since negative-sequence currents produce a backward field.

Suppose now that *two* balanced 2-phase voltage sources *of opposite phase sequence* are connected in series and applied simultaneously to the motor, as indicated in Fig. 11-17a, where phasor voltages V_{mf} and jV_{mf}

applied, respectively, to windings m and a form a balanced system of positive sequence and phasor voltages V_{mb} and $-jV_{mb}$ form another balanced system but of negative sequence. The resultant voltage V_m applied to winding m is, as a phasor,

$$V_m = V_{mf} + V_{mb} \qquad (11\text{-}29)$$

and that applied to winding a is

$$V_a = jV_{mf} - jV_{mb} \qquad (11\text{-}30)$$

If, for example, the forward, or positive-sequence, system is given by the phasors V_{mf} and jV_{mf} in Fig. 11-17b and the backward, or negative-sequence, system is given by the phasors V_{mb} and $-jV_{mb}$, then the resultant voltages are given by the phasors V_m and V_a. An unbalanced 2-phase system of applied voltages V_m and V_a has thus been synthesized by combining two symmetrical systems of opposite phase sequence.

The symmetrical component systems are, however, much easier to work with than is their unbalanced resultant system. Thus it is easy to compute the component currents produced by each symmetrical component system of applied voltages, because the induction motor operates as a balanced 2-phase motor for each component system. By superposition, the actual current in a winding then is the sum of its components. Thus if I_{mf} and I_{mb} are, respectively, the positive- and negative-sequence component phasor currents in winding m, then the corresponding positive- and negative-sequence component phasor currents in winding a are, respectively, jI_{mf} and $-jI_{mb}$ and the actual winding currents I_m and I_a are

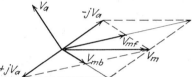

Fig. 11-18. Resolution of unbalanced 2-phase voltages into symmetrical components.

$$I_m = I_{mf} + I_{mb} \qquad (11\text{-}31)$$
$$I_a = jI_{mf} - jI_{mb} \qquad (11\text{-}32)$$

The inverse operation of finding the symmetrical components of specified voltages or currents must often be performed. Solution of Eqs. 11-29 and 11-30 for the phasor components V_{mf} and V_{mb} in terms of known phasor voltages V_m and V_a gives

$$V_{mf} = \tfrac{1}{2}(V_m - jV_a) \qquad (11\text{-}33)$$
$$V_{mb} = \tfrac{1}{2}(V_m + jV_a) \qquad (11\text{-}34)$$

These operations are illustrated in the phasor diagram of Fig. 11-18. Obviously, similar relations give the phasor symmetrical components I_{mf} and I_{mb} of the current in winding m in terms of specified phasor currents

I_m and I_a in the 2 phases; thus

$$I_{mf} = \tfrac{1}{2}(I_m - jI_a) \tag{11-35}$$
$$I_{mb} = \tfrac{1}{2}(I_m + jI_a) \tag{11-36}$$

Resolution of the stator-mmf wave into its forward and backward components, as in Fig. 11-2c, may help to complete a physical picture of what is happening in the machine when one applies the symmetrical-component transformations of Eqs. 11-35 and 11-36. In Fig. 11-19a, I_m and I_a are rotating time phasors whose projections on the real axis are proportional to the instantaneous currents in the windings. Figure 11-19b is a space-phasor diagram in which the dash-dot lines m and a represent the winding axes and the phasors F_m and F_a represent the instantaneous values of the pulsating mmf wave produced by each winding. For simplicity, the phasors are shown in their positions at the moment when

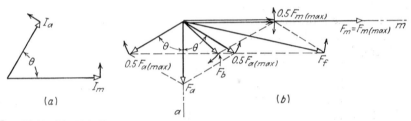

FIG. 11-19. (a) Unbalanced 2-phase currents and (b) phasor resolution of mmf waves into forward and backward components.

i_m, and therefore F_m, has its instantaneous maximum $F_{m(max)}$. Consequently, when F_m is resolved into its forward and backward half-amplitude revolving components (in the manner of Fig. 11-2c and Eq. 11-4), the components at this instant are in line with the axis m, as shown by the two oppositely revolving components $0.5F_{m(max)}$. At this same instant, however, i_a has passed beyond its maximum value by the time angle θ (Fig. 11-19a) and therefore the forward- and backward-revolving components $0.5F_{a(max)}$ are in the two positions shown in Fig. 11-19b. The space phasors representing the resultant forward and backward fields F_f and F_b are the phasor sums of the components, as in Fig. 11-19b. Because of the space angle between the 2 windings, the angle between the two revolving-field components $0.5F_{m(max)}$ and $0.5F_{a(max)}$ for the forward field is 90° less than the time-phase angle θ between the currents and for the backward field is 90° greater. Consequently the phasor summations by which the mmfs F_f and F_b are obtained in Fig. 11-19b are exactly similar to those of Eqs. 11-35 and 11-36 for obtaining the symmetrical-component currents. Thus, when the currents are resolved into symmetrical components, the stator mmf is thereby resolved into forward and backward components.

Example 11-2.   The equivalent-circuit constants of a 5-hp 220-volt 60-cps 2-phase squirrel-cage induction motor are given below, in ohms per phase:

$$r_1 = 0.534 \qquad x_1 = 2.45 \qquad x_\varphi = 70.1$$
$$r_2 = 0.956 \qquad x_2 = 2.96$$

This motor is operated from an unbalanced 2-phase source whose phase voltages are, respectively, 230 volts and 210 volts, the smaller voltage leading the larger by 80°. For a slip of 0.05, find:

  a. The positive- and negative-sequence components of the applied voltages
  b. The positive- and negative-sequence components of the stator phase currents
  c. The effective values of the phase currents
  d. The internal mechanical power

  Solution.   *a.* Let V_m and V_a denote the voltages applied to the 2 phases, respectively.   Then

$$V_m = 230\underline{/0°} = 230 + j0 \text{ volts}$$
$$V_a = 210\underline{/80°} = 36.4 + j207 \text{ volts}$$

From Eqs. 11-33 and 11-34, the forward and backward components of voltages are, respectively,

$$V_{mf} = \tfrac{1}{2}(230 + j0 + 207 - j36.4)$$
$$= 218.5 - j18.2 = 219.5\underline{/-4.8°} \text{ volts}$$
$$V_{mb} = \tfrac{1}{2}(230 + j0 - 207 + j36.4)$$
$$= 11.5 + j18.2 = 21.5\underline{/57.7°} \text{ volts}$$

  b. From Eqs. 11-18 and 11-19, the forward-field impedance is, for a slip of 0.05,

$$Z_f = 16.46 + j7.15 \text{ ohms}$$
$$r_1 + jx_1 = \underline{0.53 + j2.45} \text{ ohms}$$
$$16.99 + j9.60 = 19.50\underline{/29.4°} \text{ ohms}$$

Hence the forward component of stator current is

$$I_{mf} = \frac{219.5\underline{/-4.8°}}{19.50\underline{/29.4°}} = 11.26\underline{/-34.2°} \text{ amp}$$

For the same slip, from Eqs. 11-22 and 11-23 the backward-field impedance is

$$Z_b = 0.451 + j2.84 \text{ ohms}$$
$$r_1 + x_1 = \underline{0.534 + j2.45} \text{ ohms}$$
$$0.985 + j5.29 = 5.38\underline{/79.5°} \text{ ohms}$$

Hence the backward component of stator current is

$$I_{mb} = \frac{21.5\underline{/57.7°}}{5.38\underline{/79.5°}} = 4.00\underline{/-21.8°} \text{ amp}$$

  c. By Eqs. 11-31 and 11-32, the currents in the two phases are, respectively,

$$I_m = 13.06 - j7.79 = 15.2\underline{/-31°} \text{ amp}$$
$$I_a = 4.81 + j5.64 = 7.40\underline{/49.2°} \text{ amp}$$

Note that the currents are much more unbalanced than the applied voltages.   Even though the motor is not overloaded in so far as shaft load is concerned, the losses are appreciably increased by the current unbalance and the stator winding with the greatest current may overheat.

d. The power delivered to the forward field by the 2 stator phases is

$$P_{gf} = 2I_{mf}^2 R_f = 2 \times 126.8 \times 16.46 = 4{,}175 \text{ watts}$$

and the power delivered to the backward field is

$$P_{gb} = 2I_{mb}^2 R_b = 2 \times 16.0 \times 0.451 = 15 \text{ watts}$$

Thus, according to Eq. 11-17, the internal mechanical power developed is

$$P = 0.95(4{,}175 - 15) = 3{,}950 \text{ watts}$$

If the core losses, friction and windage, and stray load losses are known, the shaft output can be found by subtracting them from the internal power. The friction and windage losses depend solely on the speed and are the same as they would be for balanced operation at the same speed. The core and stray load losses, however, are somewhat greater than they would be for balanced operation with the same positive-sequence voltage and current. The increase is caused principally by the $(2 - s)$-frequency core and stray losses in the rotor caused by the backward field.

11-9. Two-phase Control Motors.

The general construction and applications of the 2-phase control motor have already been described in Art. 6-8. When appropriate assumptions are made, the symmetrical-component methods of Art. 11-8 provide simple and effective means for analyzing the steady-state performance of control motors and acquiring insight into their dynamic behavior.

The analysis is greatly simplified if the currents and voltages are considered to be sinusoidal, if the effects of the source impedances are neglected, and if the motor is assumed to have identical 2-phase stator windings. The motor then is simply a symmetrical 2-phase motor operating from an unbalanced 2-phase source. The more elaborate theory of Art. 11-10 is required to account for the effects of unbalanced impedances.

Example 11-3. A symmetrical 2-phase induction motor develops a maximum internal torque at a reverse speed of 0.50 per unit when balanced 2-phase voltages are applied to its stator terminals. The Q of its Thévenin equivalent circuit (see Art. 10-3) is 3.0. This motor is to be used as a 2-phase control motor with constant voltage of 1.00 per unit applied to its reference phase and variable voltage applied to its control phase, these voltages being considered to be in time quadrature.

Plot a family of internal-torque-speed characteristics for per-unit values of the control-phase voltage of 1.00, 0.80, 0.60, 0.40, 0.20, and 0, covering a speed range from -1 to $+1$ per unit. Express the torque in per unit, considering the unit of torque to be the internal torque developed at standstill when balanced 2-phase voltages of 1.00 per unit are applied to the two stator phases.

The torque-slip curves obtained in this example are those plotted in Fig. 6-17.

Solution. The speed for maximum torque, the Q, and the stalled torque for balanced 2-phase voltages fix the curve for $V_a = 1.00$. This curve can readily be determined from the normalized torque-slip curves of Fig. 10-7. The rest of the family then can be computed from this curve by resolving the applied voltages into 2-phase symmetrical components.

Since the speed for maximum torque is given as -0.50 per unit, the slip for maximum torque $s_{\max T} = 1.50$. At standstill, then,

$$\frac{s}{s_{\max T}} = \frac{1.00}{1.50} = 0.667$$

From Fig. 10-7 for $Q = 3.0$, the corresponding torque ratio at standstill is

$$\frac{T_{\text{stalled}}}{T_{\max}} = 0.938$$

But $T_{\text{stalled}} \equiv 1.00$ per unit, by definition. Hence $T_{\max}$ is $1/0.938$, or 1.066 per unit.

Data for the torque-speed curve for $V_a = 1.00$ in Fig. 6-17 can now be obtained from Fig. 10-7. The data are shown in Table 11-1. The first column gives the slip ratios, and the corresponding torque ratios are read from the curve for $Q = 3.0$ in Fig. 6-17. The actual slip s in column 3 is found by multiplying column 1 by $s_{\max T} = 1.50$. The corresponding torque T_f' in column 4 is found by multiplying column 2 by $T_{\max} = 1.066$. For balanced conditions ($V_a = 1.00$) there is no backward torque, and column 4 gives the net torque from which the curve labeled $V_a = 1.0$ in Fig. 6-17 is plotted.

Table 11-1
Computations for Example 11-3

$\dfrac{s}{s_{\max T}}$	$\dfrac{T}{T_{\max}}$	s	T_f'	$2 - s$	T_b'
0	0	0	0	2.0	1.03
0.133	0.32	0.2	0.34	1.8	1.055
0.267	0.565	0.4	0.60	1.6	1.06
0.40	0.745	0.6	0.795	1.4	1.06
0.533	0.86	0.8	0.92	1.2	1.045
0.667	0.94	1.0	1.00	1.0	1.00
0.80	0.98	1.2	1.045	0.8	0.92
0.933	0.995	1.4	1.06	0.6	0.795
1.067	0.995	1.6	1.06	0.4	0.60
1.20	0.99	1.8	1.055	0.2	0.34
1.33	0.965	2.0	1.03	0	0

When the voltages are unbalanced, they can be resolved into symmetrical components. Let the per-unit magnitude of the control-phase voltage be V_a, and assume that this voltage leads the reference voltage V_m by 90°. The phasor expression for the control-phase voltage then is jV_a, and Eqs. 11-33 and 11-34 reduce to

$$V_{mf} = \tfrac{1}{2}[1 - j(jV_a)] = \tfrac{1}{2}(1 + V_a) \qquad (11\text{-}37)$$
$$V_{mb} = \tfrac{1}{2}[1 + j(jV_a)] = \tfrac{1}{2}(1 - V_a) \qquad (11\text{-}38)$$

Both forward and backward fields are now present. The slip for the backward field is $2 - s$, as in column 5 of Table 11-1. Column 6 gives the values of backward torque T_b' that would be developed with negative-sequence voltages of 1.00 per unit and is obtained from column 4. (For example, the value of T_b' at a backward-field slip $2 - s = 1.8$ is the same as the value of T_f' at a forward-field slip $s = 1.8$.)

Now recall that the internal torque developed by a polyphase induction motor varies as the square of the voltage. The forward and backward torques therefore are

$$T_f = V_{mf}^2 T_f' \tag{11-39}$$
$$T_b = V_{mb}^2 T_b' \tag{11-40}$$

where V_{mf}, V_{mb} are the per-unit values of the positive- and negative-sequence components of the unbalanced applied voltages (Eqs. 11-37 and 11-38) and T_f', T_b' are the forward and backward torque corresponding to positive- and negative-sequence applied voltages, respectively, of 1.00 per unit, as given in columns 4 and 6. The net internal torque T is

$$T = T_f - T_b \tag{11-41}$$

The torque developed at any chosen values of V_a and slip can now be determined. For example, from Eqs. 11-37 to 11-40,

At $V_a = 0.60$:

$$V_{mf} = 0.80 \qquad T_f = 0.64 T_f'$$
$$V_{mb} = 0.20 \qquad T_b = 0.04 T_b'$$

Values of T_f' and T_b' can be read from Table 11-1. For example,

At $s = 0.20$:

$$\begin{aligned} T_f' &= 0.34 & T_f &= (0.64)(0.34) &= 0.218 \\ T_b' &= 1.055 & T_b &= (0.04)(1.055) &= \underline{0.042} \\ & & T &= T_f - T_b &= \overline{0.176} \end{aligned}$$

Data for the family of curves in Fig. 6-17 can be computed by repeating these simple calculations for other assumed values of V_a and slip. The calculations can be arranged systematically in tabular form.

The nondimensional curves of Fig. 6-17 are approximately applicable to all 2-phase control motors since nearly all of them are designed to develop maximum torque at about the same per-unit speed and to have about the same Q. The slip $s_{\max T}$ at maximum torque and the Q fix the shape of the characteristics, so long as the rotor resistance is constant and the effects of saturation are negligible. Fairly wide variations in the parameters $s_{\max T}$ and Q have relatively little effect on the characteristics over the normal operating range.

11-10. Revolving-field Theory of Unsymmetrical Two-phase Induction Machines.

We have seen that the double-revolving-field concept leads to a useful method of analyzing 2-phase machines with identical quadrature stator windings. The question naturally arises: Can the same thought processes be applied to machines having unsymmetrical stator circuits? Specifically, the problem we should like to solve is indicated in Fig. 11-20 which shows a 2-phase induction motor connected to two voltage sources V_m and V_a through unbalanced circuits of impedance Z_{em} and Z_{ea}. The motor has a uniform air gap and a symmetrical polyphase or cage rotor. The stator windings are in electrical space quadrature but may have unequal turns and unequal leakage impedances.[1] If an attack

---

[1] For a general treatment of machines in which the windings need not be in quadrature, see W. V. Lyon and Charles Kingsley, Jr., Analysis of Unsymmetrical Machines, *Trans. AIEE*, vol. 55, no. 5, pp. 471–476, May, 1936. For an analysis of the quadrature case, see F. W. Suhr, Symmetrical Components as Applied to the Single-phase Induction Motor, *Trans. AIEE*, vol. 64, no. 9, pp. 651–656, September, 1945.

along these lines should be successful, the results would be applicable to a wide variety of induction-machine types. For example, split-phase and capacitor motors would be the special case in which V_m equals V_a. Single-phase operation would be the special case in which I_a is zero. In fact, the preceding investigations of Arts. 11-6 and 11-8 may be considered simply as exploratory ones, finally leading up to the generalized point of view to be investigated next.

a. Generalized Theory. The stator-circuit phasor voltage equations for the generalized 2-phase motor of Fig. 11-20 can immediately be written as

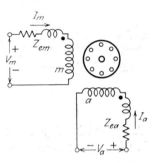

$$V_m = I_m Z_{1m} + E_m \qquad (11\text{-}42)$$
$$V_a = I_a Z_{1a} + E_a \qquad (11\text{-}43)$$

where V_m, V_a are the phasor source voltages; I_m, I_a are the phasor phase currents; Z_{1m}, Z_{1a} are each the phasor sum of the external-circuit impedance and the leakage impedance of a stator phase; and E_m, E_a are the counter emfs generated in the stator windings by the resultant air-gap flux. In order to proceed further, the internal reactions of the air-gap

FIG. 11-20. Two-phase induction motor with unbalanced stator circuits.

flux waves must now be studied. The previous experience of Art. 11-8 leads one to suspect that a way to proceed is to resolve the stator currents into two sets of components that would produce, respectively, forward and backward mmf waves. The counter emfs can then be expressed in terms of the internal impedances to the component revolving fields. Only fundamental space distributions of flux and mmf will be considered.

Let N_m and N_a be the effective turns in windings m and a, respectively. By effective turns is meant the number of turns corrected for the effects of winding distribution in so far as fundamental space distribution of mmf is concerned. Exactly as in a balanced 2-phase motor, a constant-amplitude revolving field would result if the currents in the 2 windings produced equal-amplitude mmfs in time quadrature. The direction of rotation of the field would depend on the phase sequence of the currents. A constant-amplitude forward field would result if a set of phasor currents I_{mf} and I_{af} in the windings m and a, respectively, satisfied the phasor relationship

$$N_a I_{af} = j N_m I_{mf} \qquad (11\text{-}44)$$

or

$$I_{af} = j \frac{I_{mf}}{a} \qquad (11\text{-}45)$$

where a is the effective turns ratio N_a/N_m. Similarly, a constant-amplitude backward field would result if another set of phasor currents I_{mb} and

I_{ab} satisfied the phasor relationship

$$I_{ab} = -j\frac{I_{mb}}{a} \tag{11-46}$$

If both sets of currents existed simultaneously, the actual winding currents I_m and I_a would be

$$I_m = I_{mf} + I_{mb} \tag{11-47}$$

$$I_a = I_{af} + I_{ab} = j\frac{I_{mf}}{a} - j\frac{I_{mb}}{a} \tag{11-48}$$

and both a forward and a backward field would be present. Solution of these equations for the component currents I_{mf} and I_{mb} in terms of the actual winding currents I_m and I_a gives

$$I_{mf} = \tfrac{1}{2}(I_m - jaI_a) \tag{11-49}$$

$$I_{mb} = \tfrac{1}{2}(I_m + jaI_a) \tag{11-50}$$

Compare with Eqs. 11-35 and 11-36. Note that aI_a is simply the current in winding a referred to winding m, as in static-transformer theory.

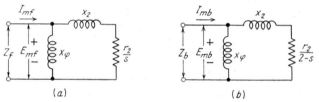

FIG. 11-21. Equivalent circuits representing the reactions of (a) the forward and (b) the backward fields as viewed from the main winding.

From the viewpoint of winding m, the internal reactions of the forward and backward fields are just like those in a balanced 2-phase motor. Thus, if the rotor and magnetizing impedances are referred to winding m, the forward- and backward-field impedances Z_f and Z_b as viewed from winding m are given by the equivalent circuits in Fig. 11-21 and the component counter emfs E_{mf} and E_{mb} generated in winding m by the forward and backward fields, respectively, equal the voltages across these impedances. The total counter emf E_m generated in winding m is, as a phasor,

$$E_m = E_{mf} + E_{mb} = I_{mf}Z_f + I_{mb}Z_b \tag{11-51}$$

Because of the stator turns ratio, the component counter emfs generated in winding a will be a times the corresponding component voltages generated in winding m. Because of the directions in which the fields rotate, the forward-field component generated in winding a leads and the backward-field component lags the corresponding component generated in winding m. The total counter emf E_a generated in winding a by both fields therefore is

$$E_a = jaE_{mf} - jaE_{mb} = jaI_{mf}Z_f - jaI_{mb}Z_b \qquad (11\text{-}52)$$

Note that aE_{mf} and aE_{mb} are merely the voltages of winding m referred to winding a.

Substitution of Eqs. 11-47, 11-48, 11-51, and 11-52 in Eqs. 11-42 and 11-43 then gives

$$V_m = (I_{mf} + I_{mb})Z_{1m} + I_{mf}Z_f + I_{mb}Z_b \qquad (11\text{-}53)$$

$$V_a = \left(j\frac{I_{mf}}{a} - j\frac{I_{mb}}{a} \right)Z_{1a} + jaI_{mf}Z_f - jaI_{mb}Z_b \qquad (11\text{-}54)$$

Rearrangement of terms in these equations and multiplication of Eq. 11-54 by $-j/a$ gives

$$V_m = I_{mf}(Z_{1m} + Z_f) + I_{mb}(Z_{1m} + Z_b) \qquad (11\text{-}55)$$

$$-j\frac{V_a}{a} = I_{mf}\left(\frac{Z_{1a}}{a^2} + Z_f\right) - I_{mb}\left(\frac{Z_{1a}}{a^2} + Z_b\right) \qquad (11\text{-}56)$$

Note that V_a/a and Z_{1a}/a^2 are, respectively, the phase a voltage and stator-circuit impedance referred to winding m.

These equations can be solved for the currents in terms of the voltages and impedances, but experience with the symmetrical-component method, as in Art. 11-8, leads one to suspect that a rearrangement which introduces the symmetrical components of the applied voltages may lead to worthwhile simplifications. Such a rearrangement is readily made; thus, addition of Eqs. 11-55 and 11-56 and division of the result by 2 gives

$$\frac{1}{2}\left(V_m - j\frac{V_a}{a} \right) = I_{mf}\left(\frac{\frac{Z_{1a}}{a^2} + Z_{1m}}{2} + Z_f \right) - I_{mb}\frac{\frac{Z_{1a}}{a^2} - Z_{1m}}{2} \qquad (11\text{-}57)$$

Similarly, subtraction of Eq. 11-56 from Eq. 11-55 and division of the result by 2 gives

$$\frac{1}{2}\left(V_m + j\frac{V_a}{a} \right) = -I_{mf}\frac{\frac{Z_{1a}}{a^2} - Z_{1m}}{2} + I_{mb}\left(\frac{\frac{Z_{1a}}{a^2} + Z_{1m}}{2} + Z_b \right) \qquad (11\text{-}58)$$

Now let

$$V_{mf} \equiv \frac{1}{2}\left(V_m - j\frac{V_a}{a} \right) \qquad (11\text{-}59)$$

$$V_{mb} \equiv \frac{1}{2}\left(V_m + j\frac{V_a}{a} \right) \qquad (11\text{-}60)$$

By comparison with Eqs. 11-33 and 11-34, these new voltages can be recognized as symmetrical components of the applied voltages referred to phase m. From Eqs. 11-59 and 11-60, the relations for the actual winding voltages in terms of the symmetrical components are

$$V_m = V_{mf} + V_{mb} \tag{11-61}$$
$$V_a = jaV_{mf} - jaV_{mb} \tag{11-62}$$

For further simplification of the notation, let

$$Z_o = \frac{1}{2}\left(\frac{Z_{1a}}{a^2} + Z_{1m}\right) \tag{11-63}$$

$$Z_d = \frac{1}{2}\left(\frac{Z_{1a}}{a^2} - Z_{1m}\right) \tag{11-64}$$

where Z_o is the average value of the impedances referred to the main winding and Z_d is half their difference (subscript d for difference).   Sub-

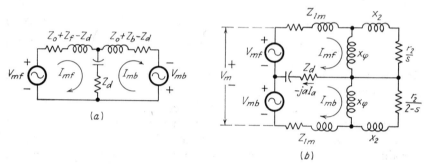

FIG. 11-22. Generalized equivalent circuits for 2-phase induction machines.

stitution of the defining relations (Eqs. 11-59, 11-60, 11-63, and 11-64) in Eqs. 11-57 and 11-58 then gives

$$V_{mf} = I_{mf}(Z_o + Z_f) - I_{mb}Z_d \tag{11-65}$$
$$V_{mb} = -I_{mf}Z_d + I_{mb}(Z_o + Z_b) \tag{11-66}$$

Equations 11-65 and 11-66 are also the voltage equations for the coupled circuit shown in Fig. 11-22a, which is therefore an equivalent circuit for the motor.   From Eqs. 11-63 and 11-64

$$Z_o - Z_d = Z_{1m} \tag{11-67}$$

Also recall that the impedances Z_f and Z_b are parallel combinations of the rotor and magnetizing branches (Fig. 11-21).   The equivalent circuit therefore can be redrawn as in Fig. 11-22b.   The impedance Z_d is drawn as a capacitive impedance, because that is what it is in the important case of a capacitor motor.   This impedance acts as a coupling, just like a mutual impedance, between the forward and backward fields and shows the manner in which these fields influence one another.   The current in this impedance is

$$I_{mf} - I_{mb} = -jaI_a \tag{11-68}$$

Equations 11-65 and 11-66 and the equivalent circuit of Fig. 11-22 are applicable to a wide variety of induction-motor types. For example, if the stator-circuit impedances are equal when referred to the same winding, then $Z_d = 0$ and the forward and backward fields are independent of one another; this special case is exactly like that of the symmetrical motor of Art. 11-8 after all quantities have been referred to the same winding. If $Z_d = 0$ and if the referred voltages form a balanced 2-phase system of positive sequence, then Fig. 11-22b reduces to the equivalent circuit for balanced operation. If winding a is open, then Z_d is an open circuit; this is the special case of single-phase operation treated in Art. 11-6. For this special case $I_a = 0$, and Eqs. 11-49 and 11-50 become

$$I_{mf} = I_{mb} = \tfrac{1}{2}I_m \tag{11-69}$$

The equivalent circuit then reduces to V_m applied to the combination of $2Z_{1m}$ in series with the forward- and backward-field impedances. Division of the impedances by 2 gives the equivalent circuit of Fig. 11-14c.

Equations 11-65 and 11-66 can be solved for the currents, giving

$$I_{mf} = \frac{V_{mf}(Z_o + Z_b) + V_{mb}Z_d}{(Z_o + Z_f)(Z_o + Z_b) - Z_d^2} \tag{11-70}$$

$$I_{mb} = \frac{V_{mb}(Z_o + Z_f) + V_{mf}Z_d}{(Z_o + Z_f)(Z_o + Z_b) - Z_d^2} \tag{11-71}$$

If the motor constants and the applied voltages are known and a value of slip is assumed, the forward and backward components of the current in phase m can then be found. The power delivered to the forward field by phase m of the stator is $I_{mf}^2 R_f$, and since the internal behavior of the motor for the forward-field components is the same as that of a balanced 2-phase motor, a like contribution is supplied by phase a. As in a balanced 2-phase motor, the total power P_{gf} delivered to the forward field by both phases of the stator therefore is

$$P_{gf} = 2I_{mf}^2 R_f \tag{11-72}$$

Similarly, the total power P_{gb} delivered to the backward field is

$$P_{gb} = 2I_{mb}^2 R_b \tag{11-73}$$

The internal torque, rotor I^2R losses, and internal mechanical power can then be determined from straightforward application of revolving-field theory, as in Eqs. 11-13, 11-16, and 11-17.

b. Starting Torque. The starting condition is an important and simple special case. With the rotor stationary, the current in each winding can be determined from its own applied voltage and impedance (including any series impedances), there being no mutual effect between phases at standstill when the windings are in space quadrature. If the stator currents are now resolved into forward and backward components, the internal starting torque can then be determined from the basic torque relation (Eq. 11-13). Since the forward- and backward-field impedances are equal at standstill, the basic torque relation reduces to

$$T_{\text{start}} = \frac{2}{\omega_s} (I_{mf}^2 - I_{mb}^2) R \tag{11-74}$$

where T_{start} is the internal starting torque in newton-meters and R is the resistance of the parallel combination of $r_2 + jx_2$ and jx_φ referred to winding m. The factor 2 is the number of stator phases.

A simple and convenient relation for the starting torque can now be obtained by expressing the difference between the squares of the effective values of the forward and backward currents in terms of the resultant

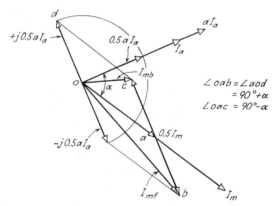

FIG. 11-23. Phasor diagram of currents and their symmetrical components.

stator currents and the phase angle between them. The resolution of the stator currents into forward backward components in accordance with Eqs. 11-49 and 11-50 is shown in the phasor diagram of Fig. 11-23. The phase angle between I_m and I_a is α. From the geometry of triangle oab,

$$(ob)^2 = (oa)^2 + (ab)^2 - 2(oa)(ab) \cos \angle oab \tag{11-75}$$

or, in terms of the effective values of the currents,

$$I_{mf}^2 = (0.5I_m)^2 + (0.5aI_a)^2 + 2(0.5I_m)(0.5aI_a) \sin \alpha \tag{11-76}$$

Similarly, for triangle oac

$$I_{mb}^2 = (0.5I_m)^2 + (0.5aI_a)^2 - 2(0.5I_m)(0.5aI_a) \sin \alpha \tag{11-77}$$

Substitution of the difference between Eqs. 11-76 and 11-77 in Eq. 11-74 then gives

$$T_{\text{start}} = \frac{2}{\omega_s} I_m a I_a R \sin \alpha \tag{11-78}$$

c. Capacitor and Split-phase Motors.   Capacitor and split-phase motors are the special case in which

$$V_m = V_a = V \tag{11-79}$$

where V is the single-phase line voltage.   Equations 11-59 and 11-60 then reduce to

$$V_{mf} = \frac{V}{2}\left(1 - \frac{j}{a}\right) \tag{11-80}$$

$$V_{mb} = \frac{V}{2}\left(1 + \frac{j}{a}\right) \tag{11-81}$$

In Eqs. 11-63 and 11-64, the impedance Z_{1m} is the leakage impedance of the main winding.   The impedance Z_{1a} is the leakage impedance of the auxiliary winding plus (in the case of capacitor motors) the impedance of the capacitor.   The single-phase line current is the phasor sum of the winding currents.   The application of the theory to the numerical calculation of performance characteristics can be illustrated by means of an example.

Example 11-4.   A ¼-hp 110-volt 60-cps 4-pole two-value capacitor motor (capacitor-start, capacitor-run) has the following constants:
  Rotor referred to m: $r_2 = 4.12$ ohms, $x_2 = 2.12$ ohms
  Magnetizing reactance referred to m: $x_\varphi = 66.8$
  Main winding: $r_{1m} = 2.02$, $x_{1m} = 2.79$
  Auxiliary winding: $r_{1a} = 7.14$, $x_{1a} = 3.22$
  Starting capacitor: $r_c = 3.00$, $x_c = -14.5$
  Running capacitor: $r_c = 9.00$, $x_c = -172$
  Effective turns ratio $N_a/N_m = a = 1.18$
  No-load core loss = 24 watts
  No-load friction and windage = 13 watts
  a. For standstill conditions, compute the current in each winding, the line current and power factor, the voltage across the capacitor, and the internal torque.
  b. With the starting capacitor still in the circuit, repeat (*a*) for a slip of 0.50.
  Solution.   From the constants of the rotor and magnetizing reactance referred to the main winding, the forward- and backward-field impedances Z_f and Z_b can be computed at the specified values of slip.   The results are as follows:

$s = 1.0$:

$$Z_f = Z_b = Z$$
$$= 3.87 + j2.29$$

$s = 0.5$:

$$Z_f = 7.62 + j2.97$$
$$Z_b = 2.58 + j2.16$$

  a. At standstill, the motor is a static circuit with no mutual effects between phases. The impedance at the line terminals of the main phase is

$$Z_m = Z_{1m} + Z = 2.02 + j2.79 + 3.87 + j2.29$$
$$= 6.89 + j5.08 = 7.78\underline{/40.8°} \text{ ohms}$$

With the line voltage V as reference phasor,

$$I_m = \frac{V}{Z_m} = \frac{110}{7.78} \underline{/-40.8°} = 14.14 \underline{/-40.8°} \text{ amp}$$
$$= 10.7 - j9.23$$

The rotor and magnetizing impedance referred to the auxiliary winding is

$$a^2 Z = (1.18)^2 (3.87 + j2.29) = 5.38 + j3.18$$

The impedance of the starting capacitor in series with the auxiliary-winding leakage impedance is

$$Z_{1a} = 3.00 - j14.5 + 7.14 + j3.22 = 10.14 - j11.28$$

The impedance at the line terminals of the auxiliary phase is

$$Z_a = Z_{1a} + a^2 Z = 10.14 - j11.28 + 5.38 + j3.18 = 15.52 - j8.1$$
$$= 17.5 \underline{/-27.5°} \text{ ohms}$$

$$I_a = \frac{V}{Z_a} = \frac{110}{17.5} \underline{/+27.5°} = 6.29 \underline{/+27.5°} \text{ amp}$$
$$= 5.57 + j2.91$$

Line current $I = I_m + I_a = 16.27 - j6.32 = 17.5 \underline{/-21.3°}$ amp

Power factor $= \cos 21.3° = 0.932$

Impedance of starting capacitor $= \sqrt{r_c^2 + x_c^2} = 14.8$ ohms

Capacitor voltage at starting $= I_a Z_c = (6.29)(14.8) = 93$ volts

In Eq. 11-78

$$\omega_s = {}^{377}\!/\!_2 = 188.5 \qquad \alpha = 27.5° + 40.8° = 68.3°$$
$$\sin \alpha = 0.929$$

$$T_{\text{start}} = \frac{2}{188.5} (14.14)(1.18)(6.29)(3.87)(0.929)$$
$$= 4.00 \text{ newton-m, or } 2.95 \text{ lb-ft}$$

b. With the rotor in motion the motor is no longer a simple static circuit, and the forward and backward currents must be computed by means of Eqs. 11-70 and 11-71. From Eqs. 11-80 and 11-81 with the line voltage as reference phasor

$$V_{mf} = 55 - j\frac{55}{1.18} = 55 - j46.6 = 72.1 \underline{/-40.3°}$$
$$V_{mb} = 55 + j46.6 = 72.1 \underline{/+40.3°}$$

With the starting capacitor, from part a

$$\frac{Z_{1a}}{a^2} = \frac{1}{(1.18)^2} (10.14 - j11.28) = 7.30 - j8.10$$
$$Z_{1m} = 2.02 + j2.79$$

From Eqs. 11-63 and 11-64

$$Z_o = 4.66 - j2.66$$
$$Z_d = 2.64 - j5.45 \qquad -Z_d^2 = +22.7 + j28.9$$

At $s = 0.50$, from the beginning of the solution,

$$\begin{array}{ll}
Z_f = 7.62 + j2.97 & Z_b = 2.58 + j2.16 \\
Z_o = 4.66 - j2.66 & Z_o = 4.66 - j2.66 \\
\overline{Z_o + Z_f = 12.28 + j0.31} & \overline{Z_o + Z_b = 7.24 - j0.50}
\end{array}$$

Substitution of numerical values in Eqs. 11-70 and 11-71 then gives

$$I_{mf} = \frac{946\underline{/-35.0°}}{114.0\underline{/11.6°}} = 8.30\underline{/-46.6°} = 5.69 - j6.03$$

$$I_{mb} = \frac{577\underline{/16.8°}}{114.0\underline{/11.6°}} = 5.05\underline{/5.2°} = 5.03 + j0.46$$

Main-winding current I_m = sum = $10.72 - j5.57 = 12.1$ amp

In Eq. 11-48,

$$j\frac{I_{mf}}{a} = 5.11 + j4.82$$

$$-j\frac{I_{mb}}{a} = 0.39 - j4.27$$

Auxiliary-winding current $I_a = 5.50 + j0.55 = 5.53$ amp
Line current $I = I_m + I_a = 16.22 - j5.02 = 17.0\underline{/-17.2°}$
Power factor = $\cos 17.2° = 0.955$
Capacitor voltage = $(5.53)(14.8) = 81.8$ volts

In Eqs. 11-72 and 11-73,

$$P_{gf} = (2)(8.30)^2(7.62) = 1{,}048 \text{ watts}$$
$$P_{gb} = (2)(5.05)^2(2.58) = \underline{\quad 132}$$
$$\text{Difference} = \quad 916$$

From Eq. 11-13,

$$T = \frac{916}{188.5} = 4.86 \text{ newton-m, or } 3.59 \text{ lb-ft}$$

Data for the curves of internal torque and capacitor voltage shown in Fig. 11-24 were computed by repeating similar calculations for other assumed values of slip. The general shape of the characteristics is typical of capacitor-start motors. Notice the rather rapid increase in the voltage across the capacitor for increasing speed above

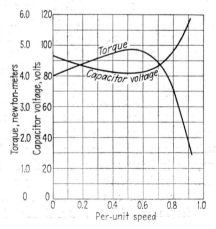

FIG. 11-24. Computed curves of torque and voltage across starting capacitor for ¼-hp 110-volt two-value capacitor motor of Example 11-4.

about 0.7. As the motor speed increases, its reactance increases and a condition analogous to resonance is approached. One of the problems confronting the designer is the proper choice of the correct combination of auxiliary-winding constants, turns ratio, and capacitor rating so that a suitable torque characteristic is obtained without causing excessive voltage across the capacitor.

11-11. Résumé. The main theme of this chapter is a continuation of the induction-machine theory of Chaps. 6 and 10. This theory is expanded by a step-by-step reasoning process from the simple revolving-field theory of the symmetrical polyphase induction motor. The basic concept is the resolution of the stator-mmf wave into two constant-amplitude traveling waves revolving around the air gap at synchronous speed in opposite directions. If the slip for the forward field is s, then that for the backward field is $2 - s$. Each of these component fields produces induction-motor action, just as in a symmetrical polyphase motor. From the viewpoint of the stator, the reflected effects of the rotor can be visualized and expressed quantitatively in terms of simple equivalent circuits. The ease with which the internal reactions can be accounted for in this manner is the essential reason for the usefulness of the double-revolving-field theory.

For a single-phase winding, the forward- and backward-component mmf waves are equal, and their amplitude is half the maximum value of the peak of the stationary pulsating mmf produced by the winding. The resolution of the stator mmf into its forward and backward components then leads to the physical concept of the single-phase motor described in Art. 11-1 and finally to the quantitative theory developed in Art. 11-6 and to the equivalent circuits of Fig. 11-14.

The next step is investigation of the possibilities of applying the double-revolving-field resolution to a symmetrical 2-phase motor with unbalanced applied voltages, as in Art. 11-8. This investigation leads to the symmetrical-component concept, whereby an unbalanced 2-phase system of currents or voltages can be resolved into the sum of two balanced 2-phase component systems of opposite phase sequence. Resolution of the currents into symmetrical-component systems is equivalent to resolving the stator-mmf wave into its forward and backward components, and therefore the internal reactions of the rotor for each symmetrical-component system are the same as those which we have already investigated. A very similar reasoning process, not considered here, leads to the well-known 3-phase symmetrical-component method for treating problems involving unbalanced operation of 3-phase rotating machines. The ease with which the rotating machine can be analyzed in terms of revolving-field theory is the chief reason for the usefulness of the symmetrical-component method.

In so far as basic concepts are concerned, it is a simple matter to modify the symmetrical-component method of Art. 11-8 so that the effects of unequal turns in the stator windings of a 2-phase motor can be taken into account as in Art. 11-10. All that is necessary is that the currents and voltages be referred to the appropriate winding by use of the effective turns ratio, in the same manner as in static-transformer theory. The effects of unequal stator-circuit impedances also are included, but no new concepts are thereby introduced; only the algebra becomes somewhat longer. The effect of unbalanced stator impedances is to make the two symmetrical-component systems mutually interrelated, as shown in the equivalent circuit of Fig. 11-22b. This equivalent circuit applies to a wide variety of induction-motor types, of which capacitor and split-phase motors are important examples.

It is only natural to compare the symmetrical-component transformations of Arts. 11-8 and 11-10 with the dq transformations used freely in Part II of the book. Both are simply mathematical changes of variables. Their purpose is to obtain new variables which can be dealt with rather easily and which have rather clear physical significance. Both transformations illustrate the value of physical pictures. If one has a clear physical concept of what goes on in simple situations, then more complex situations usually can be resolved into the net effect of simple elements. The symmetrical-component method is a good example.

PROBLEMS

11-1. What type of motor would you use in the following applications? Give reasons. Vacuum cleaner. Refrigerator. Washing machine. Domestic oil burner. Desk fan. Sewing machine. Emery wheel. Clock. Food mixer. Record player. Portable electric drill.

11-2. At standstill, the currents in the main and auxiliary windings of a capacitor-start induction motor are $I_m = 14.14$ amp and $I_a = 7.07$ amp. The auxiliary-winding current leads the main-winding current by 60°. The effective turns per pole—i.e., the number of turns corrected for the effects of winding distribution—are $N_m = 80$ and $N_a = 100$. The windings are in space quadrature.

Determine the amplitudes of the forward and backward stator-mmf waves.

Suppose it were possible to adjust the magnitude and phase of the auxiliary-winding current. What should be its magnitude and phase to produce a pure forward mmf wave?

11-3. Find the mechanical power output of the ¼-hp 4-pole 110-volt 60-cps single-phase induction motor, whose constants are given below, at a slip of 0.05:

$$r_{1m} = 1.86 \text{ ohms} \qquad x_{1m} = 2.56 \text{ ohms} \qquad x_\varphi = 53.5 \text{ ohms}$$
$$r_2 = 3.56 \text{ ohms} \qquad x_2 = 2.56 \text{ ohms}$$
$$\text{Core loss} = 35 \text{ watts} \qquad \text{Friction and windage} = 13.5 \text{ watts}$$

11-4. For the single-phase induction motor of Example 11-1 running at a slip of 0.05, determine the ratio of the backward flux wave to the forward flux wave. Plot a half wave of the resultant flux distribution for instants of time corresponding to $\omega t = 0$, 45°, 90°, 135°, and 180°, zero time being chosen as the instant when the forward and backward flux waves are in space phase. If the forward and backward flux waves are represented by space phasors like the mmf phasors f and b in Fig. 11-2c, draw a diagram showing the components and the resultant for the same five instants of time. Sketch the locus of the tip of the phasor representing the resultant air-gap flux wave. What kind of curve do you think this locus is?

11-5. Derive an expression in terms of Q_2 for the nonzero speed of a single-phase induction motor at which the internal torque is zero (see Eq. 11-21).

11-6. A small 2-phase 2-pole induction motor has the following constants at 60 cps:

$$r_{1m} = 375 \text{ ohms} \qquad r_2 = 255 \text{ ohms}$$
$$x_{1m} = x_2 = 50 \text{ ohms} \qquad x_\varphi = 920 \text{ ohms}$$

The main and auxiliary windings have the same number of turns. This motor is used as a tachometer with a 60-cps reference voltage applied to its main winding, as in Fig. 11-15. Compute the speed voltage sensitivity in volts output per volt input per radian per second near zero speed. Also compute the phase angle of the output voltage relative to the input voltage.

11-7. a. Find the starting torque of the motor given in Example 11-2 for the conditions specified.

b. Compare the result of (a) with the torque which the motor would develop at starting when balanced 2-phase voltages of 220 volts are applied.

c. Show, in general, that, if the stator voltages V_m and V_a of a 2-phase induction motor are in quadrature but unequal, the starting torque is the same as that developed when balanced 2-phase voltages of $\sqrt{V_m V_a}$ volts are applied.

11-8. The induction motor of Example 11-2 is supplied from an unbalanced 2-phase source by a four-wire feeder having an impedance of $1.0 + j3.0$ ohms per phase. The source voltages can be expressed as

$$V_m = 240\underline{/0°} \text{ volts} \qquad V_a = 200\underline{/75°} \text{ volts}$$

For a slip of 0.05, show that the induction-motor performance is such that the motor's terminal voltages correspond more nearly to those of a balanced 2-phase system than those at the source.

11-9. The equivalent-circuit constants in ohms per phase referred to the stator for a 2-phase 1.5-hp 220-volt 4-pole 60-cps squirrel-cage induction motor are given below. The no-load rotational loss is 200 watts.

$$r_1 = 3.2 \qquad r_2 = 2.4$$
$$x_1 = x_2 = 3.2 \qquad x_\varphi = 100$$

a. The voltage applied to phase m is $220\underline{/0°}$ volts, and the voltage applied to phase a is $220\underline{/60°}$. At a slip $s = 0.04$, $Z_f = 41.9 + j27.2$ ohms, and $Z_b = 1.20 + j3.2$ ohms. What is the net air-gap torque?

b. What is the starting torque with the applied voltages of (a)?

c. The applied voltages are readjusted so that $V_m = 220\underline{/0°}$ and $V_a = 220\underline{/90°}$. Full load on the machine occurs at $s = 0.04$. At what value of slip does maximum torque occur? What is the value of maximum air-gap torque in newton-meters?

d. While the motor is running as in (c), phase a is open-circuited. What is the horsepower developed by the machine at slip $s = 0.04$?

e. What voltage appears across the open phase a terminals under the conditions of (d) at $s = 0.04$?

11-10. Simplified dynamic considerations relating to 2-phase control motors are presented in Example 6-6 on the basis of linearity of the torque-speed curves of Fig. 6-17 at low speeds. A similar approximate investigation is called for here.[1]

The control motor has identical 2-phase stator windings and a high-resistance rotor and is supplied from a low-impedance source. When balanced sinusoidal voltages are applied, the torque-slip curve is linear over the range of interest; i.e.,

$$T = kV_1^2 s$$

where k is a constant and V_1 the balanced stator voltage.

a. For control-motor usage as in Art. 11-9, show that the forward and backward torques are given by

$$T_f = k\left(\frac{V_a + V_m}{2}\right)^2 \left(1 - \frac{\omega_o}{\omega_s}\right)$$

$$T_b = k\left(\frac{V_a - V_m}{2}\right)^2 \left(1 + \frac{\omega_o}{\omega_s}\right)$$

where ω_o is the shaft angular velocity and ω_s is the synchronous angular velocity.

b. The motor drives a load having moment of inertia J and a torque requirement $f_v\omega_o$ proportional to speed. Neglect motor losses. With the motor at rest and the voltage V_m on the reference field, the rms voltage V_a is suddenly applied to the control field. Determine the velocity ω_o as a function of time. Ignore electrical transients.

c. For small values of control-field voltage, V_a^2 may be neglected in comparison with V_m^2. What is the time constant in (b) under this assumption?

d. Using the assumption in (c), determine the transfer functions relating shaft velocity and shaft position angle to the control-field signal.

11-11. The motor of Prob. 11-6 is used as a 2-phase control motor. When the reference-field voltage is 100 volts and the control-field voltage is 70 volts and leads the reference voltage by 90° (both voltages at 60 cps), compute:

a. The ratio of the backward flux wave to the forward flux wave at standstill

b. The ratio of the backward flux wave to the forward flux wave at a slip $s = 0.80$

c. The internally developed mechanical power in watts at $s = 0.80$

11-12. For the 2-phase induction motor of Example 11-3, plot a family of curves of rotor power loss and internal power developed for per-unit values of control-phase voltage of 1.00, 0.50, and 0, covering a speed range from -1 to $+1$ per unit. The applied voltages are in quadrature. Express the power in per unit based on the power delivered to the air gap by the stator windings at standstill when balanced 2-phase voltages of 1.00 per unit are applied to the 2 stator phases.

11-13. A small 2-pole squirrel-cage induction motor for use in servo systems has symmetrical 2-phase stator windings. At standstill, the input impedance measured at the terminals of each stator winding at 60 cps is $305 + j51$ ohms. For the purposes of this problem rotational and core losses may be neglected. Three points on the torque-slip characteristic of this motor with balanced 2-phase voltages of 100 volts at 60 cps applied to its stator terminals are given below:

Torque, newton-m	0.064	0.082	0.088
Slip, per unit	0.50	1.00	1.50

[1] A more comprehensive examination along these lines can be found in A. M. Hopkin, Transient Response of Small Two-phase Servomotors, *Trans. AIEE*, vol. 70, pp. 881–886, 1951.

If the reference-phase voltage is held constant at 100 volts, 60 cps, and the control-phase voltage is reduced to 50 volts (the two voltages being in time quadrature), compute:

  a. The standstill torque, in newton-meters
  b. The power input to the reference phase at standstill
  c. The power input to the control phase at standstill
  d. The total rotor I^2R loss at standstill
  e. The torque at $s = 0.50$

11-14. For the 2-phase control motor of Prob. 11-13 at standstill with 100 volts applied to the reference phase and variable voltage applied to the control phase, plot curves of the following variables as functions of the standstill torque:

  a. Total rotor copper loss
  b. Control-phase stator copper loss
  c. Reference-phase stator copper loss
  d. Power input to control phase
  e. Power input to reference phase

11-15. A symmetrical 2-phase control motor produces a torque of 1.25 lb-ft at standstill with balanced voltages of 100 volts applied.

If the motor is required to produce an acceleration at zero speed of 64.4 rad/sec^2 in a load having no friction but having an inertia of 0.5 lb-ft^2, what voltage must be supplied to the auxiliary winding when the main winding is supplied with 100 volts in time quadrature?

11-16. At starting (rotor stationary) the currents in the main and auxiliary windings of a capacitor-start single-phase induction motor are, respectively,

$$I_m = 15 \text{ amp} \qquad I_a = 10 \text{ amp}$$

with I_a leading I_m by 60°.   The auxiliary and main windings are in space quadrature, and the ratio of effective turns in the auxiliary winding to effective turns in the main winding is 1.50.

For starting conditions, compute:

  a. The ratio of the amplitude of the forward stator-mmf wave to the amplitude of the backward stator-mmf wave
  b. The ratio of the amplitude of the forward air-gap flux wave to the amplitude of the backward air-gap flux wave
  c. The ratio of the forward torque to the backward torque
  d. The ratio of the forward torque to the net starting torque

11-17. It is possible to design a capacitor motor and its capacitor so that the backward field is eliminated at one specified value of slip.   At this slip the motor runs as a balanced 2-phase motor.   For the motor of Example 11-4, find the value of resistance and reactance of the capacitor which will result in balanced 2-phase operation at a slip $s = 0.04$.

11-18. While the capacitor motor of Example 11-4 is running at a slip $s = 0.5$, the auxiliary winding and starting capacitor in series accidentally are disconnected from the 110-volt supply and short-circuited.   For $s = 0.5$, find the currents in the main and auxiliary windings and the net internal torque.

APPENDIX A

The Per-unit System

Very often, computations relating to machines, transformers, and systems of machines are carried out in per-unit form—i.e., with all pertinent quantities expressed as decimal fractions of appropriately chosen base values. All the usual computations are then carried out in these per-unit values instead of the familiar volts, amperes, ohms, etc.

There are two advantages to the system. One is that the constants of machines and transformers lie in a reasonably narrow numerical range when expressed in a per-unit system related to their rating. The correctness of their values is thus subject to a rapid approximate check. The other is that the analyst is relieved of the worry of referring circuit quantities to one side or the other of transformers. For complicated systems involving many transformers of different turns ratios, this advantage is a significant one in that a possible cause of serious mistakes is removed. The per-unit system is also very useful in simulating machine systems on analog and digital computers for transient and dynamic analyses.

Quantities such as voltage V, current I, power P, reactive power Q, volt-amperes VA, resistance R, reactance X, impedance Z, conductance G, susceptance B, and admittance Y can be translated to and from per-unit form as follows:

$$\text{Quantity in per unit} = \frac{\text{actual quantity}}{\text{base value of quantity}} \qquad \text{(A-1)}$$

where *actual quantity* refers to the value in volts, amperes, ohms, etc. To a certain extent, base values may be chosen arbitrarily, but certain relations among them must be observed for the normal electrical laws to hold in the per-unit system. Thus, for a single-phase system,

$$P_{\text{base}}, Q_{\text{base}}, VA_{\text{base}} = V_{\text{base}} I_{\text{base}} \qquad \text{(A-2)}$$

$$R_{\text{base}}, X_{\text{base}}, Z_{\text{base}} = \frac{V_{\text{base}}}{I_{\text{base}}} \qquad \text{(A-3)}$$

$$G_{\text{base}}, B_{\text{base}}, Y_{\text{base}} = \frac{I_{\text{base}}}{V_{\text{base}}} \qquad \text{(A-4)}$$

In normal usage, values of VA_{base} and V_{base} are chosen first; values of I_{base} and all other quantities in Eqs. A-2 to A-4 are thereby established.

The value of VA_{base} must be the same over the entire system concerned. When a transformer is encountered, the values of V_{base} are different on each side and must be in the same ratio as are the turns on the transformer. Usually the rated or nominal voltages of the respective sides are chosen. The process of referring quantities to one side of the transformer is then taken care of automatically by the use of Eqs. A-1 to A-4 in finding and interpreting per-unit values. The procedure thus becomes one of translating all quantities to per-unit values, using these values in all the customary circuit-analysis techniques, and translating the end results back to the more usual forms.

When only one electrical device, such as a transformer, is involved, the device's own rating is generally used for the volt-ampere base. When expressed in per unit on the rating as a base, the characteristics of power and distribution transformers do not vary much over a wide range of ratings. For example, the exciting current usually is between 0.02 and 0.06 per unit, the equivalent resistance usually is between 0.005 and 0.02 per unit (the smaller values applying to large transformers), and the equivalent reactance usually is between 0.015 and 0.10 per unit (the larger values applying to large high-voltage transformers). Similarly, the per-unit values of synchronous- and induction-machine constants fall within a relatively narrow range. When several devices are involved, however, an arbitrary choice of volt-ampere base must usually be made in order that the same base be used for the over-all system. Per-unit values may be changed from one volt-ampere base to another with the same voltage base by the relations

$$(P,Q,VA,G,B,Y)_{\text{pu on base 2}} = (P,Q,VA,G,B,Y)_{\text{pu on base 1}} \frac{(VA)_{\text{base 1}}}{(VA)_{\text{base 2}}} \quad \text{(A-5)}$$

$$(R,X,Z)_{\text{pu on base 2}} = (R,X,Z)_{\text{pu on base 1}} \frac{(VA)_{\text{base 2}}}{(VA)_{\text{base 1}}} \quad \text{(A-6)}$$

Example A-1. The exciting current measured on the low-voltage side of a 50-kva 2,400:240-volt transformer is 5.41 amp. Its equivalent impedance referred to the high-voltage side is $1.42 + j1.82$ ohms. Take the transformer rating as a base.

a. Express the exciting current in per unit on the low-voltage side and also on the high-voltage side.

b. Express the equivalent impedance in per unit on the high-voltage side and also on the low-voltage side.

Solution. The base values of voltages and currents are

$$V_{\text{base } H} = 2{,}400 \text{ volts} \qquad V_{\text{base } X} = 240 \text{ volts}$$
$$I_{\text{base } H} = 20.8 \text{ amp} \qquad I_{\text{base } X} = 208 \text{ amp}$$

where subscripts H and X indicate the high- and low-voltage sides, respectively.

From Eq. A-3,

$$Z_{\text{base } H} = \frac{2,400}{20.8} = 115.2 \text{ ohms}$$

$$Z_{\text{base } X} = \frac{240}{208} = 1.152 \text{ ohms}$$

a. From Eq. A-1,

$$I_{\varphi X} = \frac{5.41}{208} = 0.0260 \text{ per unit}$$

The exciting current referred to the high-voltage side is 0.541 amp. Its per-unit value is

$$I_{\varphi H} = \frac{0.541}{20.8} = 0.0260 \text{ per unit}$$

The per-unit values are the same referred to either side. The turns ratios required to refer currents in amperes from one side of the transformer to the other are taken care of in the per-unit system by the base values for currents on the two sides when the volt-ampere base is the same on both sides and the voltage bases are in the ratio of the turns.

b. From Eq. A-1 and the value for $Z_{\text{base } H}$,

$$Z_{eqH} = \frac{1.42 + j1.82}{115.2} = 0.0123 + j0.0158 \text{ per unit}$$

The equivalent impedance referred to the low-voltage side is $0.0142 + j0.0182$ ohm. Its per-unit value is

$$Z_{eqX} = \frac{0.0142 + j0.0182}{1.152} = 0.0123 + j0.0158 \text{ per unit}$$

The per-unit values are the same, the referring factors being taken care of in per unit by the base values.

When applied to 3-phase problems, the base values for the per-unit system are chosen so that the relations for a balanced 3-phase system hold among them:

$$(P_{\text{base}}, Q_{\text{base}}, VA_{\text{base}}) \text{ 3-phase} = 3 VA_{\text{base per phase}} \qquad \text{(A-7)}$$

$$V_{\text{base (line to line)}} = \sqrt{3}\, V_{\text{base (line to neutral)}} \qquad \text{(A-8)}$$

$$I_{\text{base (per phase } \Delta)} = \frac{1}{\sqrt{3}} I_{\text{base (per phase Y)}} \qquad \text{(A-9)}$$

In dealing with 3-phase systems the 3-phase kva base and the line-to-line voltage base are usually chosen first. The base values for phase voltages and currents then follow from Eqs. A-7, A-8, and A-9. Equations A-2, A-3, and A-4 still apply to the base values per phase. For example, the base value for Y-connected impedances is given by Eq. A-3 with V_{base} taken as the base voltage to neutral and I_{base} taken as the base current per phase Y; the base value for Δ-connected impedances is also given by

Eq. A-3 but with V_{base} taken as the base line-to-line voltage and I_{base} taken as the base current per phase Δ. Division of Eq. A-8 by Eq. A-9 shows that

$$Z_{\text{base (per phase Δ)}} = 3Z_{\text{base (per phase Y)}} \qquad (A\text{-}10)$$

The factors of $\sqrt{3}$ and 3 relating Δ and Y quantities in volts, amperes, and ohms in a balanced 3-phase system are thus automatically taken care of in per unit by the base values. Such 3-phase problems can be solved in per unit as if they were single-phase problems, without paying any attention to the details of the transformer connections except in translating volt-ampere-ohm values into and out of the per-unit system.

In dynamic analyses of machines, it may also be advantageous to express machine inertia in per-unit form. For induction and synchronous machines, the inertia constant H is used. This inertia constant is defined as the stored energy in the rotating mass at synchronous speed, the energy being expressed in kilowatt-seconds and normalized by dividing by rated kva input or output for the machine. Thus, in terms of moment of inertia J in mks units,

$$H = \frac{0.5J(2\pi n/60)^2 10^{-3}}{\text{rating in kva}} = \frac{5.48 \times 10^{-6}Jn^2}{\text{rating in kva}} \qquad (A\text{-}11)$$

where n is the synchronous speed in rpm. Alternatively, when the weight times the square of the radius of gyration is given as Wk^2 lb-ft², the inertia constant H is

$$H = \frac{0.231 \times 10^{-6}(Wk^2)n^2}{\text{rating in kva}} \qquad (A\text{-}12)$$

Typical values of H range from 4 to 7 for turbine-generators and 2 to 4 for water-wheel generators, both including the turbine. For induction motors, H is about 0.5; for synchronous motors it ranges from 0.5 to 1.5 (motor alone).

Normalized Solutions for Linear Second-order Differential Equations

The form of second-order equation frequently encountered is

$$a \frac{d^2x}{dt^2} + b \frac{dx}{dt} + cx = f(t) \qquad \text{(B-1)}$$

where a, b, and c are constants, x is the dependent variable, and t is the independent variable. To cite a simple example, it may be the equation for charge in a series RLC circuit on which a voltage which is an arbitrary function $f(t)$ of time is impressed. We shall be particularly interested in a system initially at rest ($x = 0$ and $dx/dt = 0$ at $t = 0$) and on which is impressed a forcing function $f(t)$ which is zero until $t = 0$ and which assumes the constant value d thereafter. The equation is then

$$a \frac{d^2x}{dt^2} + b \frac{dx}{dt} + cx = d \qquad \text{(B-2)}$$

The normalizing process is based on reduction of the number of quantities in the equation and its solution by using ratios of quantities and ultimately plotting the results to dimensionless coordinates. For greatest usefulness, it is highly desirable that new quantities replacing ratios of old quantities have definite physical significance. For this reason, judicious choice of new quantities is to a considerable extent based on knowledge of the solution of the equation in its ordinary form.

The first step here is to divide Eq. B-2 by a, giving

$$\frac{d^2x}{dt^2} + \frac{b}{a} \frac{dx}{dt} + \frac{c}{a} x = \frac{d}{a} \qquad \text{(B-3)}$$

Then let

$$\frac{c}{a} = \omega_n^2 \qquad \text{(B-4)}$$

and

$$\frac{b}{2\sqrt{ac}} = \zeta \qquad \text{(B-5)}$$

547

whereupon Eq. B-3 becomes

$$\frac{d^2x}{dt^2} + 2\zeta\omega_n\frac{dx}{dt} + \omega_n^2 x = \frac{d}{a} \tag{B-6}$$

As will be seen below, ω_n is the *undamped natural angular frequency* of the system. The quantity ζ is called the *damping ratio* of the system; it has a physical significance which will also become apparent.

The steady-state solution, or *particular integral*, of Eq. B-6 is

$$x_\infty = \frac{d}{a\omega_n^2} \tag{B-7}$$

The force-free equation, which yields the transient portion of the solution, or so-called *complementary function*, is

$$\frac{d^2x}{dt^2} + 2\zeta\omega_n\frac{dx}{dt} + \omega_n^2 x = 0 \tag{B-8}$$

The solution is of the form

$$x = A\,\epsilon^{st} \tag{B-9}$$

where s can be found by substitution of Eq. B-9 in Eq. B-8. When the trivial possibility that $A\epsilon^{st} = 0$ is discarded, this procedure yields

$$s^2 + 2\zeta\omega_n s + \omega_n^2 = 0 \tag{B-10}$$

as the *characteristic equation*. The roots are

$$s_1,\, s_2 = -\zeta\omega_n \pm \omega_n\sqrt{\zeta^2 - 1} \tag{B-11}$$

The complete solution of Eq. B-6 is then

$$x = x_\infty + A_1\epsilon^{s_1t} + A_2\epsilon^{s_2t} \tag{B-12}$$

in which the constants A_1 and A_2 can be found from the initial conditions that at $t = 0$ both x and dx/dt must be zero.

The final form of Eq. B-12 with A_1 and A_2 evaluated depends on whether ζ is less than, equal to, or greater than unity. When $\zeta < 1$,

$$\frac{x}{x_\infty} = 1 - \frac{1}{\sqrt{1 - \zeta^2}}\,\epsilon^{-\zeta\omega_n t}\sin\left(\sqrt{1 - \zeta^2}\,\omega_n t + \phi\right) \tag{B-13}$$

where

$$\phi = \tan^{-1}\frac{\sqrt{1 - \zeta^2}}{\zeta} \tag{B-14}$$

When $\zeta = 1$,

$$\frac{x}{x_\infty} = 1 - \epsilon^{-\omega_n t}(1 + \omega_n t) \tag{B-15}$$

When $\zeta > 1$,

$$\frac{x}{x_\infty} = 1 - \frac{1}{2\sqrt{\zeta^2 - 1}}\left(\frac{\epsilon^{(-\zeta+\sqrt{\zeta^2-1})\omega_n t}}{\zeta - \sqrt{\zeta^2 - 1}} - \frac{\epsilon^{(-\zeta-\sqrt{\zeta^2-1})\omega_n t}}{\zeta + \sqrt{\zeta^2 - 1}}\right) \tag{B-16}$$

These results are plotted to the dimensionless coordinates x/x_∞ and $\omega_n t$ in the curves of Fig. B-1 for a series of values of ζ. They are then universal curves depicting the solution of the second-order equation B-2 *for initial-rest conditions*. Inspection of Fig. B-1 and Eqs. B-13 to B-16 shows that the numerical value of damping ratio determines whether the response is oscillatory or overdamped, with $\zeta = 1$ representing the

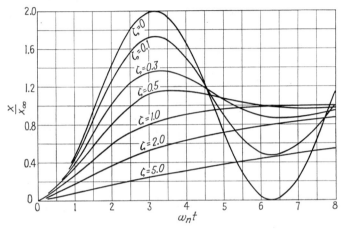

FIG. B-1. Normalized solutions of second-order linear differential equation for initial-rest conditions.

critically damped response which is the border line between the other two. Since $\zeta = 1$ for critical damping, ζ in general has the significance

$$\zeta = \frac{\text{actual damping}}{\text{damping for critical response}} \tag{B-17}$$

For an oscillatory response, the *damped angular frequency* is

$$\omega_d = \omega_n \sqrt{1 - \zeta^2} \tag{B-18}$$

Since Eq. B-18 reduces to ω_n when $\zeta = 0$, ω_n is obviously the undamped angular frequency.

The curves of Fig. B-1 are of value, not only in permitting the simple computation of response with specified parameters, but also in greatly aiding the determination of parameters for a specified response. Thus, if the object is simply for the system to settle down to a steady state as soon as possible and if all parameters but ζ are fixed, it is evident that ζ should lie in the range from about 0.5 to unity but that it makes relatively little difference where it lies in that range. On the other hand, values of the response in the neighborhood of the final steady-state value are reached earlier for the lower end of this range.

APPENDIX C

Voltages and Magnetic Fields
in Distributed A-C Windings

Both amplitude and waveform of the generated voltages and armature mmfs in machines are determined by the winding arrangements and general machine geometry. These configurations in turn are dictated by economic use of space and materials in the machine and by suitability for the intended service. In this appendix we shall supplement the introductory discussion of these considerations in Chap. 3 by analytical treatment of a-c voltages and mmfs in the balanced steady state. Attention will be confined to the time-fundamental component of voltages and the space-fundamental component of mmfs.

C-1. Generated Voltages. In accordance with Eqs. 3-42 and 3-45, the rms generated voltage per phase for a concentrated winding having N_{ph} turns per phase is

$$E = 4.44fN_{ph}\Phi \tag{C-1}$$

f being the frequency and Φ the fundamental flux per pole.

A more complex and practical winding will have coil sides for each phase distributed in several slots per pole. Equation C-1 may then be used to compute the voltage distribution of individual coils. To determine the voltage of an entire phase group, the voltages of the component coils must be added as phasors. Such addition of fundamental-frequency voltages is the subject of this article.

a. Distributed Fractional-pitch Windings. A simple example of a distributed winding is illustrated in Fig. C-1 for a 3-phase 2-pole machine. This case retains all the features of a more general one with any integral number of phases, poles, and slots per pole per phase. At the same time, a *double-layer winding* is shown. Double-layer windings usually lead to simpler end connections and to a machine which is more economical to manufacture and are found in all machines except some small motors below 10 hp in size. Generally, one side of a coil, such as a_1, is placed in

550

the bottom of a slot, and the other side, $-a_1$, is placed in the top of another slot. Coil sides such as a_1 and a_3 or a_2 and a_4 which are in adjacent slots and associated with the same phase constitute a *phase belt*. All phase belts are alike when an integral number of slots per pole per phase are used, and for the normal machine the peripheral angle subtended by a phase belt is 60 electrical degrees for a 3-phase machine and 90 electrical degrees for a 2-phase machine.

Individual coils in Fig. C-1 all span a full pole pitch, or 180 electrical degrees; accordingly, the winding is a *full-pitch winding*. Suppose now that all coil sides in the tops of the slots are shifted 1 slot counterclockwise, as in Fig. C-2. Any coil, such as a_1, $-a_1$, then spans only $\frac{5}{6}$ of a

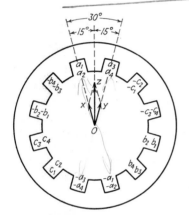
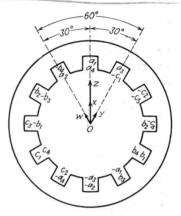

FIG. C-1. Distributed 3-phase 2-pole full-pitch armature winding with voltage phasor diagram.

FIG. C-2. Distributed 3-phase 2-pole fractional-pitch armature winding with voltage phasor diagram.

pole pitch or $(\frac{5}{6})(180) = 150$ electrical degrees, and the winding is a *fractional-pitch*, or *chorded, winding*. Similar shifting by 2 slots yields a $\frac{2}{3}$-pitch winding, and so forth. Phase groupings are now intermingled, for some slots contain coil sides in phase a and b, a and c, and b and c. Individual phase groups, such as that formed by a_1, a_2, a_3, a_4 on one side and $-a_1$, $-a_2$, $-a_3$, $-a_4$ on the other, are still displaced by 120 electrical degrees from the groups in other phases so that 3-phase voltages are produced. Besides the minor feature of shortening the end connections, fractional-pitch windings will be found to decrease the harmonic content of both the voltage and mmf waves.

The end connections between the coil sides are normally in a region of negligible flux density, and hence altering them does not significantly affect the mutual flux linkages of the winding. Allocation of coil sides in slots is then the factor determining the generated voltages, and only that allocation need be specified in Figs. C-1 and C-2. The only requisite is that all coil sides in a phase be included in the interconnection in such a manner that individual voltages shall make a positive contribution to the total. The practical consequence is that end connections can be made according to the dictates of manufacturing simplicity; the theoretical consequence is that, when computational advantages result, the coil sides in a phase may be combined in an arbitrary fashion to form equivalent coils.

One sacrifice is made in using the distributed and fractional-pitch windings of Figs. C-1 and C-2 compared with a concentrated full-pitch winding: for the same number of turns per phase, the generated voltage is lower. The harmonics are, in general, lowered by an appreciably greater factor, however, and the total number of turns which can be accommodated on a fixed iron geometry is increased. The effect of distributing the winding in Fig. C-1 is that the voltages of coils a_1 and a_2 are not in phase with those of coils a_3 and a_4. Thus the voltage of coils a_1 and a_2 may be represented by phasor OX in Fig. C-1, and that of coils a_3 and a_4 by the phasor OY. The time-phase displacement between these two voltages is the same as the electrical angle between adjacent slots, so that OX and OY coincide with the center lines of adjacent slots. The resultant phasor OZ for phase a is obviously smaller than the arithmetic sum of OX and OY.

In addition, the effect of fractional pitch in Fig. C-2 is that a coil links a smaller portion of the total pole flux than if it were a full-pitch coil. The effect may be superimposed on that of distributing the winding by regarding coil sides a_2 and $-a_1$ as an equivalent coil with the phasor voltage OW (Fig. C-2), coil sides a_1, a_4, $-a_2$, and $-a_3$ as 2 equivalent coils with the phasor voltage OX (twice the length of OW), and coil sides a_3 and $-a_4$ as an equivalent coil with phasor voltage OY. The resultant phasor OZ for phase a is obviously smaller than the arithmetic sum of OW, OX, and OY and is also smaller than OZ in Fig. C-1.

The combination of these two effects may be included in a *winding factor* k_w to be used as a reduction factor in Eq. C-1. Thus, the generated voltage per phase is

$$E = 4.44 k_w f N_{ph} \Phi \qquad \text{(C-2)}$$

where N_{ph} is the total turns in series per phase and k_w inserts the departure from the concentrated full-pitch case. For a 3-phase machine, Eq. C-2 yields the line-to-line voltage for a Δ-connected winding and the line-to-neutral voltage for a Y-connected winding. As in any balanced Y connection, the line-to-line voltage of the latter winding is $\sqrt{3}$ times the line-to-neutral voltage.

b. Breadth and Pitch Factors. By considering separately the effects of distributing and of chording the winding, reduction factors may be obtained in generalized form convenient for quantitative analysis. The effect of distributing the winding in n slots per phase belt is to yield n voltage phasors phase-displaced by the electrical angle γ between slots, γ being equal to 180 electrical degrees divided by the number of slots per pole. Such a group of phasors is shown in Fig. C-3a and, in a more convenient form for addition, again in Fig. C-3b. Each phasor AB, BC, and CD is the chord of a circle with center at O and subtends the angle γ at the center. The phasor sum AD subtends the angle $n\gamma$, which, as noted previously, is 60 electrical degrees for the normal, uniformly distributed

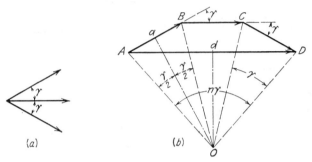

FIG. C-3. (a) Voltage phasors in a distributed winding, and (b) addition of these phasors.

3-phase machine and 90 electrical degrees for the corresponding 2-phase machine. From triangles OAa and OAd, respectively,

$$OA = \frac{Aa}{\sin (\gamma/2)} = \frac{AB}{2 \sin (\gamma/2)} \qquad (C\text{-}3)$$

$$OA = \frac{Ad}{\sin (n\gamma/2)} = \frac{AD}{2 \sin (n\gamma/2)} \qquad (C\text{-}4)$$

Equating these two values of OA yields

$$AD = AB \frac{\sin (n\gamma/2)}{\sin (\gamma/2)} \qquad (C\text{-}5)$$

But the arithmetic sum of the phasors is $n(AB)$. Consequently the reduction factor arising from distributing the winding is

$$k_b = \frac{AD}{n(AB)} = \frac{\sin (n\gamma/2)}{n \sin (\gamma/2)} \qquad (C\text{-}6)$$

The factor k_b is called the *breadth factor* of the winding.

The effect of chording on the coil voltage may be obtained by first determining the flux linkages with the fractional-pitch coil. Thus, in Fig. C-4 coil side $-a$ is only ρ electrical degrees from side a instead of the full 180°.   The flux linkages with the coil are

$$\lambda = NB_{\text{peak}}lr\,\frac{2}{P}\int_{\alpha}^{\rho+\alpha}\sin\theta\,d\theta \qquad\qquad (C\text{-}7)$$

$$\lambda = NB_{\text{peak}}lr\,\frac{2}{P}\,[\cos\alpha - \cos(\alpha + \rho)] \qquad (C\text{-}8)$$

where l is the axial length of the coil side, r the coil radius, and P the number of poles.   With α replaced by ωt to indicate rotation at ω electrical radians per second, Eq. C-8 becomes

$$\lambda = NB_{\text{peak}}lr\,\frac{2}{P}\,[\cos\omega t - \cos(\omega t + \rho)] \qquad (C\text{-}9)$$

The addition of cosine waves required in the brackets of Eq. C-9 may be

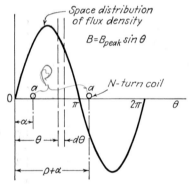

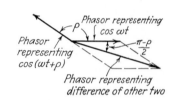

FIG. C-4. Fractional-pitch coil in sinu-   FIG. C-5. Phasor addition for fractional-
soidal field.   pitch coil.

performed by a phasor diagram as indicated in Fig. C-5, from which it follows that

$$\cos\omega t - \cos(\omega t + \rho) = 2\cos\frac{\pi-\rho}{2}\cos\left(\omega t - \frac{\pi-\rho}{2}\right) \quad (C\text{-}10)$$

a result which may also be obtained directly from the terms in Eq. C-9 by the appropriate trigonometric transformations.   The flux linkages are then

$$\lambda = NB_{\text{peak}}lr\,\frac{4}{P}\cos\frac{\pi-\rho}{2}\cos\left(\omega t - \frac{\pi-\rho}{2}\right) \qquad (C\text{-}11)$$

and the instantaneous voltage is

$$e = \omega NB_{\text{peak}}lr\,\frac{4}{P}\cos\frac{\pi-\rho}{2}\sin\left(\omega t - \frac{\pi-\rho}{2}\right) \qquad (C\text{-}12)$$

The phase angle $(\pi - \rho)/2$ in Eq. C-12 merely indicates that the instantaneous voltage is no longer zero when α in Fig. C-4 is zero. The factor $\cos (\pi - \rho)/2$ is an amplitude-reduction factor, however, so that the rms voltage of Eq. C-1 is modified to

$$E = 4.44 k_p f N_{ph} \Phi \tag{C-13}$$

where the *pitch factor* k_p is

$$k_p = \cos \frac{\pi - \rho}{2} \tag{C-14}$$

When both the breadth and pitch factors apply, the rms voltage is

$$E = 4.44 k_b k_p f N_{ph} \Phi \tag{C-15}$$

which is an alternate form of Eq. C-2.

C-2. Armature-MMF Waves. Distribution of a winding in several slots per pole per phase and the use of fractional-pitch coils influence not only the emf generated in the winding but also the magnetic field produced by it. Space-fundamental components of the mmf distributions will be examined in this article.

a. Concentrated Full-pitch Windings. We have seen in Art. 3-2 that a concentrated winding of N turns in a P-pole machine produces a rectangular magnetic-potential-difference wave around the air-gap circumference. With excitation by a sinusoidal rms current I, the time-maximum height of the space-fundamental component of the wave is, in accordance with Eq. 3-6,

$$\frac{4}{\pi} \frac{N}{P} (\sqrt{2}\, I) \qquad \text{amp-turns per pole} \tag{C-16}$$

For a polyphase concentrated winding, the amplitude for 1 phase becomes

$$\frac{4}{\pi} \frac{N_{ph}}{P} (\sqrt{2}\, I) \qquad \text{amp-turns per pole} \tag{C-17}$$

where N_{ph} is the number of series turns per phase. It is this last amplitude which is designated by the symbols $F_{a(\max)}$, $F_{b(\max)}$, or $F_{c(\max)}$ in Eqs. 3-53 to 3-55 and by the common symbol $F_{\max}$ in the balanced 3-phase case considered in Eqs. 3-56 to 3-59.

Each phase of a polyphase concentrated winding creates such a pulsating standing mmf wave in space. This situation forms the basis of the analysis leading to Eq. 3-59. Equation 3-59 may accordingly be rewritten

$$F_\theta = \frac{3}{2} \frac{4}{\pi} \frac{N_{ph}}{P} (\sqrt{2}\, I) \cos (\theta - \omega t) \tag{C-18}$$

The amplitude of the resultant mmf wave in a 3-phase machine in ampere-turns per pole is then

$$F_A = \frac{3}{2}\frac{4}{\pi}\frac{N_{ph}}{P}(\sqrt{2}\,I) = 0.90\,\frac{3N_{ph}}{P}\,I \tag{C-19}$$

Similarly, it may be shown that for a q-phase machine, the amplitude is

$$F_A = \frac{q}{2}\frac{4}{\pi}\frac{N_{ph}}{P}(\sqrt{2}\,I) = 0.90\,\frac{qN_{ph}}{P}\,I \tag{C-20}$$

In Eqs. C-19 and C-20, I is the rms current per phase. The equations include only the fundamental component of the actual distribution and apply to concentrated full-pitch windings with balanced excitation.

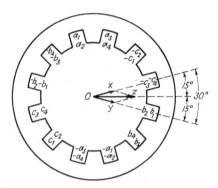

FIG. C-6. Distributed 3-phase 2-pole full-pitch armature winding with mmf phasor diagram.

b. *Distributed Fractional-pitch Windings.* When the coils in each phase of a winding are distributed among several slots per pole, the resultant space-fundamental mmf may be obtained by superposition from the preceding simpler considerations for a concentrated winding. The effect of distribution may be seen from Fig. C-6, which is a reproduction of the 3-phase 2-pole full-pitch winding with 2 slots per pole per phase given in Fig. C-1. Coils a_1 and a_2, b_1 and b_2, and c_1 and c_2 by themselves consti- tute the equivalent of a 3-phase 2-pole concentrated winding because they form three sets of coils excited by polyphase currents and mechan- ically displaced 120° from each other. They therefore produce a rotating space-fundamental mmf; the amplitude of this contribution is given by Eq. C-19 when N_{ph} is taken as the sum of the series turns in coils a_1 and a_2 only. Similarly, coils a_3 and a_4, b_3 and b_4, and c_3 and c_4 produce another identical mmf wave, but one which is phase-displaced in space by the slot angle γ from the former wave. The resultant fundamental mmf wave for the winding may be obtained by adding these two sinusoidal contributions.

The contribution from the $a_1a_2b_1b_2c_1c_2$ coils may be represented by the phasor OX in Fig. C-6. Such phasor representation is appropriate because the waveforms concerned are sinusoidal, and phasor diagrams are simply convenient means for adding sine waves. These are space sinusoids, however, not time sinusoids. Phasor OX is drawn in the space position of the mmf peak for an instant of time when the current in phase a is a maximum. The length of OX is proportional to the number of turns in the associated coils. Similarly, the contribution from the $a_3a_4b_3b_4c_3c_4$ coils may be represented by the phasor OY. Accordingly, the phasor OZ represents the resultant mmf wave. Just as in the corresponding voltage diagram, the resultant mmf is seen to be smaller than if the same number of turns per phase were concentrated in 1 slot per pole.

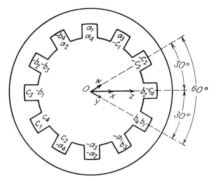

Fig. C-7. Distributed 3-phase 2-pole fractional-pitch armature winding with mmf phasor diagram.

In like manner, mmf phasors can be drawn for fractional-pitch windings as illustrated in Fig. C-7, which is a reproduction of the 3-phase 2-pole ⅚-pitch winding with 2 slots per pole per phase given in Fig. C-2. Phasor OW represents the contribution for the equivalent coils formed by conductors a_2 and $-a_1$, b_2 and $-b_1$, and c_2 and $-c_1$; OX for a_1a_4 and $-a_3-a_2$, b_1b_4 and $-b_3-b_2$, and c_1c_4 and $-c_3-c_2$; and OY for a_3 and $-a_4$, b_3 and $-b_4$, and c_3 and $-c_4$. The resultant phasor OZ is, of course, smaller than the algebraic sum of the individual contributions and is also smaller than OZ in Fig. C-6.

By comparison with Figs. C-1 and C-2, these phasor diagrams may be seen to be identical with those for generated voltages. It therefore follows that the pitch and breadth factors previously developed may be applied directly to the determination of resultant mmf. Thus, for a distributed fractional-pitch polyphase winding, the amplitude of the space-fundamental component of mmf may be obtained by using $k_bk_pN_{ph}$

instead of simply N_{ph} in Eqs. C-19 and C-20. These equations then become

$$F_A = \frac{3}{2}\frac{4}{\pi}\frac{k_b k_p N_{ph}}{P}\left(\sqrt{2}\,I\right) = 0.90\,\frac{3k_b k_p N_{ph}}{P}\,I \tag{C-21}$$

for a 3-phase machine and

$$F_A = \frac{q}{2}\frac{4}{\pi}\frac{k_b k_p N_{ph}}{P}\left(\sqrt{2}\,I\right) = 0.90\,\frac{q k_b k_p N_{ph}}{P}\,I \tag{C-22}$$

for a q-phase machine, where F_A is in ampere-turns per pole.

Table of Constants and Conversion Factors for Rationalized MKS Units

Permeability of free space............... $\mu_0 = 4\pi \times 10^{-7}$ weber/amp-turn m

Permittivity (capacitivity) of free space... $\epsilon_0 = 8.854 \times 10^{-12}$ coulomb²/newton-m²

Acceleration of gravity................. $g = 9.807$ m/sec²

Conversion Factors

Length.................... 1 m $= 3.281$ ft
$= 39.37$ in.

Mass...................... 1 kg $= 0.0685$ slug
$= 2.205$ lb (mass)

Force..................... 1 newton $= 0.225$ lb
$= 7.23$ poundals

Torque................... 1 newton-m $= 0.738$ lb-ft

Energy................... 1 joule (watt-sec) $= 0.738$ ft-lb

Power.................... 1 watt $= 1.341 \times 10^{-3}$ hp ~~~~~~~~ 746 watt = 1hp

Moment of inertia.............. 1 kg-m² $= 0.738$ slug-ft²
$= 23.7$ lb-ft²

Magnetic flux............... 1 weber $= 10^8$ maxwells (lines)

Magnetic flux density........ 1 weber/m² $= 10,000$ gauss
$= 64.5$ kilolines/in.²

Magnetizing force............ 1 amp-turn/m $= 0.0254$ amp-turn/in.

Index